Refuse Collection Practice

The activities of the municipal refuse collection departments are more continuously in the public eye and relate more closely to the daily lives of citizens than those of any governmental service. There is no better opportunity to promote good relations between the public and the municipal administration than by providing courteous, sanitary, efficient removal service. The collection of refuse in Chicago is shown above.

Refuse Collection Practice

Third Edition

●

Prepared by the

COMMITTEE ON SOLID WASTES

AMERICAN PUBLIC WORKS ASSOCIATION

●

Technical Assistance Provided by

PUBLIC HEALTH SERVICE

U. S. DEPARTMENT OF HEALTH, EDUCATION, AND WELFARE

●

PUBLIC ADMINISTRATION SERVICE
1313 East Sixtieth Street
Chicago, Illinois 60637

COMMITTEE ON SOLID WASTES OF THE
AMERICAN PUBLIC WORKS ASSOCIATION

ABRAHAM MICHAELS, *Chairman*, Consulting Engineer, Philadelphia, Pa.

ROBERT L. ANDERSON, Superintendent of Public Works and Village Engineer, Winnetka, Illinois[1]

RALPH BLACK, Chief, Solid Wastes Engineering Unit, U. S. Public Health Service, Washington, D.C.

FRANK R. BOWERMAN, Assistant Chief Engineer, Los Angeles County Sanitation Districts, Los Angeles, California

THEODORE C. EPPIG, Deputy Commissioner, Department of Streets and Sanitation, Chicago, Illinois

E. STEANE HARE, Assistant City Engineer, Engineering Department, Vancouver, B.C., Canada

J. GRADY PHELPS, Director, Department of Sanitation, Miami, Florida

CASIMIR A. ROGUS, Director of Engineering, Department of Sanitation, New York, New York

RALPH C. TAYLOR, Superintendent, Waste Collection Division, Cincinnati, Ohio

JOHN S. WILEY, Project Engineer, Office of Solid Wastes, U.S. Public Health Service, Chattanooga, Tennessee

WILLIAM A. XANTEN, Consulting Engineer, Washington, D.C.

JOHN ZEMLANSKY, Principal Sanitarian, New Jersey State Department of Health, Trenton, New Jersey

[1]Retired

FOREWORD TO THIRD EDITION

The publication of this third edition of *Refuse Collection Practice* marks a quarter century since the first edition was issued in 1941, with the second edition appearing in 1958.

Among the reasons dictating the preparation of this third edition was the fact that the second edition, like the first before it, was out of print. Equally important was the need for up-to-date information on systems, methods, finance, and equipment to reflect the changes that had taken place since 1958.

It also reflects the growing realization of the importance of solid waste collection and disposal as indicated, for instance, by the enactment of the Solid Wastes Act of 1965 and by the establishment of the American Public Works Association Institute for Solid Wastes. Future work in this field will be handled by the Institute, rather than the Committee on Solid Wastes, which undertook the present revision of this volume.

The data that served as the basis for this third edition was obtained by means of a comprehensive survey conducted by the APWA in cooperation with the United States Public Health Service, which tabulated the replies to the questionnaire.

Committee members undertook the task of revising the text to reflect the survey results and their own and their colleagues' experiences with refuse collection practices. New photographs were also obtained to illustrate recent developments in equipment and operations.

APWA Executive Director Robert D. Bugher and staff members undertook the task of assembling and correlating the data thus obtained and arranged for its publication by the Public Administration Service. Robert L. Anderson, past president of APWA, a member of the Committee on Solid Wastes and, until his recent retirement, Superintendent of Public Works and Village Engineer of Winnetka, Illinois, did the final editing of the entire text before publication to help insure the highest possible degree of accuracy.

Finally, with the publication of this third edition, we acknowledge our indebtedness to the APWA committee and staff members who, with the cooperation of colleagues and others, prepared the first and second editions.

ABRAHAM MICHAELS, *President*
Institute for Solid Wastes of the
American Public Works Association

FOREWORD TO SECOND EDITION

The technology of municipal refuse practice has undergone vast changes in recent times. Automation, population trends, new products and processes, as well as increasing demands for more and better service, have all made their mark. Municipal officials responsible for the collection and disposal of refuse experienced an increasing need for accurate and reliable informational material such as data on acceptable criteria and current practice. The American Public Works Association's book *Refuse Collection Practice* published in 1941 was out of print. Further, much of the data reported therein no longer applied. No other comprehensive up-to-date text on American practice existed.

In April, 1955, the President of the American Public Works Association appointed a Refuse Collection Committee charged with the responsibility of preparing a revised edition of *Refuse Collection Practice*. Financial support was provided by the American Public Works Association's Research Foundation. Work was begun by developing a plan of procedure based in large part on the use of questionnaires to obtain the necessary information on current practices from the various cities. The Committee recognized the difficulties of obtaining reliable and accurate data for comparative purposes through this method. However, it represented the only economically feasible method of procedure, and it was felt that information of real value to those working in this field could be supplied if the collected data were carefully interpreted. The survey was carried out in two phases. The first consisted of forwarding a questionnaire to all cities in the United States and Canada having more than 5,000 population. The second phase was the forwarding of a more detailed questionnaire to over 100 cities that represented, in the opinion of the Committee members, a group which would be better able to provide more accurate and more complete information on the desired operational, quantity, and cost data.

Of the general questionnaire mailed to all cities of over 5,000 population, 908 or about 38 per cent were returned for analysis. Of the 125 comprehensive questionnaires mailed to selected cities, 89 were returned. In the latter group, replies received included cities ranging from a population of 13,000 (Winnetka, Illinois) to over 8,000,000 (New York City) located in 34 states plus the District of Columbia. All data reported is on experience in 1955 or later.

The cooperation of the U. S. Public Health Service in the tabulation and analysis of the data contained in the returned questionnaires was most helpful. The Committee is particularly fortunate in having had Mr. Leo Weaver as its Secretary. His continuing efforts have been of great value in bringing the Committee's task to a successful conclusion. Mr. Weaver formerly served as a Senior Sanitary Engineer and chief of the Refuse Sanitation Unit of the U. S. Public Health Service and became Director of Research for the American Public Works Association during the last stage of the preparation of this publication.

Mr. Donald F. Herrick, former Executive Director of the American Public Works Association, was most helpful throughout the Committee's activity. Mr. Robert D. Bugher, present Executive Director of the Association, rendered much valuable assistance in the preparation of the questionnaire forms and in making analyses throughout the study.

Final editing and indexing of the volume were accomplished through the Public Administration Service and ably performed by Mrs. Eleanor R. Batson. To Mrs. Batson, the Committee attributes much of the credit for the physical arrangement and clarity of presentation of the material in the text.

The Committee is grateful for the excellent work the previous Committee on Refuse Collection and Disposal performed in the preparation and publication of the 1941 edition of *Refuse Collection Practice*. The soundness and thoroughness of that edition has made its revision immeasurably easier than it otherwise would have been.

The Association and the Committee are of course greatly indebted to the numerous directors of public works and refuse collection officials throughout the country whose valuable and cooperative assistance made possible the basic study leading to this revised volume. I am particularly grateful for the sincere personal efforts which each member of the Refuse Collection Committee has so freely devoted in carrying out his own personal assignments and in reviewing the preliminary drafts of his fellow members.

It is the judgment of the Committee that the text as it now appears in this volume is a representative description and appraisal of current refuse collection practice in American cities.

WARREN A. SCHNEIDER, *Chairman*
Refuse Collection Committee

FOREWORD TO FIRST EDITION

This study of municipal refuse collection practice had its beginnings in 1935 when the Joint Administrative Board of the American Society of Municipal Engineers and the International Association of Public Works Officials established a program which involved the preparation of manuals of practice in the fields of street cleaning and refuse collection and disposal. The purpose of the program was to provide authoritative reference volumes on the operation and management of these municipal services as guides to city officials as well as to others seeking information on modern methods and practices.

The Committee on Refuse Collection and Disposal, to which this present work was assigned, began its work in 1936 by preparing an outline of the subject matter to be covered. The various sections were assigned to outstanding engineers and administrators, who prepared reports for the Committee.

The two associations merged in January 1937 to form the American Public Works Association. A few months later, the Spelman Fund of New York made a grant to the Association to enable it to conduct a program of research in the management and operation of public works activities. The first study, STREET CLEANING PRACTICE, was completed in 1938 and the second, SEWER RENTALS, in 1939. An additional grant from the Spelman Fund in 1939 made it possible to undertake a large program of assembling information on refuse collection practices, by correspondence and by extensive field study, of 190 cities of the United States and Canada. Data on methods, operating experiences, administration, and costs of refuse collection operations were secured from municipalities ranging in population from the very largest to those having but a few thousand inhabitants. Communities of 41 states and 7 provinces of Canada are included.

Eight of the most important chapters of this work (Chapter II to VII inclusive, and Chapters XI and XII) were issued individually in bulletin form and given wide distribution. The threefold purpose of this procedure was to make the information available to officials as soon as possible, to present the material periodically to administrators and supervisors in small sections which are more likely to be read immediately rather than kept for reference, and to get the benefit of the suggestions and criticisms of many authorities and officials engaged in refuse collection work before final publication of the material in book form.

We are particularly fortunate in having had the services of Mr. Stanley I. Pinel, the Association's Director of Research. Mr. Pinel has studied the refuse collection operations of 40 cities in the field and has had extensive correspondence with public works and health officials of more than a hundred other municipalities. He has ably assembled and organized the data, prepared the manuscript of the book, and illustrated the various chapters.

Mr. Frank W. Herring, Executive Director of the American Public Works Association, on leave, and now Assistant Director of the National Resources Planning Board, is deserving of much credit for his organizational work at the outset of this study and his continued helpfulness throughout. Mr. Joseph F. Base, member of the Association's research staff, rendered valuable assistance in preparing numerous tabulations and in making analyses during the early part of the study. Also acknowledgment is due Mr. Harvey Karlan, research staff member, for his contributions to the chapter on personnel and public relations and for his help in preparing parts of the manuscript for printing.

The Association is indebted to directors of public works and refuse collection officials all over the country without whose valuable and enthusiastic cooperation this study would not have been possible. I am particularly grateful to the members of the Committee on Refuse Collection and Disposal who have so freely devoted much time and effort to the evaluation and criticism of the preliminary drafts and preprints of the various parts of the book. Of this Committee Carl Schneider, Consulting Engineer, deserves special mention for his valued participation in the activities of both this committee and an earlier committee of the Joint Administration Board. All of the drafts have been given close scrutiny and the Committee believes that the work as it now appears is a faithful description and appraisal of current refuse collection practice in American cities.

> STUART M. WEAVER, *Chairman*
> Committee on Refuse Collection and Disposal

Members of committee responsible for preparation of First Edition:

William J. Galligan	Carl Schneider
David W. Godat	Ralph C. Taylor
John V. Lewis	Jean L. Vincenz

CONTENTS

Cooperation Among Departments and Divisions, 302; Internal Organization, 302; The Refuse Collection Administrator, 302; Provision for Line Activities, 303; Provision for Staff Activities, 306; Organization Charts, 307.

13. PERSONNEL 314

Essentials of Sound Personnel Management, 315; Effect of Existing Personnel Policies, 315; Personnel Practices in Refuse Collection Organizations, 317; Recruitment, 317; Wages and Hours, 318; Task System, 319; Fringe Benefits, 321; Working Conditions and Safety, 323; Employee Training, 326; Rules and Regulations, 326; Employee Suggestion Systems, 327; Service Ratings, 328; Employee Organizations, 329; Labor-Management Relations, 332; Summary, 335.

14. EQUIPMENT MANAGEMENT 336

Organization for Equipment Management, 336; Management and Operation, 337; Function of Equipment Organization, 337; Purchasing Equipment, 338; Truck Chassis, 340; Control of Equipment, 341; Identification of Equipment, 342; Inventory Control, 342; Equipment Rental Plan, 342; Assignment of Equipment, 343; Plant Facilities, 343; Preventive Maintenance, 344; Cleaning the Equipment, 352: Retirement of Equipment, 353; Training and Equipment Operation, 354; Renting Private Equipment, 355; Amount of Equipment Needed, 356; Insurance, 356; Accident Prevention Programs, 357; Equipment Records and Reports, 358; Summary, 359.

15. REPORTING, COST ACCOUNTING, AND BUDGETING 360

Measurement of Performance and Efficiency, 360; Field Reporting of Removal Operations, 364; Present Status of Field Reporting, 365; Content of Field Reports,368; Summary Statements of Performance and Cost, 369; Summaries of Performance, 369; Summaries of Unit Costs, 371; Cost Accounting for Refuse Collection, 371; Preparing Work Programs, 375; Forecasting the Amount of Work, 376; Determining Standard Costs, 377; Consolidating Forecasts and Costs, 377; Changes in Work Programs, 378; Budgetary Control, 378; Data Processing—Solid Wastes Collection Application, 379; Summary, 380.

16. PUBLIC RELATIONS 381

Policies of the Municipal Government, 381; Influences of Personnel Practices, 382; Employee Contacts with Citizens, 383; Training for Contacts, 383; Personal Contacts, 384; Contacts

Through Correspondence, 386; Contacts by Telephone, 386; Handling Complaints, 386; Good Relations Through Effective Operation, 389; Public Education, 391; Organization for Public Education, 393; Development of a Campaign, 396; Enforcement of Ordinances and Regulations, 399; Summary, 406.

appendices

chapter 1

THE REFUSE COLLECTION PROBLEM

The collection and removal of municipal refuse—one of the major problems of American cities—has been given less attention than this essential public function deserves. Only within relatively recent years have most municipal officials been willing to admit that refuse disposal is a technical management problem worthy of their attention and study. Much progress has been made, but still only a minority of communities are using the administrative techniques which generally have proved most satisfactory. Not that methods, equipment, and practices should be uniform over the country. Conditions vary, and it is vital that procedures vary to meet them. However, the problem should be approached the same way in all communities, should be analyzed in terms of sound administrative management, and should receive the same consideration usually given other public health aspects of government.

What is the refuse collection problem? From the public administration point of view, it is to determine the best method or methods of collecting refuse produced by the community in a sanitary manner consistent with the desires of the inhabitants. After determining health and service level standards, reliable and efficient collection procedures should be established.

NECESSITY FOR REFUSE REMOVAL

People living in cities and towns continuously produce large quantities of waste materials which they cannot ordinarily dispose of safely, effectively, or economically by themselves. Garbage results from processing, marketing, storing, and preparing food; rubbish of all kinds accumulates through the normal processes of living; and ashes are produced wherever coal, coke, or wood is burned. Such materials cannot be accumulated on individual properties without menacing public health, creating fire hazards, utilizing valuable space needed for other purposes, causing nuisances, and generally detracting from community appearance. Refuse removal so greatly affects public interest that it is almost universally agreed that municipal governments must be responsible for seeing that suitable arrangements are made for collection and disposal.

Whether the complete removal of all refuse is necessary, however,

1

depends to some extent on the size of the community and the relative density of its population. Very small municipalities may need but little organized collection service, particularly where houses are far apart and businesses are neither large nor numerous. Even in such places, however, garbage must be removed frequently and regularly because it decomposes rapidly and soon produces foul odors and provides breeding places for flies. In some cases, it may be possible to bury the material on the individual properties, but this practice is discouraged in modern communities. It may not be necessary to have any regular removal service for ashes and rubbish where the combustible rubbish can be burned on the properties without creating nuisances, and the noncombustible rubbish and ashes can be accumulated without ill effect and occasionally removed by the residents themselves.

FIG. 1-1. Large quantities of refuse accumulate on properties in densely populated areas unless frequent collection service is given. One of the very important problems is to provide for the temporary storage of the refuse in such a manner that public health is not endangered, nuisances are not created, and communities are not made unsightly. The refuse shown above has been very carelessly handled. Proper containers would eliminate such littering.

As communities become larger and people live closer together, however, it is increasingly unsatisfactory to burn refuse or to store it on individual properties. Also, it becomes more difficult for householders to get rid of their own rubbish and ashes, and the nuisances caused by such individual disposal become more important. Gradually, organized service for the removal of all classes of refuse becomes essential, not only in the interests of protecting public health and avoiding nuisances, but also in the interest of over-all economy.

RESPONSIBILITY FOR REFUSE COLLECTION

Since the storage, collection, and disposal of refuse affect the health and welfare of a community, local government must accept the responsibility for regulating these functions and services. The refuse collection service may be performed by a governmental agency, by a refuse collection contractor under contract with government, by a contractor under direct contract with the resident or refuse producer, or by the refuse producer himself. However, regardless of who collects and hauls the refuse, the government should police the activity to insure conformity to regulations. Although in the final analysis the residents of the community determine the level of refuse collection service desired, government establishes the refuse storage and collection standards insofar as they affect the community's health.

Two types of standards must be recognized when considering refuse collection: public health and public convenience. These are intimately related and must be considered simultaneously when standards are established. The community is largely responsible for establishing convenience standards such as collection source, i.e. curb side vs. back yard, collection frequency (when greater than minimum required from health standpoint), and combined vs. separate collections. The local government must establish operational ordinances and public health standards such as refuse storage regulations, minimum collection frequencies, refuse collection vehicle regulations, etc., and these standards should be reviewed regularly in recognition of changing conditions.

STANDARD OF SERVICE

The public health standards will be influenced by such factors as population density, climate, age of the community, and disposal methods. The public convenience standards will be influenced by all of the health factors plus historical practices, economic level of the community, and public interest. Although these factors do vary, and although there is no measuring method available to determine the effectiveness of a particular collection system, adequate public health environmental standards should be established for each community. These standards should be determined by competent health authorities taking into account such factors as insect and rodent breeding and feeding habits.

COOPERATION OF HOUSEHOLDERS

The effectiveness of a collection system and the cost of the operation depend to a great extent on the cooperation of the householders in providing proper containers, preparing and storing the refuse in accordance with regulations, and regularly placing the material for collection. It is not enough to prepare and adopt suitable ordinances and regulations. Officials must see that the code of practice is followed. Public education is the most effective and economical means of securing the assistance of citizens, but if a well planned and continuous educational

FIG. 1-2. The cooperation of householders is essential to the proper handling and removal of refuse. This picture was taken on a Philadelphia street before a campaign was inaugurated to improve the appearance of the community and to reduce the cost of street cleaning.

program fails to secure desired results the ordinances should be rigidly enforced. Unfortunately, many cities do neither, and the collection work is far more difficult, time-consuming, and expensive than necessary.

EFFECT OF DISPOSAL METHODS

The means used to dispose of refuse influence collection practices to such a great extent that the disposal methods must be determined and the disposal sites selected before the collection system can be intelligently studied. The size and kind of equipment depend on the length of the haul to the disposal points and on the nature of the refuse collected. It is obvious, therefore, that a change in disposal method or in the location of the plants or dumps requires a reappraisal of the collection methods, equipment, and procedures, and the adjustment of them to conform to the new conditions. All too frequently, the collection arrangements are made with little or no consideration of the disposal situation. In such cases, the cost of the work is likely to be much too high.

SEASONAL AND DAILY VARIATIONS

The amount of refuse produced varies considerably with the seasons of the year. The quantity of garbage is greatest in the summer months when fresh fruits and vegetables are plentiful and smallest in the winter months. Yard rubbish is most plentiful in spring and fall, although some must be collected throughout the summer. Ashes are normally produced only in the cold months. In resort places the total amount of refuse may vary considerably with the seasonal population.

FIG. 1-3. Philadelphia regulations require that all rubbish be placed in suitable containers or be carefully bundled and tied. This is the same street shown in Fig. 1-2 shortly after the city secured the cooperation of householders. By the expenditure of very little effort, communities can be kept attractive and refuse collection and street cleaning expense can be substantially reduced.

Such variations add to the difficulty of administering refuse collection services. The collection force and the number of vehicles must be equal to times of peak production, which means that operating procedures must be flexible enough to permit the work to be conducted economically at all times. Sometimes crews and vehicles can be shifted from one class of collection to another or to some other municipal activity. In other cases, the size of the force must be adjusted to the work load. If the size of the force is kept constant, a variation in the hours of work will be necessary.

In addition to seasonal variation, the quantity of refuse may also be considerably different even from one collection to the next. Supervisors must constantly be in close touch with the operations so that the irregularities are known and necessary adjustments made. No refuse collection system can be so routine and mechanical that it will run efficiently by itself.

REFUSE COLLECTION METHODS

There are several methods of getting the refuse to the collection vehicles from the points where householders place it: (1) The material may be transferred from regular containers located at curbs or in alleys. (2) The full containers may be carried from back doors or basements and the empty receptacles returned. (3) The material may be emptied from the containers into carrying tubs or baskets and then carried to the vehicles. (4) Full cans may be exchanged for clean empty ones. (5) Large portable containers may be located at strategic points and picked up and emptied or carried to the disposal site using specially designed hoisting and carrying equipment. (6) Disposable refuse bags may be used for curb, alley, or back door collections. Sometimes the refuse is shoveled from piles on the ground or from alley vaults, but this practice is considered undesirable and is rapidly disappearing. Also, separate

FIG. 1-4. Methods and equipment must be adapted in each community to the existing conditions. The density of population, the unit weight of the refuse, the width of streets as shown here in Philadelphia, and many other factors must be taken into consideration.

set-out and set-back crews may be employed. The wise choice is dictated partly by the citizens and partly by a careful analysis of conditions.

The methods of organizing crews also vary widely among cities. Each crew may operate independently on a daily or weekly route basis with one or more collection vehicles, or two or more crews may be integrated in different ways on larger routes. The problem is to determine the method that permits the most effective work at the least cost.

COLLECTION EQUIPMENT

Collection equipment is usually selected for reasons of economy, sanitation, and appearance. Available are trucks, semi-trailers, trailers, container trains, motorized carts, and bodies in a wide range of types, sizes, and capacities. The goal is to obtain the equipment which is best suited to satisfactorily meet local conditions.

It is the citizens who ultimately set the standards of appearance and sanitation of collection equipment which will produce adequate service for the community. The administrator must decide which kind, size, and capacity of vehicle is the most economical and effective for particular conditions. The size of the chassis must be proportioned to the capacity of the body of a vehicle according to the unit weight of the refuse to be handled and according to the length of haul to the disposal point. Numerous other factors such as loading height, mechanical loading and unloading devices, covers, turning radius, watertightness, use of automatic drives, compaction devices, and safety features influence the over-all economy as well as the effectiveness of the equipment. Furthermore, it may be desirable to select vehicles that can also be used for other municipal work.

Under certain circumstances it is uneconomical to transport the refuse to the disposal site in the collection vehicles. If the most suitable equipment is not efficient for long hauls, it is well to transfer the collected material to other vehicles. If the disposal areas cannot be reached by highways, supplemental transportation by railroad or boat becomes necessary. Consequently, transfer stations must sometimes be provided to facilitate the shifting of the refuse to another conveyance.

PLANNING REFUSE COLLECTION OPERATIONS

The importance of sound planning of refuse collection operations must not be underestimated. All too often, refuse administrators are content to lay out collection systems and select methods and equipment by rules of thumb, guesses, estimates, or prejudiced opinions.

Sound planning involves a thorough analysis of all the factors affecting the collecting problem. These include a factual survey of the community refuse problem, the effects of the established methods, materials to be handled, the types of equipment available or selected, the physical layout of the area, factors affecting personnel practices, and the financial potential of the operating division. Studies are underway to determine the feasibility of using computers for refuse collection systems analysis.

Such an analytical approach may sound very complex and time consuming. True, considerable study and work are necessary, but the savings that will result through economical collection will pay many times over for the expense of investigation and analysis. Moreover, the equalization of the work made possible by such studies will promote better relations between the collectors and their superiors.

SPECIAL PROBLEMS

In addition to the many questions pertaining to the regular collection activities, numerous other matters, related more or less directly to the removal work, are important in the administration of a refuse removal agency. Among these are: the control and regulation of scavengers, private collectors, and contractors; the removal of market refuse; the handling of condemned food; the collection of dead animals; the management of annual or semi-annual clean-up campaigns; the coordination of the removal of street cleaning dirt and litter with regular municipal refuse; and the control of refuse hauling by citizens. Many such special problems arise in every community and must be given considerable attention and study if satisfactory results are to be secured.

FIG. 1-5. Refuse collection equipment must be selected in accordance with local standards of sanitation and community appearance as well as for economy of operation and safety. The enclosed-body vehicles of Los Angeles keep all loaded refuse from view, prevent the dissemination of odors, provide easy loading by collectors, and present a good appearance.

FINANCING REFUSE COLLECTION

Traditionally, refuse collection service for residential communities has been financed from general tax revenues. However, the practice of using service charges has increased in recent years as a means of financing refuse collection service. Some communities use special assessments or specific taxes to obtain funds for this service.

The removal of refuse from commercial properties constitutes one of the most difficult problems. It is just as important for public health and community appearance to have complete refuse collection in the business areas as in residence sections, but the amount of service required by some places is so great that it seems unfair to provide it free of charge. Several ways of dealing with this problem have been tried. Some cities will not make any collection from business places on the grounds that the removal work is a legitimate business expense and the service should not be provided by the city at large. Other cities collect from all properties but have a maximum limit so that very large producers are not unduly favored. Still others charge for all of the commercial refuse collected or for all over a stipulated amount. In some cases, tickets are sold to refuse producers, each ticket being for the removal of a specified quantity of material. Billing for such service charges or extra charges may be much the same as for water service, and sometimes the refuse charges are placed on water or electric bills. No matter what methods for financing are chosen, the character of the refuse collection service must ultimately depend on the success of such methods in raising the required funds.

ORGANIZATION

There is no one best plan of organization for a refuse collection unit. The plan chosen in any particular locality depends on the form of government in the city, size of the community, density of population, kind of service to be rendered, and numerous other factors. Whether the city is to be the active collecting agent or is merely to supervise contract or private collection will determine the character and scope of the organization.

If the first method is used, the refuse collection agency may be a separate and complete unit, it may be combined with other sanitation services in a separate department, or it may be a part of the general public works or public health department.

If the city acts solely, or in part, in a supervisory capacity, the problem is mainly one of safeguarding public health and regulating the activities of collectors and citizens to see that the ordinances and rules are obeyed. A health department, public works department, or even a police department may be made responsible.

In practice, refuse collection organizations are arranged by American cities in every possible way—and this cannot in itself be condemned, for the benefits and disadvantages of each plan must be considered in the light of the local circumstances. The internal organization of the refuse collection unit can also be arranged according to many different schemes. The work may be divided according to the separation of refuse or on a geographical basis into areas, districts, or even collection routes. It may be feasible to follow a functional arrangement, allowing a single group to conduct operations of the same kind throughout the city, or the work may be combined with street cleaning or other activities. For a particular community, a combination of these various types may offer the best solution, and this best solution must be found if the work of collecting refuse is to be well administered, adequately supervised, and properly coordinated with other municipal activities.

FIG. 1-6. Refuse collection forces are uniformed in some cities to increase the morale of the employees, to make the service more attractive, to promote safety, and to identify the municipal employees. The uniform on the right is worn by all refuse collectors and truck drivers of the New York City Department of Sanitation. A supervisor's uniform is shown on the left.

PERSONNEL

Unless personnel are intelligently handled, the administration and supervision of refuse collection activities are extremely difficult and costs are much greater than necessary. When personnel practices are unwise, the work suffers in quality and effectiveness, friction is created within the service itself, and the best interests of the community are not served.

The policies of personnel procedure and employment practices and benefits are established in most municipalities for the entire service. These policies must be thoroughly studied and understood by the officials responsible for establishing and administrating a collection unit. *Esprit de corps* and high morale are valuable assets and are reflected in performance. The personnel administrator for the municipality can provide valuable advice and assistance to the refuse administrator in such areas as recruitment, performance rating, record keeping, supervision, and relations with unions.

Although many of the tasks performed by the refuse collection personnel are in the unskilled categories, employee training is extremely important. Safety of the individual worker, of his fellow worker, job safety, and efficient use of energy and equipment must be stressed. Training in public relations should be given every employee, regardless of rank in the organization to assure those attitudes which enhance this relationship.

Training in the lower echelons can form a basis for training for promotions and betterment of self and the service, assuring an adequate reservoir of properly indoctrinated men for filling higher positions.

MANAGEMENT OF EQUIPMENT

Inadequately maintained, worn out, or unsuitable equipment means inefficient refuse collection. Because refuse collection is basically a materials handling and transporting problem, the question of equipment maintenance and management is particularly important.

The administration of refuse collection equipment on a rental basis, either as a part of a central municipal equipment service or separately for the collection agency, has proved very effective in the cities in which it is employed. Under this plan the cost of equipment is definitely known and is accurately charged to activities, classes of refuse, districts, or routes as required. Not only is good administration of the whole service made easier, but the detailed cost and performance records make possible sound equipment management. Cities that lack such effective control probably have costs higher than necessary and service less effective than should reasonably be expected.

PUBLIC RELATIONS

There is no other service offered by a community which has so intimate a contact with the individual citizen as the refuse collection service. Because of this close contact it is vitally important that each man in the service have the proper "public relations attitude."

He should be imbued with a genuine desire to provide good service. This service should be impartial, performed in a neat and efficient manner, and the employees should be competent, willing and efficient. When the refuse collection service is of such a caliber, it will take its place successfully in the larger framework of a city's public relations program and can greatly influence the success or failure of any administration.

Every employee in the refuse collection service should be trained in contacting the public whether his job calls for contact in person, by telephone, or by letter. All requests for information and all complaints should be acknowledged promptly and courteously. If possible, a personal contact on the ground should be made as soon as possible and then if necessary followed up by proper written reply. Decisions should be backed by the logic of operational problems rather than flat recitals of codes, ordinances, or rules. But more important than the settling of complaints is the carrying out of the work in such a manner as to eliminate the cause in the beginning. The chief causes of complaints are the rough handling of containers, spillage of refuse, damage to lawns and shrubbery by collectors, and incomplete removal service. These can be minimized by the training of personnel and by instilling in them a desire to do a good job. The training of drivers to operate their equipment properly is also important. The impression which city equipment makes on the citizen depends on its use as well as on its appearance. A reckless driver or an inconsiderate driver is not liked under any circumstance, but if he is driving a municipal vehicle his offense is doubly magnified. A driver training program will pay dividends not only in improved public relations but in reduced costs.

SUMMARY

The success of the administration of a refuse collection system depends in a large measure on the extent to which the many aspects of the problem are recognized and constructively handled. The task of managing a removal service is a tremendous one, comparable to that of a large business enterprise. It cannot be ignored as an activity too humble in nature for the serious attention of officials, administrators, or citizens. Competent supervisors must be placed in charge of the work and all of the techniques of modern administrative management must be employed if effective and economical service is to be realized.

chapter 2

REFUSE MATERIALS

The many previous attempts, including the first two editions of *Refuse Collection Practice,* to standardize the definitions of refuse and its constituent materials have not been as successful as desired. The fact that refuse is highly heterogeneous increases the importance of specific definitions of its various components to avoid confusion. Too often a city uses the term "garbage" to mean all of the materials accepted for collection. Garbage has a specific meaning and should not be used as a synonym for refuse or to include other constituents of refuse such as rubbish. Many cities specify in ordinances or codes the various refuse materials acceptable for collection and disposal. Lack of common terminology for these categories of refuse makes it difficult to interpret the literature on this subject. This confusion may be especially important in connection with court decisions.

Even though the constituents of refuse are constantly changing in character and amounts, it seems essential in this discussion to define the terms used to identify different classes of refuse and to state as precisely as possible what materials make up each class. It is hoped that greater use of the following terminology will be made, particularly in ordinances and codes as cities initiate or revise their refuse collection and disposal requirements.

DEFINITIONS OF REFUSE MATERIALS

The following definitions of refuse and its component materials apply throughout this volume and represent the most widespread meanings of the terms.

Waste

The word waste refers to the useless, unwanted, or discarded materials resulting from normal community activities. Wastes include solids, liquids, and gases. Atmospheric wastes consist of particulate matter, such as dust and smoke, fumes, and gases. Liquid wastes consist mainly of sewage and industrial wastewaters, including both dissolved and suspended matter. Solid wastes are classed as refuse. The physical state of wastes may change in their conveyance or treatment. Dewatered sludge from wastewater treatment plants may become solid wastes;

garbage may be ground and discharged into sewers becoming water-borne wastes; and fly ash may be removed from stack discharges and disposed of as solid or as water-borne wastes.

Refuse

Refuse comprises all of the solid wastes of the community. It also includes semi-liquid or wet wastes with insufficient moisture and other liquid contents to be free-flowing.

The component materials of refuse can be classified in several different ways. In connection with some problems, its point of origin is important. From this standpoint, it can be considered made up of domestic, institutional, commercial, industrial, agricultural, or street refuse. In other problems the point of origin is not so important as the nature of the material itself, and classification may be made on the basis of organic or inorganic character, putrescibility or nonputrescibility, combustibility or noncombustibility. One of the most useful classifications is based on the character of materials, and includes garbage, rubbish, ashes, bulky wastes, street refuse, dead animals, abandoned vehicles, construction and demolition wastes, industrial refuse, agricultural wastes, and special wastes. Table 2-1 represents such a grouping of refuse materials, describes each category, and indicates in a general way its origin.

Most of the duties of the refuse collection agency consist of the collection of garbage, rubbish, and ashes either separately or together. When combined collection of garbage and rubbish is practiced, the term "refuse" should be used whether or not ashes and yard wastes are included. Because of the ill-defined nature of the term "trash," it is recommended that the term "rubbish" be used instead in cases where the storage and collection of garbage is separated.

Bulky wastes may require collection from residential and commercial areas or from public property and vacant lots. They are given a separate classification because often special collection vehicles and trips are required for their collection. Not all types of collection trucks are suitable.

Street refuse is generally collected as a part of the street maintenance and cleaning functions. While removal and disposal of dead animals may be included in the duties of the refuse collection agency, it is generally managed as a special problem rather than as a routine activity. Responsibility for removal of abandoned vehicles may rest with the street cleaning agency or the police department. Construction and demolition wastes may be the responsibility of the contractor, private collector, or the refuse collection agency, but requirements for their disposal should be established by the municipality or other administrative agency.

Ordinarily, industrial solid wastes are the responsibility of the industry, but there is a trend towards city collection of some types of "trade" refuse. With expanding metropolitan areas, agricultural activities

TABLE 2-1
Classification of Refuse Materials

Refuse (Solid Wastes)	Garbage	Wastes from the preparation, cooking, and serving of food Market refuse, waste from the handling, storage, and sale of produce and meats		From: households, institutions, and commercial concerns such as: hotels, stores, restaurants, markets, etc.
	Rubbish	Combustible (primarily organic)	Paper, cardboard, cartons Wood, boxes, excelsior Plastics Rags, cloth, bedding Leather, rubber Grass, leaves, yard trimmings	
		Noncombustible (primarily inorganic)	Metals, tin cans, metal foils Dirt Stones, bricks, ceramics, crockery Glass, bottles Other mineral refuse	
	Ashes	Residue from fires used for cooking and for heating buildings, cinders		
	Bulky Wastes	Large auto parts, tires Stoves, refrigerators, other large appliances Furniture, large crates Trees, branches, palm fronds, stumps, flotage		From: streets, sidewalks, alleys, vacant lots, etc.
	Street refuse	Street sweepings, dirt Leaves Catch basin dirt Contents of litter receptacles		
	Dead animals	Small animals: cats, dogs, poultry, etc. Large animals: horses, cows, etc.		
	Abandoned vehicles	Automobiles, trucks		
	Construction & Demolition wastes	Lumber, roofing, and sheathing scraps Rubble, broken concrete, plaster, etc. Conduit, pipe, wire, insulation, etc.		
	Industrial refuse	Solid wastes resulting from industrial processes and manufacturing operations, such as: food-processing wastes, boiler house cinders, wood, plastic, and metal scraps and shavings, etc.		From: factories, power plants, etc.
	Special wastes	Hazardous wastes: pathological wastes, explosives, radioactive materials Security wastes: confidential documents, negotiable papers, etc.		Households, hospitals, institutions, stores, industry, etc.
	Animal and Agricultural wastes	Manures, crop residues		Farms, feed lots
	Sewage treatment residues	Coarse screenings, grit, septic tank sludge, dewatered sludge		Sewage treatment plants, septic tanks

are often engulfed by residential or commercial development. Where disposal of manures or crop residues can no longer be done on the farm without public health or nuisance hazards, these wastes require consideration in the over-all refuse collection and disposal plan. There is a trend towards more culling, cleaning, and even packing of fruits and vegetables in the fields, leaving wastes which may putrefy causing fly and odor problems, unless they are suitably removed or treated.

Garbage

Garbage is the animal and vegetable waste resulting from the handling, preparation, cooking, and serving of foods. It is composed largely of putrescible organic matter, and its natural moisture content. While it normally includes only a minimum amount of free liquids, collection vehicles for garbage must still be water-tight. The term garbage does not include food-processing wastes from canneries, slaughterhouses, packing plants, or similar industries; large quantities of condemned food products; or oyster or clam shells. Garbage originates primarily in home kitchens, stores, markets, restaurants, hotels, and other places where food is stored, prepared, or served.

Garbage decomposes rapidly, particularly in warm weather, and may soon produce disagreeable odors. When carelessly stored, it is a source of food for rats and other vermin and serves as a breeding place for flies.

The terms, "swill," "slops," and "offal," which are frequently found in city ordinances to define garbage, are not properly synonymous with garbage. "Swill" and "slops" connote semi-liquid waste material consisting of garbage and free liquids. Where cities do not collect such materials, hog raisers operating as private collectors frequently collect it from restaurants, hotels, and institutions. The word "offal" has had so many different meanings that its use is avoided in this volume, except to refer to intestines and discarded parts from the slaughter of animals.

Market Refuse

Market refuse comes from wholesale and retail stores and markets as a result of the handling, storage, and selling of foods. It originates principally in poultry, fish, meat, vegetable, and fruit markets, and includes large quantities of putrescible garbage along with some rubbish such as wooden crates and cardboard boxes. It also includes some condemned foods but not large quantities of spoiled material.

Because of the high putrescibility of market wastes, the protection of the fresh food supply and the appearance of the community make frequent collection necessary.

Rubbish

Rubbish consists of a variety of both combustible and noncombustible solid waste materials from households, stores, and institutions. This waste is defined more specifically as "combustible rubbish" and "noncombustible rubbish," but whenever the term "rubbish" is used alone it means a combination of combustible and noncombustible rubbish. When other materials such as garbage or ashes are collected with rubbish, the mixture should then be designated as "combined" refuse.

Combustible Rubbish. Combustible rubbish consists of miscellaneous burnable materials. In general, it is the organic component of rubbish, such as paper, rags, cartons, boxes, wood, excelsior, bedding, rubber, leather, grass, leaves, yard trimmings, plus combustible inorganic materials such as plastics. Combustible rubbish, primarily organic, is generally not highly putrescible and therefore may be properly stored for relatively long periods without being a nuisance. It has a high heat value and when dry burns freely without forced draft or auxiliary fuel. While garbage is also largely organic and combustible, it is generally classified separately from combustible rubbish because of its putrescibility and high moisture content.

Noncombustible Rubbish. Noncombustible rubbish consists of miscellaneous refuse materials that are unburnable at ordinary incinerator operating temperatures (1300° F to 2000° F). For the most part, it is the inorganic component of rubbish, such as tin cans, metals, dirt, ceramics, glass, and the like. Although noncombustible rubbish is very stable, it is esthetically objectionable and may harbor rodents and other vermin if it is carelessly stored.

Tin cans and bottles that once contained food may have a residue of putrescible material clinging to them when discarded. Under ordinary conditions, this organic matter desiccates rather than putrefies. In a warm, moist atmosphere, however, the remnants of food in noncombustible containers may serve as breeding places for flies and other insects and may necessitate more frequent collection than normally required for noncombustible rubbish.

Yard Rubbish. Yard rubbish consists of prunings, grass clippings, weeds, leaves, and general yard and garden wastes. When collected, it often contains some earth clinging to the roots of grass, weeds, and discarded plants. Much of the yard rubbish is green vegetation which, when kept moist or stored in large masses, decomposes rather rapidly. While not ordinarily objectionable, these materials may serve as a breeding place for insects under certain conditions. This green material can be burned in an incinerator, but normally will not sustain a fire alone. Dried vegetation, dead leaves, and plants do not cause any sanitary or nuisance hazard and will burn readily in an open fire.

Yard rubbish is really a part of combustible rubbish, rather than a main class by itself, but it is separately defined because cities frequently make different arrangements for its collection, or even exclude it entirely from their collection service. Yard rubbish may be collected with other rubbish, but cities often specify different types of containers or bundles of certain maximum size for its storage on the premises.

Ashes

Ashes are the residue from the burning of wood, coal, coke, and other combustible material in homes, stores, institutions, and small industrial establishments for the purposes of heating, cooking, and disposing of waste combustible material. Cinders that are produced in large quantities at steam-generating plants are not included within the meaning of the term.

Ashes are usually composed of a mixture of fine powdery residue, cinders, clinkers, and small portions of unburned or partially burned fuel or other material. Some metal, glass, and combustible materials are usually found in ashes when they are presented for collection. The residue may be a fire hazard as it may still contain live coals. Since the mixture is mostly inorganic, it is valuable for making fills on low land, even in or near built-up communities; and it is acceptable in some cases as cover material in sanitary landfills. Except for the dust that they may create, ashes are not objectionable from a nuisance or esthetic standpoint. Where there is a separation for collection purposes between combustibles and noncombustibles, many cities ask that noncombustibles such as broken crockery, cans, bottles, and all metals be discarded with the ashes.

The residue from household refuse incinerators and from yard rubbish burners is classed as ashes, as are the remains from burning leaves and yard rubbish in open fires. However, when garbage is only partly burned in low temperature or inefficiently-operated domestic incinerators, local authorities may require that the contents of incinerator pits be stored and collected as garbage or combustible refuse, or they may refuse them for collection. In such cases, the incinerator or the operation thereof should be modified so that garbage will be burned to a proper ash, or attempts to incinerate such material should be discontinued.

The residue from central or municipal incinerators should be classified under industrial refuse, rather than under ashes. Incinerator residue may be quite substantial in amount and generally contains most of the items listed under noncombustible rubbish (see Table 2-1).

Bulky Wastes

Bulky wastes are large items of refuse such as appliances, furniture, large auto parts, trees and branches, palm fronds, stumps, flotage, etc. These may be generated in residential or commercial areas, on public property such as parks, streets, alleys, and beaches, or they may be abandoned on vacant lots. Some bulky wastes may require special collection arrangements and vehicles.

Some items, such as boxes and crates, can be greatly reduced in size on the premises so that they may be stored in regular containers or tied in bundles for collection. In cities where there are many trees, particularly on public property, special trimming and collection service may be required and the use of chippers to reduce volume may be indicated.

Street Refuse

Street refuse is material picked up by manual and mechanical sweeping of streets and sidewalks, litter from public litter receptacles, and dirt removed from catch basins. It includes dirt, leaves, paper, and the like. Some cities assign the task of collection of street refuse to the regular refuse collection agency, while others assign it to the street department.

Dead Animals

As a class of urban refuse, dead animals are those that die naturally or from disease or are accidentally killed. Condemned animals or parts of animals from slaughterhouses or similar places are not included in this term, but are regarded as industrial refuse.

Dead animals may be classified according to size. The large animals are horses, cows, goats, sheep, hogs, and the like. These have value because of the grease and tankage that can be produced from them in rendering plants. Their hides also have some value. Collection of large animals is usually a separate operation and may require special equipment. Small animals are dogs, cats, rabbits, squirrels, chickens, and rats. These can be effectively handled in the routine collection service.

Dead animals are particularly offensive from both sanitary and esthetic viewpoints and usually must be collected promptly—often on an emergency call basis. They putrefy rapidly, particularly in warm, moist atmospheres, and have a strong attraction for flies and other vermin. Animal traffic victims are sometimes crushed by many vehicles passing over them and therefore must be picked up promptly.

Abandoned Vehicles

This class of refuse includes passenger automobiles, trucks, and trailers that are no longer useful as such and have been left on city streets and in other public places. Usually they are found stripped of tires, wheels, lights, and other easily salvaged parts. They must be removed by municipal authorities or under local governmental control. This task may be part of the work of the regular refuse collection agency, or a duty of the street cleaning, highway, or police department.

Construction and Demolition Wastes

Construction and demolition wastes are the waste building materials and rubble resulting from construction, remodeling, repair, and demolition operations on houses, commercial buildings, pavements, and other structures. They comprise a great variety of rejected matter, such as excavated earth, stones, concrete, bricks, plaster, roofing, sheathing, lumber, insulation, and wastes from installation or demolition of plumbing, heating, and electrical systems.

Small amounts of this refuse material may be accepted as normal waste from households and stores, but the larger, bulkier amounts require special collection either by private industry or by the municipality. With the great increase in metropolitan populations, new housing and shopping developments, slum clearance, urban redevelopment, and freeway construction, the problem of collection and disposal of construction and demolition wastes is becoming urgent in many areas.

Industrial Refuse

Industrial refuse consists of the solid waste materials from factories, processing plants, and other manufacturing enterprises. It is usually of a special character, peculiar to a specific industry, and its removal should be the responsibility of the industry. Refuse of this class may include putrescible garbage from food-processing plants and slaughterhouses; condemned foods; cinders and ashes from power plants, central incinerators, and large factories; and miscellaneous manufacturing wastes. Because putrescible industrial refuse may cause serious nuisances and even endanger public health, its storage, hauling, and disposition should be subject to municipal control.

Industrial refuse should not be confused with commercial refuse or so-called "trade wastes" which emanate from stores, hotels, restaurants, markets, and similar concerns operated for profit. Responsibility for its collection and disposal varies but is subject to local governmental control.

Special Wastes

Special wastes are defined as hazardous wastes by reason of their pathological, explosive, radioactive, or toxic nature. They require very careful handling and disposal to render them innocuous or safe from human and animal contact for an adequate decay period. While most of these wastes will be disposed of by the institution or industry generating them, others from residential or commercial areas may be put out for regular municipal collection. These are mainly solid wastes or liquids in containers, generally explosive or highly flammable in nature, which should be carefully segregated at the source or at the time of pickup. They present hazards to collectors and may cause dangerous explosions or flash fires at incinerators, grinding plants, sanitary landfills, or refuse dumps.

Animal and Agriculture Wastes

Agricultural wastes are principally the manures and crop residues from various agricultural pursuits, including dairying and the raising of livestock and poultry. Although agriculture is normally thought of as separated from municipalities, in many areas the rapid growth of cities and suburbs has engulfed various types of farms and small ranches. In some cases, residential, commercial, or industrial developments spring up on one or more sides of a farm and the usual farm methods of storage and disposal of wastes are impractical or create nuisance and health hazards.

Animal wastes include, in addition to those mentioned above, wastes from stables, kennels, pet pens, chicken coops, veterinary establishments, and the like. These wastes are often public health and nuisance problems.

Where cities expand to include some agricultural installations or where the refuse collection area is enlarged to include the entire county or special districts with both urban and rural activities, major sanitary problems of animal and agricultural waste disposal are generated which cannot be ignored. Such wastes are largely organic and readily decomposable so that they must be disposed of in a sanitary manner or converted to safe useful products. Although large quantities of agricultural wastes may not be collected along with municipal refuse, their joint treatment or disposal may be most satisfactory and economical.

Sewage Treatment Residues

These wastes consist of coarse screenings, grit, and dewatered or air-dried sludge from sewage treatment plants, and pumpings of cesspool or septic tank sludges which require disposal with municipal solid wastes. While the latter sludges are actually liquid wastes and may be disposed of by approval in certain sewers or at sewage treatment plants, this is often impractical or unacceptable, requiring another method of disposal. Most coarse sewage screenings and grit, even including washed grit, contain substantial amounts of highly putrescible matter and require a sanitary method of disposal. Dewatered raw sludges from sewage treatment plants require careful handling and disposal and, in some cases, air drying and disposal of digested sludges present health or nuisance hazards. These sewage solids may most conveniently be disposed of or further treated along with the municipal refuse or rubbish. Where sewage treatment plants are absent or inadequate, septic tank and cesspool pumpings are often disposed of in sanitary landfills under rigid controls to avoid nuisances.

Problem Wastes

The 1964 APWA refuse questionnaire showed that less than half of the cities reporting provided for either direct collection or collection by authorized contractors or private collectors for the following classes of refuse: bulky wastes, dead animals, abandoned vehicles, construction and demolition wastes, industrial refuse, tree debris, and evictions (debris of no value) (see Chapter 10). Some of these wastes are generally collected or disposed of by those creating them, particularly industrial refuse, and construction and demolition wastes. However, many of these wastes simply accumulate in unauthorized dumping areas or litter our streets, highways, and byways. They are extremely unsightly and may cause very serious health, fire, safety, or nuisance hazards.

This uncontrolled dumping of everything from abandoned automobiles, appliances, and dead animals to tin cans, bottles, and paper is already a serious problem and may be expected to increase unless appropriate steps are taken to prevent it. President Johnson has forcefully called for the elimination of such eyesores along with a program to landscape and beautify our cities, highways, and countryside. On February 8, 1965, the President said, "we must each and every day, dispose of a half billion pounds of solid waste. These wastes—from discarded cans to discarded automobiles—litter our country, harbor vermin, and menace our health. Inefficient and improper methods of disposal increase pollution of our air and streams . . . We must rescue our cities and countryside from blight with the same purpose and vigor with which, in other areas, we moved to save the forests and the soil."

The quantity of problem wastes is generally unknown because they are disposed of privately by clandestine dumping or littering. While the amounts are presumably included in subsequent figures on total refuse production, they are not included in the amounts shown as collected refuse. These wastes will undoubtedly vary from area to area depending on the adequacy of the official collection services and the degree of education and enforcement against unauthorized dumping and littering. It is recommended that they be taken into account in planning refuse collection and disposal facilities.

QUANTITIES

Total refuse quantities, as well as the amounts of various classes of refuse, vary widely from city to city and, within a city, they also vary widely from section to section, from season to season, and from day to day. There are also great differences from city to city between the refuse quantities *produced* and the quantities *collected*. The following factors greatly affect the proportions collected as related to the totals produced: frequency of collection; amount of segregation required; amount and types of on-site burning permitted, such as outdoor burning, burning in fireplaces or furnaces; use of domestic and apartment house incinerators; the extent of use of food waste grinders; and unlimited collection versus collection restrictions or charges based on collected amounts. Finally, there are general trends which occur to a greater or lesser extent on a nation-wide basis, depending on the economy, standard of living, new product development, and other factors.

During the past decade, there have been general decreases in the per capita quantities of garbage and ashes but increases in the amounts of combustible rubbish, particularly paper and plastics. The decrease in ashes is due to greater use of oil, gas, and electricity, rather than coal and wood, as fuels for heating and cooking. The other changes are due to greater use of packaged and frozen foods, ready to serve or to cook, and less marketing of fresh foods or those requiring extensive culling, trimming, and preparation for serving by the housewife. These changes are noticeable in a great increase in *volume* of refuse and a considerably lesser increase in *weight* of refuse. Refuse is therefore appreciably more bulky and less dense now than it was ten years ago.

It is important to know within reasonable limits the amount of refuse that a government agency must collect or supervise the collection of, and how it is to be disposed of. This information is essential in determining the most suitable and economical plan for collecting the refuse, establishing collection routes, selecting the right kinds of collection equipment, determining the best disposal method, and providing the number of men and vehicles necessary to do the work efficiently. Some cities keep accurate records, by classes, of the amount of refuse they collect, and effectively use these data in the administration of their collection and disposal program. For example, the data can disclose trends that can be used as a basis for determining future facility needs; and the data can be used to help judge operational efficiency. Many city agencies, however, have little or no information on the amount of refuse they handle, and therefore must use the experiences of other cities to determine how much refuse they will probably have to collect and dispose of.

Measuring Quantities

Some cities weigh combined refuse, and others only weigh garbage or garbage and combustible rubbish, and still others weigh different constituents, generally depending on the method of collection. The amounts of various classes of refuse are usually reported in tons per day, week, month, or year. For convenience in determining the amount of refuse collected on a population basis, however, pounds per capita per calendar day or per year are usually used. As used here a "day" refers to a calendar day and not necessarily a collection day. If collections are made 5, 5½, or 6 days per week, amounts reported per day have been converted to a 7-day week basis.

A great many cities do not have scales for weighing refuse, but keep data regarding quantities on a volume basis. The cubic yard, as measured in the collecting vehicle, is the unit used. If the volume is carefully measured or estimated, the resulting data are of value to local authorities. For comparative purposes, however, there are several reasons why volume is not as satisfactory as weight. In some cities refuse is loosely thrown into collection vehicles, while in others various degrees of compaction are obtained either by use of compaction-type vehicles or by breaking up bulky articles and compression of loads by trampling.

The volume, and therefore the density, of a given class of refuse varies greatly with the type of truck used, the method used by the crew in loading it, and the completeness of loading. An open truck may carry from 150 to 300 lb/cu yd of the same type of rubbish, depending on how it is loaded and trampled. An enclosed truck can vary even more markedly in the weight it carries per cubic yard. In a modern compaction truck, the density of refuse can vary from 150 lb/cu yd if the crew neglects to load it properly to more than 500 lb/cu yd if the refuse is properly loaded and compacted. A load of noncombustible rubbish with a high ash content may weigh as much as 1,000 lb/cu yd.

Scales are not available at most dump sites or at many sanitary landfill sites. Reporting of quantities is therefore done on a volume basis which at best is only a rough estimate of the quantity actually handled. It is thus impossible to make accurate efficiency or cost accounting studies of either collection or disposal, to compute reliably the density of refuse, or even to plan realistically for future refuse collection and disposal activities. It is important, therefore, to weigh all refuse that is collected in all except very small operations.

Relation of Refuse Produced to Refuse Collected

The amount of refuse picked up by the regular collection agency is always somewhat less than the amount produced in the community. The difference depends largely on the amount of self-disposal by industry and residents, the efficiency, extent, cost, and timing of the service, the amount of on-site disposal, and the amount of refuse salvaged before collection.

Some garbage and combustible rubbish is burned in household fireplaces, furnaces, and stoves, not only for the heat but also because it may be more convenient for the householder than collection and it may cost less if direct collection charges are made. Household and yard rubbish is often burned in backyard burners because it is easier and less offensive esthetically than to store large amounts of refuse until the regular collection day. Some garbage and rubbish is also burned in apartment house incinerators, either because of convenience or local requirements. As a result, in some cities the amount of combustible refuse collected is very small and less than half of the total refuse produced is actually collected.

The amount of material salvaged from household or business refuse is closely related to the market value of the materials. Paper, cardboard, ferrous and other metals, bottles, cullet, rags, bones, and other materials are sold when there is a demand for them. At such times the quantity of refuse collected is considerably reduced. Scavengers, when permitted, often pick up part of the refuse that has been placed for collection. Civic and charitable organizations also collect certain savable materials.

Some garbage, especially from hotels, restaurants, and food-processing plants, is frequently sold to hog farmers for feed, even if the city agency would collect it without charge. Hog raisers take a large part of the commercial garbage of some cities, thus substantially reducing the amount collected by the regular agency. Because the trend has been for farmers to charge for removing garbage, there is more demand for municipal collection and disposal of commercial garbage. The number of cities requiring separate collection of domestic garbage for disposal by hog feeding has been greatly decreased since regulations requiring the cooking of garbage were adopted in all of the States. More and more new houses, apartments, and commercial establishments are equipped with garbage grinders. These alone have generally reduced the amount of garbage to be collected from 25 per cent to about 10 per cent of the total refuse.

City collections may therefore only amount to 50-75 per cent of the total refuse produced and, if there is appreciable hauling by householders, the amount may be less than half. While the amount collected by the official agency can be accurately determined by weighing, it is virtually impossible to measure the total refuse produced in a community. Administrators of refuse collection and disposal agencies ordinarily are only concerned with the amounts of wastes they have to handle. These amounts can be determined by day-by-day measurements or estimates based on experience in similar jurisdictions. In long-range planning, however, provision should be made for changes in amounts of various classes of refuse based on the current trends.

TOTAL AND PER CAPITA REFUSE PRODUCTION IN THE UNITED STATES

Quantities of municipal refuse produced in the United States continue to increase at an alarming rate due primarily to two factors:

population increase and per capita increase in refuse production. Figure 2-1 shows the estimated per capita refuse *production* in the United States from 1920 to the middle 1980's. Individual refuse production in 1965 is estimated at about 4.5 lb/cap/day or 1,650 lb/cap/yr. It is assumed that the straight line trend from 1955 to date will continue at an increase of about 0.07 lb/cap/day or 25 lb/cap/yr.

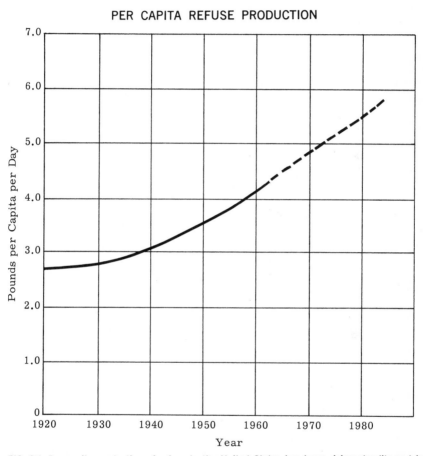

PER CAPITA REFUSE PRODUCTION

FIG. 2-1. Per capita production of refuse in the United States has been rising steadily and is expected to reach almost six pounds per person each day by the middle 1980's. From: Solid Waste Handling in Metropolitan Areas, Division of Environmental Engineering and Food Protection, Public Health Service, Department of Health, Education, and Welfare, September 1963.

Just as in the last ten years, the increase in per capita refuse production is expected to be largely in paper, plastics, and other types of packaging or wrapping materials, and in construction and demolition wastes. Americans now use an estimated 475 lb/cap/yr of paper. By 1970 that average is expected to increase another 45 pounds. In 1964, 27 billion new glass bottles and jars were used in the U.S. or about 140 per capita. This was more than any previous year. While the amounts of paper and glass wasted each year are not equivalent to the amounts produced, constantly increased production results in corresponding increases in refuse quantities.

Superimposing the population increase on the per capita increase gives the anticipated total refuse *production* in the U. S. shown in Figure 2-2. This results in an expected increase from 150 million tons per year in 1963 to about 260 million tons in 1980, or more than 73 per cent. Of the increase of 110 million tons/yr, about half is expected from the per capita increase in amount of refuse and about half from the total population increase (to about 259 million by 1980). Total refuse production is expected to double the amount in 1963 by 1985. The U. S.

TOTAL REFUSE PRODUCTION IN THE U.S.

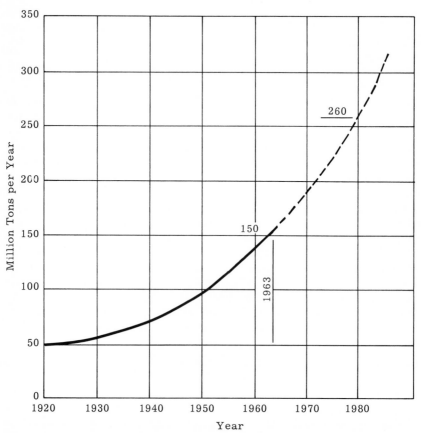

FIG. 2-2. The estimated increase in per capita refuse production from the present time to the middle 1980's (see Fig. 2-1) plus the projected population increase during the same period is expected to result in total refuse production of more than 300 million tons a year by the middle 1980's. From: Solid Waste Handling in Metropolitan Areas, Division of Environmental Engineering and Food Protection, Public Health Service, Department of Health, Education, and Welfare, September 1963.

population is expected to double by the year 2000. Most of this population growth, possibly 75 per cent, is expected to occur in our cities and their surrounding urbanized areas.

Increase in Paper Consumption

As an example of the increase in paper and paperboard, U. S. consumption increased by 16.6 per cent from 1958 to 1962, from 35 to 42 million tons. This increase was much greater than the comparable population increase of only 7.5 per cent. Figure 2-3 and Table 2-2 further il-

TABLE 2-2

Paper and Paper Board Consumption
from: American Pulp & Paper Association[1]

	1963	1980
Total U. S. Consumption, Tons	43,000,000	76,000,000
Per Capita Consumption, lb/cap/yr	460	640
Waste Paper Reused, lb/cap/yr	96	130
Paper in Buildings and to Storage, lb/cap/yr	54	75
Balance to Disposal, lb/cap/yr	310	435
Percentage Increase Per Capita, %	—	40

[1]From: Wegman, Leonard S.—Planning a New Incinerator, *Proceedings 1964 National Incinerator Conference*, ASME.

lustrate past and projected increases of the paper and paper board industry. The increases noted have occurred in spite of the facts that one ton of paper now covers as much as 50 per cent more than it once did and the basic weight of some packaging paperboard has been reduced from 60 pounds to 40 pounds without any reduction in weight-sustaining capacity. These factors confirm the trend of increasing refuse bulk at a faster rate than the increase of refuse weight.

In the Hartford, Connecticut, Capitol Region Study it was revealed that increases occurred in the population of 30 per cent, refuse weight 67 per cent, and refuse volume 75 per cent during the period 1950 to 1962. The increase in refuse weight was 2.3 per cent/cap/yr and in volume was 2.6 per cent/cap/yr. In the same study, Mr. Leonard S. Wegman developed a table which in his judgment represents the average refuse quantities and densities in the United States (Table 2-3). These figures serve well to illustrate today's low quantity of garbage and large quantity of combustible rubbish as compared to the total refuse amount.

Quantities of Refuse Collected Per Capita

A special questionnaire was completed by on-the-spot surveys made in the spring of 1965 by APWA Solid Wastes Committee members. As shown in Table 2-4, the values are reported for residential refuse, commercial and industrial refuse, and all refuse *collected*. Residential refuse varied from 386 lb/cap/yr or 1.1 lb/cap/day to 1,152 lb/cap/yr or 3.2 lb/cap/day. The lowest quantity occurred in Cedar Rapids, Iowa, where considerable on-site burning is practiced.

Commercial and industrial refuse collected varied from 480 lb/cap/

PAPER CONSUMPTION INCREASES COMPARED WITH POPULATION INCREASE IN THE U.S.

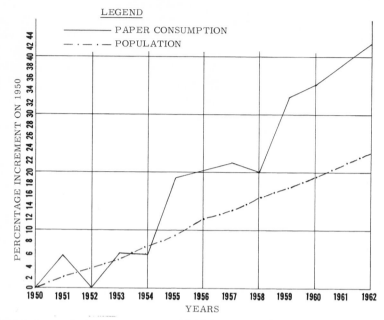

FIG. 2-3. Paper consumption in the United States increased almost twice as much percentagewise as the population in the years 1950-1962, thus contributing to the trend toward greater refuse bulk compared to refuse weight. From: Proceedings of 1964 National Incinerator Conference, ASME.

TABLE 2-3
Annual Quantities of Raw Refuse Per Capita[1]

Class	Weight Lb	% By Weight	Uncompacted Volume, Cu yd	% By Volume	Specific Weight, Lb/cu yd
Garbage	150	9.5	0.15	4.0	1000
Rubbish and all combustibles (except garbage)	1000	62.5	3.15	81.0	320
All noncombustibles	450	28.0	0.60	15.0	750
Total	1600	100	3.90	100	410

[1]From: Wegman, Leonard S.—Planning a New Incinerator, *Proceedings 1964 National Incinerator Conference,* ASME.

yr or 1.3 lb/cap/day to 955 lb/cap/yr or 2.6 lb/cap/day. However, one city was non-industrial and one collected none of the industrial refuse. Most cities reporting did not include demolition or construction wastes.

The quantities of total refuse collected varied widely from 856 lb/cap/yr or 2.3 lb/cap/day to 2,373 lb/cap/yr or 6.5 lb/cap/day, the latter including demolition wastes. Non-industrial cities and those not reporting industrial wastes are Philadelphia, Garden City, Chandler, and Winnetka. The median value of all refuse collected (Table 2-4) is 1,435 lb/cap/yr or 3.9 lb/cap/day, but, because of the wide variation of local conditions and practices, this value should not be generally considered as representing the amount to be expected in any given community.

TABLE 2-4
Pounds of Refuse Collected Per Capita
1965 APWA Survey

City	Lb/cap/yr	Lb/cap/day	Remarks
Residential Refuse Only, All Classes			
Cedar Rapids, Iowa	386	1.1	Original data in cu yd only; backyard burning is practiced
Vancouver, B. C.	454	1.2	
Washington, D. C.	565	1.6	Some commercial garbage included
Philadelphia, Pa.	571	1.6	
Seattle, Wash.	603	1.7	
Cincinnati, Ohio	721	2.0	Some commercial combustible included
New York, N. Y.	768	2.1	
Los Angeles, Calif.	780	2.1	
Trenton, N. J.	782	2.1	Small amount of little commercial establishments
Evanston, Ill.	996	2.7	
Chandler, Ariz.	1100	3.0	Some commercial included
Winnetka, Ill.	1152	3.2	
Median	745	2.0	
Commercial and Industrial Refuse, All Classes			
Winnetka, Ill.	480	1.3	Non-industrial city
Cincinnati, Ohio	514	1.4	Part of original data in cu yd only
Philadelphia, Pa.	555	1.5	No industrial, not all of commercial refuse
New York, N. Y.	715	2.0	Combustible construction and demolition wastes included
Seattle, Wash.	905	2.5	Extrapolated
Vancouver, B. C.	933	2.6	
Washington, D. C.	955	2.6	Extrapolated
Median	715	2.0	
All Refuse			
Newark, N. J.	856	2.3	Limited to 100 lbs. per pickup
Chandler, Ariz.	1100	3.0	Non-industrial city
Philadelphia, Pa.	1126	3.1	No industrial, not all commercial refuse
Cincinnati, O.	1235	3.4	Non-combustible rubbish given in cu yd
Garden City, N. Y.	1308	3.6	No industrial
Vancouver, B. C.	1387	3.8	
New York, N. Y.	1483	4.1	Combustible construction and demolition wastes included
Seattle, Wash.	1508	4.1	Extrapolated
Washington, D. C.	1545	4.2	
Neptune, N. J.	1565	4.3	
Winnetka, Ill.	1632	4.5	Non-industrial city
Los Angeles, Calif.	2373	6.5	Demolition wastes included
Median	1435	3.9	

The general trend of median values for total refuse collected is as follows: 1939–794 lb/cap/yr; 1955–834 lb/cap/yr; 1957-1958–1,430 lb/cap/yr; and 1965–1,435 lb/cap/yr.

Only two cities reported separate collections of garbage. Philadelphia showed 128 lb/cap/yr of residential garbage only. The extrapolated figure for Washington was 200 lb/cap/yr or 0.55 lb/cap/day which amounted to about 13 per cent of the total refuse collected.

In Philadelphia, where the various classes of refuse have been weighed for the last 10 years, the total amount of refuse per capita has increased an average of about 2 per cent per year. Partial data from San Francisco and Atlanta indicate increasing trends in total refuse collected per capita.

Because of the trend toward greater use of combined refuse collection, it is becoming more difficult to estimate the quantities of the various classes of refuse. Where collections are of combined refuse or of mixed classes of refuse, it appears that the only way to classify the refuse is by sampling and physically sorting weighed amounts. This procedure is quite tedious and is usually employed only in research or special studies.

Of the 11 and 12 cities reporting on all refuse collected in the surveys of 1957-1958 and 1965, respectively, six were the same cities reporting in both. The per capita amounts are shown in Table 2-5 along with the 1955 data from three of the same cities. In the two latest surveys the quantities reported were greater in 1965 in three of the six cities. In two of the cities, some classes of refuse were not included in the latest report. The most notable change occurred in Los Angeles where the amount was reported to be 1,667 lb/cap/yr in 1957-1958 and increased to 2,373 lb/cap/yr or 6.5 lb/cap/day in 1965.

TABLE 2-5
Pounds of All Refuse Collected Per Capita
From Same Cities Reported in Two or More Surveys

City	1955 Survey		1957-1958 Survey		1965 Survey	
	Lb/ cap/yr	Lb/ cap/day	Lb/ cap/yr	Lb/ cap/day	Lb/ cap/yr	Lb/ cap/day
Chandler, Ariz.	—	—	1587	4.3	1100[1]	3.0[1]
Garden City, N. Y.	1187	3.3	1438	3.9	1308[1]	3.6[1]
Los Angeles, Calif.	—	—	1677	4.6	2373	6.5
New York, N. Y.	826	2.3	1325	3.6	1483	4.1
Seattle, Wash.	842	2.3	1370	3.8	1508	4.1
Washington, D. C.	—	—	1638	4.5	1545	4.2

[1]Excludes industrial refuse.

The wide ranges in quantities of refuse collected, as shown in Tables 2-4 and 2-5, serve to emphasize the extreme differences from city to city. In estimating refuse quantities for a particular city or area, an individual survey or study should be made rather than using data from another city or a median value for a number of cities.

Seasonal Fluctuations in Quantity of Refuse

Seasonal variations in the quantities of various classes of refuse produced in a community may be large and may differ greatly from city to city. An important factor that influences seasonal changes is climate. In northern climates the quantity of ashes shows sharp winter peaks while that of garbage and combustible rubbish will have marked spring or summer peaks. Yard rubbish may account for an appreciable proportion of the total refuse in spring and summer. Spring cleanups may produce enormous amounts of rubbish in some areas. In moderate climates seasonal fluctuations tend to be less prolonged and less fuel is used for heating; often heating is by non-ash-producing fuels.

Combined collection of refuse, especially that including garbage and ashes, tends to result in more uniform quantities throughout the year. Even then, however, there may be increases of 15 to 30 per cent during the summer and similar decreases during the winter. Such variation is believed due to the greater summer increases of garbage and combustible rubbish over that of the winter increases of noncombustible rubbish.

Seasonal changes in quantity and density of combined residential refuse are shown for three cities in Table 2-6 and Figure 2-4 from studies made by Purdue University during the period 1959-1962. The density was measured in open trucks or containers except for the two values measured in packer trucks at Milwaukee. In the cities of Bloomington and Indianapolis, Indiana, considerable on-site burning of combustible rubbish is practiced by the residents, resulting in extremely low per capita quantities.

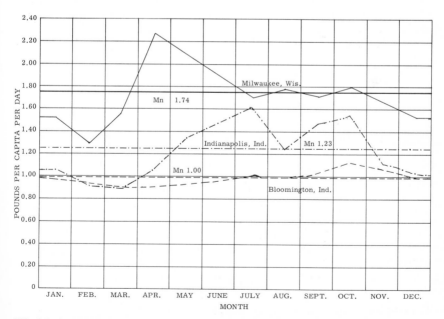

FIG. 2-4. Graph shows monthly per-capita quantities of combined residential refuse in selected cities, 1959-62.

The peak monthly quantity varied from spring (April) to fall (October). The maximum quantity varied from 14 to 31 per cent above the mean. Seasonal lows occurred in winter or spring (December to March) and were 9 to 27 per cent below the mean. Milwaukee and Indianapolis exhibited greater seasonal differences than did Bloomington.

Bulk refuse density was greater at Indianapolis than at the other two cities. In Milwaukee little difference in density was shown between winter and summer measurements. The peak density at Bloomington and Indianapolis occurred in October while the minimum density was in July and March, respectively. In general the peak density occurred when the weight of refuse was greatest rather than when the volume of refuse was the least. Per capita volume was generally highest in summer and lowest in winter or early spring.

The Southeastern Oakland County Incinerator Authority, Berkley, Michigan, reported in 1963 that the quantity of rubbish disposed of was 640 lb/cap/yr or 1.75 lb/cap/day. The maximum quantity was 2.45 lb/cap/day in June and the minimum was 1.27 lb/cap/day in February. These deviations were about +40 per cent and −28 per cent from the mean.

Daily Fluctuations in Quantity of Refuse

Daily variations in amounts of refuse collected may greatly exceed the seasonal variations. In any system of collection the daily amounts will be increased to some extent after weekends and holidays. Rain or snow may increase the weight of refuse as will the cleanup after floods, storms, and the like. Where refuse is collected weekly, the amounts vary little from day to day but reflect the seasonal variations. However, when collections are twice or three times a week, daily amounts during the first half of the week may be as much as double those of the last half. This reflects not only the scheduling with uneven number of days between collections, but also the greater amount of rubbish discarded over the weekends.

Density of Refuse

Knowledge of the density of various classes of refuse is valuable for prescribing the size of containers, for selecting collection equipment, for designing storage bins or hoppers, and for planning disposal methods. Usually the density is determined individually for each community by weighing known volumes of refuse and expressing it in pounds per cubic yard. The several classes of refuse vary considerably in unit weight and, particularly the classes of combined refuse, rubbish, and bulky wastes, vary widely within each class. With the trends of increased refuse production and decreased density of loose refuse, greater use of compactor trucks has been made. Greater compaction has been sought and the size of trucks has been increasing to attain greater payloads. Refuse is almost always weighed in the collection vehicles and the influence of type and size of the vehicle on the density can be very significant. Although the density of loose refuse is continually

TABLE 2-6
Monthly Quantity and Density of Combined Residential Refuse
Three Cities, 1959-1962
From Studies Made by Purdue University

Month	Milwaukee, 1959-1960			Bloomington,[1] 1961-1962			Indianapolis,[1] 1961-1962		
	Weight Lb/cap/day	Weight % of Mean	Density[2] Lb/cu yd	Weight Lb/cap/day	Weight % of Mean	Density Lb/cu yd	Weight Lb/cap/day	Weight % of Mean	Density Lb/cu yd
January	1.52	87	Winter: 378 (405 in packer)	0.98	98	302	1.05	85	464
February	1.29	74		0.94	94	308	0.91	74	473
March	1.57	90		0.91	91	319	0.90	73	452
April	2.27	131		0.91	91	305	1.05	85	473
May	2.05	118		0.94	94	292	1.34	109	497
June	1.85	106	Summer: 373 (405 in packer)	0.96	96	284	1.48	120	513
July	1.71	98		1.02	102	281	1.61	131	500
August	1.79	103		1.00	100	300	1.25	102	475
September	1.73	99		1.02	102	294	1.47	119	551
October	1.80	104		1.14	114	327	1.56	127	619
November	1.71	98		1.09	109	311	1.13	92	462
December	1.55	89		1.00	100	294	1.04	85	511
Mean	1.74	100		1.00	100	301	1.23	100	502

[1]Considerable on-site burning of combustible rubbish and garbage is practiced by the residents.

[2]Density is measured in open trucks or containers unless otherwise specified.

decreasing, the better compaction being attained in modern trucks appears to have more than offset this up to now.

Table 2-7 shows the density of various classes of refuse as reported in the APWA survey of 1965. All densities were measured in compactor trucks except as noted. The density of combined refuse varied from 300 to 750 lb/cu yd with a median value of 475 lb/cu yd.

TABLE 2-7
Refuse Density, 1965

Class of Refuse	City	Density Lb/cu yd	Remarks[1]
Combined	Evanston, Ill.	525	
	Los Angeles, Calif.	500,570	Different size trucks
	Neptune, N. J.	600	
	Newark, N. J.	450	
	New York, N. Y.	390	Municipal collection
		480	Private collection
	Philadelphia, Pa.	450	
	San Francisco, Calif.	324	Estimated
	Seattle, Wash.	350,470	Different contractors
	Trenton, N. J.	450	
	Vancouver, B. C.	432	Different truck models
		582,683,712	
	Winnetka, Ill.	300	Commercial
		750	Residential
Rubbish	Atlanta, Ga.	400	
	Cincinnati, O.	580,600	Combustibles; different size trucks
		670,700	Noncombustibles; different size trucks
	Philadelphia, Pa.	350,509,625	Different size trucks
	Washington, D. C.	222	Open truck
Garbage	Los Angeles, Calif.	1,325	Non-compactor; restaurants only
	Philadelphia, Pa.	900	Non-compactor; residental only
	Washington, D. C.	1,000	Non-compactor
Bulky Wastes	Philadelphia, Pa.	200	Open trucks
Ashes	Philadelphia, Pa.	800	Non-compactor

[1]All densities were measured in compactor trucks unless otherwise noted.

Rubbish density in compactor trucks varied from 350 to 700 lb/cu yd with a median of 590 lb/cu yd. The densities reported at Cincinnati indicate that noncombustible rubbish is more dense than combustible rubbish by about 100 lb/cu yd. The density of rubbish in open trucks was reported to be 222 lb/cu yd at Washington.

Three cities reported the density of garbage collected in non-compactor trucks to range from 900 to 1,325 lb/cu yd with a median value of 1,000 lb/cu yd. Philadelphia reported an average density of bulky wastes in open trucks of 200 lb/cu yd and of ashes in non-compactor trucks of 800 lb/cu yd.

The trend in density of various classes of refuse is indicated in Table 2-8 where values obtained in three APWA surveys are reported. The density of garbage has apparently remained about the same at approximately 1,000 lb/cu yd as collected in non-compactor trucks. It is believed that these figures apply to unwrapped garbage. The density of rubbish has shown a consistent and large increase since 1939. This is believed to be due both to greater use of compactor trucks for collection and to gradual improvements in packer truck design rather than to any increase in density of loose rubbish. On the contrary, loose rubbish has been decreasing in density because of the increased proportion of such light materials as paper, plastics, and cardboard.

The densities of the other classes of refuse with the exception of combined refuse, as shown in Table 2-8, are based on data from only one city each and therefore may not be representative. With the tendency toward combined refuse collection, fewer cities are reporting separate collections of ashes, combustibles, and noncombustibles. Combustible rubbish including garbage appears to have become more dense since 1955 as measured in compaction trucks, probably for the same reasons as given above concerning all rubbish. The great decrease in density of noncombustible rubbish from 1939 to 1955 is thought to be the result of a lower content of ashes from decreasing use of solid fuels. This trend may now have been reversed due to the greater compaction being attained in modern collection trucks.

Combined refuse showed a decrease in unit weight of 41 per cent from 1939 to 1955 when the median value declined from 604 to 356 lb/cu yd. The causes are believed to be reductions in the proportions of both ashes and garbage and an increase in proportion of combustible rubbish. This downward trend in density has been significantly reversed as the median value has now increased to 475 lb/cu yd. Again, compaction appears to play the predominant role.

It is probable that the density of combined refuse in loose form is increased from 1½ to 2½ times by compaction in a modern packer-type truck.

Comparison of the density of combined refuse with size of compactor trucks is given in Table 2-9.

Except for the 25-cu yd packer trucks, the densities show a decided decrease in general with increasing size of compaction vehicles. Individual results from the different cities, however, vary widely for the same truck size, as illustrated in the figures for 16- and 20-cu yd vehicles. One reason for such wide variation may lie in the age and state of repair of the particular trucks.

Physical Components of Refuse

The classification of refuse according to major component materials may be done by making a single breakdown into (1) organic (mostly combustible) and (2) inorganic materials (mostly noncombustible). These two general classes may then be broken down by further sorting into such physical components as (1) garbage, paper, wood, plastics, grass and trimmings, and (2) metals, glass, ashes, ceramics, stones,

TABLE 2-8
Density of Various Classes of Refuse, Lb/cu yd

Class of Refuse	1939				1955				1965[1]			
	No. Cities	Min	Md	Max	No. Cities	Min	Md	Max	No. Cities	Min	Md	Max
Garbage	7	798	936	1540	—	—	—	605	3	900	1000	1325
Rubbish	5	200	214	677	5	60	383	—	3	350	590	700
Ashes	—	1150	1250	1400	—	—	—	—	1	—	800	—
Garbage and Combustible Rubbish	5	214	442	800	3	234	392	502	1	580	—	600
Rubbish and Ashes	7	400	692	1000	—	—	—	—	—	—	—	—
Noncombustible Rubbish[2]	4	747	883	1165	3	396	543	605	1	670	—	700
Combined Refuse	6	500	604	1000	7	300	356	667	11	300	475	750

[1] In 1965 all densities are reported for compactor trucks except for garbage and ashes.

[2] Includes some ashes.

Data are from APWA surveys.

TABLE 2-9
Density of Combined Refuse Compared to
Size of Compactor Trucks
8 Cities, 1965 APWA Survey

Truck Capacity Cu Yd	Density Lb/cu Yd
6	625
9	500
16	390, 580
20	324, 350, 432, 450, 480, 500, 600
21	450
25	570, 683, 712
26	222

dirt. In any method of sorting there will usually be some "miscellaneous" materials too fine for further separation but, if the sorting is fairly complete, the percentage of these unclassified materials will be small.

Table 2-10 shows a physical classification of combined refuse in New York City in 1939 and in Chicago in 1956-58. In the New York classification the seasonal changes in components was quite pronounced; less variation occurred in the more recent study in Chicago. The most significant differences between the two cities are the substantial changes in garbage, ashes, and paper contents that apparently developed in the intervening 17-19 years. Thus, Chicago's garbage is but 28 per cent and ashes 44 per cent of New York's 1939 vintage, whereas the paper content is over 250 per cent higher. A sound comparison is possible between these two carefully performed studies.

Table 2-11 shows the composition of what is termed "average municipal refuse" based on studies made by Purdue University in terms of both physical classification and chemical analysis. The refuse classification figures appear to represent a good average for combined refuse collection: rubbish (mostly combustible)—64 per cent; garbage (including fats]—12 per cent; and noncombustible rubbish—24 per cent. Paper is the predominant subclassification—42 per cent. The amount of tin cans in refuse is generally approximated at about 7 per cent which tends to verify the metals figure of 8 per cent.

Overall the refuse appears to be relatively dry (20.7 per cent moisture) but this value, of course, varies widely from day to day in a given locality. Moisture probably ranges generally from 15 or 20 per cent to 50 or 60 per cent. Values for volatile matter, considered as the organic constituent, are logically highest in the combustible rubbish classification, lowest in the noncombustible rubbish. The value for garbage was 53.3 per cent on a dry-weight basis which, with a moisture content of 72 per cent, results in a value of only 20.3 per cent on a wet-weight basis.

The chemical analysis is of interest to those planning or operating composting, incineration, or other types of plants for treatment of refuse. They are not of much interest in the sanitary landfill method of disposal except insofar as water pollution may be involved. The calorific value is of **great** importance in incinerator design and operation. The

TABLE 2-10

Physical Components of Combined Refuse
in New York City, 1939, and Chicago, 1956-1958

Month	Year	Per Cent by Weight									
		Organic						Inorganic			
		Garbage	Paper	Wood	Grass	Misc.	Total	Metal	Glass	Ashes	Total
New York City, New York[1]											
Jan.	1939	5.7	12.4	0.3		1.0	19.4	4.3	4.0	72.3	80.6
Feb.		9.0	12.6	0.7		1.7	24.0	6.6	4.9	64.5	76.0
Mar.		9.7	20.6	0.3		2.1	32.7	7.4	7.3	52.6	67.3
Apr.		18.1	21.6	2.0		2.8	44.5	7.4	6.9	41.2	55.5
May		26.7	23.0	3.1		3.3	56.1	7.1	6.8	30.0	43.9
June		35.1	24.3	4.6		3.8	67.8	6.4	6.8	19.0	32.2
July		43.8	25.5	5.9		4.1	79.3	6.6	6.3	7.8	20.7
Aug.		23.1	37.6	3.8		7.4	71.9	11.6	5.1	11.4	28.1
Sept.		12.6	26.7	4.9		5.6	49.8	8.2	9.1	32.9	50.2
Oct.		10.1	31.0	2.6		3.8	47.5	8.9	4.0	39.6	52.5
Nov.		6.6	18.0	2.1		1.9	28.6	3.8	2.9	64.7	71.4
Dec.		3.5	9.0	0.8		0.8	14.1	3.1	1.9	80.9	85.9
Avg.		17.0	21.9	2.6		3.2	44.7	6.8	5.5	43.0	55.3
Chicago, Illinois[2]											
Mar.	1956	6.4	50.1		*		56.5	18.5		25.0	43.5
Apr.		7.4	64.0		*		71.4	13.9		14.7	28.6
May		5.6	57.3		11.9		74.8	14.0		11.2	25.2
June		2.5	60.7		6.5		69.7	13.6		16.7	30.3
Oct.		3.5	56.0		4.5		64.0	11.9		24.1	36.0
Feb.-Mar.	1957	6.1	49.2		*		55.3	17.5		27.2	44.7
Apr.		3.2	53.3		19.7		76.2	(9.3)	5.9	8.6	23.8
Sept.		3.6	42.0		23.0		68.6	(7.4)	5.4	18.6	31.4
Nov.		2.3	59.3		3.7		65.3	(5.2)	6.5	23.0	34.7
Feb.	1958	5.7	57.6		*		63.3	(11.6)	9.3	15.8	36.7
Feb.		1.5	56.3		*		57.8	(7.5)	6.0	28.7	42.2
Feb.		2.6	70.4		*		73.0	(8.0)	6.9	12.1	27.0
Apr.		1.5	63.7		*		65.2	(8.1)	5.8	20.9	34.8
June		0.8	54.7		34.4		89.9	(6.2)	3.5	0.4	10.1
Avg.		4.8	56.5		9.6		70.9	14.8		18.7	33.5

* Analysis not performed; grass included with paper. ( ) Not included in average.

Note: Chicago—Each sample consists of one truck load of refuse (approximately three tons); March 1956 - March 1957 represents analysis of 4 to 10 loads each, April 1957 - June 1958 represents analysis of 1 to 3 loads each.

[1]from: Casimir A. Rogus, "Refuse Quantities and Characteristics," *APWA Proc. National Conference on Solid Waste Research*, 17-27, December 1963.

[2]from: *Municipal Refuse Disposal*, APWA, 1961.

average value on a dry-weight basis was 6,203 Btu/lb, or 4,917 Btu/lb on a wet-weight basis at 20.7 per cent moisture. On a dry-weight, ash-free, metal-free basis, the value was 9,048 Btu/lb. The extremely low value of nitrogen (0.33 per cent) indicates the low nutrient value of refuse due to continual decrease in garbage content and sharp increases in paper and other rubbish, both combustible and noncombustible. Garbage alone has a nitrogen content of 3.3 per cent. Generally the other major plant nutrients, phosphorous and potash, are thought to be quite low in municipal refuse, 0.5-0.1 per cent or less. These values are of importance in biological treatment of the refuse, as in compost or sew-

TABLE 2-11

Composition and Analysis of an Average Municipal Refuse
From Studies Made by Purdue University

Component	Per cent of All Refuse by Wt.	Moisture Per cent by Wt.	Volatile Matter	Carbon (C)	Hydrogen (H)	Oxygen (O)	Nitrogen (N)	Sulfur (S)	Non-Comb.[1]	Calorific Value Btu Per Lb.
				Rubbish, 64%						
Paper	42.0	10.2	84.6	43.4	5.8	44.3	0.3	0.20	6.0	7572
Wood	2.4	20.0	84.9	50.5	6.0	42.4	0.2	0.05	1.0	8613
Grass	4.0	65.0	—	43.3	6.0	41.7	2.2	0.05	6.8	7693
Brush	1.5	40.0	—	42.5	5.9	41.2	2.0	0.05	8.3	7900
Greens	1.5	62.0	70.3	40.3	5.6	39.0	2.0	0.05	13.0	7077
Leaves	5.0	50.0	—	40.5	6.0	45.1	0.2	0.05	8.2	7096
Leather	0.3	10.0	76.2	60.0	8.0	11.5	10.0	0.40	10.1	8850
Rubber	0.6	1.2	85.0	77.7	10.4	—	—	2.0	10.0	11330
Plastics	0.7	2.0	—	60.0	7.2	22.6	—	—	10.0	14368
Oils, paints	0.8	0.0	—	66.9	9.7	5.2	2.0	—	16.3	13400
Linoleum	0.1	2.1	65.8	48.1	5.3	18.7	0.1	0.40	27.4	8310
Rags	0.6	10.0	93.6	55.0	6.6	31.2	4.6	0.13	2.5	7652
Street Sweepings	3.0	20.0	67.4	34.7	4.8	35.2	0.1	0.20	25.0	6000
Dirt	1.0	3.2	21.2	20.6	2.6	4.0	0.5	0.01	72.3	3790
Unclass.	0.5	4.0	—	16.6	2.5	18.4	0.05	0.05	62.5	3000
				Food Wastes, 12%						
Garbage	10.0	72.0	53.3	45.0	6.4	28.8	3.3	0.52	16.0	8484
Fats	2.0	0.0	—	76.7	12.1	11.2	0	0	0	16700
				Noncombustibles, 24%						
Metals	8.0	3.0	0.5	0.8	0.04	0.2	—	—	99.0	124
Glass and Ceramics	6.0	2.0	0.4	0.6	0.03	0.1	—	—	99.3	65
Ashes	10.0	10.0	3.0	28.0	0.5	0.8	—	0.5	70.2	4172
				Composite Refuse, as Received						
All Refuse	100	20.7	—	28.0	3.5	22.4	0.33	0.16	24.9	6203

[1]Noncombustibles—ash, metal, glass, and ceramics

age treatment plants. The protein content of refuse, based on the formula 6.25 N was only 2.1 per cent on a dry basis.

Fats, oils and paints, plastics, and rubber have the highest heat values of the components of refuse, 11,330-16,700 Btu/lb. Ashes may neither detract nor add to the burning of all refuse because of their similar heat values, 4,000-5,000 Btu/lb on an as-received basis. Because of the inorganic nature of most noncombustibles (metals, glass, ceramics, etc.), the heat value of these items depends only on small amounts of combustible matter clinging to them (papers, plastics, paint, garbage, dirt, and other contaminants). For this reason, the heat value for the noncombustibles is generally below 200 Btu/lb but it is not necessarily zero as the classification implies.

SUMMARY

Standardization of the definitions of refuse and its various components is needed if uncertainties and errors of interpretation in published information are to be avoided. As in previous editions of this manual and the companion manual, *Municipal Refuse Disposal*, the various classes of refuse are defined in accordance with the most widespread use of the terms. Two classes of refuse, bulky wastes and agricultural wastes, have been added because of the special problems they create in the environment.

Quantities of all refuse produced are continuing to increase on both total and per capita bases. The estimated total refuse production is now 4.5 lb/cap/day and some cities report amounts as high as 8 lb/cap/day. Refuse is becoming more bulky and less dense due to large increases in quantity of such materials as paper and plastics. Amounts of garbage and ashes are continuing a downward trend. Quantities of bulky wastes, abandoned vehicles, and construction and demolition wastes are increasing and pose serious problems in storage, collection, and disposal.

There is a trend towards less separation of refuse classes on the premises and greater use of combined refuse collection. However, in the larger cities more agencies, municipal, contract, and private, are performing the actual collection service. This makes difficult the task of determining the amounts of refuse collected. In the APWA surveys of 1957-58 and 1965, no significant difference was observed in the median per capita quantities of total refuse collected. This should be interpreted with caution, however, because there is a wide variation in cities depending upon collection practices, habits regarding salvage, on-site disposal, and individual hauling, and the completeness of the survey data. For planning and implementing refuse collection services, studies should be made in each community rather than using data from elsewhere.

While the density of loose refuse continues to decrease, that in modern compaction-type vehicles has thus far shown an increasing trend. This is due to improvements in compaction mechanisms. To cope with the increasing bulk of refuse, communities are turning towards larger collection vehicles and transfer units with greater packing forces. But a limit may soon be reached in the refuse density attainable in compaction vehicles.

In any community, seasonal and daily fluctuations in both weight and volume of refuse collected may be large. The variations can only be estimated accurately in a given area by means of a local study. The same is true if it is necessary to determine the classification of the refuse materials.

chapter 3

PREPARATION OF REFUSE FOR COLLECTION

The householder is responsible for the refuse he produces until it is collected by the municipal forces. The manner in which householders prepare and present refuse for collection is, therefore, an important factor in determining the effectiveness and efficiency of the municipal collection operation. At one extreme, the refuse may be carefully separated by classes; the garbage carefully drained, wrapped, tied, and placed neatly in watertight covered cans; the rubbish placed in covered receptacles or carefully bundled and put beside the containers; and the ashes kept in covered metal cans. At the other extreme, all refuse may be dumped indiscriminately in a heap in a backyard or alley. In the latter case, the work of collecting and disposing of it is difficult and expensive, to say nothing of the nuisance and the menace to public health that is created.

Municipal officials have found that most people disapprove of indiscriminate refuse handling practices and the resultant extra burden on public funds and agree that some measure of municipal control is essential. Consequently, it has become a definite part of the responsibility of city governments to regulate and define local requirements, specifying proper practices for separating, handling, and storing refuse, and placing it for collection.

The creation of a code of practice, of course, does not guarantee universal compliance. In fact, it is tremendously difficult to gain the cooperation of all of the people. Tact, perseverance, patience, public education, and vigilance are always needed and sometimes drastic enforcement methods are required. The natural resistance of the American people to what they consider undue restriction or regulation, however, must be taken into account; their desires and established customs must be recognized; and the peculiar conditions in certain districts or the special needs of certain classes of the population must be considered. The task of the public official is to achieve a reasonable balance between public convenience and satisfaction on one hand and the essential requirements for public sanitation, for municipal cleanliness, and for economical collection and disposal on the other.

The practices that may properly be required of refuse producers are on the whole neither complicated nor burdensome. From a public health standpoint, putrescible refuse must be stored so that disease vectors such as rats and flies cannot have access to it and so that liquids cannot leak from the containers. For the prevention of nuisances, refuse of all kinds must be stored so that it cannot be scattered by the wind or animals; disagreeable odors are not created; and accumulations are not unsightly. To achieve economical and effective collection and disposal, it is essential that suitable containers of proper size be provided, that they

FIG. 3-1. Improper handling of refuse by householders not only creates nuisances and insanitary conditions in a community but also increases the work and cost of collecting the material.

be kept or placed where they are easily accessible to the collectors, and that the various classes of refuse be separated to conform to the particular collection and disposal methods used.

From an administrative point of view, careful preparation of refuse is the key to successful and economical operation of the collection and disposal systems. Any lapse by householders is almost immediately reflected in less effective service or in increased municipal costs. A refuse collection superintendent, therefore, must accept a large part of the responsibility for seeing that refuse is properly handled and stored on private premises. It is up to him to win the cooperation of the citizens so that they will follow closely the rules agreed upon. He can of course call upon other municipal departments, such as the Health Department, for assistance. In some major cities, the Police Department, and on special drives, even the Fire Department assist in this activity.

The most important preparatory operations for which the householder must be responsible are: (1) separation of refuse by classes or kinds of material; (2) special handling of garbage or rubbish, such as draining, wrapping, and bundling; (3) storage in proper receptacles; (4) placing the receptacles for collection at a suitable location; and (5) the avoidance of excess quantities. These operations, together with some other matters dealing with ordinances, public education, and enforcement, will be discussed in the following sections.

FIG. 3-2. A very little effort and expense on the part of each householder will insure healthier and more attractive neighborhoods. The provision of suitable containers and the following of simple rules for preparing refuse for collection are all that he must do.

SEPARATION OF REFUSE FOR COLLECTION

The disposal method used for various types of refuse is undoubtedly the primary reason for requiring certain classes of refuse to be kept separate from the time they are produced until they are collected, but there are other factors which at times may become very important. For example, the frequency of the collection service may influence the needed degree of separation. Sometimes it may be advisable to require separation, even beyond that called for by the method of disposal or the extent of service, in order to facilitate collection, use equipment to better advantage, reduce the cost of collection and transportation, salvage certain materials or insure the sanitary storage of garbage pending its removal.

To set up ideal, or at least desirable, practices to fit a particular set of circumstances may be relatively simple, but to secure universal adoption of them under actual working conditions is quite another matter. Indifferent attention to separations at the point of origin will influence every part of the collection and disposal process. Quite naturally, the economy of the whole refuse service, even the performance of individual crews and workmen, will be affected. Requirements as to separation of refuse should, therefore, be based upon careful study of all phases of the problem. Only then can collection and disposal operations be intelligently planned and the most suitable provisions be made for securing compliance with the different separations established.

Present Separation Practices

The majority of cities collect all refuse together and do not require householders to separate the material by classes, but many cities do require one or more separations, depending usually upon the kinds of collection that are made. In some cities, there is a considerable difference between practices in residential districts and those in commercial areas, as a result of differences in the extent of service given, the character of the refuse produced, and the local conditions that affect refuse storage and collection. However, general practices may be the same in residential and commercial areas excepting that more frequent service is provided in the commercial areas or swill may be collected separately.

Effect of Disposal Methods on Separation

As stated earlier, the disposal method used for various classes of refuse is the most important single factor influencing the manner of separation needed. In fact, if certain disposal operations are to be successfully and economically carried out, it is virtually mandatory that the required segregation be made at the point of origin. The degree to which the individual producer's observance of regulations is obtained will be reflected throughout the disposal operations and contribute directly to the effectiveness of the administration of this important public service.

There are a number of reasons which may dictate special separations. Garbage, for example, may be used for hog feed, or disposed of by the reduction or grinding process; combustibles, including garbage, may be destroyed by incineration; noncombustibles simply by landfill or by salvage processing. Ashes may be used to good advantage on certain classes of streets, roads, and alleys. The various disposal methods usually employed by municipalities and the separation required in each instance are discussed below and summarized in Table 3-1.

Separation for hog feeding. Where garbage is disposed of by feeding it to hogs, it is essential that householders separate it from other kinds of refuse. Unless the separation is well made, "foreign material" may make the garbage unsuitable for disposal by this method. Such things as needles, razor blades, broken glass, and tin cans are, of course, harmful to hogs, and an appreciable amount of paper or other rubbish reduces the nutritive value of the garbage, makes heat treatment more difficult,

FIG. 3-3. Separation of refuse by householders is necessary in some communities because certain classes of refuse are not collected by the city. In this case, garbage and rubbish are picked up regularly but ashes are not collected at all.

requires the transportation of unproductive material to the hog ranch, and increases the residual disposal problem at each ranch.

Consequently, for this method of disposal, now becoming extinct, it is preferable that the garbage be kept unwrapped and entirely separate from all other refuse. Separation is also almost mandatory since most states now require the disinfection of the garbage (usually by boiling for at least 30 minutes before it is fed to animals).

Separation for central grinding. Some cities, whose number is lessening, dispose of garbage by grinding it and discharging it into the sewerage system. In such cases, tin cans, bottles, broken glassware and crockery, metals, ashes, and similar refuse must be kept separate. Their inclusion makes manual or mechanical sorting necessary at the disposal plant, and this is a costly operation. In the grinding process small amounts of paper are not considered objectionable.

Separation for incineration. If incineration is employed as the method of disposal, the usual practice is separation of the refuse at its point of origin into combustibles and noncombustibles. This permits garbage and combustible rubbish to be collected from one set of containers and hauled to the incinerator for burning, while ashes and noncombustible refuse may be collected from a different set of containers and disposed of by dumping. If ashes or other materials that will not burn are mixed

TABLE 3-1
Influence of Disposal Methods on Separation of Refuse

Method of Disposal or Use	Suitable Materials for Disposal	Usual Preparation and Collection Practices
Hog feeding	Garbage	Should not be wrapped or mixed with other classes of refuse.
Reduction	Garbage	Should not be wrapped.
Grinding	Garbage	Preferably should not be wrapped. In some instances small amounts of paper with the garbage are not objectionable. Other materials, such as metals and glass, must be sorted out.
Incineration	Combustible materials	Garbage should be drained and wrapped. Combustible rubbish should be kept dry. Sometimes combustible rubbish collected separately. Sometimes all classes of refuse collected together, when proportion of non-combustibles is relatively small.
Sanitary fill	All refuse	All classes of refuse collected together.
Used for cover material on dumps	Ashes and other mineral matter	Must be collected separately from other refuse.
Used for street, road, alley improvement	Ashes	Nails, broken glass, sharp metal, and tin cans should not be placed with ashes. Sometimes clinkers are undesirable and must be removed.
Composting	Refuse materials of value	All classes of refuse collected together. Sometimes garbage collected separately and disposed of by one of above methods; all rubbish and ashes collected together. Sometimes specified materials, such as paper, are kept separate by the householders.
Recovery and sale	Garbage, organic Rubbish Ashes	No usual practice yet established. Hard metals, glass, crockery and other inert material might be collected separately or extracted at composting plant if required.

with the combustible refuse, the efficiency of incineration will be reduced. Furthermore, it becomes necessary to rehandle such materials along with the incinerator ashes. Some cities incinerate only combustible rubbish; in those cases garbage is usually collected separately and noncombustible rubbish and ashes are collected together. Empty tin cans ,and glass from residences are usually included with the material disposed of by incineration; their disposal by open dumping can cause considerable nuisance. According to some operators, the cans provide open spaces in the incinerator fire bed and thereby improve combustion. However, a large amount of cans will necessitate frequent dumping of grates, while glass generally shatters or melts, depending on temperature range.

Separation for open burning. Frequently cities use open spaces remote from the residential areas to burn large bulky materials such as tree branches, cartons, boxes, and large quantities of paper. If open burning is used, the combustible material should be kept separate from other classes of refuse by the householder. It is obvious that no garbage or putrescible materials of any sort should be permitted with this class of refuse. Serious objections and complaints are made about objectionable odors from the attempted burning of garbage in open fires. In addition, the presence of incompletely burned food scraps usually results in insect and rodent infestation. More stringent air pollution ordinances and enforcement in major cities are reducing the practice of open burning.

Separation for open dumping. Refuse such as ashes, masonry building rubble and similar materials may be disposed by open dumping. Putrescible material should not be included with refuse disposed of in open dumps because of the insanitary conditions that such refuse creates. This means that garbage should be excluded, requiring its separation by the householder. In some cities, combustible material of any kind is objectionable on open dumps because of the possibility of fires, or because paper and other light rubbish is scattered by the wind. In such cases, the separation regulations should designate the kinds of materials that may be included.

Separation for sanitary fill. When the sanitary fill method of disposal is used, no separation is required. However, a compaction problem may at times be presented by bulky rubbish, such as large tree branches, and it may be desirable to separate such material from the other refuse for disposal by other means.

Separation of ashes for cover material. Some cities, using open dumping or the sanitary fill method of disposal for garbage or rubbish, provide for the separation of ashes and other mineral matter for use as a covering for the top or exposed faces of the dumps. Such use of ashes serves the double purpose of reducing the total amount of refuse dumped, and the amount of other cover material that must be secured.

Separation of ashes for street, road, and alley maintenance. Many communities that have a large proportion of unimproved streets and alleys find it convenient and economical to utilize ashes for maintaining them in passable condition throughout the year. Such practice, of course, calls for the complete separation of ashes from all other refuse. Nails, sharp pieces of metal, and broken glass cause much trouble on road surfaces. The presence of even small amounts of combustible or noncombustible rubbish or garbage in a load of ashes prohibits its use for this purpose. The use of ashes to eliminate slippery conditions on icy walks and pavements may be acceptable under some conditions.

Separation for composting. Although composting is not yet a proven method of municipal refuse disposal, the amount of current experimental work on this method and its potential for the future warrants its mention. Presently at least, it appears desirable to separate heavy metal objects, glass, crockery, and bulky items from garbage, paper, rags, small amounts of wood, grass, and similar material. Interest in composting is increasing, particularly in those areas of the country where soil conditioning is necessary and in areas where great amounts of vegetation, such as palm fronds, are disposed of.

Separation for disposal by recovery and sale. Cities sometimes sort out of the collected refuse all materials that have sufficient market value to make the process worthwhile. Generally, the city does not require separation of the salvagable materials at the point of origin, but does the necessary operations at a salvage plant. In some cases, all refuse is collected together and taken to the salvage plant; in others, rubbish is kept separate by the householders and only this part is handled at the plant. Sometimes, however, the city requires householders to assist in the sorting process. Garbage, tin cans, bottles, paper, or rags may be collected separately where the salvage operation is limited to one or two kinds of materials. Several cities salvage only a few kinds of refuse, such as paper, tin cans, and rags, and in such cases there is no salvage plant. The householders are required to keep the designated materials separate, and the collectors either make separate collections of them or the collecting vehicles are provided with compartments for holding the different kinds of rubbish. The collectors sometimes sort out certain kinds of materials while on the trucks.

Effect of Sanitation Requirements on Separation

In some cities, where separation of refuse may not be required by economic reasons or the disposal methods used, segregation of garbage may be required for purposes of sanitation. The highly unstable nature of garbage makes it essential to keep it in watertight, covered containers, regardless of whether or not it is mixed with other refuse. Consequently, if putrescible material is mixed with all other refuse, the entire quantity must be kept in standard garbage receptacles to prevent nuisance.

Effect of Collection Practices on Separation

Some cities divide the responsibility for refuse collection between two different agencies, which means that the kinds of material handled by each group must be kept separate. Sometimes a contractor collects part and a municipal agency another part. Or two different departments of the city government may each collect part of the refuse.

Differences in the frequency of collection can necessitate the separation of refuse into several classes. Unwrapped garbage should be collected at least twice weekly during the summer and at least once each week during the cold season because it putrefies rapidly. However, where garbage is properly wrapped, many communities apparently consider year-round collection once per week as a satisfactory frequency. When all refuse is collected together, the schedules must be the same as for garbage alone. Rubbish and ashes may be collected as seldom as once a month or even less frequently, but a weekly collection is usually desirable. It is sometimes more economical to collect garbage separately from other refuse and to provide less frequent collections for rubbish and ashes. Such an arrangement necessarily requires the separation of garbage even though all refuse may be disposed of in the same manner.

Frequently tree branches and shrubbery are kept separate from other refuse because of the difficulty in loading them into trucks. Sometimes they are collected by special vehicles, as are household appliances and large bulky trash items.

SPECIAL TREATMENT OF GARBAGE, RUBBISH, AND ASHES

In order to insure better sanitation, more economical collection, or more effective disposal, it is frequently required that garbage and certain kinds of rubbish be given special preparation before being placed in containers or otherwise presented for collection.

Preparation of Garbage

Because of its high putrescibility and greater difficulty of disposal, garbage is usually given the most attention by the city officials responsible for the collection and disposal of refuse. Usually it must be drained

FIG. 3-4. The use of systems in which a whole truck body is placed on site for collecting refuse—especially construction or industrial material—then picked up by a crane-equipped truck has become increasingly popular. Shown here is a Load Lugger in dumping position.

of free moisture, often it has to be wrapped in paper, and in some instances the bundles must be tied.

Draining garbage. Garbage, as it is usually defined in ordinances and regulations describing what will be collected,[1] is the solid waste material resulting from the preparation, cooking, storing, and marketing of foods, without any free liquids. Liquid wastes are easily and economically disposed of through the sewerage systems, but when mixed with garbage, they cause nuisance, inconveniences, and added expense at every stage of the collection and disposal process. If free liquids are present to any appreciable extent, metal garbage cans rust and corrode rapidly, the material is much more disagreeable for the collectors to handle, absolutely watertight bodies must be provided on the collection vehicles, and most of the disposal processes are seriously impaired.

Wrapping garbage. Many cities specify that all garbage must be wrapped in paper before being placed in the containers. Sometimes this requirement is simply for purposes of sanitation, but where incineration is employed the paper also serves as supplementary fuel. In any case, it is generally recognized that the practice of wrapping garbage is bene-

FIG. 3-5. All leading refuse body manufacturers make portable storage containers where refuse is stored—principally on commercial routes—then picked up and emptied into trucks with lifting devices. This is a 20-yard Loadmaster equipped with a one through six-cubic yard container mechanism.

[1]The ordinary meaning of the word "garbage" is "offal," "refuse or waste matter from a kitchen market or store", "any worthless, offensive, or filthy material." But the cities are not in complete accord as to the meaning of the term "garbage" as used in ordinances relating to its removal and disposition. McQuillons, *The Law of Municipal Corporations* (Chicago: Callaghan & Company, 1949), Vol. 7, Chap. 24, Sec. 247.

ficial alike to householders, the collectors, and the general public. Wrapping assures that there will be rather complete draining of the garbage, makes it almost impossible for flies to get to it or escape from it, and to a large extent prevents the escape of odors. Wrapping keeps containers dry and therefore cleaner and more sanitary. Since the garbage does not come in contact with the metal, the containers are not corroded by the garbage acids and consequently have a much longer life. In addition, since the garbage will not freeze to the cans in cold weather, it is much easier for the collectors to dump the contents into the vehicles, and the destructive pounding that is otherwise necessary to empty the cans during the winter months is almost wholly eliminated. In collection vehicles, loads of wrapped garbage are usually dry, making the task of collection less disagreeable, and giving longer life to the collection equipment. Moreover, flies are not attracted to such loads and the odor is hardly noticeable.

In short, where garbage is wrapped, the householders' premises, the collection vehicles, and the disposal sites are cleaner, more sanitary, freer from nuisances, and can, if necessary, be served by less frequent collection.

On the other hand, wrapped garbage is objectionable in some methods of disposal. When hog feeding or grinding is used, for example, wrapping is usually not permitted. In the incineration and sanitary fill processes, however, it is desirable to have the garbage wrapped.

The practice of wrapping is rather widespread. In 1964, 47 per cent of the 606 cities for which data were available for residential districts reported that all garbage was required to be wrapped for collection.

Tying bundles of wrapped garbage. Some cities require householders to tie the packages of wrapped garbage securely before they place them in the garbage cans for collection. The primary purpose of tying is to prevent the bundles from coming unwrapped in the containers, during the collection or transfer operations, or at the disposal site. As a refinement on wrapping it has considerable merit because it insures careful wrapping and complete and uniform achievement of the advantages of this preparation of garbage.

Lining cans with paper. In several cities the regular garbage cans must be lined with paper before garbage is placed in them. This is a compromise between no protection at all and complete wrapping. Presumably it is of greatest value in those cities where the disposal methods do not permit wrapping.

Preparation of Rubbish

To reduce the cost of collecting certain kinds of bulky material many cities require special preparation of rubbish for collection. They have found that such rubbish, in its original condition, takes up so much space in the collection vehicles that a different type may be necessary or more frequent trips to the disposal points may be required, adding greatly to the expense of handling. Some cities collect bulky materials of all kinds

FIG. 3-6. When garbage is carefully drained and wrapped in paper it is much less disagreeable to handle for both the householders and the collectors. Such preparation has become a matter of habit in St. Petersburg, Florida, requiring a minimum of regulatory control by the city.

in any manner the householder may present them. Others do not collect such rubbish at all because of the excessive cost. The most generally suitable course is a compromise: require the consolidation of bulky articles by the citizens before they are set out for collection.

Cartons and boxes. The wider use of cartons and boxes in the shipment of merchandise has resulted in an important increase in the total volume of rubbish produced. This is naturally of greater significance in commercial areas, but it is by no means a negligible factor in residential areas. To take care of this increasing bulk, many cities that provide collection service for this kind of rubbish insist that the boxes and cartons be broken apart, laid flat, and tied in bundles that can be conveniently loaded by the collectors.

In residential districts, cartons, boxes, and similar containers are usually collected when any rubbish collection service at all is rendered. This would seem to indicate a rather general acceptance of complete collection of all classes of refuse as a municipal responsibility. Nevertheless, cities must require citizens' cooperation if they are to provide such broad service for the funds which can be made available.

Tree branches. Tree branches and shrubbery present a serious problem to refuse administrators. As it is usually presented, this class of refuse is so bulky and so inconvenient to handle that the cost of its collection is unduly high. Several cities have rather satisfactorily solved this difficulty by requiring the householder to prepare the tree branches and shrubbery so as to reduce their bulk and to make them easier for the collectors to handle. Typical regulations stipulate that branches and other unwieldy rubbish be cut into lengths of not more than four feet and tied securely and compactly in bundles. The weight of bundles is usually limited to what one man can lift easily. Typical cities regard 75 pounds as the maximum weight. The bundles usually do not have to be put into containers but may be placed beside or on top of them.

Tin cans. Tin cans are very bulky and in addition often contain food particles that may become a source of nuisance or insanitary condition on dumps. Although it is hardly practical to ask the householders to do anything about compacting them, such a requirement may not be unreasonable when applied to a business normally discarding large quantities of cans. Filling stations, for example, have rapidly extended the dispensing of oil from individual quart cans, and the collection and disposal of the empty containers has become a large problem. It would not be unreasonable to require such places to provide a hand press to flatten the cans before they are presented for collection.

Tin cans and other receptacles containing food particles have long presented a problem that has caused sanitary engineers and public health officials concern. Such cans are sometimes unwanted at disposal plants, and on open dumps they may attract insects and rodents and create odors. A possible and practical solution would be to require householders to rinse out tin cans immediately after the contents have been emptied so that practically all of the organic matter is removed. This proposal has been advanced on different occasions, but it is not known that any city has put it into effect on other than a voluntary basis.

Many cities accept tin cans with regular garbage or combined refuse and run them through the incinerators. Special screening equipment is installed to separate the cans and other retrievable material which is then sold on a salvage contract.

Household furniture and appliances. Discarded household furniture also presents difficulties in collection. The smaller articles can be handled easily, but they occupy an unreasonable amount of space in the collection vehicles. Large pieces cause much more trouble and expense. Stoves, davenports, tables, mattresses, bed springs, and other bulky pieces are sometimes collected by special trucks and crews because of the vehicle space required and the likelihood that several men may be needed to load a single piece. Many administrators believe that such special service is not a proper municipal activity. Some cities have satisfactorily met the situation by requiring that furniture be broken apart and placed in regular containers or tied in bundles that can be readily loaded by one collector. In some cases, charitable organizations help by making at least limited collections, and in other cases, some cities salvage large metal objects. In the case of refrigerators, householders should be cautioned to remove the doors to avoid the possibility of children being locked in and suffocated before the equipment is picked up.

Dangerous rubbish. Some kinds of materials that would ordinarily be classed as rubbish may be extremely dangerous for collectors or disposal crews to handle. Explosives, poisons, acids, caustics, and infected materials from sick rooms may cause injury to refuse workers. Most cities make it unlawful to place these kinds of materials with the refuse to be collected by the city forces. In many cases they must be disposed of by the individuals directly. Discarded bedding, articles of clothing, furnishings, and similar articles that may be infected are often required to be removed under the supervision of the health authorities. In other cases, they must be taken directly to the place of refuse disposal.

Preparation of Ashes

Ashes do not cause any serious difficulties either in collection or disposal. Most cities, however, have a regulation prohibiting householders from presenting hot coals or hot ashes for collection and specify proper containers. Loads of refuse have often been set afire by such material; considerable loss has been experienced because such fires are difficult to extinguish.

RECEPTACLES FOR REFUSE

There is probably no single feature of refuse collection which has caused municipal officials more concern than refuse receptacles. It is rare indeed to find a city where there are enough suitable containers to hold the refuse that accumulates between collections. Some cities do not have suitable regulations and if there are regulations, citizens often fail to observe them and officials often do not enforce them. In some cities garbage and other refuse materials are placed for collection in every conceivable kind of container from cartons or lard cans to oil drums and huge boxes. Sometimes refuse is merely piled in yards or alleys. Most municipalities have enacted ordinances or have adopted regulations which stipulate in great detail the kind, number, and size of receptacles; the manner in which they shall be used and cared for; and the persons who are responsible for providing them. Some of these ordinances, in fact, specify as complete and sanitary a service as could be desired by anyone. Yet typically these provisions are not uniformly put into practice. Sometimes the failure to provide satisfactory receptacles is more or less citywide. More often, householders in the better residential districts and proprietors of commercial establishments obey the regulations fairly well while those in the poorer districts fail to store their refuse adequately. Their failure, of course, is largely caused by economic conditions, but a good program of public education can do much to improve refuse storage practices.

The importance of suitable containers for the temporary storage of refuse cannot be overemphasized. Separation, draining, or wrapping is

FIG. 3-7. The containers provided by this store include a wash tub, a paper carton, a wooden barrel, an oil drum, three oil drums cut down, and two regular refuse cans. None of them is provided with a cover. Some of the makeshift receptacles may cause injury to the collectors.

of little value without adequate receptacles to protect the material until the collectors pick it up. It would seem logical, therefore, that public officials would emphasize citizen compliance with the regulations. Numerous reasons for the lack of enforcement have been advanced. In the past the one given most frequently is that the people in the poorer districts cannot afford to purchase suitable containers, or if they do, the cans or other receptacles are soon stolen. Another reason is that elected officials are often unwilling to incur temporary public disfavor by supporting uniform enforcement of the existing ordinances. This attitude is rather widely held, and it may easily be the real root of the difficulty. Rigid and impartial enforcement of regulations requiring the provision of suitable containers is not impossible except in instances of extreme poverty, when the containers could quite properly be furnished by relief agencies or by the city itself. With satisfactory cooperation by the police force, thefts could be reduced to a minimum. In the few cities where refuse receptacles are furnished by the municipalities, practically no containers have been stolen. In other words, the solution of the container problem lies in the hands of the citizens, their chosen representatives, and the administrative officials.

Kinds of Receptacles

There are several kinds of refuse containers that insure sanitary storage of garbage, prevent the escape of refuse, and provide for economical collection. The fundamental requirements for garbage containers are that they be watertight, have tight-fitting covers, and be easy to clean. For rubbish, the containers should be such that the material cannot leak through crevices or be blown from the top. Containers for ashes should be leakproof and fireproof. All containers should be easy to empty and be equipped with suitable handles.

Garbage containers. Data on the refuse collection practices of 710 cities reveal that in the great majority of cases the containers must be made of durable metal and must be provided with tight-fitting covers. Many cities also specify suitable handles.

Containers that meet these requirements are available at most hardware stores in many different designs and styles. Typically, they are cylindrical, in tapered shape, and have a diameter large enough in proportion to height to give stability. Their cost is not great, usually within the means of any family. It varies somewhat, however, with the thickness of the metal, with the amount of reinforcing, and with the kind of special features provided.

Smaller cans are usually equipped with bails for easy carrying and dumping. Larger ones have two side handles. The bottoms are given particular attention by can manufacturers because it is usually the bottoms that rust and break out first. Extra heavy metal or double bottoms are sometimes used. Frequently the sides project below the floor of the can so that the bottom itself will not come in contact with the earth or with damp or wet floors. The covers for galvanized iron cans are designed to fit tightly enough to prevent the entrance of flies or other insects and to make it impossible for dogs to displace them. The usual cover fits snugly over the top of the can; the edge has a slight flare so that with increased pressure the cover is fixed more firmly in place. Many ingenious devices have been used to permit the cover to be fastened positively to the can or to make it unnecessary to remove the cover completely to put in garbage.

Since underground vaults for garbage containers were introduced they have enjoyed a somewhat limited use. The cans are effectively concealed under an iron cover flush with the ground; they cannot be tipped over. The cost of the vaults is quite high, and some difficulty is experienced in the winter in the northern part of the country when the vaults become covered with snow or when the covers freeze shut. Also, their use has been limited in certain areas due to high ground water table.

Another plan calls for wet strength bags, to be used only once (as liners). The bags are loaded into the collecting vehicle and both bags and garbage are disposed of together. The plan offers considerable convenience and sanitation, but has proved rather costly for general use.

FIG. 3-8. Well constructed garbage containers are essential to good premises storage practice. They should be durable, watertight, easy to clean, and have tight-fitting lids.

Plastic Containers. Some cities report an increase in the use of plastic containers. Their advantages include their lightness, which makes handling easy for both the householder and collection crew. Some cities, however, report that rodents can enter plastic containers easily, that they tend to crack in cold weather, and that they are susceptible to fire.

Paper Bags and Holders. Experimentation with paper bags and holders has been conducted in ˜some smaller towns and villages, as well as sections of the larger metropolises. Disposal bags are provided at a minimum price, and in some instances, at no cost to the householder, whose responsibility it is to affix the bag to the holder after each collection is made. Reports indicate that the paper bags have proven highly sanitary, easy to handle, and require no return operation—as in the case of metal containers. Some cities report this type of operation permits a reduction of up to 50 per cent in the collection staff.

A special study on paper bags for household refuse handling was conducted by the American Public Works Association Research Foundation (Research Project No. 115) published in August of 1963 as special report No. 26.

Rubbish containers. Specifications for rubbish containers are usually less rigid than those for garbage cans. Sanitation is not usually a primary factor and consequently more kinds of receptacles are used. Data on the types and sizes of containers used for rubbish in 1,156 cities are shown in Tables 3-2 and 3-3. Numberous cities require the same kind of receptacles for both garbage and rubbish, which may account, in part, for the large number of cities that specify the use of galvanized iron or metal rubbish cans. A large number of the cities shown in Table 3-2 require that all containers be covered and have suitable handles.

Many refuse collection administrators are not greatly concerned about the kinds of rubbish containers used. They are interested mainly in keeping the rubbish from leaking from the receptacles or being blown from them by the wind. Where combustible rubbish is incinerated, a special effort is usually made to keep the material reasonably dry, either by covering the receptacles or by keeping them under a shelter of some kind. The use of burlap or canvas bags offers some advantages. They are rather easily handled and if properly designed are not difficult to empty. Where combustible rubbish is involved, however, storage fire hazards are undoubtedly increased.

FIG. 3-9. Burlap bags for holding rubbish are supplied to each householder by the city of Fredericksburg, Virginia. Uniform garbage containers are also provided.

Some cities still permit the use of large concrete or brick vaults at the

TABLE 3-2

1964 Regulations of 1156 Cities Concerning Use and Type of Containers, by Class of Refuse

Class of Refuse	Container Required			Durable Metal	Tightfitting Lids	Suitable Handles
	Yes	No	N.R.[1]			
Garbage..........	710	27	422	399	405	195
Rubbish..........	496	91	578	192	193	101
Combined refuse..	742	67	454	336	346	175
Other............	43	13	1098	21	7	7

1. No report.

TABLE 3-3

1964 Regulations of 1156 Cities Concerning Size of Refuse Containers and Weight When Filled, by Class of Refuse

Class of Refuse	Maximum Volume (gallons)										Minimum Volume (gallons)						Maximum Weight Filled (pounds)							
	0-9	10-19	20	21-29	30-32	33-54	55	55 & up	No Limits	N.R.[1]	1-5	6-9	10	11-50	No Limits	N.R.	1-24	25-49	50-74	75-99	100	101 & up	No Limits	N.R.[2]
Garbage..........	9	73	163	59	278	67	11	6	18	472	83	9	95	104	54	811	5	23	115	123	74	13	41	762
Rubbish..........	5	14	90	39	167	63	22	12	36	707	26	8	47	69	58	947	1	15	102	100	67	18	33	820
Combined refuse..	2	23	137	59	281	80	22	8	38	506	49	8	86	107	73	833	0	17	133	141	73	12	53	726
Other...........	3	7	7	5	3	8	0	1	5	1117	3	0	1	7	6	1139	0	5	9	7	11	2	6	1116

1. No report.
2. Includes 24 unclassifiable answers.

alley line or even in or near the streets. These vaults are extremely unsatisfactory. In most places they were originally intended for rubbish or ashes, but frequently garbage is also deposited in them. In addition to inducing slovenly preparation of refuse by the householders, these bins or vaults sooner or later become very insanitary and cause disagreeable odors. It is extremely difficult, if not impossible, to clean them thoroughly. Unless they are well enclosed, rats are able to enter them easily to obtain food or to nest. Because vaults are difficult to empty, collection is slowed down, refuse is often spilled into the alley. Finally, it is difficult to service vaults in freezing temperatures.

FIG. 3-10. This refuse vault is used to store garbage, ashes, and rubbish until it is collected by the city. Although substantially built, it is neither sanitary nor does it prevent the release of garbage odors. A great many suitable refuse receptacles could be bought for the money required to build this vault.

Kinds of ash containers. Municipal requirements for ash receptacles are very much the same as those for rubbish containers. Actually, however, ashes are presented in all kinds of boxes, baskets, barrels, metal cans, and oil drums. Specifications for ash containers generally permit considerable latitude as to type, but rather uniformly stipulate that they be made of fireproof material, have suitable handles, and tight-fitting lids.

The use of concrete or brick vaults is probably not quite as objectionable for ashes as for garbage or rubbish. They are used mostly in those cities that collect ashes only once or twice during the winter. In such cases, vaults are preferable to ash piles in back yards or alleys.

Size of Receptacles

The capacity of those refuse containers in use varies from that of small lard pails to that of 55-gallon oil drums. Sometimes huge wooden boxes are used which when full require the combined efforts of several men to lift.

Factors affecting proper size. The weight of the filled receptacle is a primary criterion for establishing the size of receptacles to be used for different classes of refuse. If combustible rubbish is collected with gar-

FIG. 3-11. Some refuse vaults are unsightly as well as insanitary. The collectors must expend much more time and effort to load refuse by shoveling than by handling standard cans. More important, however, these vaults can never be made really clean.

bage, for example, the containers could probably be relatively large because of the light unit weight of the combined material. Rubbish containers could be still larger. However, far too much attention has been given to trying to proportion the size of receptacles to the frequency of collection or to the size of families. A more sensible approach would be to determine the capacity that can be handled most easily and economically by the collectors and then require that sufficient containers be provided to hold the material that accumulated between collections.

It is usually agreed that collectors in good physical condition can lift containers weighing from 75 to 100 pounds throughout an eight-hour shift without undue strain. The proper size of receptacles, then, can easily be determined if the weight of the empty cans and the unit weight of the

FIG. 3-12. Oil drums do not make good refuse containers. They are so heavy that they may cause injuries to collectors if they attempt to lift them. To avoid lifting them, collectors often dump the contents and shovel the material into the vehicles from the ground or from the drums.

class of refuse is known. Table 3-4 shows the weights of typical sizes of cans when they are filled with refuse of different unit weights.

The use of very small receptacles increases the loading time for the

TABLE 3-4

Weight of Containers and Their Contents When Filled
With Refuse of Different Densities

Containers		Combined Weights of Container and Refuse for Various Weights of Refuse per Cubic Yard							
Size (gallons)	Weight[1] (pounds)	1200	1000	800	600	500	400	300	200
5	5.1	35	30	25	20	17	15	13	10
7	5.7	47	40	34	27	23	20	16	13
8	6.4	54	46	38	30	26	22	18	14
10	7.1	67	57	47	37	32	27	22	17
12	8.5	80	68	56	44	38	32	26	19
15	13.3	102	88	73	58	50	43	36	28
18	14.5	122	104	86	68	59	50	41	32
20	15.2	134	113	95	75	65	55	45	35
25	16.7	165	141	116	91	79	66	54	42
30	18.7	197	167	138	108	93	78	63	48
35	20.5	228	194	160	125	107	90	73	55
40	22.3	260	220	181	141	121	102	82	62
55[2]	55.0	381	327	273	218	191	164	137	109

[1]The can weights used in this table are those of average metal receptacles, exclusive of covers.

[2]Oil drums (these are considered unacceptable as residential or commercial establishment refuse containers.)

collectors and therefore raises the collection cost. Such containers, of course, are easily handled. The larger sizes, when full, cannot be lifted by one man and sometimes not even by two, without undue exertion and strain.

There is a much greater tendency to permit or specify large receptacles for rubbish or ashes than for garbage, probably because of the usually greater interval between collections. From the householder's viewpoint, it is probably somewhat more satisfactory to have one large receptacle than several smaller ones particularly if the large container can be left at the alley line. Where they must be carried to the curb by the householder, however, smaller containers are generally preferred.

Provision of Receptacles

Refuse containers may be furnished by the owners of properties, by the occupants or householders, by the city, by refuse collection contractors, or by private collectors. The vast majority of cities require the owners or occupants of the premises to provide refuse receptacles. Large portable containers are sometimes provided by the city at commercial establishments, such as produce markets, where it is to the city's advantage because of sanitation and economy to provide the receptacles.

The owners rather than the occupants of large apartment buildings are ordinarily held responsible for providing the necessary receptacles for refuse. Several cities specify that in buildings containing living quarters for more than four families, the owner must provide suitable containers. Other cities place the limit as two, three, five, or six families.

A few cities have long practiced the exchange system, an empty can being left at each point of collection when the full one is removed. The full containers are hauled to the point of disposal, emptied, cleaned, and made ready for distribution. Private collectors that serve hotels and restaurants frequently provide the necessary receptacles, and leave clean empty ones in place of the full ones that are hauled away. In this way, sanitary collection can be secured without requiring the operators to purchase watertight, covered truck bodies.

Care of Receptacles

The average citizen is apt to believe that refuse receptacles have a very short life, the general impression being that garbage acids and coal ashes will corrode any metal or wood container very quickly. Actually, given proper care, galvanized iron cans will last at least three to five years. With this life expectancy and the relatively low first cost of cans, appropriate receptacles should be within the means of all families. The frequent statement that low-income families cannot afford to have proper refuse receptacles may be an admission that they are unwilling to take proper care of such containers by keeping them clean and in good repair.

Keeping receptacles clean will pay dividends in more sanitary conditions as well as in reduced container replacement and expense. Cans should be washed with hot water, and scoured, if necessary, to remove all food particles. If garbage is carefully wrapped, less frequent cleaning will be required. The cans should be allowed to dry before they are used again.

Disinfectants sometimes are used in the cans to sterilize them. This is an excellent practice that should prevent any possibility of bad odors or insanitary cans, but disinfectants should be used in addition to washing, not as a substitute for it.

It is also important to keep the outside of the can as dry as possible. If the containers are kept directly on the ground or on floors that are damp or wet a large part of the time, the bottoms of the cans will rust quickly. A very satisfactory plan is to keep the receptacles on pipe racks or on wooden platforms that are elevated a foot or more above the ground. They should not be kept under eaves or downspouts or in other places where water may get inside them.

Some collection officials recommend painting the cans inside and outside as added insurance for longer life. Painting is particularly effective when the galvanizing is chipped or cracked, after cans are repaired, or after dents are straightened out. Otherwise rusting and corrosion are apt to be rapid.

FIG. 3-13

FIG. 3-14

FIG. 3-15

FIG. 3-16

Vaults and other "homemade" structures, built to conceal refuse awaiting collection, as shown in Figures 3-13, 3-14, and 3-15, often pose problems for collectors or cause unsanitary conditions. The straightforward practice of using easily accessible, properly covered cans, shown in Figure 3-16, is more satisfactory.

The frequent theft of refuse containers has troubled many cities and has often led to the refusal of householders to supply proper cans. Sometimes the fault for this situation lies with the householder, but more often local collection practices are such that proper protection of the containers against theft is difficult if not impossible. Cans are rarely stolen from the back yard, particularly when they are kept near the house;

FIG. 3-17. With care, refuse receptacles will last three to five years. This can is kept on a raised platform to protect the bottom from rusting, and is located inside the fence so vehicles cannot damage it, but it is accessible to collectors.

they are much more liable to theft when they are kept permanently in or near the alley. When it is the practice for collectors to empty the cans into carrying baskets, it is feasible for householders to fasten the cans to fences, posts, or houses by means of chains. This kind of protection is not practical, of course, if the cans must be carried any distance by the collectors or if they must be emptied directly into vehicles. Many cans, however, are lost or damaged because of the failure of the householder to exercise reasonable care. They are left at curbs or in alleys for long periods after they have been emptied by the collectors, often in violation of regulations. Also many householders leave the cans permanently in or near alleys so they will not have to go to the trouble of setting them out at each regular collection period.

LOCATION OF RECEPTACLES

Naturally at collection time, the receptacles must be at the place from which the regular collectors will accept them. In many cases householders find such locations also the most convenient places to keep the containers between collections. When collection is made from the curb,

FIG. 3-18. Collections are made from the curbs in some places where there are no alleys. Sometimes city employees carry the receptacles from their regular locations just before the collecting vehicles arrive. In other places, the householders must place the refuse at the curbs at the proper time.

however, the receptacles must be kept regularly at other places. Some cities require that the emptied container be removed from the curb within a specified length of time after the collection has been made. The location of containers for collection is largely a matter of municipal regulation; the location at other times is for the householder's convenience.

Location for Collection

The location of receptacles for collection is very closely related to the method of collection used by a particular municipality and will be discussed fully in Chapter 5, "Collection Methods." There are some aspects of the problem, however, that affect the householders directly and influence the preparation of refuse. Only such factors will be mentioned here.

FIG. 3-19. Many householders find it more satisfactory to keep their refuse containers just inside the alley gates so that they will not have to be responsible for carrying them to the alleys on collection days. Some cities specify that cans must be within a stipulated distance from the alley line.

Cities collect refuse from many different locations, depending in large measure on the existence of suitable alleys and on the amount of money available for the collection service. Refuse is collected from curbs, alleys, back porches, back yards, at front or back building lines, from basements and even from inside buildings. Of more than 1,000 cities reporting on refuse receptacle location requirements in 1964, 61 per cent specified alley and/or curb collection; 31 per cent authorized front of house or back of house collection along with curb or alley collection; and 8 per cent reported that no particular collection point was specified. The above percentages indicate usual practices, but in nearly all cities special local conditions make it necessary to prescribe different locations for particular properties. Ordinarily, the official in charge of the collection service is given the authority to specify the place where containers must be placed for collection.

FIG. 3-20. Concrete boxes are still used in some cities, but are being replaced with portable containers because the use of the concrete box is slow and insanitary, involving both shoveling and spilling of refuse.

Numerous cities have found it more satisfactory to collect refuse from the place the householder keeps the containers, although in most cases this involves extra time for each pick-up and therefore additional cost. Such extra service is given because householders frequently forget to transfer receptacles to the collection point at the proper time, and if the refuse is not collected then they are inconvenienced and insanitary conditions are often created through lack of containers to hold the accumulated material. Frequently special trips are made by the collectors to pick up refuse that has not been set out in time. This problem must be faced with every refuse collection administrator. The solution lies either in the willingness of the citizens to pay for more collection service or in the rigid enforcement of sanitary ordinances. It is argued by some collection officials, however, that householders cannot be induced to cooperate sufficiently, and that it is cheaper and more satisfactory in the long run to pick up the refuse from the back of the houses or other locations on the householder's premises. In fact, some cities which limit their activities to the collection of garbage only because of insufficient funds to provide complete collection service, pick up that garbage from back doors at considerable extra expense when compared with alley or curb collection. However, in the majority of cities the location of the containers at the time of collection is at the alley or curb. Only a relatively small per cent pick up containers from inside the building, with the exception of the collection of garbage from restaurants or hotels.

Location of Containers Between Collections

Either for convenience or to hide them from view, householders keep their refuse receptacles in all sorts of places between collections. They are kept on porches, under porches, in basements, in kitchens, in garages, in clumps of shrubbery, in back yards, in alleys, and in specially built structures. If they are left in or near the alleys or in garages it is usually not for convenience, because this necessitates carrying refuse considerable distances several times a day. When receptacles are kept in or near alleys, the purpose sometimes is to keep possible insanitary conditions as far as possible from the houses but usually to have the cans in place at all times for collection. When they are kept in garages, in shrubbery clumps, or under porches, the primary reason may be to conceal them.

The advisability of keeping containers in alleys is sometimes open to question. This practice often leads to insanitary conditions, filthy alleys, and neighborhood quarrels. The containers are battered by passing vehicles or by the automobiles of residents in maneuvering to get into or out of alley garages. They may be tipped over by dogs and the contents scattered. Scavengers have free access to them and frequently spread quantities of refuse over the alley as they sort out salvagable materials. Most of the complaints of theft of containers occur in those places that use the alleys as permanent locations for the cans. It is true that when the containers are in the alley they are usually out of the sight of residents, but it is also true that insanitary alleys may be far worse than visible cans and have more serious consequences.

EFFECT OF QUANTITY LIMITATIONS ON PREPARATION

The desirability of complete refuse collection by municipalities is becoming generally accepted. In many cases, however, such ideal service is economically impractical and certain limits must be imposed. Some municipal authorities find it necessary to regulate the quantity of refuse, by weight or volume, which will be collected from a single residence

FIG. 3-21. Refuse may not be placed outside of the property line in some cities. The purpose of such a regulation is to prevent street littering and to keep the streets more attractive. The containers shown here are kept in the basement garage between collection periods.

or place of business at one collection. The purpose of the regulations is twofold: first, to maintain the degree of service rendered on a somewhat uniform basis; and second, to insure a more or less constant collection from week to week. If left unregulated, careless producers might permit large quantities of refuse to accumulate on their premises over long periods and place abnormal amounts out for collection at irregular intervals, thus upsetting the collection schedule. Regulation is especially applied to large wholesale, industrial, and manufacturing enterprises which in the great majority of cases are required to dispose of all or part of their refuse themselves, at their own expense.

The maximum quantities permitted by regulation should obviously be sufficient to take care of a normal accumulation at a household over the established interval between regular collections. In commercial districts the maximum quantity limitations are often fixed on arbitrary bases rather than on normal production. Total quantities of refuse can also be controlled by restricting the kinds of material which will be collected. Both types of regulations serve to keep the scope of municipal refuse collection and disposal operations within reasonable or desired bounds.

Quantity Limitations for Residential Properties

Unusually large accumulations of refuse at residences are caused principally by abnormal production of rubbish, particularly yard rubbish and the material discarded during moving and house-cleaning periods.

FIG. 3-22. Frequently it is more convenient to keep the refuse containers near the kitchen door. Some cities collect the material from such points. In other cases, the householder must carry the cans to the locations designated by municipal officials. Containers are concealed in or near shrubbery clumps on some properties.

Nevertheless, the failure of householders to prepare or to set out garbage and ashes regularly as these kinds of refuse are produced is also responsible for unreasonable quantities.

Some cities have encouraged citizens to burn yard rubbish and other combustible rubbish on their premises in order to reduce the load on the regular collection agency and to keep the public expense as low as possible. A definite limit on the amount which will be collected is sometimes imposed. In numerous cases open yard fires are permitted, but many cities require such burning to be done in covered wire baskets or in yard incinerators. There are numerous kinds of such burners available. They are not necessarily unattractive, and in many cases they can be concealed by shrubbery or fences. Some manufacturers of precast

FIG. 3-23. A few of the many types of yard rubbish burners available to property owners. Burning of rubbish is prohibited in some cities because of air pollution.

concrete burners have designed incinerators that are well suited to residential yards. In some communities, however, the fire laws prohibit outdoor fires of any kind during certain seasons. Moreover, such burning may contribute to local air pollution problems, and therefore the trend is against it. In such cases, combustible rubbish must be removed by the regular collection agencies, by the householders, or by private collectors.

Many cities, which impose limitations on the kind and quantity of refuse that is collected, provide for spring clean-up periods during which all accumulations of rubbish are removed by city forces. The advocates of complete municipal service, however, contend that regular collection of all classes of refuse will prevent any accumulation on the premises and thus prevent unattractive heaps of refuse and smooth out the total collection load. This position is well demonstrated in those cities

TABLE 3-5
Air-Pollution Control Practices in 995[1] Cities—1964

Local Air Pollution Regulations		Backyard Burning Permitted	On-site Burning of Demolition Wastes Permitted	Flue-fed Incinerators Permitted	Domestic Incinerators Regulated
Yes—374	Yes	181	116	228	276
cities	No	191	248	108	76
	No Ans.	2	10	38	22
	Total	374	374	374	374
No—493	Yes	241	175	254	197
cities	No	133	183	79	143
	No Ans.	119	135	160	153
	Total	493	493	493	493
No Answer	Yes	24	15	25	32
—128 cities	No	26	34	9	8
	No Ans.	78	79	94	88
	Total	128	128	128	128
Total—995	Yes	446	306	507	505
cities	No	350	465	196	227
	No Ans.	199	224	292	263
	Total	995	995	995	995

[1]To the 1964 survey question "Are there any local air pollution control regulations?" 374 cities replied "yes," 493 replied "no" (perhaps interpreting the question as referring to "industrial" air pollution control), and 128 gave no reply. However, many cities replying in the negative and cities giving no response indicated restrictions on backyard burning, on-site burning of demolition wastes, and use of flue-fed and domestic incinerators—presumably under other sections of municipal codes and ordinances.

that have complete service and the householders cooperate by placing their refuse regularly for collection.

Cities generally will accept all garbage in residential areas without quantity limitation. Rubbish and ashes are sometimes limited to specific amounts or to the quantity that can be placed in one or more standard containers. These regulations are primarily to prevent unreasonable abuse, because collectors are often instructed to accept occasional excess accumulations. Severe quantity restrictions usually result in the employment of private collectors by citizens who can afford to pay for such service or in promiscuous dumping of the excess by those unable or unwilling to hire private collectors.

Quantity Limitations for Commercial Establishments

The amount of refuse produced by business and industrial establishments varies greatly. Some types of business produce very little, while others may have to dispose of several truck loads each day. It would obviously be impossible to establish uniform quantity limits based on normal accumulations. Many cities, however, assume full responsibility for the collection of commercial garbage, even from hotels, restaurants, markets, and food stores. Others limit the amount of garbage as well as other classes of refuse that will be collected without charge.

REGULATIONS FOR THE PREPARATION OF REFUSE

Every city has specific regulations governing the householder's responsibilities in the handling of refuse and the preparation of it for collection, regardless of whether the material is picked up by city forces, contractors, or private collectors. Often these regulations are prescribed by ordinance, sometimes in great detail. In other places, much of the formal control of practices is left to the municipal officials who have supervision of the collection work or who have charge of the collection operations. In most cases, the ordinance provisions are written in rather technical language and are usually not clear to the average citizen and certainly not to the more illiterate or foreign groups. Consequently, it is usual to interpret the ordinance requirements and other regulations in a form suitable for general use.

Ordinances, enforcement, and public education methods are discussed in other chapters. It is intended here to present only the means by which citizens are informed more or less officially of the municipal requirements for preparing refuse for collection.

There is some difference of opinion as to the form in which such rules for the guidance of the public can best be presented. Some cities make a practice of distributing printed instructions, giving in more or less detail a practical interpretation of the salient provisions of the ordinance, together with such additional explanations and directions as may be deemed essential in establishing good collection practice. While these tend to become the more fixed rules for the conduct of the service, there are undoubtedly a host of other informal and verbal arrangements which never find their way into the published practices.

House Cards

The formal instructions are usually printed in the form of "house cards" of varying dimensions, simply and attractively arranged to encourage preservation by the householders. Emphasis is placed upon those things required of each householder, including the number and type of containers to be furnished, the necessary separations of refuse to be made, the house treatment of various classes of refuse to be collected, the care to be given containers, and the locations where containers shall be placed for collection. Information is usually given on numerous general matters, including the designations of the materials which will not be collected, the means for handling complaints, the provisions for reporting dead animals and other insanitary conditions, the statement of penalties for violation, and other similar matters. Some house cards also include the collection hours and days for the particular collection districts. Due to the frequency with which the collection schedules are altered in some places, some officials believe that district boundary maps and schedules of collection dates might well be published separately.

Rather than make the "house card" a formal and forbidding legal document, a number of cities look upon this medium as an unusual opportunity for public education and for gaining the householder's cooperation. Attractively designed folders, pamphlets, and colored cards convey the necessary information and instructions in an informal and

REFUSE COLLECTING RULES
IN THE CITY OF MADISON

1. The collection of refuse such as tin cans, ashes, paper and glass is under the direction of the Superintendent of Streets. Grass, leaves, and small tree or shrub trimmings will be collected with regular refuse when in containers.
2. The owner or occupant of each house shall provide suitable containers in which to store such refuse in a safe manner between collections.
3. Containers should be a bushel basket or its equivalent for non-combustible material. The containers with their contents should not exceed in weight that which one person can lift. (About 50 pounds). Pressed paper drums are permitted for combustible material, such as paper, rags and light-weight noncombustible, such as tin cans. They should not be over 30 inches high or 24 inches in diameter. The above 50 pound weight limit applies.
4. Fifty gallon metal drums or wooden barrels will NOT be emptied regardless of the contents or weight.
5. Building material of any kind will NOT be collected.
6. Containers of refuse should be placed at the curb edge of the street for collection.
7. Placing of refuse in the gutter is prohibited by Ordinances of the City of Madison and provides a penalty.
8. Containers of refuse shall be kept off streets until 12 hours prior to the day of collection in your ward, but placed at the curb by 7 a. m. of the collection day.
9. For day of collection in your ward, see opposite side of this card.
10. No special collections of refuse will be made. Special collections required when people move may be ordered by Building Inspection or Health Department and costs billed to party moving. Large items, such as, stove, refrigerator, davenport, table, etc., will be picked up by separate trucks on regular collection day if Madison citizens place a phone call to this office.
11. If scheduled collection date falls on a holiday, collections will be made on the following working day. WATCH LOCAL NEWS-PAPERS FOR ANNOUNCEMENTS.
12. Direct requests for information to the street department operating headquarters at:
    East Side—City Market—266-4685
    West Side—Badger Road—266-4681
    Excluded from Regular Refuse Collection Schedule, but included in the Street Department Service will be the continued collection of shrub and small bush or tree trimmings, providing they meet the following regulations:
    a. The material will be tied securely in bundles not over 4 feet long and not exceeding 50 lbs. in weight.
    b. Every area in the City during the summer months will have two such collections per month. These will be made on the week when your regular rubbish is not collected and on the same day of the week. For example, if your regular rubbish collections are on the 1st and 3rd Mondays, the brush collection will be on the 2nd and 4th Mondays of the month. Grass clippings if placed in containers will also be collected at this time.

FIG. 3-24

RULES PERTAINING TO
GARBAGE COLLECTION

1. The garbage of the City of Madison is collected under the supervision of the Superintendent of Streets, Sewers and Sanitation. In the residential area the collection is made at least once each week.
2. The owner or occupant of each house, apartment, flat, restaurant or hotel shall provide a sufficient number of portable, metallic cans; said cans to be watertight, provided with handles, and close-fitting covers which shall not be removed except when necessary.
3. Garbage cans of residents must not be **less than 5** gallons nor **more than 20** gallons in size. Garbage cans of restaurants and hotels shall not be **more than 35 gallons** in size. If more capacity is needed, additional cans must be furnished.
4. All garbage from residences shall be drained and wrapped in paper before being placed in garbage vessels, and garbage from hotels and restaurants shall be deposited in the garbage vessels, **after** draining, without wrapping.
5. Put into the garbage can all animal and vegetable refuse from the kitchen.
6. It shall be unlawful for any person to place in the garbage cans any ashes, earth, tin cans, crockery, excess paper, paper boxes or any other refuse other than garbage. Cans containing any of the above will not be emptied by the collector.
7. Cans must be placed on the ground floor easily accessible to the collector, and when filthy, leaky, or in any way defective, be replaced by new cans.
8. You are not entitled to the services of this department unless you conform to these rules.
9. After you have complied with the above rules, report all complaints to office of Superintendent of Streets, Sewers and Sanitation, West Side 266-4681, East Side 266-4685.
10. The above rules are in accordance with section 7.26, General Ordinances of the City of Madison.

JAMES A. BROPHY
Supt. Streets, Sewers and Sanitation

"HANG THIS UP IN YOUR KITCHEN"

FIG. 3-25

The house cards used in Madison, Wisconsin, clearly state the regulations governing separation, containers and their location, and where to report complaints.

pleasing manner. On the whole, the purpose of the cards or folders would seem to be a bid for public cooperation rather than a threat for noncompliance.

Emphasis is usually placed on presenting the necessary information concisely and simply so it can be readily understood by almost all citizens. Sometimes translations are made in communities where there are rather large numbers of foreigners who cannot read English. Catch phrases are used in some house cards to make the regulations easier to remember. Pictures, cartoons, maps, and diagrams are also used to good advantage.

House cards are given to all householders. Sometimes they are mailed, but more frequently are distributed by refuse collection supervisors and foremen. Special emphasis is usually given to informing new residents in the city or in collection districts of the regulations on preparation. Many cities insist that the foremen make personal contact with a responsible citizen in each household when the cards are distributed so that any questions can be answered and certain special rules can be explained. During such visits, the location of refuse containers is agreed upon, particularly if peculiar local conditions make it advisable to adjust the general rules slightly.

Informal Regulations

Numerous special conditions must be given individual attention in any community. Conditions on particular properties may make different collection treatment necessary. Temporary measures may have to be taken because of severe storms or other emergencies such as strikes, epidemics, or serious breakdowns in disposal plants. Unusual kinds of refuse or exceptionally large quantities produced at residences may require different handling and preparation or may require some limitation as to quantity. Some cities treat individually all commercial properties which produce rather large quantities of refuse. The amount and kind of collection to be rendered is agreed upon and in some cases the amount to be charged such properties for service in addition to that provided at public expense.

Notices in local newspapers are used to inform citizens of any unusual changes in the regulations or of temporary requirements that may be necessary to meet emergencies. Often householders are advised of the regular seasonal changes made in frequency or character of collection service through advertisements or articles in newspapers.

SUMMARY

It is evident that the preparation of refuse for collection assumes greater importance than is ordinarily realized. In fact it is one of the most significant factors in the whole problem of refuse collection and disposal. Its direct relationship to disposal has been especially emphasized.

Cooperation of the householders and commercial producers is unquestionably an imperative first step to successful operation, from both the standpoint of health and economics. This necessarily involves attention to prescribed details, including separations of the refuse into designated classes, preparing these for collection, providing suitable receptacles for their accumulation, and setting these out for collection at regular intervals at stated locations.

It seems evident that with the ever-increasing demands and requirements of the public for extended refuse collection service, wholehearted public understanding and cooperative assistance are absolutely essential if good service is to be maintained within the economic limitations set by the funds available.

chapter 4

FACTORS AFFECTING REFUSE COLLECTION COST

Conditions and practices in the field of refuse collection vary so much from place to place that it can be truly said that no two cities present exactly the same situation. First, there are many physical differences between cities that influence collection operations, including differences in size, density of population, climate and topography, and alleys or lack of them. Second, there are wide differences in the amount and kind of collection service provided by city governments—differences in what will be collected, in the place from which it will be collected, and in the frequency with which it will be collected. Third, there are important variations in public attitudes and personal habits that affect the amount of refuse produced, the way it is prepared for collection, the character of the service provided, and the amount of work involved in making the collections. Sometimes the convenience of the house-holders is subordinated to economy of operation; at other times the desires of the public control refuse collection and disposal practices.

These particular local conditions all are reflected in the amount of effort, equipment, and money required to provide refuse collection service. In addition, when reported costs are considered, other differences must be taken into consideration. The wages paid to collectors and equipment operators differ greatly from place to place, and accounting methods and practices are so different that the cost figures reported may not be properly comparable.

It is easily seen that under these circumstances it is difficult to make inter-city comparisons of the cost of refuse collection. If total costs or per capita costs are used, all of the possible variations mentioned above may be significant. If unit costs are studied, some of the variables are taken into account, such as differences in the amount of material collected and in the extent of the service, but many other important variations still exist.

The purpose of this chapter is to show in some detail just how cities differ in providing refuse collection service and how these differences influence the cost of conducting the work. There has been a strong tendency, among municipal officials as well as laymen, to compare cities and services solely on the basis of reported costs. Comparisons can be valid only when all important influencing circumstances are properly accounted for. The administrator of a refuse collection service will find accurate costs from another city having a closely similar problem extremely valuable. But when cost reports are used without interpretation, conclusions may be wholly erroneous.

INTERPRETATION OF REFUSE COLLECTION COST DATA

Good refuse collection cost data are essential to intelligent management. They expose inefficient procedures and suggest more effective methods. Once costs are determined, it is natural to attempt comparisons with those of other cities, in the belief that the relative efficiency of differing operating plans may be discovered. Unfortunately, such worthy aims are often negated by the countless dissimilarities in working conditions and the quality and extent of service rendered.

Unless all dissimilar conditions are appraised, comparisons of such municipal cost data are worse than useless. Hastily considered comparisons penalize those cities which, in order to produce data that are administratively valuable, include all elements of cost in their reported figures. Such comparisons also jeopardize progress in refuse collection practices and in public health generally, for they tend to drive the level of service in all cities down to that of the most inadequate. It is safe to use information from other communities only when all of the salient facts behind the figures are known and are taken into account.

Often it is quite difficult to understand just how much must be known about conditions in other cities to make comparisons valid. It is not unusual to find per capita figures used in an attempt to gauge the effectiveness of collection systems, even though such information eliminates only one of the many significant variations that may exist, that of population. The range in per capita cost per year for refuse collection is still extremely wide. In 1960, for 38 cities, the range was $0.24 to $7.40. Obviously such figures cannot disclose relative efficiency, the amount of service, or the kind of service. All that can be gleaned from such data is that on the average with a normal amount of service given and average working conditions, it may be expected that the cost per capita per year will be somewhere between the figures. As will be pointed out, very high or very low costs may be explained in terms of different conditions or service.

It becomes apparent that some of the more important differences must be eliminated if one is to get closer to the real relation of one community to another. Thus, when the cost of collecting a ton or a cubic yard of refuse is studied, or when the amount of effort or equipment required for such a single unit is computed, differences in the amounts of refuse produced or in the amounts accepted for collection are no longer of great significance, provided there are not material differences in population densities or in the amounts of refuse collected per capita. It would not be reasonable, however, to compare a city which collects garbage only with one which collects all refuse together. Consequently it is necessary to inquire into the costs or other pertinent factors on a per-ton or a per-cubic-yard basis for each class of refuse, depending on the kind of separation effected. Table 4-1 shows the range of collection costs in 1965 reported by selected cities.

It might have been expected that these performance cost figures would not show great dispersion, but it can be seen that the cost of collecting a unit of refuse may vary considerably. The collection of a ton of garbage, for example, may be more than three times as costly in one city as in another. It is evident that such discrepancy is far too great to be explained in terms of relative efficiency or character of service.

TABLE 4-1
Collection Operating Costs (Dollars per Ton)
For Selected Cities, 1965

City	Labor	Equip-ment	Over-head	Total	Notes
Los Angeles....	6.76	2.61	3.37	12.74	Combined refuse—residential.
	16.16	3.41	11.43	31.00	Garbage—commercial.
Washington.....	—	0.61[1]	—	14.11	Combined refuse less residential garbage.
	—	1.47[1]	—	24.06	Garbage—residential and commercial.
Cedar Rapids...	—	—	—	14.00	Records list $49.92 a load. Density of 450 pounds per cubic yard assumed to arrive at $14.00.
Evanston.......	8.88	1.78	0.71	11.37	Combined refuse—residential.
Winnetka.......	7.04	1.46	0.87	9.37	Combined refuse—residential.
	8.06	1.22	0.98	10.26	Combined refuse—commercial.
Newark.........	—	—	—	9.15	Combined refuse—residential, commercial, some industrial.
Trenton........	—	—	—	12.40	Combined refuse—commercial.
Cincinnati......	7.39	1.97[2]	2.14	11.50	Combustible and non-combustible rubbish—residential, commercial, and industrial. Labor benefits included in overhead. Set-out system used.
Philadelphia....	6.21	1.95	2.67	10.83	Combined refuse less residential and commercial garbage. Labor benefits in overhead.
	14.00	1.95	4.04	19.99	Bulk.
	—	—	—	7.83	Some garbage. Net Cost.
Vancouver.....	7.48	3.10	1.08	11.66	25 cubic yard trucks—combined refuse, residential, commercial and some industrial.
	8.60	3.57	1.08	13.25	25 cubic yard trucks—same as above.
	7.16	2.03	1.08	10.27	16 cubic yard trucks—same as above.
	3.81	2.63	1.08	7.52	20 cubic yard trucks—same as above.
	8.40	1.76	1.08	11.24	26 cubic yard trucks—same as above.
	7.09	2.62	1.08	10.79	Average—use with caution.
New York City..	19.28	4.44	1.24	24.96	Combustible and non-combustible rubbish. Combined refuse—residential.

[1]Depreciation portion includes maintenance only.
[2]Depreciation not included.

What are the important differences, then, that must be considered in order to get an accurate comparison among communities? Some of the fundamental factors are: (1) climate and geographical differences; (2) form in which refuse is presented for collection; (3) frequency of collection; (4) place from which the refuse is collected (curb, alley, back door, or basement); (5) length of haul; (6) character or number of classes of refuse collected; (7) manner of collection of the various classes, in combination or separately; (8) wage rates of collectors and drivers; (9) population density; (10) general overtime, holiday, vacation and sick-time allowance policies; (11) kind of service demanded by citizens; (12) character of administration and supervision; and (13) accounting and field reporting practices.

Since the medium for expressing relations among the communities is their reported cost figures, it would be neither fair nor productive of valid conclusions to begin the process by uncritical acceptance of figures which may not include all cost elements or at least the same elements. Sometimes certain direct costs are omitted and many times indirect costs and overhead are unknown. Consequently, the cities must be grouped at the outset to place them on a comparable basis, depending on whether such cost elements as equipment expense, equipment depreciation, and overhead are included.

In other words, the minimum requirements for comparability of cost figures are that they be expressed in terms of units of work performed, that they refer to the collection of the same materials, and that they include the same cost elements. If these requirements are not met, attempts to appraise a city's efficiency by comparing its reported costs with those of another may result in an unjust charge of inefficiency, on the one hand, or undeserved commendation for economical operation, on the other. What appear to be high costs may represent a high standard of service and a complete accounting system; what appear to be low costs, may be due to a low standard of service and incomplete accounting of the cost of what is done.

But even when these requirements for comparability are met there are still a great many important circumstances outside the control of administration that have a heavy influence on operating costs. The whole situation must be analyzed in each case. The extent of service provided is influenced by the frequency of collection and the place from which the garbage is accepted by the city forces. Some of the conditions which may critically affect the cost of providing the service are the wage rates of employees, the relative density of population, and the length of haul. Probably the most significant factor is the place from which the refuse is collected because of the great amount of additional time and effort required to make a collection from a back door instead of from the curb or alley.

Other factors that influence collection costs are climatic and geographical differences, the kind of equipment used, topography, cooperation of householders, and relative density of population. When these have been taken into consideration, remaining differences in unit costs can safely be ascribed to the efficiency of the management of the collection systems. Undoubtedly costs are greatly affected by administrative practices as well as by conditions fixed by ordinance, existing physical circumstances, or demands of citizens. Such elements as personnel management, organization, route layout, scheduling, and collection methods may make important differences in costs and cannot be ignored in interpreting data.

The interpretation of reported cost data in this manner makes it possible to make sound evaluations or comparisons and at the same time portray the facts in true perspective. Comparison of cost data is helpful in expressing relations and indicating differences, but the limitations of the comparative method must be kept constantly in mind. Some of the factors influencing costs are not themselves susceptible to precise measurement and consequently there is no way of adjusting the costs of different cities to produce wholly comparable figures. The following sections are devoted to a rather detailed analysis of the influence of the numerous variations in refuse collection systems on costs. Variations in the extent and character of the service are examined first, after which consideration is given to physical and cultural differences, wage rates, limitation of funds, attitude of officials, and effect of disposal methods.

VARIATIONS IN THE SERVICE RENDERED

Probably the most fundamental variations in municipal refuse collection lie in the extent and character of the service provided. In general, a city is entirely free to provide for the collection of municipal refuse in any manner it desires. One city may decide that complete service should be provided by municipal forces, that all classes of refuse should be collected without limitation on quantity, that all properties should be served, that refuse should be collected frequently and in a sanitary manner, and that it should be collected from whatever point on an individual property is most convenient for the householder. Another city may decide that each resident should be responsible for disposing of the refuse he produces, and the municipality should do no more than regulate that disposal. Between these two extremes are innumerable possibilities for placing limitations on the kind or amount of refuse that will be accepted, the classes of properties that will be served, the frequency of collection, and other determinants of the amount of work that will be done. Actually, there are almost as many service patterns as there are cities.

It is not always easy to understand how or why the many differences in service arose. In most cities refuse collection service began rather modestly, often with the collection of garbage only; additional materials were included when the citizens would not dispose of them economically themselves. With the growth of the service, certain restrictions on the kind of materials that would be collected and other limitations on the extent of service came into existence. Such restrictions may have been occasioned by the opinion that complete service should not be financed from general tax revenues, or that only certain classes of properties should have collection service at general city expense. There is no doubt that some restrictions have been brought about by limitations on municipal financial ability. In some cities, in all likelihood, the limitations have become traditional and are being continued long after the original reasons for them have disappeared. Frequently, curtailed service prevails in the face of spirited clamoring by citizen groups that it be improved and increased.

FIG. 4-1. A separate collection for yard rubbish is provided in St. Petersburg, Florida. House-holders are requested to place the yard trash, such as grass cuttings, in cardboard cartons and asked to tie branch trimmings and the like into bundles. These are placed at the curb for the collection.

It is not intended to imply that all cities should provide unlimited service or that the same service should be given by all communities. It is the intention, rather, to emphasize the fact that the municipal task is widely different from city to city.

Limitations on Kinds of Materials Collected

The work of collecting a city's refuse obviously is influenced by the amount and the nature of the material that is collected. Methods, equipment, practices, and management may all be drastically affected by limitations which exclude certain materials. In some cities, entire broad classes of refuse, such as ashes or rubbish, are not accepted for collection; in others certain component materials, such as tree, shrubbery, or grass trimmings, furniture, or dead animals may be excluded from the collectible types.

Considering first the inclusion or exclusion of entire classes of refuse materials by municipalities, it becomes apparent that there is a great diversity of both policy and practice. For the purpose of this discussion eight major classes of refuse are considered: *Residential:* (1) garbage (2) ashes, (3) noncombustible rubbish, and (4) combustible rubbish, *Commercial:* (1) garbage, (2) ashes, (3) noncombustible rubbish, and (4) combustible rubbish. The broad service patterns of 1,142 collection systems are shown in Table 4-2. If some regular service is provided for a class, either with or without charging a fee by direct municipal service, contract, or private collection, the collection system is credited with collecting that class. However, such inclusion does not mean that all kinds of materials within each class are collected. It is thus evident that substantial quantities of wastes must be disposed of by property owners and private firms not regularly engaged in the refuse collection business.

Table 4-3 gives data on the service patterns provided by 428 municipalities which have municipally operated collection systems only.

Table 4-3 indicates that even municipal collection systems operating exclusively in a given area are somewhat incomplete in terms of a comprehensive refuse collection. The nature of the service given in any one city may be governed by certain limitations of disposal facilities, or by the opinion of the legislative body as to the proper extent of munic-

TABLE 4-2

Class of Refuse Collected in 1964 by 1,142 Collection Systems Including Municipal, Municipal-Contract, and Private Collectors (in Per cent)

Class of Refuse Collected	Yes	No
Combined refuse	76.0%	24.0%
Garbage	94.6	5.4
Combustible rubbish	93.1	6.9
Noncombustible rubbish	93.3	6.7
Abandoned automobiles	7.6	92.4
Industrial refuse	34.5	65.5
Contractors' building or demolition wastes	16.9	83.1
Ashes	78.0	22.0
Dead animals	42.5	57.5
Tree debris	35.5	64.5
Bulk refuse	43.0	57.0
Evictions	35.9	64.1

ipally financed service. Cities may collect garbage only, or they may collect everything but garbage. (In some cases the latter is prompted by a city's complete reliance on the encouraged installation and use of household and commercial garbage grinders for garbage disposal.) They may exclude commerical garbage, or commercial ashes, or just one or both

TABLE 4-3

Class of Refuse Collected in 1964 in 428 Communities Having Only A Municipally Operated Refuse Collection System

Class of Refuse Collected	Yes	No
Combined refuse	77.8%	22.2%
Garbage	99.3	0.7
Combustible rubbish	97.9	2.1
Noncombustible rubbish	97.7	2.3
Abandoned automobiles	7.0	93.0
Industrial refuse	38.2	61.8
Contractors' building or demolition wastes	9.3	90.7
Dead animals	59.5	40.5
Tree debris	48.5	51.5
Bulk refuse	48.0	52.0
Evictions	37.1	62.9

types of commercial rubbish; or they may exclude ashes throughout the city.

In addition to excluding entire classes of refuse from municipal service, it is not uncommon for cities to exclude certain kinds of materials from the classes that *are* collected. Such materials as yard rubbish, grass cuttings, tree branches, furniture, building materials, cartons, boxes, market refuse, and dead animals are typical of the kinds of refuse that various municipal agencies will not handle.

The type of service given by municipal collection systems to residential and commercial refuse producers is detailed in Table 4-4, which indicates that municipal refuse collection agencies prefer combined collections rather than the collection of selected classes of refuse.

TABLE 4-4

Residential and Commercial Refuse, by Class, Collected by 543 Municipal Forces in 1964 (in Per Cent)

Class of Refuse Collected	Residential		Commercial	
	Yes	No[1]	Yes	No[1]
Combined collection	77.0%	23.0%	66.2%	33.8%
Garbage	19.1	80.9	17.0	83.0
Ashes	13.0	87.0	9.0	91.0
Rubbish	19.0	81.0	15.5	84.5
Other	20.0	80.0	12.0	88.0

[1]Includes "no answer" and unusable responses.

Limitations of Service

Classes of property served. Another type of limited service is found in those cities that deny refuse collection service to certain classes of property. Such a limitation is most often applied to commercial properties, or multiple dwellings, but other forms of property-class limitation are also found.

Quantity collected. The maximum amount of refuse that will be accepted at any one collection is specified in a number of cities. A control of this sort is not so far reaching, of course, as is a denial of all collection service or the exclusion of an entire class of refuse from collection. Variations in such restrictions from city to city, however, may account for large differences in total quantities collected and in the cost of providing the service.

A limitation on the quantity that will be accepted at one collection in residential areas is, in some instances, designed to encourage the regular and orderly discarding of refuse as it accumulates and to prevent the presentation of large quantities for collection after periodic cleanup operations. Such control may also be found necessary to halt abuses or to prevent unreasonably large quantities from some premises at every collection. In some of the cities which give no commercial collection service it has been found that the proprietors of small shops may even haul their business refuse to their homes in the residential areas in order to have it collected at municipal expense. Actually, however, quantity limitations are not widely applied.

FIG. 4-2. Some cities give complete service to commercial properties while others give none at all or accept only certain classes of refuse. Rather wide differences in methods, practices, and costs often may be justified because of the scope or extent of municipal service rendered.

Control of the quantity of refuse is of considerably more significance in connection with commercial than with residential properties. If unlimited quantities of commercial refuse were to be accepted for collection, a substantial increase in personnel and equipment would be necessary in some communities. Some legislators feel that a quantity limitation is called for in the interest of fair and equal treatment, since some enterprises produce little or no refuse while others produce great quantities. The limitations imposed are quite similar to those for residential districts, both as to the units of measurement and the amounts, but in most cases the collections are more frequent in commercial areas, resulting in less severe restriction.

Frequency of collection. The character of refuse collection service varies also with the frequency with which the several classes of material are removed from the householder's premises. Within reasonable limits, the more frequently collections are made the more satisfactory and convenient it is for the citizens. When refuse is removed often, fewer and smaller containers are needed, garbage does not putrefy in the cans, and it cannot serve as a breeding medium for flies and other insects or as food for rodents.

It has been observed that more refuse per capita is collected when frequent service is given because there is usually no need for house-holders to burn refuse or to dispose of it privately by other means since there is usually ample container capacity. However, the cost of collection increases with frequency by more than can be accounted for by increase in quantity. When frequent collections are made, smaller quantities are set out on each collection day and trucks must travel farther and make more stops to obtain a full load. Hence, extra labor, time, mileage, and equipment is required.

The proper frequency to give the most satisfactory and economical service is governed by the amount of refuse that must be collected, the climate, and the demands of citizens. For the collection of refuse containing garbage the maximum period should not be greater than:

1. The normal time for the accumulation of the amount of refuse that can be placed in a container of reasonable size.
2. The time it takes fresh garbage to putrefy and to give off foul odors, under average conditions of storage.
3. The length of the fly-breeding cycle. Unwrapped garbage should be removed from the premises at regular intervals spaced according to the minimal time required for the development of flies from eggs to mature larvae. During the hot summer months this is frequently less than 7 days.

The frequency of collection by municipal agencies generally meets the standards described above. This is demonstrated in Table 4-5, concerning combined refuse collections, which account for the bulk of the municipal refuse collection activities.

TABLE 4-5

Frequency of Combined Refuse Collections from Residential and Commercial Areas During the Summer by Municipal Collection Agencies in 1964[1]

Frequency of Collection	Residential	Commercial
(Number of communities responding)	(418)	(359)
Once a week	46.7%	8.1%
Twice a week	48.5	11.4
Three times a week	3.6	3.6
Four times a week	0.0	1.1
Five times a week	0.0	11.7
More than five times a week	0.0	29.3
Fortnightly	0.5	0.0
Monthly	0.0	0.0
Variable	0.7	34.8
Cleanup drives	0.0	0.0
	100.0	100.0

[1]The frequency of collections during the winter varies only slightly from that in the summer.

The frequency for the collection of rubbish and ashes generally is based on the size of containers, the amount produced, and the funds available.

Different conditions existing within a single community may easily make it desirable to use different frequencies for different districts or for different classes of property. Although small cities generally find it more satisfactory and more economical to serve all areas equally, larger cities commonly collect more frequently in commercial than in residential districts. A few cities find it desirable to vary the period between collections from one residential section to another.

The actual frequency of municipal collection of the various classes of refuse reported by 924 collection agencies for residential areas is given in Table 4-6. The frequency of private collections usually varies widely, depending upon the character and extent of service each customer is willing or able to purchase.

TABLE 4-6

Frequency of Refuse Collection from Residential Areas in 1964 by 924 Collection Systems Including Municipal, Contract and Private Collection Arrangements, by Class

	Number of Collection Systems				
Frequency of Collection	Combined Refuse		Garbage	Ashes	Rubbish	Other
3 collections per week....	S	27	12	0	0	1
	W	19	10	0	0	1
2 collections per week....	S	309	101	6	15	2
	W	289	75	10	16	1
1 collection per week.....	S	288	45	44	84	45
	W	363	71	48	84	34
1 collection ea. 2 weeks..	S	2	0	13	21	7
	W	3	1	13	21	7
1 collection per month....	S	1	1	8	11	13
	W	1	2	7	11	13
Cleanup drives............	S	—	0	1	0	45
	W	—	0	1	0	34
Variable..................	S	11	1	12	8	33
	W	22	1	12	7	32

S = Summer
W = Winter

It can readily be seen that the most usual year-round service for refuse containing garbage (combined refuse, garbage separately) is once or twice a week. Some agencies provide less frequent collection in the winter when garbage production is low, putrefaction proceeds at a slower rate, and fly breeding is not a significant threat.

Refuse that does not contain garbage (ashes, combined rubbish, noncombustible rubbish, combustible rubbish, garden rubbish, and all rubbish and ashes) is usually collected once a week or even less frequently.

In commerical districts, as shown in Table 4-7, the most usual col-

FIG. 4-3. Not only the quantity of refuse produced, but the condition in which it is accepted for collection may strongly influence the cost of collection. Here the piles of rubbish must be loaded by the relatively slow process of shoveling, after which the loose, small particles must be gathered and loaded if the alley is to be left in a reasonably neat condition.

lection frequency for refuse containing garbage is six or more times a week.

Refuse that does not contain garbage is commonly collected once a week, as it is in residential districts, although many cities provide six collections a week for combustible rubbish or for combined rubbish.

Location of refuse containers. The location of the refuse container at the time of collection is an important factor in determining not only the cost of operation but also the nature of the collection service itself. In some cities the refuse is picked up from back doors, from back porches, and even from basements, and carried by the collectors to the street or to the alley for loading. In other cities, the householders do a part of the work themselves by carrying the containers to the curb or to the alley just before the scheduled time of collection so that the collector's task is limited to emptying the containers. The householders then must return the containers to the place they are regularly kept. Practices in this regard are discussed in detail in Chapter 3. The subject is reintroduced here because local decisions as to the division of work between the householder and the collection agency may be of great importance in judging the relative costs of service. Similarly, those cities that remove ashes and other refuse from basements spend con-

TABLE 4-7

Frequency of Refuse Collection from Commercial Establishments in 1964 by 924 Collection Systems Including Municipal, Contract and Private Organizations, by Class

Frequency of Collection		Number of Collection Systems				
		Combined Refuse	Garbage	Ashes	Rubbish	Other
6 or more collections per week..............	S	145	31	11	21	7
	W	145	31	12	21	7
5 collections per week....	S	80	22	0	7	0
	W	79	22	0	7	0
4 collections per week....	S	5	1	0	0	0
	W	5	1	0	0	0
3 collections per week	S	24	7	0	4	0
	W	20	4	1	4	0
2 collections per week....	S	68	28	10	14	2
	W	70	25	9	13	2
1 collection per week.....	S	53	13	18	37	19
	W	56	18	22	37	18
Cleanup drives............	S	0	0	0	0	20
	W	0	0	0	1	15
Variable (On call).........	S	242	39	19	24	28
	W	241	40	19	24	27

S = Summer
W = Winter

siderably more than those giving less complete service to the householder. On the other hand, high costs are occasioned in some places by the necessity of shoveling refuse from piles on the ground or pavement. In comparing costs, it is essential that the extent of service given be known and evaluated.

Limitation of Available Funds

It must be recognized that many cities are giving incomplete service and that some are not even rendering minimum adequate service. Usually the public officials and citizens in such places understand the desirability of better or more complete service but find that sufficient public funds cannot be made available to provide it. Where the municipal service is inadequate, those citizens who can afford it are able to secure satisfactory service by employing private collectors to supplement municipal collection. If sound appraisal of total expenditures and services is desired, it is necessary to consider both public and private collection activities and costs. Usually it is not possible to obtain satisfactory data on private operations, but they should not be ignored in the appraisal of refuse collection systems.

Some cities that are unable or unwilling to finance refuse collection and disposal from general municipal revenues prefer to operate those services on a service-fee basis rather than to license private collectors. The operating practices and conditions in the cities which charge fees for refuse collection are not greatly different from those which do not, except that there are not any restrictions imposed on quantities or the classes of property to be served. Each customer who is willing and able to pay the fee is given complete collection service. In service-fee cities a part of the population may not request and therefore not receive any service at all. This situation can normally be averted, however, by properly enforced ordinances requiring city-wide use of the collection service.

EFFECT OF DISPOSAL METHODS ON COLLECTION

The refuse collection system obviously must be carefully coordinated with the system of disposal. Sometimes disposal methods can be selected so that the most economical and effective collection practices can be employed. More frequently, however, there are definite limitations on the possible disposal methods and on the location of disposal sites, and it becomes necessary to design the collection system to fit the arrangements for disposal. Undoubtedly many cities are faced with more difficult collection problems and with increased expense because of this necessity, and it should not be ignored in appraising or studying any particular collection service.

This does not mean that the proper economic balance between collection and disposal is always attained. On the contrary, many disposal systems have been adopted without due consideration of collecting the refuse and hauling it to the disposal sites. Collection cost is ordinarily much greater than disposal cost, and the relative cost of the different methods of collection and the different kinds of collection equipment should have considerable bearing on the selection of disposal facilities. Increased length of hauls, different separations of refuse, and special conditions at the disposal points may cause abnormally high collection expense.

Influence of Hauling Distance

In planning collection methods and selecting proper equipment, the distance that refuse must be hauled is of prime significance. Under normal conditions, shorter hauls indicate lower cost of service. Long hauls require more, and frequently larger, equipment, and occasionally the refuse must be transferred from one collection vehicle to another for transport to the disposal points. When it is considered that the length of hauls may vary from a half mile to twenty miles or more in different communities, it will be seen that this factor must be carefully studied in any evaluation of particular collection systems.

In explaining the cost involved, the distance the refuse must be hauled may be less significant than the amount of time required to haul a load to a disposal site and return, because the conditions of travel differ considerably and time lost at the disposal points may vary. Certainly where all or a substantial part of the haul is through urban areas, the speed of travel will be much less than on rural highways. Traffic density, stop streets, stop and go lights, and cross traffic influence the average speed of travel and total time for a trip. Further, the condition of the roadway surfaces may be an important factor in the hauling time required and also in the cost of keeping the equipment in good condition.

Influence of Separations

The disposal methods used usually dictate the manner of separating refuse into classes for collection. Economical operation of some types of incinerators requires that combustible materials be separated from noncombustibles (some recent types will permit inclusion of household noncombustibles with combustibles); garbage must be separated from other refuse for hog feeding, grinding, and reduction; if ashes are to be used for street maintenance, they must be separated from other refuse. Such separations generally increase collection difficulties and expense. Presumably, however, they are justified by improved service, elimination of nuisances, or reduced cost of disposal.

Frequently certain kinds of materials must be kept separate either because the places of disposal differ or because some of the refuse is salvaged. In some places, tree branches, yard rubbish, and large cartons and boxes are burned in open fires at separate dumps or near the regular disposal sites. Such material is usually separated by the collectors as it is loaded, although separate collections are made in some places. When the collectors must make the separations, collection effort and cost are increased somewhat. Even where the material is kept separate by householders and is loaded into different compartments of the vehicles, the collection work is more expensive than where the refuse can be handled without separation.

The problems of refuse collection and refuse disposal must be viewed together. Broad inquiries into the suitability and economy of the service must take both parts into consideration. For example, a particular collection service may seem needlessly complicated and unduly expensive, but the limitations of refuse disposal methods or the comparative expense of disposal may explain such conditions.

VARIATION IN WAGE RATES

Normally the expense for labor (collectors, truck drivers, and helpers) is from 60 to 80 per cent of the total cost of refuse collection. Obviously, therefore, the wage level in a community is an important cost factor. If wage rates were substantially the same in all cities, corrections would not be necessary for valid comparisons of expenditures and costs. Actually, however, labor rates vary greatly, as indicated in Table 13-3 in Chapter 13. The data from 669 cities show that wages range on an hourly basis from under $1.00 to over $3.00, with most cities (411) paying in the $1.75 to $1.99 range. It is possible, then, for one city to pay two or three times as much as another for the same amount of labor service. Thus ignoring all other differences that may exist, the difference between two cities in wage rates alone may easily account for total expenditures in the ratio of two to one.

EFFECT OF LOCAL PHYSICAL CONDITIONS

Refuse collection practices, and therefore costs, are materially affected by certain physical conditions and by the general character of the community. Some of the more important factors are size, topgraphy, existence and condition of alleys, climate, character of districts, and character of inhabitants.

Size of City

It may seem at first glance that the size of a city would not have an important bearing on the refuse collection system. Standards of public health and sanitation should not vary with the number of people in a community. Similar operating practices are used in both large and small cities. Nevertheless, size does have an influence on collection activities, particularly on the extent of service and the selection of methods.

Very small communities cannot economically conduct a municipal collection service because the total amount of work is insufficient to warrant the full-time employment of a minimum collection crew. In such places, the residents dispose of their own refuse or use such private collection facilities as are available. Often garbage is collected by farmers from the nearby rural areas without cost to the householders. Sometimes collection service of this sort is given practically no attention by city officials, while in other cases it is regulated by municipal ordinance and inspected by municipal officials. Many small cities and towns have a formal system of garbage collection, although in many cases garbage and other refuse is collected by farmers or by private collectors under municipal supervision. Many cities of less than 50,000, however, do not provide regular collection service for rubbish and ashes and sometimes neither actively regulate the practices of private collectors nor license them. In the larger and more densely populated cities, the difficulty in maintaining a reasonable standard of sanitation is increased. Irregular, incomplete, or infrequent collections, which in smaller places might not be serious, have a much greater effect upon public health, general sanitation, and community appearance. As a general rule, the larger the community, the more regular and complete must be the collection service.

City size also influences to some extent the collection methods and equipment. The full range of methods and procedures is available to the large community, except that the haul from collection routes to disposal or transfer sites is generally longer, making the methods that go best with short hauls not generally usable. The districts and routes can be as large as desirable and relatively large collection vehicles can be operated economically. The smaller city, on the other hand, may easily find that there is a definite limit on the methods and equipment that can be economically and effectively used. Routes may be too short to permit the best balance between collecting and hauling time, and the total amount of work to be done may be too small for certain practices and management techniques which have proved very valuable in larger cities.

Topography

The influence of topography on refuse collection is strong enough to make consideration of it an important item in a study of the problems of any one city and an essential one in a comparative study of different cities. In extreme cases, topography may control the selection of equipment, the layout of routes, and even the points from which refuse is collected. Topographical differences may also be responsible for substantial differences in operating costs.

Certain kinds of equipment are not safe or economical for use in hilly terrain. Trailer trains, for example, are not well adapted to steep grades, and there are serious objections to certain kinds of trucks and semi-trailers. In any case, specifications for vehicles used on hilly streets must be carefully prepared so as to provide the adequate and safe brake, power, power transmission, and stability features required for heavy duty service.

Route planning is more difficult in hilly districts. There are likely to be numerous dead-end or impassable streets and alleys. Furthermore, efforts must be made to avoid travelling the steepest grades when the vehicles are heavily loaded. Unless the planning is done with great care some crews may have to do considerable unproductive travelling to get from one part of their routes to another.

The work of carrying refuse from the back yard to the curb or alley is greatly increased in rugged areas. In some places containers must be carried up or down long flights of steps or extremely steep walks or driveways. The added labor, the increased time required, and the greater probability of injury to the collectors may influence the extent of the service to be given and the selection of collection methods. It may be decided that the extra cost and increased risk of collecting refuse from back doors or yards outweigh the values to be derived from that added service, and the householder may be required to place his refuse at the curb or alley at the proper time for collection. In other cases, the use of separate set-out and set-back crews to carry the refuse from the yards to curbs or alleys may prove to be economical, because it avoids the slowing down of the collection vehicle when the loaders do the carrying work.

Existence and Condition of Alleys

The very existence of alleys greatly influences the collection methods and practices that can properly be employed. In a corresponding fashion it affects the cost of the service. In general, the collection of refuse from an alley is more desirable than collection from a front street. It is usually easier to carry the material to the alley than to the street from the place where it is regularly stored. Also, when collection is from the alley the street is free of the congestion caused by collectors

have relatively little garden or yard refuse. However, there is an extremely wide variation in municipal practices in regard to the collection of this kind of refuse and consequently operating data may give no clue as to amounts actually produced. In all parts of the country there are cities that make complete collection of yard rubbish and cities that collect none or only limited amounts of it. In those places where yard rubbish is not permitted to be burned in open fires, it may be expected that the amount of refuse collected will be greater.

It would seem rather logical to suppose that garbage would have to be collected much more frequently in the very warm latitudes than in the northern sections of the country. An examination of operating practices of cities, however, does not disclose any marked difference. In southern cities having substantially the same climatic conditions the frequency of collection varies from daily to once, twice, or three times a week. Similar variations in frequency are found in many northern cities. Humidity is an important factor which must be considered with temperature. In a dry atmosphere the frequency can normally be reduced somewhat. In the few instances where northern cities collect garbage three times a week, in the summer time, such frequency of collection can in all probability be attributed more to a desire for a high degree of service than to climatic requirements.

Certain conditions that prevail in a cold climate also directly affect working conditions and operating costs. Snow and sleet storms cause serious interruptions in collection schedules and make the work unusually difficult and time consuming. After heavy snowfalls heavy containers may have to be lifted or carried over high snowbanks, an operation which not only slows up the service but causes undue hardship and strain on the collectors. Refuse often freezes to the containers, particularly where garbage is not wrapped in paper, and emptying it is a task accomplished only with great difficulty. Sometimes such containers are not emptied until the material thaws.

ATTITUDE OF MUNICIPAL OFFICIALS

It can be fairly assumed that municipal officials reflect the wishes and attitude of the citizens of the community in matters of appropriations, extent of service, frequency of collection, and the like. There are some actions of administrative, executive, and legislative officials, however, which cannot be accepted as originating with the citizens or even as desired by them, and which may strongly influence collection costs.

In most instances the failure to enforce regulations dealing with such matters as the separation of refuse, the provision of containers, and the placing of refuse for collection can be attributed to elected officials, who fear that any real effort to enforce regulations might cause them to lose some political support. Most administrative officials are fully aware of the added costs caused by the lack of proper preparation of refuse

and if they had authority would insist on general compliance with th
municipal requirements.

Some officials, furthermore, are unwilling or unable to refuse individ
ual requests for special or extra service regardless of how unreasonabl
they may be. A single special favor may be quite inexpensive, but al
most inevitably other householders begin to ask for special treatmen
and before long a regular practice of more extensive service develops
Some of this unplanned growth of service may be desirable and sound
but many activities so created are not sound at all and may result in th
curtailment of operations which are more essential.

One of the most serious weaknesses of administrative and executiv
officers is the failure to recognize the need for sound management prin
ciples in the administration of the refuse collection service. Too fre
quently the task of directing this work is considered unworthy of seriou
administrative effort. In many communities such matters as proper in
ternal organization, modern personnel administration, planning and pro
gramming, scientific job analysis, route determination, field reporting
and cost analysis are neglected entirely. The inevitable results are highe
costs and decreased effectiveness of the service.

EFFECT OF THE CHARACTER OF DISTRICTS

The character of urban development is another important factor af
fecting refuse collection costs. Widely different conditions are found i
residential, market, retail business, wholesale business, and industria
areas. There also may be great differences within any one of these broa
classes. In residential areas, for example, intensity of development ma
vary from relatively open areas, such as small farms or estates to solidl
built-up apartment areas. In a sparsely settled area where the houses ar
far apart and set far back from the roadway, the amount of refuse mate
rial collected may have little influence on costs, being greatly out
weighed by the time of travel between houses and the time of makin
a single collection. On the other hand, it is sometimes possible to obtai
an entire truckload of refuse from a single block of apartment houses. I
market districts a great amount of garbage or rubbish may also be col
lected in a very small area. Obviously any comparison between suc
districts in terms of dollars per capita, per cubic yard, or per ton of ref
use would show wide differences. While the examples represent ex
treme conditions and may be relatively unimportant when considerin
the refuse collection problem of the city as a whole, it may also serv
to influence the over-all cost so much that unless the situation is taken
into consideration any interpretation of the cost figures may be quit
misleading.

CHARACTER OF POPULATION

The personal as well as the civic habits of the people that live in a
community have an important bearing on the amount of refuse that i
presented for collection, on the orderly preparation of refuse, and i

general on the cost of the collection service. Frugal families may discard only very small amounts of refuse and there may be large areas, particularly those in which foreign-born groups predominate, in which a considerable amount of home salvage has evidently been practiced. On the other hand, there are areas in which the residents are extremely wasteful. The wealthier part of the population generally produces a greater amount of refuse per capita, but the areas of large refuse production are not confined to the high-class residential districts. In some very poor residential districts the per capita amount of refuse presented for collection is well above the average for the community as a whole.

Use of Garbage Grinders

The extent to which a refuse collection service will be called upon to collect garbage will be affected by the number or percentage of residences in the municipality that are equipped with household grinders. Certain cities prohibit garbage grinders, some permit them at the option of the householder, while some cities have passed laws requiring that units be installed in all new residential units, and/or commercial establishments such as restaurants or hotels. Although the convenience sanitary, and aesthetic value of the use of grinders for disposal of food wastes to the sewerage system is well recognized, those municipalities which prohibit the use of grinders usually do so because of the inadequacy of their sewers and/or their sewage treatment facilities. In any event, the problem of collecting noncombustible and combustible rubbish, which represent most of the volume of municipal refuse, still exists.

SUMMARY

In view of the many differences that may exist in physical conditions, in the extent of service provided, in the attitudes and demands of the public, in the amount of funds available for refuse collection, and in other factors, a comparison of the costs in one city with those in others is useless and unwise unless all pertinent conditions are known and properly evaluated. However, the material in this chapter is not presented to discourage sound comparative studies of municipal refuse collection service. A very valuable avenue to administrative improvement is through an intensive examination of the actual operating practices of different cities. The many possible variations in the collection processes and problem conditions have been given in considerable detail to help toward an understanding of the scope of the problem and to point out the factors that must be taken into consideration in evaluating the merits of different services.

In particular, it is pointed out that unexplained and unqualified comparisons of costs of different collection services and communities are of dubious value. If the many unequal conditions and practices are not all evaluated, or at least mentioned in qualification of the costs presented, the conclusions drawn from such comparisons are likely to be unsound. On the other hand, it is realized that it may be difficult or even impos-

TABLE 4-8

Cities Responding to 1964 APWA Survey That Prohibit Use of
Garbage Grinders

City	Prohibits Residential	Prohibits Commercial
Lethbridge, Alberta	x	
Cranbrook, British Columbia	x	x
Victoria, British Columbia		x
Watsonville, Calif		x
Coral Gables, Fla		x
Eau Gallie, Fla		x
Winter Haven, Fla	x	
Gainesville, Ga		x
Newman, Ga	x	x
Chicago		x
Lake Forest, Ill	x	x
Sioux City, Iowa		x
Florence, Ky	x	
Baltimore County, Md	x	x
Seat Pleasant, Md	x	x
Hancock, Mich	x	x
Wyoming, Mich		x
Fergus Falls, Minn		x
North Kansas City, Mo		x
Kearney, Nebr	x	x
York, Nebr	x	x
Belmar, N. J	x	x
Butler, N. J	x	x
Du Mont, N. J	x	x
Fair Lawn, N. J	x	x
Morristown, N. J	x	x
Oradell, N. J	x	
Ramsey, N. J	x	x
Rutherford, N. J	x	x
Teaneck, N. J		x
Gallup, N. M	x	x
East Hills, N. Y	x	x
Geneva, N. Y	x	x
Hempstead, N. Y		x
Middletown, N. Y	x	x
Mount Kisco, N. Y		x
New York City	x	x
Rye, N. Y	x	x
Graham, N. C		x
Thomasville, N. C		x
Norman, Okla		x
Westlake, Ohio	x	x
Forest Hill, Ont	x	x
Oakville, Ont	x	x
Ottawa, Ont	x	x
Port Credit, Ont	x	x
Scarborough, Ont	x	x
Toronto	x	x
Welland, Ont	x	
Abington, Pa		x
Philadelphia		x
West York Borough, Pa	x	x
York, Pa	x	x
Chattanooga	x	x
Falfurrias, Texas	x	x
Wichita Falls, Texas	x	x
Fredericksburg, Va	x	x
Newport News, Va		x

sible to adjust actual cost figures for all of the differences that may exist between the services being studied. Perhaps a sensible compromise is to adjust the cost figures for the important differences and, by way of qualification, to call attention to differences that have not been taken into account.

In short, it must be recognized that the task of refuse collection is different in each community and that to a great extent the plan of operation must be adapted to actual conditions. This does not mean that valuable lessons cannot be learned from the experience of other cities, but it does mean that practices which have proved desirable in one place cannot be blindly applied in another.

chapter 5

REFUSE COLLECTION METHODS

The refuse collection methods used by municipal agencies differ rather widely as a result of varying local conditions and requirements. While the reasons for the use of certain methods are discussed in this chapter, major consideration is given to descriptions and an analysis of the various techniques available to a refuse collection official. The selection of methods or equipment to meet a given set of circumstances is discussed in Chapter 7, "Planning Refuse Collection Systems."

That the actual situations faced by refuse collection agencies differ greatly as a result of variations in laws, regulations, habits of citizens, climate, and other local conditions, has been pointed out in preceding chapters. It is reasonable to expect, then, that actual operating practices will be substantially varied to conform to these circumstances. Two basic methods have been developed which, with many possible combinations, provide a wide range of practice. These include:

1. Definite task assignment for individual crews
   a. Daily route method
   b. Large route method
   c. Single load method
   d. Definite working day - irregular frequency method

2. Integration of the work of several crews
   a. Swing crew method
   b. Variable size crew method
   c. Inter-route relay method
   d. Reservoir route method

Refuse collection methods fall rather naturally into three distinct parts, depending on the scope of the work and the complexity of the operations, and will be discussed in their logical sequence. The first section of this chapter concerns the conduct of the separate tasks of the refuse collectors, such as lifting containers, carrying them, emptying them into vehicles, stowing the material in the vehicle bodies, and similar duties. The second section deals with the combination and coordination of these tasks into methods for getting the refuse into the collection vehicles from the point where the householders place it. These methods include the collection from containers at curbs or alleys, carrying the refuse from the premises to vehicles, the use of the set-out and set-back plan, and the exchange of wet strength bags. The third and final section covers the broader methods of organizing the work and equalizing the load among crews and also integrating the operations of several crews.

METHODS OF HANDLING REFUSE CONTAINERS

The tasks involved in handling refuse are fundamental to any of the more comprehensive systems of refuse collection. Economies in operation can often be realized through careful studies of these individual tasks, and a reduction of effort for the men can also be brought about. The key to the correction of any particular situation may be found as frequently in the minor operations as in the broader collection methods.

Lifting and Carrying Containers

The refuse collectors must carry the cans of garbage or other refuse to the collection vehicles from the locations at which the householders place their material. This may be a matter of only a very few feet if the containers are left at the curb or at the alley lines. On the other hand, containers have to be carried considerable distances if they are accepted at back doors or at other points on the householders' premises. Efficiency in can carrying is normally not given much attention by refuse collection officials, probably because of the lack of uniformity of conditions. Some cans are very small, some are extremely large, some are very heavy, some are quite light, some have handles or bails, and some have no handles at all. Moreover, the men themselves are of different stature, and trucks often are of varying loading heights. Nevertheless, if the cans are substantially uniform in size, it should be possible through a series of trials and studies to determine a one best method of lifting and carrying the refuse containers, so that the least time is lost and the least effort and strain are required. Frequently no instruction whatever is given to refuse collectors as to the easiest and safest ways of doing their work. As a result, some valuable employees have been lost to the collection services. Either they find the work too strenuous or they strain themselves seriously in trying to make a good impression the first days on the job.

Because conditions among cities are not uniform, it may be desirable to allow experienced employees to experiment to see if they can develop better methods of lifting and carrying containers. Then after the easiest method has been found for a particular community, the collectors should be trained to use it.

Lifting containers. Some collectors prefer to lift the containers to their shoulders or heads for carrying them to the collection vehicles. Others seem to find it easier to carry them in lower positions until they reach the trucks, simply lifting them slightly off the ground by the handles, bails, or even by the rims, and carrying them in a "trail" position. Often two or more containers can be carried in this manner while it is difficult to carry more than one on the head or shoulders.

The easiest way to lift a can to any appreciable height is to raise it quickly and evenly to about knee height, and then, without loss of momentum, to boost it with the knee high enough to get a hand under the bottom of the container at about shoulder height. From this position the containers can easily be placed on the shoulders or head or the lift can be continued by pushing the receptacles into collecting vehicles. The

FIG. 5-1. Collector lifting a heavy refuse receptacle to his shoulder preparatory to carrying it to the collection vehicle in the street. Note that the collector's back is straight and that the lifing is done with the legs.

first lift should be made with the legs and not the back. Inexperienced collectors almost invariably bend over at the waist to lift a can from the ground. The proper method is to stoop by bending the knees, keeping the back as straight and vertical as possible, and to rise with the load by straightening the knees. Proper coordination of movement comes only with practice.

Carrying containers. Carrying refuse containers is ordinarily less difficult and less strenuous than lifting, but under some circumstances can be quite hazardous. If the carrying distances are short, if the terrain is relatively flat, if reasonable amounts are carried, and if undue hurrying is avoided, the work is usually not very arduous or dangerous. Overstrain and injuries may result from attempting to carry too much or trying to proceed at too fast a pace. Such practices are usually the result of work incentives such as allowing the crews to go home when they have done a specified amount of work. Intelligently applied, such incentives are excellent, but the operations must be controlled to avoid the natural consequences of inferior work and rushing. To avoid extra trips, employees may attempt to carry two or more containers at a time, particularly if the distance to the collecting vehicle is great. Consequently, rather strict rules must be adopted to prevent overstrain, ruptures, and other injuries to employees.

In hilly areas, carrying refuse containers becomes harder and more hazardous. Cans may have to be carried up or down long flights of stairs or very steep driveways or walks. Special care must be exercised to avoid accidents, particularly in wet weather or when walks or steps are covered with ice. Many experienced collectors prefer to carry containers on their backs on hills or steps. Some of them use belts or twisted strips of burlap to hold the containers in place on their backs, much as furniture movers carry heavy chairs, barrels, and boxes.

Rolling containers. It is not always necessary to carry refuse cans. Sometimes it is more convenient to roll the heavier ones. The can is

FIG. 5-2. One method of transporting containers to collection vehicle as used in Hartford, Connecticut. Bottom can is held on with a slip hook. Two, three and four containers can be taken at a time in this fashion.

tilted from a vertical position so that its weight is balanced over the point where the bottom edge rests on the ground. The angle depends on the proportions of the can and the amount and weight of the refuse it contains. The receptacle is rotated, maintaining the same angle, causing it to advance in the direction of the rotation. The course of a rolling container may be changed by slightly adjusting the angle of tilting. Many collectors become very adept at rolling cans by manipulating the top rims. Sometimes they are able to carry a container in one hand and roll another with the other hand. Where there are many steps or terraces, or where lawns must be crossed, rolling may not be feasible.

Loading refuse from large containers. Special problems and annoyances for refuse collection supervisors are created by refuse containers too heavy for one man to carry safely. The use of such containers should be forbidden by ordinance or regulation. However in almost every community some very heavy receptacles are found every day. Such containers should be equipped for handling by mechanized systems.

FIG 5-3. Where large volumes of refuse are produced, mobile containers sometimes are used. Hartford, Connecticut, has successfully used one-cubic yard containers with especially equipped trucks in 3 to 6 family dwelling areas where no driveways are available.

Emptying Containers

Containers are emptied directly by the collectors from the ground. The loading height of the vehicles and their type and design are the main factors governing the method used.

Emptying by groundmen. Equipment with mechanical means for ʁaising or distributing the refuse into the body has a very low loading ʁeight, and the collectors can empty the containers from the ground ʁith little effort. Vehicles with enclosed bodies also commonly have low ʒading heights, and in most instances the bodies are equipped to com-

FIG. 5-4. The low loading height of modern collection vehicles permits much easier loading by the collector.

pact and consolidate the refuse toward the back or front and thus obvi- ate the need of careful stowing.

Occasionally collectors empty containers into the vehicle even where much greater lifts are required. In such cases, though, it is usually necessary to provide steps—not always so much to make it possible for the men to empty the containers as to provide access for spreading the refuse in the body and pushing it away from the dumping side.

Emptying by men on trucks. Where open-top trucks are used, top men are sometimes stationed in the refuse collection bodies to receive the loaded refuse containers, empty them, and return them to the collec- tors. In addition, they usually are required to compact the material and stow it efficiently. This practice is followed in practically all communi- ties which have vehicles of high loading height or which load the trucks high above the normal level. It is usually advantageous, regard- less of loading height, where relatively large trucks are used and rapid loading is more essential, and where rubbish is collected.

FIG. 5-5. Containers that weigh more than 100 pounds when full are difficult to load. Th speed of the work is reduced when two or three men must lift a single receptacle, the cos of the operation is increased, and the possibility of accidents to the collectors is greate

Stowing Refuse in Trucks

The primary objective in stowing refuse in trucks is to place th maximum amount of material in the space available. The effectiv capacity of a vehicle is increased to a maximum through consolidation mechanically or otherwise.

Consolidating refuse in vehicles. When most refuse reaches the collect ing vehicles it is subjected to considerable volume reduction. Un wrapped garbage or ashes collected alone, however, can be condensed very little. The rubbish component of refuse is made up of much bulky material which can be compressed or broken up or can be placed to require the least amount of space. Where compaction-type vehicles are used, refuse is compacted mechanically. Where open-top trucks are used, the man or men in the vehicle bodies must effect consolidatior by trampling the refuse already placed. A substantial compression of the rubbish occurs through the normal operation of walking back and forth with the containers to different parts of the vehicle body in order to distribute the material more or less uniformly.

While refuse collection equipment is discussed in detail in the next chapter, the opportunity is taken here to point out that the necessity for piling great amounts of refuse on open vehicles results primarily from the use of unsuitable types and sizes of equipment bodies. When refuse weighs very little even after some consolidation in the vehicles, the bodies must be quite large in relation to the chassis. Some officials severely condemn any appreciable surcharge of open bodies. They criticize the appearance of the heaped vehicles and believe that the losses due to scattering refuse, overturned loads, and extra effort in

FIG. 5-6. The containers are handed into the vehicles when the receptacles are heavy or when the loading height is great. These collectors in Washington, D. C., are passing a large bundle of lightweight rubbish to the topman. The high loading height is necessary to provide the volumetric capacity necessary to secure economical loads.

loading and stowing make the practice uneconomical compared with providing adequate equipment.

The use of vehicles of the open body type should be discouraged in all municipalities for regular refuse collection. The open body truck has a special use for hauling heavy bulky waste; however, the truck should be equipped with hydraulic tail gate lift in order to prevent accidental injury to the men.

METHODS OF GETTING REFUSE FROM PREMISES TO VEHICLES

Methods for getting the refuse into the collection vehicles from the points at which the householders leave it depend on the extent of service demanded by citizens, local preparation practices, density of population, physical characteristics, and to some extent on traditional practices or individual preferences of refuse collection administrators.

Collecting from Containers at Curb or Alley

The most rapid and cheapest refuse collection is the loading of standard containers directly from the curbs or the edges of alleys into the collection vehicles—a plan which involves very little lost motion and little lost time. In many cases the trucks can be kept advancing continuously at a rate of 1½ or 2 miles per hour, the speed, of course depending greatly on the density of the population, the amount of refuse, and many other factors. Some cities do not consider this method aesthetically acceptable, however. Also, when the refuse is not collected shortly after it is placed for collection, considerable difficulty may be experienced due to scattering of refuse.

Loading refuse into the vehicles. The sequence of operations for removing the refuse from a single container is: (1) removing the cover and placing it on the ground or sidewalk; (2) lifting the can; (3) tossing it into the collection vehicle or carrying it to the vehicle; (4) emptying the container; (5) replacing it on the ground or sidewalk; (6) replacing the cover; and (7) advancing to the next container.

Normally, the distance from the containers to the vehicles is not great. In alleys the cans will be right beside the vehicle and can be lifted and emptied with little walking. Sometimes in extremely narrow alleys there is not enough room to load from the side; in such cases it is easiest to wait until the truck has passed the can and then load it into the back. Even in the widest alleys the containers will usually be not more than six or seven feet from the vehicles.

When refuse is collected from the streets if traffic is not extremely heavy and the pavement not excessively wide, it may be practical to move the refuse vehicle along the right side of a pavement and yet collect from both sides. While this operation would necessarily involve some delays and somewhat slower loading, it might still be more efficient than collecting from only one side at a time. The usual procedure on business and arterial streets, and sometimes even on other main streets, is to collect the refuse from the right side only—which means that each street must be traveled in both directions. Compensating somewhat for this greater travel, the distance which cans have to be moved is usually less and speed is increased a little. However, it is not always easy to utilize to the best advantage a full crew for two-side loading when it must operate on only one side.

Left to his own devices, a refuse collection operator would probably use two-side loading and drive the trucks down the center of all but the widest and busiest thoroughfares. Complaints by automobile drivers or police officials, or bad accident records, usually arise to limit the practice to local streets. In Los Angeles, for example, it has been found

FIG. 5-7. Storage in proper containers reduces time and cost of collection and presents a more pleasing neighborhood appearance on collection day.

necessary in practically all areas to collect refuse from only one side of street at a time. When refuse must always be loaded from one side of the vehicles, the amount of working space is reduced and the probability of workers' interfering with each other is greater, although if the practice is more or less continuous the size of the crew and truck can be proportioned to this kind of operation.

Replacing containers. When refuse containers are emptied, they are usually replaced where they were found. In most municipalities collectors are instructed to place the cans upright on the curb so that they will not obstruct sidewalks or driveways or fall into the street. In alleys they are required to place them as close as possible to the alley property lines. Such regulations arise from the efforts of administrators to prevent the unsatisfactory practices which collectors develop when the truck speed is too high for them to keep up or when they hurry to complete the day's work. Tossing cans to the ground or sidewalk; leaving them on their sides so they can roll to the center of alleys, into drive ways, or into the streets; leaving them partly suspended over curbings, or leaving them where they interfere with either vehicular or pedestrian traffic may cause the containers to be damaged, may contribute to accidents, and may be responsible for unnecessary disorder in streets or alleys. Naturally, citizens will complain about these practices.

Replacing can covers. Frequently the collectors are required to re place the covers on the empty containers. The reasons given for this practice are that it insures the container's being replaced in an upright position, protects the covers against damage or loss, and gives better appearance to the streets and alleys. Officials who prefer to have the collectors leave the covers on the ground maintain that to replace them requires too much time and additional expense. Furthermore, supervisors and inspectors can tell at a glance whether the collections have been made or not.

Time limits for leaving cans at curbs or in alleys. Municipal ordinances or the administrative regulations usually specify the time when the refuse containers must be placed at the curbs or in the alleys for collection and also the length of time they may be left out after they have been emptied. Most householders do not follow such regulations, nor is much attention given to their enforcement. In some places, however, the require ments are rather carefully observed, but of course there are always some who fail to place the material out in time and leave the empty cans out too long. Inevitably there are some places where no one is at home to replace the containers, and it must be recognized that citizens cannot always arrange to have the cans removed.

However, there are certain incentives to cooperation on the part of the individual residents. Because it is inconvenient and undesirable to have large quantities of refuse on hand, very few householders fail reg ularly to place the full containers in time for collection. More likely they are put in place too far ahead of the collection time. Frequently the containers are set out the night before the regular collection day to avoid missing early pick-ups, and often they are placed early in the morning even though the regular collection time is late in the day. While some cities have tried to enforce the maximum limits for leaving full refuse cans at the curbs or alleys, on the whole the attempts have been found to be impractical.

Householders are very definitely benefited by removing the empty cans soon after the collections have been made, to protect them from damage or theft. Empty containers left in streets and alleys seem to be highly attractive playthings for children, who may roll both covers and con tainers about, battering them or leaving them where they are liable to be run over by automobiles. Nor is it unusual for covers or entire containers to be stolen when they are not removed promptly.

Size of crew. When refuse cans are loaded from curbs or alleys, the progress of the work is ordinarily so rapid that the driver of a motor vehicle must remain in the cab. Not infrequently the vehicles are kept moving almost all the time.

The most satisfactory size of crew depends entirely on local conditions, among which are population density, vehicle size and type of refuse collected, and the ratio of collection time to hauling time. A typical crew for loading a compactor type vehicle consists of a driver and two collectors, one loading from each side of a street. In certain instances where large capacity trucks are used, the collection crew is larger. Sometimes two collectors are used on each side of a street.

Variations in the method. The method of curb and alley collection described has been varied by some communities in an attempt to reduce the more unsatisfactory features. Instead of requiring the containers to be placed at curbs, they ask that they be placed on private property immediately adjacent to the sidewalk or at the building lines. For an alley collection, they ask that the containers be placed just inside the property lines rather than in the alleys. Advocates believe that this adjustment prevents much of the street littering and interference with the cans by children and scavengers. There is no doubt that the appearance of the streets and alleys is improved. This practice is used in parts of New York City with much success. Of course, because the collectors have to walk farther with each container, the collection process is slowed up considerably by these changes and the cost is increased. In alleys the increase in distance and cost is not so great and it is a big improvement to keep the cans out of the alleys at all times.

Advantages and disadvantages. The advantages of loading containers from curbs or alleys lie mainly in the rapidity of making collections, with resulting lower costs. Also, usually, it is unnecessary for the collectors to enter private property. If the operations are properly planned, this collection method is cheapest, although the amount of service provided is low in comparison with other methods. It requires householders to do part of the work and to put up with some inconvenience to compensate for the reduced expense. However, it eliminates a number of variables, and the amount of service given each householder is more uniform.

The objections to this method of collection arise out of the increased bother and nuisance to householders and the long time the full and empty containers are in the streets or alleys. Many citizens dislike having to remember to place the material for collection at specific times and object to doing part of what they consider the collector's work. The inconvenience and nuisances resulting from the failure to set out the refuse regularly have been mentioned, as has the increase in the number of citizen complaints. Perhaps the most unsatisfactory feature of collection from curbs and alleys is the unsightly appearance of streets on refuse collection days. Frequently many containers remain on curbs all day, and only in rare cases is an entire block free from more or less unsightly cans at any time during the days on which collections are made. When cans are in public streets and alleys for rather long periods, it is not unusual for refuse to be strewn over the streets, alleys or

FIG. 5-8. When refuse in improper containers is left at curbs overnight or for several hours in the daytime, some containers will be upset, material will fall out of uncovered receptacles, and often the streets will be extremely untidy. Street-cleaning expense is undoubtedly increased in many cases.

yards. Sometimes entire containers are tipped over by vehicles or children, and scavengers add to the litter as they search through the cans. The result is increased street cleaning expense and generally untidy streets.

Set-Out and Set-Back Method

The set-out and/or set-back method was developed through attempts to combine the important advantages of curb and alley collection from standard containers with the advantages of collection from back doors without many of the disadvantages of either method. To a large extent this objective has been attained. Briefly the method consists of the following operations: (1) carrying the full refuse containers from back doors or other places on the householder's premises to the curbs or alleys a few minutes before the collection vehicle arrives; (2) loading the refuse in the same manner as when it is placed at curbs or alleys by the householders, leaving empty containers at the curbs or alleys; and (3) returning the empty cans to their regular locations within a short time after they are emptied. Variations of this operation are: (1) setting out the containers but not returning them after they are emptied; and (2) having the collectors set the cans out and back during otherwise idle time while the truck is dumping, instead of having a separate set-out and set-back crew. The main purpose of the plan is to make it possible to load the trucks as rapidly as possible, thus reducing to a minimum the idle time for the equipment. The other features of the method have been adopted chiefly to insure a sanitary service free from nuisances.

FIG. 5-9. Special hand trucks are used for tubbing refuse in Detroit, Michigan. They reduce the number of trips into some properties, make the work easier for the men, and under suitable conditions will lessen the cost of the set-out work.

Setting out containers. The refuse containers must be brought out from householders' premises to the curbs or to the alley lines before the collection vehicles arrive. The most satisfactory arrangement is to have the set-out crews precede the collection vehicles by only a very few minutes so the cans are in the streets or alleys as brief a period as possible. Obviously this cannot always be done, and some latitude is usually allowed to prevent delays to the collection forces and equipment when the setting-out operation involves exceptionally long carrying distances or a large number of containers.

In actual practice it is usual to have the set-out crews begin work from 40 minutes to an hour ahead of the collection forces. Under some circumstances the set-out gangs may increase the lead, but in planning the operations an effort is made to have the collection crew gradually catch up with the set-out crew so that at the end of a day's work the two forces are practically together. It can be seen that the actual time the refuse containers are at the curbs before collection would vary considerably but would usually be somewhere between a few minutes and an hour.

The size of the set-out crew will vary considerably with the number of containers to be handled, the distances they must be carried, the speed of collection forces, and other local factors. Sometimes one set-out man can keep ahead of a collection crew, but under ordinary circumstances some additional help must be provided. It may be necessary to assign two set-out men to a crew but frequently it is practicable to have a crew of three serve two routes or a crew of four set out for three routes. Of course, if a large collection force is provided to speed up the collection process, the number of set-out men per collection crew must also be increased.

FIG. 5-10. A set-back man returning the emptied cans so that within a few minutes after the collection is made the streets are completely cleared of cans and other refuse receptacles.

When only one truck is assigned to a route and hauls are fairly long, the collectors have time enough to set out refuse to make a second load while the driver takes the filled truck to and from the disposal point. This plan does not permit great flexibility, but where the time balance is such that both the equipment and the collectors are employed most effectively, it has some advantages. Under such an arrangement, the collectors can begin the day's work a half hour or an hour ahead of the equipment so that the loading can progress rapidly when the actual collection is started, or the first load can be collected much more slowly by having the truck wait while the collectors carry out each container.

The set-out men should be thoroughly familiar with their routes so that all the refuse will be brought to the curbs. They must know where the refuse containers are normally kept on each property, the best way to reach these locations, and the existence of dangerous conditions which must be avoided.

Normally the set-out men enter properties by means of driveways or sidewalks and proceed to the back doors or other locations where the containers are kept. Usually they remove the covers from the cans and place them on the ground. They lift one or more containers and carry them to the curb and place them so they will be easily available to the collection crew. Sometimes two or more trips must be made for a single household. The set-out men are soon able to size up quantities of refuse and estimate the number of trips that will be necessary. The natural tendency is for the men to try to carry too much at a time to avoid making extra trips. Supervisors have some difficulty in training these workers to limit their loads to the amount they can carry safely and easily. In some cities the covers are not removed but are carried with the containers to the curbs. This is particularly necessary if the containers must remain at the curbs for a considerable period or if unwrapped garbage is in them.

Setting containers back. After the refuse is emptied by the collection forces, the cans are replaced on the curbs. Usually when they have been set out by special crews they are also returned to the places where they are normally kept. In some places, however, a part of the responsibility is shifted to the householders at this point by making it their duty to replace the empty cans. In Hartford, Connecticut, for example the collectors leave the empty receptacles at the front property lines.

Sometimes the set-out men double back and return the empty cans to the places they are regularly kept. In other cases it is more satisfactory to have employees permanently assigned to follow the trucks and re-place the receptacles. Under the first arrangement the routes will proba-bly be somewhat smaller and it will be easier for the men to remember where the containers belong. There may be a considerable amount of extra walking, however, in alternating ahead of the collection vehicle and behind it, particularly if the empty cans are to be taken back rather soon after they are dumped, which of course is desirable in the inter-ests of keeping the streets as attractive as possible. Unless a collection crew moves with exceptional speed, it is usually possible for one em-ployee to return the empty cans behind it and keep up with it most of the time.

Several empty containers can ordinarily be carried at a time, and it is probable that the total number of trips to return cans will be less than the number for carrying out the refuse. The return loads are not likely to be very heavy because the cans are so bulky that it is difficult to handle very many.

Advantages. There are some very important advantages to the set-out and set-back method. In the first place, the householders are relieved of all responsibility for remembering to set out their refuse for collection and of the work of carrying out the filled cans. Furthermore, the containers are on the street only a very short time, usually less than two hours, and the extent of the untidiness in any street is limited to this period. More important, the material is placed so that it cannot become strewn over the streets and the time is normally too short for dogs to upset cans or for scavengers or other persons to disturb the material. Since the streets are not littered, some saving in street cleaning expense is possible and, of course, the improved appearance of the streets is a real benefit. Routing and scheduling are made somewhat easier when the householders do not set out the containers for collection. If for some reason unusual delays are experienced, a part of a route can be left for the next day without any inconvenience. Usually in such cases it will be possible to catch up in a day or two. When the cans are set out by householders, however, it is absolutely essential that an entire route be collected, regardless of breakdowns or other emergencies. It may also be cited as an advantage that under the set-out and set-back method it becomes necessary for householders to supply standard refuse receptacles. This may mean, however, that the plan is practicable only when all the residents provide such receptacles.

Disadvantages. The major disadvantage of the set-out and set-back method is the increased cost of conducting the collection work. Various estimates place the additional expense at 25 to 50 per cent over the amount needed for regular curb or alley collection. Such estimates, however, do not take into consideration the difference in street cleaning expense, so the net increase probably is much less in many cities. The method subordinates efficiency in the use of labor to the most effective use of equipment. It may be considered a disadvantage, for example, that at least two trips into each property are required, one for the full container and one to replace the container, when under other plans one trip is enough. It is the total cost that must be considered, however, and not the cost of one part of the operation. Some officials believe the fact that the collectors must enter private property is a drawback because of the danger of being bitten by dogs and because of charges by householders that collectors steal from the premises. It should also be mentioned in this summary that in some communities the fact that the cans are on the streets part of the time would be considered a disadvantage.

Table 5-1 gives information on set-out, set-back practices in 23 cities.

Removal from Premises to Vehicles

Objections to the setting out of refuse containers in streets and alleys gave rise to a method of refuse collection in which the material is carried from where it is usually kept directly to the collecting vehicles Under this plan the vehicles keep pace with the collectors, which results in considerably slower loading although labor efficiency is increased in some respects.

The normal operation consists of these steps: (1) taking an empty carrying tub or basket from the collecting vehicle to the place on a householder's premises where the refuse is regularly kept; (2) transferring the accumulated material from the householder's containers to the carrying tub or basket; (3) carrying the refuse to the street or alley; and (4) dumping it into the collection vehicle. The important aspect of this procedure is that ordinarily only one trip into a householder's premises is required to complete the collection operation.

TABLE 5-1

Refuse Collection Data From 23 Cities Using Set-Out
and/or Set-Back System

City	Class of Refuse[1]					Average Time Containers Are at Curb	Typical Number in Crew	
							Set-Out	Set-Back
1. Birmingham, Alabama...	G					2 hours	1	
2. Glendale, California......	G	R				½ minute	2	
3. Pasadena, California.....			NCR			1 minute	2	
4. Pomona, California......	G		NCR	CR		18 hours	3	
5. Denver, Colorado........					C	21 minutes	2	2
6. Hartford, Connecticut....	G		NCR	CR		75 minutes	8³	
7. Norwich, Connecticut....					C	2 hours	4	4
8. Stamford, Connecticut...					C	2 hours	6	6
9. St. Petersburg, Florida...					C	2 hours	2	
10. Columbus, Georgia.......					C	1-8 hours	3	
11. Oak Park, Illinois........	G			CR		....	2	2
12. Rockford, Illinois........					C	....	2	
13. Gloucester, Mass........				CR		....	2	
14. Detroit, Michigan........		R				....	2	2
15. Montclair, New Jersey...					C	1 hour	10	6
16. Newark, New Jersey.....					C	1 hour	3	
17. Cincinnati, Ohio........	G		NCR	CR		1 hour	3	
18. Dayton, Ohio...........	G			CR		....	1	1
19. Dallas, Texas...........					C	....	2	2
20. El Paso, Texas..........					C	4 minutes	3	3
21. Salt Lake City, Utah.....	G			CR		2-3 hours	2-3	
22. Milwaukee, Wisconsin....			NCR			1-2 hours	2	2
23. Victoria, Br. Columbia....	G					5 minutes	2	2

[1]G—garbage; R—rubbish; NCR—noncombustible rubbish; CR—combustible rubbish; C—combined refuse.
[2]Number in set-out and/or set-back crew not specified.
[3]Crew serves entire district (5 trucks).

When more than one trip is needed to collect the refuse from the householder's premises, it is an indication that an additional weekly collection should be provided. In some municipalities this may mean two or three collections per week.

Collection practices. The collection of refuse by removal from the premises is not the fastest method. It takes time to enter each separate property, transfer the material, clean up any part that spills over, and carry out the refuse. However, the collectors become quite expert in transferring material quickly and without spilling, in filling their carrying receptacles to capacity, and in carrying loads. Moreover, there are short cuts which some collectors use although they are not permitted in some communities. To save an extra trip the collectors may carry some of the larger articles in their free hands, in addition to the loaded re-

FIG. 5-11. Lightweight plastic carry-out barrels are preferred by collectors in St. Petersburg, Florida for carrying out well wrapped household refuse from the premises to the collection vehicle.

ceptacle. Unless such overloading is carried to extreme, it probably saves considerable time. When production of refuse is not particularly heavy, collectors sometimes enter two or even three properties in succession and make the collections before they empty their carrying receptacles. The time saved by accumulating the refuse from several households may make an impressive total in the course of a day, but the effort expended in carrying loaded or partially loaded containers such long distances may be too severe for the practice to be approved as a standard operation. After all, the total distance saved is only a few feet at each property if the collectors have to return to the front sidewalk or to the alley in order to enter the adjacent property, although it may be much greater if short cuts can be used. When there are no fences or other barriers, the collectors have a strong tendency to walk across lots wherever possible. This practice has been the cause of numerous complaints in some municipalities and has been stopped completely in a few of them. The collectors have been charged with breaking through hedges, leaping fences, walking through gardens or shrubbery, or across newly planted lawns. With discretion, the practice can probably be handled satisfactorily and some definite gains made. The most satisfac

ory plan is for the supervisor of the collection work to approve each
hort cut used, and to change the arrangement if any complaint is

FIG. 5-12. A lightweight, 32-gallon plastic butt can is used to transfer garbage from household
container to collection in Philadelphia, Pennsylvania.

made. The refuse collection contract in Seattle specifically states that
collectors shall not cross from one property to another.

Carrying refuse receptacles to vehicles. As a rule, it is not economical
to carry the householders' containers from the places they are usually
kept to the collection vehicles because of the extra trip required to return
the empty cans. In some situations, however, this practice is quite
sound and relatively inexpensive. As mentioned, the operation is feasible when there is enough refuse at one location to require more than one
trip to the street or alley. The practice may also be less expensive when
the distance from the regular place of the containers to the vehicle is
quite short. This would be true in the case of a side entrance to a corner
lot, or when collection is made from the alley and the containers are

within 30 feet of the alley. Under such conditions, the extra distance
can be traveled in less time than it takes to transfer the refuse can
into the carrying receptacles.

Advantages. A summary of the advantages of carrying refuse from
premises to vehicle must emphasize the high degree of service rendered
to the householders. The cans are never left in streets or alleys even for a
few minutes and there is none of the littering and unattractiveness
which results from other methods. Residents do not have to concern

FIG. 5-13. In Lincoln, Nebraska, a motor scooter is used to good advantage for "carrying
out" refuse in certain suburban areas where the houses are located on tracts of land about
150 feet by 135 feet and frequently driveways are quite long.

themselves with setting out containers or returning them, and they can
be kept at the place most convenient to the householders. This means
that they do not have to be in or near alleys where they are liable to
theft and more liable to interference by scavengers or children. From
the standpoint of operation, only one trip to individual properties is
normally necessary, route layout is more flexible, and administration is
easier because a day's work does not necessarily have to stop at a particular point. If a few properties more or less are not serviced in a day, a

does not make much difference as long as all are given the required number of collections a week. Possibly another advantage, at least for the officials, is that the containers may be somewhat below the standard desirable for cans that must be carried.

Disadvantages. The disadvantages of this method are mostly economic. Equipment is operated quite inefficiently. Considerable time is consumed at each property in transferring and carrying the refuse, and consequently the trucks are necessarily loaded very slowly. The inevitable result is that unit collection costs are higher than under some other methods. One study resulted in the conclusion that provision of 100 per cent "carry out" service in a community required doubling the hauling equipment as compared to 100 per cent curb and alley collection, using a constant crew of a driver and two loaders. The only serious disadvantage from the viewpoint of the householders is that in many cases the collectors must enter private property. This may lead to complaints of gates left open, of having to keep dogs indoors on collection days, and of theft. If the collectors pick up the refuse from the basements, the cost is still greater, the inconvenience and lost time are increased, and the probability of additional complaints is magnified.

METHODS OF ORGANIZING WORK

The assignment of crews to particular parts of the whole job of collecting the refuse in a municipality will be discussed in Chapter 7 as one aspect of planning the operations of the collection system. However, certain general methods of arranging or assigning work loads will be mentioned here to round out the discussion of the different means of operation available to a refuse collection administrator. These methods may be divided into two main types: (1) Definite tasks are assigned to individual collection crews. (2) Operations of several or many crews are coordinated or integrated for the purposes of equalizing the work load and increasing the efficiency of the whole activity.

Definite Tasks for Individual Crews

Daily route method. One of the most common and perhaps the simplest distribution of the work is to divide the community into areas which provide as nearly as possible one day's work for one crew. This plan is usually called the daily route control method. Naturally, a crew will not work in such an area each day unless daily collection is provided by the municipality. If three collections a week are made, a crew will have two areas from which to collect; if twice-a-week collection is provided, each crew will have three areas; if collection is weekly, each crew will have five or six areas. A definite number of stops are made in each area, and normally a day's work is considered complete when the task of collecting from the area is finished. The amount and difficulty of the work and the time required to complete the collection on such a route or in such an area varies from day to day and from season to season. The quantity of refuse produced, the number of days between collections, the weather, and numerous other factors influence the amount of work required. A collection crew will complete a day's work very early on some days and quite late on others.

The advantages of this plan are that the householders can know definitely on which day or days the collection will be made, and usually about the time of day the crew will reach certain points. Administration is relatively easy. The arrangement is usable with any loading method and operates particularly well when the householders place refuse at the curbs or in the alleys, because it will be definitely known which properties will receive collection service on particular days. Also, supervision is made easier by the incentive provided by allowing the crews to go home when they have done the prescribed amount of work.

Disadvantages of the plan are the unequal distribution of the work, the conflict with labor policies and regulations when the collectors work more than eight hours in a single day, the tendency toward making the peak eight hours in length, and the inefficient use of equipment and labor, with consequent higher cost. Finally, breakdowns and interruptions seriously interfere with this plan.

Large route method. Another method frequently used for the assignment of work is called the large route control method and provides for the assignment of larger areas or routes to individual collection crews. The customary practice is to lay out enough work for a normal week's activity for a single crew. A crew begins a route on Monday without any rigidly fixed stopping point for the day's work. The crew may work exactly eight hours or somewhat more or less than a regular period, depending on the desires of the crew and the conditions facing it. Work begins the next day at the point reached the day before, and so on until the entire route is completed. The major stipulation is that each route must be entirely completed within the working week. Usually the head of the collection crew is responsible for dividing the work among the days of the week so that the load is fairly well equalized. Ordinarily the crew is considered to have completed its week's work when the entire area or route has been finished. Since the properties to be served in a single day cannot be definitely known, this method is most satisfactory with set-out and set-back service or where the collectors carry containers from the householders' premises to the collection vehicles. It is customarily used with once-a-week collections, although in some cases as many as two a week or as few as one a month are made.

The advantages of the large route method are that the day's work is equalized, supervision is very easy, regular collection is provided, and equipment is used efficiently. Although the daily load is equalized to a large extent, some work incentive is provided by allowing the crew to stop when the entire route is completed. Administration is simplified because the supervisors have ample time to note the relative progress on the routes and can speed up the work or provide extra assistance if necessary. Equipment breakdowns or other emergencies that cause loss of time are not disrupting to the flexible schedules nor to the smooth operation of the collection process, for the crews are usually able to catch up before the end of the routes. While the collection is not ordinarily timed as exactly as under the daily route method, for all practical purposes regular collection is insured by the stipulation that all routes be completed within the allotted time. The more uniform length of the working day makes for more effective use of equipment, which at times can be released for other work at the end of a collection period or can be made available for maintenance.

The disadvantages of this collection method are found mainly in the limitations on its use and its relative inefficiency. It cannot, for example, be used effectively when frequent collections are scheduled or when householders set out the refuse containers at the curbs. Just as under the daily route method, there is a strong tendency to plan the routes for conditions when the work is most slow and difficult. Although administrative effort is reduced, crews are busy less than full time during a large part of the year, and this increases costs. It has been charged that "soldiering" or letting the slowest man set the pace will undoubtedly occur under this method.

Single load method. A variation of the daily route method is a plan of laying out areas or routes which, under normal conditions, will each provide a full load of refuse. Usually each crew has two, three, or four such routes for a day's work, depending on the size of the crew, the capacity of the equipment, the length of haul, and other factors. As a rule, the routes assigned to a single crew are not continuous, but are selected with the idea of providing a full day's work. It is not unusual to have the first load or route located some distance from the disposal or transfer site and subsequent loads much closer.

The main advantage of the single load plan is that during normal periods a full day's work is provided for both the crew and the equipment. There are no extremely small loads to haul at the end of a day's work; neither does a crew ever arrive at the disposal point considerably before quitting time but too late to return to the route. Another advantage is that the extreme regularity of the collection makes it possible to use the plan in connection with any means of loading the refuse receptacles.

A disadvantage is that the work of a single crew is not confined to a particular area, making it more difficult for the collectors to remember their routes. This is particularly true if there must be a separate set of routes for each day of the week, as happens when collections are made once a week. With lay-offs or absence of regular route men, extra help will surely miss part of such routes. It may even be very confusing for the collectors to have from nine to twelve individual routes, as may easily be the case with twice-a-week collections. The method is not particularly satisfactory when the amount of refuse varies considerably from collection to collection or from season to season. A route may yield only a partial load during one collection and more than a full load on another occasion. This feature is partially overcome by the use of open collection vehicles which are subject to some excess loading. If enclosed vehicles are used, a considerable overrun in the quantity of refuse on a route would be a serious disadvantage. The increased amount of supervision required to make sure that the crews keep busy, that they are in the proper areas, and that they are conducting the work in an effective manner, may or may not be a disadvantage, depending on the point of view. As a general observation, the less efficient methods require little administrative effort and the supervision is quite easy. Some increased administration becomes mandatory for the proper operation of methods which provide for a full day's work for crews and equipment. Another disadvantage of this method is that it offers an incentive to make the loads more bulky by placing the refuse inefficiently. This is applicable, however, only to rubbish and mixed refuse containing rubbish. Unwrapped garbage and ashes load solidly.

Definite working day—irregular frequency method. Some cities, faced with the necessity of limiting the working period to a definite number of hours because of higher rates for overtime or because of other reasons, have adopted a method which sacrifices regularity of collections to gain uniformity in working hours. Essentially, this is a variation of the large route method. Definite routes are laid out and a crew assigned to each. The collection proceeds along a route for the length of time adopted for a working day. The next working day collections are resumed at the point reached during the previous period. This continues until the route is completely collected. The process then begins again immediately, often in the middle of a day, so that there is virtually no beginning or end to a route. The length of the route will determine the average frequency of collection, but this method is not generally used where more than one pick-up a week is necessary. The time required to complete a route will depend on the amount of refuse produced, on the weather, on the efficiency of the workmen and on other factors.

An important advantage of a definite working day is that employees do not have to put in extra time even during periods of heavy refuse production, and municipalities do not have to pay high overtime labor rates. However, where the drivers have to work longer than the collectors, in order to haul the last load to a disposal point, it may be advisable to pay the driver some overtime in order to obtain a full day's work from the collectors. This method, under adequate supervision, assures the full day's services of both the employees and the equipment.

Because of the uncertainty as to the time or even the day on which individual collections will be made, the plan is not practical where householders have to set out containers at the curbs. Another disadvantage is that the collections become less frequent at times when relatively large amounts of refuse are produced. It would obviously be more desirable during such periods to increase the frequency, if anything, because of the limited storage capacity at average households. It is possible in some cases to increase the size of the crews without great loss of efficiency. In other cases it is necessary to have a different routing plan for certain seasons. Furthermore, the method provides practically no work incentive. The collection crews gain no special advantage by working rapidly or efficiently, and supervision therefore becomes quite difficult. The irregularity of obtaining loads makes it probable that there will be only a partial load in a vehicle at quitting time or that a vehicle may have returned to a route just in time to leave for the garage.

Utilization of crews between loads. The activities of refuse collection crews, while the vehicles are traveling to and from the disposal points, are arranged in several different ways to meet most effectively the particular situations faced. The chief governing factor is the length of the haul, or, more properly, the time required for a collection vehicle to travel to the disposal site or transfer station, dump the load, and return to the route. Contributing influences are the means which have been adopted for accepting and unloading refuse receptacles, the size of the collection crew, the number of loads a day, and the arrangements at the disposal site.

When the haul is very short the elapsed period is ordinarily too brief to make it advisable or practical to use the collectors and topmen for other work. As the hauling distance increases, however, there is more and more time during which these employees have nothing to occupy them unless they are given other tasks. Any work assigned to them must be such as can readily be handled by refuse collectors. Moreover, it should be useful and necessary work which can be done efficiently by these men in their spare time. For very long hauls, it may be advantageous to supply additional vehicles so the crews can keep on loading, particularly if there is no other work which they can do effectively.

When a collection crew operates with a single vehicle, there is necessarily some time between loads when they cannot load refuse, unless, of course, only one load of refuse is collected in a full shift—an extreme case. Normally, the crews collect at least two loads a day and sometimes as many as five or six loads, depending on truck size, length of haul, and density of pick-up points. Where only two loads a day are collected, the first load will often be completed about lunch time, so the crew can take the noon recess while the truck goes to the dump. The drivers frequently eat their lunch while waiting for collectors to load, but when the drivers help with the loading they must usually take their lunch period after returning with the truck, leaving the rest of the crew to begin the collection of the second load.

When the haul is not very long, it may be advisable to use the time between loads as rest periods for the collection crew, particularly if a rapid pace is maintained during the collection work or if exceptionally heavy containers must be handled. If this is done, the crew may either remain on the route to rest or ride with the driver to the disposal point. In some cities the disposal or transfer arrangements make it advisable to have additional help during the unloading process. Of course it is only in cases of very small operations that it is practical to transport the collection crews rather than provide the necessary employees at the disposal site. To avoid the probable adverse public reaction to the sight of municipal employees idling during regular working hours, it may be better to have the crews travel with the collection vehicles. Some administrators believe that greater production is obtained by giving the collectors brief rests between loads. If the loading time is as much as 70 per cent of the whole cycle, they would use the interval for resting rather than for finding other work. On the other hand, the operation of a collection crew with a single vehicle is sometimes justified only by providing other work for the crew members while the truck is away, particularly if the hauling distance is great. The alternatives would be to provide additional vehicles or to integrate the work of several crews.

Integration of the Work of Several Crews

In an effort to overcome some of the weaknesses which develop when crews work independently, several plans of coordinating the activities of two or more crews have been tried in some municipalities. These will be discussed briefly.

Swing crew method. One of the simplest methods of compensating for unusually large amounts of refuse on certain days or at certain seasons is to provide one or more extra crews to help out any point were they are needed. Such crews are frequently called swing crews. They are used in a few places in connection with the daily route method, in which case very close contact with the regular crews is necessary if the supervisors are to know where help will be required. Frequently no accurate indication can be had before noon. Consequently it is necessary to start the swing crews much later than the regular ones and make it possible for them to finish after hours any of the regular routes left uncompleted. The plan is simpler to operate with the large route method because a checkup can be made at the close of each working day to determine which crews will not be able to complete the routes by themselves. Often under this plan the swing crews are not used until a need is demonstrated and ordinarily they work only one or two days a week. Usually they start at the end of routes and work toward the beginning points, to avoid interference with the regular forces.

Swing crews are sometimes used—unsatisfactorily—on a rather permanent basis for parts of regular and permanent routes. The practice is too often adopted solely to avoid the work and nuisance of rerouting the entire system when it becomes evident that the work load is unequally divided among the crews. The device is in no sense a satisfactory alternative for needed rerouting, and usually proves a very inefficient substitute. The swing crews are probably recruited from men who want steady jobs and it has been found in some cases that the regular collectors will help them by easing up. Under some circumstances, however, it may be quite satisfactory to handle temporary or seasonal variations by adding swing crews when only a few routes are affected and when the areas assigned to a particular swing crew are neither too small nor too far apart.

Swing crews are an advantage mainly in eliminating some of the inequalities in the work loads on the various routes. Normally the regular routes are so designed that, on the average, a crew will have a full day's work. When the loads are especially large, as frequently happens in the first part of the week, then either the employees must work overtime or additional help must be provided. In the interest of relatively uniform working days and the avoidance of paying extra compensation for overtime periods—necessary in some cities—the swing crew plan has some merit.

The plan has a number of disadvantages, however. In the first place the activities of swing crews are usually very inefficient and expensive in relation to the regular work because they must move from place to place for the collection of relatively small amounts of refuse. This is not a valid objection in connection with the large route method where it may be possible to assign a whole day's work or at least a half-day's work on a single route. Generally speaking, swing crews are not employed full-time and consequently both equipment and employees must be kept available on short notice. The most careful attention must be given to the management of swing crews to retain the incentive provided by assigning a single route to a single crew which expects no help and which strives for time off if it completes the work ahead of time. Furthermore, there is a considerable danger that the use of swing crews may be attempted as a substitute for sound planning of refuse collection activities and periodic examinations into the details of existing working arrangements. Certainly a very much higher grade of supervision is essential if the swing crews are to be used to the best advantage. If this means only that supervisory force must be especially alert in keeping watch over the operations of the entire system, it may be more of an advantage than a disadvantage. If additional supervisory employees must be secured because of the increased personal attention required, then the cost of the service may become unduly high.

Variable size of crew method. Instead of varying the number of crews and the number of collection vehicles, one simple method of integrating the refuse collection work is to provide a variable number of collectors for the individual crews, depending on the amount and conditions of work on particular routes. Ordinarily the extra collectors are shifted from one crew to another either at the beginning of a day's route, based on rather accurate knowledge of the conditions on the route, or sometime during the day when it can be seen that one crew is running behind and another ahead of anticipated progress. It sometimes happens, however, that on a particular day most of the routes will be heavier than usual, perhaps because of an intervening Sunday, and several additional collectors are needed to equalize the load. Sometimes such extra employees can be obtained easily on short notice, particularly during periods of widespread unemployment. In certain places, a scheme of alternating collectors has been adopted so that all get some time off on the days when the routes are light. This is particularly effective when the collectors work five days a week but the collection work continues six days a week. In such cases the entire force works on the one or two days when the amount of work is greatest, with smaller crews the rest of the week.

At first glance, it may seem that this method would be a lazy administrator's way of equalizing collection loads in the easiest possible manner. Undoubtedly the method is thus misapplied in some cases, but it has, nevertheless, a real place among the worth-while methods available. In the right place and intelligently applied, it can serve better than any other plan. The plan is obviously useful when collection conditions vary from one day to another because a larger or smaller amount of labor is needed to load the same amount of refuse. By adding, or withdrawing, a collector, it may be possible to maintain schedules, obtain the same number of truckloads each day, and avoid overtime work. Effective use, of course, involves an unusually complete knowledge of the collection routes and the operations of the crews. It is apparent that an especially high quality of administration is needed to secure and use accurately the necessary facts about the different routes.

The advantage of this method is that the work load throughout the week is divided so equally that a minimum of overtime is necessary; and the equipment is used economically because the same number of vehicles are used each day and, on the whole, they are used for full days. In some cases, however, the variable-sized crews will load the truck much more quickly or slowly than usual, altering the number of loads a day and disturbing the balance between loading and hauling time. This is not serious for short hauls, but on long hauls it may mean that the collectors will be idle for rather long periods.

In general, it seems reasonable that a crew is most efficient when a definite number of collectors are loading, and that a change in size would mean reduced efficiency. If this is true, it means that for the advantage of equalizing the day's work of the collectors, less effective operations are employed deliberately. Certainly before this is done the advisability of other methods or other means should be explored. The fact that strange collectors are used on routes, while not an objection for curb or alley loading, may seriously impair the effectiveness of the collection service from backdoors or basements. On the whole, the method should be used with caution, and only when complete knowledge is available on the operating conditions for each route.

Inter-route relief method. Another method has been developed which provides for regular crews to help collect other routes when their own assignments are completed. When used with daily routes, the supervisory officers must keep in close touch with the progress on each route and be in a position to make additional assignments as the crews complete the regular routes. When used with weekly routes, such close contact is not so essential because the fill-in operations can be foreseen more easily and can usually be anticipated a day ahead of the actual completion of routes. The plan, however, was developed not only to eliminate the necessity for certain crews to work much longer than others or long beyond the regular quitting time, but also to use the equipment much more effectively. In some cities it was found that, regardless of the care exercised in laying out routes, the quantities of refuse varied so much from collection to collection that vehicles sometimes were only half full when the route was finished or were completely filled with only a small volume of material still to collect. This meant either that the vehicle must make a trip to the disposal or transfer point with only a partial load or, after emptying the full load, must make a complete trip to the route and back to collect a very small quantity of refuse. In either case, the equipment was employed inefficiently. In the second case, the crew was needlessly delayed in completing the day's work.

As the method operates, the drivers of the vehicles report the progress made on the routes each time they bring a load to the disposal or transfer point. On smaller systems a foreman or clerk may record the data as to the part of the routes completed, but on larger operations a dispatcher takes the information, plots it on a control map, and gives any necessary directions to the drivers. On daily routes, the drivers must telephone the foreman or dispatcher (1) when a route is completed and the vehicles are only partially loaded, regardless of time, and (2) when it becomes apparent that there is not enough room in the vehicle to accommodate the refuse still to be collected. Drivers are reimbursed for the cost of such telephone calls. The foremen or dispatchers are in a position to make additional assignments to crews which have only partial loads as they call in. Usually a relief crew begins at the end of the route and works toward the beginning until it meets the regular crew or reaches the point where the regular crew stopped because of a completed load. Sometimes certain crews are ordered to complete their loads on other routes even though such work involves working beyond regular hours and necessitates paying overtime wage rates. Frequently it is more economical to pay one crew overtime than to send out a truck to collect a small quantity of material.

The advantages of this method are obvious. The equipment can be used at the greatest efficiency, the crews seldom have to work overtime, and there is a positive control over the entire collection system. Work incentive is not destroyed as much as would be suspected, because a crew is not helped out on its task until it has collected the number of loads which ordinarily constitute a day's work. A crew is not helped unless its vehicle will not hold all the refuse left to be collected. One disadvantage is that the method cannot be used very successfully where the collections are made from backdoors or basements, for the relief crews cannot be expected to be well enough acquainted with all the routes to be able to conduct the work satisfactorily. It is probable that the cost of supervision is somewhat higher for this method than for some others, but this is not important if over-all efficiency is raised by improving the control. Another disadvantage is that the "load" is not a very satisfactory task basis. Collectors may be able to stow the refuse very inefficiently so as to complete a load quickly. This would not be possible with garbage or ashes.

Reservoir route method. Another important refuse collection method which integrates several crews is called the reservoir route method because the basic principle involves the establishment of a central overflow route among a group of several routes. Typically three, four, or five routes are laid out around a center route and the entire group constitutes a working unit. Greater flexibility in operation is permitted within such a group because the central or reservoir route may be collected by all crews from the marginal routes after their regular route is completed. The work continues by all crews in the reservoir routes until all refuse is collected. Normally all crews will finish at the same time. When the work load is extremely heavy, during a particular day of the week or during certain seasons of the year, an additional crew may be assigned to the reservoir route, in which case the operation is conducted on the daily route plan or the inter-route relief plan previously described.

The advantages of this method are that the collection work can be arranged within a definite area so that several crews operate as a unit and strive, collectively rather than individually, to do a prescribed amount of work. The work is divided equally among the several crews and all finish about the same time. Since the operations of such a unit are confined to a fairly compact area, the method is useful in connection with backdoor and basement collection as well as with curb and alley collections. As is true with other plans for integrating operations of several crews, the supervision must be adequate, and complete data on the various routes and operations must be continuously reported and intelligently used. A possible disadvantage is that the equipment may not be utilized as efficiently as under the inter-route relief method, and it is possible for several vehicles to have only fractional loads at the completion of a day's work. There is no reason, however, why the supervisory officers cannot keep sufficiently in touch with the progress of the various crews to enable them to prevent a large part of the inefficient use of equipment by adjusting assignments toward the close of a day's operation. For example, if a truck leaves for a disposal point rather late in the day so that it would return to the route in time to do only a small amount of work, the supervisory officer could order the truck to the garage instead and assign the crew to other equipment within the reservoir route. Occasionally it might be desirable to shift an entire crew from one reservoir route to another.

SUMMARY

Each of the methods described in this chapter is in actual use in American municipalities, sometimes in the simplest form, but in other places in combination with other methods. There has been no attempt to justify or rate the various plans used except to present the obvious advantages and disadvantages, although it is probable that each is particularly well adapted to certain existing combinations of local conditions. For any particular city, there may be more bad than good in some of the methods. Other methods may be wholly unworkable because of personnel, political situations, or service requirements.

There are two fundamental criteria for the suitability of any method: (1) Does it accomplish effectively the work to be done? (2) Is it economical? Community standards of service, sanitation, and appearance enter into the evaluation of the character of the work done. The economy of the operations covers such matters as proper routing and scheduling, work incentives, and adequate supervision and administration.

It is impossible to deal properly with the selection of methods without considering equipment. Therefore methods will be reintroduced after the discussion of refuse collection equipment is presented.

chapter 6

REFUSE COLLECTION EQUIPMENT

The selection of suitable vehicles for any particular collection operation involves a thorough understanding of all local conditions that affect refuse collection and complete knowledge of the kinds and sizes of equipment available for this work.

The development of refuse collection equipment to meet conditions as they changed from generation to generation is an interesting study. It is not intended here to trace the history of refuse collection equipment but it is pertinent to mention that the advent of motor-driven vehicles caused a prolonged dispute as to the proper direction of advancement and served to delay the improvement of refuse carriers. Even after motor vehicles had become firmly established, there was for some time a considerable difference of opinion as to the relative merits of horse-drawn and motor-operated equipment for refuse collection. As a result, very little attention was given to adapting motor vehicles for refuse collection. Those that were used for this purpose were designed mainly for handling materials very much heavier than refuse, such as earth, stone, or sand. Such vehicles could not operate economically in the refuse service.

Municipal officials, of course, want the most effective and economical equipment they can obtain for a particular operation. For refuse collection this means that vehicles must be properly designed as to size and strength; must be sanitary, reliable, easy to load and unload; and must be safe for the workmen. Not a negligible factor, however, is the appearance of such equipment and frequently some efficiency is sacrificed in order to provide more elaborate or showy vehicles for the effect on public opinion and citizen support.

BASIC CONSIDERATIONS ON THE SUITABILITY OF EQUIPMENT

The adaptability of refuse collection equipment to individual local situations is of the greatest importance if the service rendered is to be sanitary, inoffensive, and effective, and at the same time as economical as possible. Numerous features of a collection service must be taken into account in selecting equipment for this work. The class of refuse collected, collection frequency, collection methods, length of haul, width and condition of streets and alleys, and a city's size, financial position and labor rates are important and determine the essential characteristics of the vehicles best suited. The basic determinations to be made include the size and capacity of vehicles, loading height, speed of loading, degree of compaction, retention of compaction, vertical clearance of loading aperture, appearance, unloading devices, whether it is easily cleanable, speed of travel, watertightness, and numerous other features of design or construction. These matters will be discussed briefly in the following paragraphs before a description is given of the equipment actually in use by collection agencies.

FIG. 6-1. Refuse collection vehicles should be designed for efficient performance under local conditions. This 25-cubic yard compactor type refuse collection vehicle is used to collect combined refuse in Los Angeles. The body is mounted on a 45,000 pound gross vehicle weight chassis. Note righthand drive adopted for a driver's convenience and safety in stepping from vehicle to assist loader.

Size and Capacity of Vehicles

One of the most important factors in equipment design is the proper relation between the volumetric capacity of the body and the weight-hauling capacity of its chassis. In the past, the tendency was to use bodies that were much too small to hold the amount of refuse which the chassis were capable of hauling. Data presented in Chapter 2 showed that rubbish may be as light as 200 pounds per cubic yard while garbage or ashes may weigh more than 1,000 pounds a cubic yard. Consequently, for the same chassis size the volumetric capacity of the body of a rubbish vehicle may be five times as great as one for garbage or ashes.

The usual approach to the selection of refuse vehicles is to determine first the volumetric capacity which best fits the local situation and then proportion the chassis to conform to the total load. In general there are three points to be considered in selecting the proper body capacity:

1. The volume should be such that a definite number of full loads will be collected in an average day. The goal is to minimize having the last load contain a small part of a complete load.

2. The size should be related to the loading speed of the crews or the collection methods used. When rapid loading is feasible the units can be large for collections from high production sources or for long hauls to disposal points. When loading is necessarily slow, or the haul to disposal points is short, smaller vehicles may be more advisable.

3. When vehicles are utilized on a relay plan, it is desirable to proportion the loading time to hauling time. Therefore the body capacity should be studied in relation to the length of haul, speed of travel, and loading time.

Loading Height

The loading height of refuse collection vehicles is one of the most critical features of their design. As a general principle, the lower the loading height the more rapidly and easily the material can be loaded. What loading height is satisfactory in any particular situation depends considerably on the weight of the individual receptacles to be handled. Excessive height may increase unduly the cost of loading material, and, what is more pertinent, it may cause physical injuries to the workmen.

The most advantageous collection body from the low loading height standpoint, is the rear-loading compaction type. Refuse materials are loaded into a hopper at the rear of the body and the material either lifted by a conveyor arrangement or hydraulically controlled swinging panel which pushes the material into the main compartment of the body. It is possible with this arrangement to have high bodies of large capacity without causing additional lifting effort by the loaders. Most manufacturers of this type of body have reduced the height of the edge of the loading hopper to below the height of the frame of the truck chassis.

Some users of open-bodied or locally fabricated enclosed-bodied trucks have been able to reduce the loading height somewhat by hinging the upper part of the side so that it can be swung downward.

Unloading Devices

The collection vehicles must be capable of rapid unloading so that a minimum of time will be lost at disposal sites or transfer stations. Several unloading arrangements or devices are used on refuse collection equipment, but the most prevalent method is the hydraulically operated dump body. For complete clearing of the load with mixed refuse or rubbish, a dumping angle of 50 to 55 degrees has been found most satisfactory. It is also important that the rear end of the body be slightly wider than the forward end, particularly on compactor-type bodies, in order to facilitate the clearing of the load.

Another widely used unloading arrangement on the modern compaction vehicles is the movable bulkhead, which does not require that the body be raised. This type may be either hydraulically operated or operated by a chain or cable.

Turning Radius of Collection Equipment

The turning radius of refuse collection vehicles should ordinarily be as short as practicable so as to cause the minimum obstruction to traffic

FIG. 6-2. One of the important attributes of modern compactor type refuse collection equipment is the low loading height body. Refuse is placed in the rear hopper and a metal plate pushes and compacts the refuse into the main compartment.

in narrow streets, and to simplify maneuvering around parked cars and at corners. When the equipment is used in alleys, particularly T-, L-, or

H-shaped alleys, short turning radius is usually mandatory. The turning problem becomes especially acute in narrow alleys, and special equipment, such as power steering, may be used to facilitate right-angle turns. In some cities the need to make collections from narrow alleys has resulted in the use of a much smaller truck than would otherwise be used. For this reason, Philadelphia, Pennsylvania, recently put into operation a number of small compaction trucks, which are both shorter and narrower than the conventional collection trucks used for street curb collections.

Cab-over-engine and cab-forward chassis have a much shorter wheel-base than other conventional type chassis with the same length of cab-to-axle dimension, and this shorter wheel-base permits a shorter turning radius. This type of chassis is manufactured in even the largest sizes and is being widely adapted for use in the refuse collection service.

FIG. 6-3. Use of the hydraulically operated dump body is a prevalent method of unloading refuse trucks. For complete clearing of a load of mixed refuse or rubbish, a dumping angle of 50-55 degrees as shown in the left picture is satisfactory.

Watertightness of Collection Bodies

To have liquids from the collected refuse drip or flow from the truck bodies onto pavements or roadways is generally recognized as extremely undesirable. Therefore, when the refuse material is so wet that liquid collects in the bottom of the body, some provision must be made to prevent its escape. This is accomplished simply by creating a shallow tank in the bottom of the body or by inclining the floor upwards to the rear.

The end gates are made watertight by the insertion of a gasket of neoprene or similar material between the end gate and body, held in place by substantial clamps. Usually, the problem of preventing leakage or seepage occurs only in connection with unwrapped garbage collection. Wrapped garbage, mixed refuse, and rubbish are ordinarily dry enough to absorb any liquids which may be present.

Safety and Comfort of Collection Crews

Properly designed refuse collection vehicles have incorporated in them devices to make it easy and safe for the collectors to load the materials and to ride on the vehicles. These include a cab for the driver and collectors, suitable steps to facilitate access to the cab, well located hand holds, adequate door fastenings, and ample racks or supports for tools, containers, and other equipment.

FIG. 6-4. Modern refuse vehicles are designed to be pleasing to the eye and minimize potential nuisance hazards. They have watertight bodies and tailgates so that liquids will not drip on roadways. In Philadelphia, loading hoppers are covered with hinged metal covers or closed off with packing blade before the vehicle travels to the disposal area.

All modern collection vehicles are now equipped with enclosed cabs for the driver and other members of the crew, usually with room enough for two loaders in addition to the driver. When the collection crew consists of more than the driver and two loaders, special provision must be made for their transportation. Also, there usually is enough space for the employees to store their lunches and extra clothing for extremely cold or rainy weather. A well-located step or hand-hold of proper design may mean the difference between safety and danger for a collector riding on the vehicle.

Safety also plays an important part in determining the arrangements for loading the collection vehicle. There is no fixed rule which can be followed because so much depends on the type of vehicle, habits of collectors, and the local traffic conditions. In any particular situation, however, it may be found that side loading is far safer than end loading, or that the reverse is true. It is probable that the curb side will be much more satisfactory than the street side.

It is interesting to note that equipment used by Los Angeles includes a number of rubbish collection vehicles equipped with right-hand drive chassis which in addition to other considerations, includes the consideration of safety for the driver who dismounts and assists the other crew members in loading heavy containers.

Adaptability of Collection Equipment for Other Work

In many instances, refuse collection equipment is purchased with the idea of adapting it to other uses in the municipal service. Sometimes such uses are purely emergency in character, such as snow plowing, snow removal, leaf collection, removal of debris after storms, and similar

FIG. 6-5. Collection crew members often ride the truck between pickups. It is important to the safety of the crew that vehicles be equipped with slip resistant type steps and secure, convenient hand holds where needed.

work in unusual circumstances. In other cases the equipment may be bought to serve part-time regularly on other than refuse collection work. In small cities particularly, where the number of pieces of equipment is necessarily limited, it is appropriate to give special consideration to transferring the vehicles to other work when they can be released from the refuse service.

It might appear at first glance that enclosed vehicles with special types of loading and compaction devices would not be suitable at all for other work. This would certainly be true in smaller cities where the equipment might be needed for construction work, general hauling, or snow hauling, but in larger cities it has been found that such vehicles serve excellently with snow plows and can be used for emergency service. In smaller communities it may be desirable at times to sacrifice some special refinements or a small degree of efficiency in refuse collection in order to provide vehicles that can also be used for other work. It is not practicable to specify a general rule for appraising such situations. It is a matter requiring careful analysis in every instance.

FIG. 6-6. Refuse collection vehicles often are adaptable to other uses in the municipal service. In New York City, collection trucks are an important part of the city's snow removal equipment. This truck is equipped with a permanent mounting for a snow plow. The plow can be attached quickly and the vehicle used in the city's emergency snow removal program, as needed, with a minimum of delay.

Appearance of Vehicles

The general appearance of refuse collection equipment is becoming more and more a factor in its selection, care, and up-keep. Not so many years ago it was rather generally accepted that such vehicles would at best be rather unpleasing in appearance, and often quite disreputable. Developments in design and construction have made it possible to secure trucks, trailers, and other vehicles which are quite pleasing in appearance and in some cases cannot be distinguished from some of the best looking commercial vehicles. As such equipment undoubtedly costs more than the plainest type, the most economical equipment is not always the logical type to select if appearance is an important factor. Many officials think that the appearance of refuse collection equipment is unconsciously taken by the average citizen as a general index to the character of the municipal government. They believe it may be desirable to sacrifice a little in economy to advertise the city and the municipal administration. Similarly, proper care of equipment will be reflected in improved public relations. Some cities keep their refuse collection vehicles scrupulously clean at all times and well painted in an attractive uniform color. Many other communities are content with occasional washings and infrequent painting. A few neglect this part of maintenance.

KINDS OF COLLECTION VEHICLES IN GENERAL USE

The kinds of refuse collection vehicles used in American cities generally fall into three types—open trucks, enclosed trucks, and enclosed compactor trucks. All are giving satisfactory service where they are used under appropriate operating conditions. Because each type has certain advantages and limitations, a sound analysis of any particular situation requires that these be understood.

FIG. 6-7. In some cities the collection and disposal of palm fronds and similar vegetation are large problems. In Miami, Florida, compactor trucks are used to transport to the disposal area palm fronds placed in piles at the curb.

The enclosed compactor truck is currently by far the most widely used type of collection vehicle. (See Table 6-1.) Planned procurement shows that this type will be even more widely used, with the open, and noncompactor enclosed trucks being given less consideration.

Collection Truck Chassis

Truck chassis have similar characteristics regardless of the type of body used or the kinds of materials to be collected. A heavy duty commercial chassis is desirable for refuse collection work and practically all standard makes are found somewhere in this service. The nominal size of the chassis ranges from $1\frac{1}{2}$ to 8 tons, with the trend going toward even larger chassis, i.e., up to 15 tons. As a rule they are able to go relatively slow and relatively fast—for example they can be driven at around $1\frac{1}{2}$ miles per hour to synchronize with the speed of the collection crew, and they can be driven at speeds of over fifty miles per hour, for travel to and from the disposal points. All the leading truck manufacturers can meet these requirements with their standard models of adequate capacity.

TABLE 6-1

Types and Sizes of Collection Vehicles Utilized—1964

A—Compactor Trucks

Capacity Cubic Yards	Daily Cities	Daily Trucks	Standby Cities	Standby Trucks
12	12	30	13	29
12-15	30	81	19	34
16	77	1448+	36	633
17-18	30	161	12	14
19-20	65	1255	22	161
21-24	12	44	0	0
25-30	20	145	9	24
30	5	24	2	3
Capacity not stated	781	7688	438	925
Total	1032	10786+	551	1823

B—Containers Used with Compactor Trucks

Capacity Cubic Yards	Daily Cities	Daily Containers	Standby Cities	Standby Containers
1	12	878	2	102
2	5	348	1	101
3	3	658	0	0
4	3	53	1	3
5	0	0	1	12
6-8	2	10	2	8
Capacity not stated	359	13824+	31	438
Total	384	15771+	38	664

NOTE: 1. The plus (+) sign next to a number in Tables A and B indicates that there was one city with more than 998 units, but the exact number is not known. Therefore 998 is included in the totals.

C—Enclosed Noncompactor Trucks

Capacity Cubic Yards	Daily Cities	Daily Trucks	Standby Cities	Standby Trucks
12	4	67	5	19
12-15	4	48	3	4
16	1	1	0	0
17-18	0	0	0	0
19-20	2	2	1	1
21-24	2	36	2	9
25-30	0	0	0	0
30	0	0	0	0
Capacity not stated	145	1272	49	91
Total	158	1426	60	124

D—Open Trucks

Capacity Cubic Yards	Daily Cities	Daily Trucks	Standby Cities	Standby Trucks
1-5	6	15	6	14
6-10	9	45	7	13
11-12	7	146	6	69
13-16	8	52	3	18
17-18	2	20	0	0
19-20	2	6	2	3
21-25	2	17	1	2
25	1	4	1	2
Capacity not stated	759	3362	205	511
Total	796	3367	231	632

E—Number of Hoisting Units

Type of Service	Daily Cities	Daily Hoisting Units	Standby Cities	Standby Hoisting Units
Municipal	77	237	16	24
Contract	25	58	5	8
Private	27	133	5	2
Total	129	428	23	34

F—Containers Used with Hoisting Units

Capacity Cubic Yards	Daily Cities	Daily Containers	Standby Cities	Standby Containers
0-5	1	1	0	0
6-9	2	141	0	0
10-11	0	0	0	0
12-13	1	3	0	0
14-15	0	0	0	0
16-17	1	34	0	0
18-20	0	0	0	0
20	2	24	0	0
Capacity not stated	106	9070	21	86 + + + + –
Total	113	9273	21	86 + + + + –

NOTE: 2. Each plus (+) sign in Table F indicates a city with more than 8 standb units, but the exact number is not known. Therefore, the total is the minimum number possible.

While on the collection route the refuse collection vehicle is sub jected to strenuous treatment—slow speed, continual starts and stops generally heavy traffic, and power loading and compacting. The fol lowing features should be considered especially in the selection of truc chassis for any particular service conditions: high-torque engine, heav duty clutch and transmission, adequate braking system, preferabl power activated in the larger sizes, conspicuous stop and turn indicators cab with good vision in all directions, rugged driving arrangement t

FIG. 6-8. Many cities use open-top trucks for rubbish collection. This truck, operated under contract with the city of Lakewood, California, is equipped with a mechanical front loading device to overcome the problem of the high loading height created by the exra large 35-cubic yard body.

reduce maintenance to a minimum, and proper weight distribution for the intended maximum usage. Indications are that trucks with torque convertor drive reduce clutch maintenance substantially.

As pointed out previously, the cab-forward and cab-over-engine chassis are experiencing considerable favor for narrow alley routes and collection routes in heavy traffic areas.

Open-Top Trucks

Open-top trucks are being replaced rapidly in the collection of mixed refuse by the more sanitary enclosed compactor trucks. Many open-top trucks however, are still being used, especially in the smaller cities, for collecting mixed refuse. Typically, those used are generally in the class of 10 to 20 cubic yards capacity. This volume is achieved usually by building up the sides. A canvas or wire mesh cover is used to keep the material from blowing.

There are several important advantages in the open-top truck. First, cost is usually less, and they are more economical to operate than other kinds of trucks. They are readily adaptable to other municipal services and can be used in emergencies for snow or debris removal. It may be counted a further advantage that the trucks are capable of surcharge above the nominal water-level line, permitting them to be loaded to the full capacity of the chassis; this advantage is, however, rapidly losing way to the higher efficiency which is being built into the most modern kind of compaction truck. The principal advantage, how-

FIG. 6-9. Collection vehicle operated by a Los Angeles industrial concern engaged in the collection and salvage of meat scraps from markets. 30-gallon containers are loaded onto the truck and covered by a tarpaulin while in transit. The truck and body are steam-cleaned and disinfected with a sanitizing solution at the end of each collection trip.

ever, for open-top trucks is that bulky items can be readily loaded where they may not fit through the openings of any of the enclosed body trucks. Even the largest cities usually employ some open-top trucks to handle those special materials which cannot be collected on the regular routes using enclosed compaction trucks.

The disadvantages of the open-top trucks may or may not be serious; these must be weighed in each case under the conditions in which they will be used. Littering with ashes and rubbish by blowing occurs with almost every type of open-top truck despite continued efforts to prevent it. Invariably, odors are given off where garbage is collected either separately or with other kinds of refuse material.

Enclosed Noncompactor Trucks

The enclosed noncompactor truck is essentially an open-top truck with a rigid or semi-rigid cover which completely envelopes the refuse material except when the doors are open during loading. This kind of collection vehicle has essentially the same characteristics as the open-top truck with the one distinct advantage over the open-top truck, i.e., complete enclosure of the refuse. This feature is important for it precludes littering and odor nuisance problems. Many of these bodies are locally fabricated in municipal shops to city specifications. Others are made by established body manufacturing plants. The initial cost of enclosed noncompactor trucks will be considerably less than that of compactor-type trucks. However, the noncompactor type trucks do not possess the advantageous features of the compactors such as low load-

FIG. 6-10. There are many types of enclosed rear-loading compactor type refuse collection bodies manufactured. Those pictured above are (1) a large unit used in heavy work in Chicago, Illinois; (2) Gar Wood Load Packer used in Wayne, Michigan; (3) Truxmore Packer used in Richmond, Virginia; (4) Heil Colectomatic, used in Milwaukee, Wisconsin; and (5) Power Packer, Daybrook Hydraulic Div., L. A. Young Spring and Wire Corp., Bowling Green, Ohio.

ing height and ability to crush and compact the refuse, thus permitting more materials to be loaded in the same size body.

Such vehicles are not usually equipped with mechanical devices for compacting the loaded refuse. Some compaction can be obtained by closing the doors and covers and raising the body with the hydraulic hoist, forcing the loaded material to the back of the body, thus allowing some consolidation by the normal weight of the materials. It should be pointed out, however, that refuse consisting predominately of lightweight rubbish does not compact well even though the body is hoisted frequently. Consequently enclosed noncompactor type trucks are now used prevailingly in the collection of garbage or ashes.

Practically all such vehicles are equipped with hydraulic hoists so that the refuse is discharged through the rear gates.

FIG. 6-11. Rear-loading compactor type vehicles are equipped with side doors so that large bulky items may be placed directly into the body. Here the collector is placing an abandoned 55-gallon oil drum into the body for transport to the disposal area.

Enclosed Compactor Trucks

The most widely used types of enclosed compactor trucks are provided with special mechanical devices for loading the refuse into the main compartment of the body, for compressing the loaded materials, and for distributing the refuse within the body. This equipment has been developed over the years in an effort to solve the ever-present problem of providing a body of sufficient capacity for the particular size of chassis used and at the same time a low loading height. Without exception, these vehicles are unloaded through large rear gates. There are several different arrangements which accomplish the same end.

Trough or bucket loader. One type of low-loading height body is the rear or side trough loader. Refuse is dumped from regular containers into a trough which has a capacity of one to one and a half cubic yards suspended at the rear or at the side of the truck body. When the trough is filled, it is raised and dumped into an opening in the top of the body, then returned to its normal position for reloading. Normally the top of the trough is about 36 inches above the ground, which makes it easy for the collectors to load the refuse.

The main part of the vehicle is covered effectively at all times, the only exposed refuse being that which is temporarily in the trough. However, during high winds some materials may be blown out onto the street and lawns, particularly at the time the contents of the trough are being dumped into the body. Side doors are usually provided for access to the main part of the body and for loading directly such items as bed springs, mattresses, large boxes and cartons.

Some of these vehicles are equipped with internal compacting devices for consolidating the material into the back part of the body.

FIG. 6-12. The trend in modern batch-loading type compactor vehicles is toward large receiving hoppers so that the collector will not be delayed while waiting for other crew members to dump containers. This type vehicle used by Maple Heights, Ohio, is designed so that 3 collectors can dump containers simultaneously.

Batch loader. Another type of enclosed compactor truck loads and consolidates in the same operation. In this type the refuse is dumped from standard containers into a low compartment or hopper sufficiently wide for several loaders at the same time and which has sufficient capacity for the contents of several containers before being emptied into the main part of the body. After the hopper is loaded, the operator by actuating a lever starts the mechanism which consists of a swinging gate or panel that revolves or swings horizontally, sweeping the refuse from the hopper into the main compartment of the body. Some types of bodies crush the material against a retaining panel; others sweep the material in and compress the material in the body with the retaining panel. The first refuse loaded simply piles on the floor of the body at the rear, succeeding refuse pushes the material forward progressively compacting and compressing it as the entire interior of the body becomes filled. Each arrangement by the several manufacturers is claimed to be superior for various kinds of refuse materials collected; the features of each should be tested for the particular conditions under which the truck will be operated in the city collection service to ensure the most efficient collection system for that city.

Escalator conveyor loader. Still another type of enclosed compactor body has an arrangement for elevating the refuse materials into the enclosed body by means of a continuous conveyor. The refuse is dumped into the low hopper at the rear of the truck from conventional containers by the collectors. The conveyor carries the refuse from the hopper up an incline to near the roof of the truck where it is discharged by gravity into the main compartment. As the refuse builds up in a pile at the rear, a compactor plate at the top of the conveyor moves the material toward the front thus filling the entire inside of the body. This type also has auxiliary side doors for loading materials which are not suitable for loading by the conveyor.

The collection truck developed by the city of New York is of this type and is proving very satisfactory in that city's refuse collection service. In operation, the refuse is dumped into the low loading hopper at the rear of the truck and carried by the blades of the conveyor up a rather steep incline to the top where it is discharged into the main compartment. The load fills up at the rear under the discharge end of the conveyor and gradually extends forward as the pile builds up. A compactor plate at the end of the conveyor also assists in moving the piled refuse forward in the body and further consolidates it. The entire mechanism is operated hydraulically from a power take-off of the vehicle and except for engaging the power take-off, full operation by the collectors is provided by controls located near the loading hopper. The New York collection vehicles are also provided with top loading doors for use when the vehicles are used in emergency snow removal. These top doors are then used to load snow from separate mechanical snow loaders. The plans and specifications of the New York unit have been made available to others, and several of the large cities are using some of a similar type in their refuse collection service.

Movable bulkhead loader. The most recent development in the enclosed compactor body field is the side loading movable bulkhead type. This type collection body is simpler in construction and operation and is finding favor among smaller municipalities where initial cost is a prime consideration. The body may be either square or round in transverse section. Loading is accomplished through openings in each side near the front of the body. As the space for loading becomes filled, a chain, cable, or hydraulically driven plate moves from the front toward the rear of the body, loading, and compacting as it moves. Thus the refuse is pushed to the rear filling the body and consolidating the refuse in the same operation. Discharge of the loaded vehicle is accomplished with the same movable bulkhead by simply opening the rear doors and moving the plate to the rear; eliminating the need for underbody hoists. This type of collection body is one of the least expensive—from the standpoint of initial capital cost—and the simplest to operate. However, it has the disadvantage of a higher loading height than the rear hopper type compactors. A further disadvantage is that previously compacted material may partially obstruct the loading opening, and the initial cost

FIG. 6-13. Collection trucks developed by the city of New York are of the escalator type of compactor. The refuse is dumped into the low loading hopper at the rear of the truck and carried by the blades of the conveyor up a rather steep incline to the top where it is discharged into the main compartment.

advantage may be offset by a faster loading cycle in the rear loaders under actual operating conditions. The side loading feature may be an advantage or a disadvantage depending on whether side or rear loading is the most advantageous in a particular instance.

Advantages and Disadvantages of Compactor Vehicles

From the stand point of a sanitary refuse collection service, enclosed compactor vehicles satisfy all of the requirements. Practically all of the disadvantages cited for other kinds of vehicles are eliminated in this type. They are easily and rapidly loaded, completely covered, and attractive in appearance. No topmen or loaders work inside the vehicles, in fact, they cannot be used in most types. The mechanical devices replace a part of the work of refuse collectors and make unnecessary one or two employees to stow and consolidate the material. The saving which results will offset in part the added initial cost and the cost of operating this kind of equipment over other types. On the whole, however, the benefits of such devices lie in the fact that they make possible a large capacity body without necessitating high loading height or exceeding the legal width and length regulations.

(1)

(2)

(3)

(4)

FIG. 6-14. There are a number of designs for enclosed side-loading compactor type refuse collection bodies. These shown are (1) Pak-Mor, Pak-Mor Mfg. Co., San Antonio, Texas; (2) MB Packer, MB Corp., New Holstein, Wisconsin; (3) Hydepak, Hyde Corporation, Fort Worth, Texas; and (4) Hydro E-Z Pack, Hercules Galion Products, Inc., Galion, Ohio.

The disadvantages of the enclosed compactor type of equipment are not numerous but may be quite important to some municipalities. The vehicles are more expensive in both first cost and in maintenance and operation. The benefits of low loading height, complete cover, and attractive appearance undoubtedly justify some increased cost in providing refuse collection service. The fact that the elevators and other devices for lifting the refuse into bodies of the vehicles cannot handle certain kinds of materials, or become jammed when the wrong kind of

FIG. 6-15. Medium-sized portable containers have been found to be useful by some producers of large amounts of refuse with limited access and storage areas. The containers are up to 4 cubic yards in size and are moved on caster type wheels to the truck for unloading. Hoisting equipment dumps and lowers the container so the operation can be performed by one man. One important advantage to this system is that the refuse collection vehicle may be used for ordinary household type collections also.

material is accidentally placed in the loading hoppers may show up as a disadvantage in those communities where the refuse is not properly prepared in the homes. It emphasizes the need for suitable regulations and strict observances. When side doors are provided, however, there should be little occasion for interrupted service because the collectors can soon learn to separate the material that can be mechanically loaded from that which must be loaded manually. While the separation and manual loading necessarily delays the operation somewhat, it can hardly be cited as an important disadvantage.

A recent development is the production of a medium size portable container the contents of which may be lifted and emptied into the body by mechanical means provided on the truck. These containers are

FIG. 6-16. Large portable refuse containers are often used for collecting refuse in commercial and multiple-dwelling areas or where large quantities of refuse are produced in densely occupied areas. Containers up to 15 cubic yards capacity are available. The containers pictured above are manufactured by the Ingersoll-Kalamazoo Div., Borg Warner Corp., Kalamazoo, Michigan; and Dempster Bros., Knoxville, Tennessee.

made in sizes up to 4 cubic yards. The container may be placed at the point of refuse generation and rolled on its casters to an accessible point for collection by the regular compactor truck. This arrangement has shown promise of widespread adoption for certain commercial, apartment house, school and institutional use since a large volume of material can be handled in a single container, thus obviating the need for many containers. Not only does it speed up the collection operation but many merchants and other commercial establishments have eliminated most of the disagreeable aspects of the refuse can storage area.

Portable Containers

Portable containers are widely used in commercial and multiple-dwelling areas, or where large volumes of refuse are generated in densely occupied areas. Containers up to 15 cubic yards in capacity are placed at convenient locations and refuse materials are emptied into them by the occupants of the establishments. A special hoisting truck services the portable containers on a scheduled basis, usually with a crew of one man, the driver. Thus, large volumes of refuse can be handled at a minimum of cost. This type of collection equipment is used in several

FIG. 6-17. Specially designed transport equipment is required to pick up and empty large portable containers. The entire operation is performed by one man. The transport units pictured are manufactured by Dempster Bros., Knoxville, Tennessee; and the Ingersoll-Kalamazoo Div., Borg Warner Corp. of Kalamazoo, Michigan.

FIG. 6-18. Where hauls are great, portable containers may be emptied into enclosed compactor type bodies of 50- to 60-cubic yards capacity for transport to the disposal area. The semi-trailers pictured are the side-loading type equipped with power units to operate the compaction plate independent of the tractor unit. They are manufactured by the Pak-Mor Mfg. Co., San Antonio, Texas; and the MB Corp., New Holstein, Wisconsin.

ways; some cities require the occupants to provide the container with the city providing the hauling service; some cities provide both the container and the service, usually at a fee; still other cities do not provide either the container or the service but permit private collectors to operate, in which case both the container and service are provided at the agreed cost between the collector and occupant. Where the hauling distance to the disposal point is great, portable containers are sometimes used in conjunction with a transfer truck or trailer. The transfer truck, or trailer, is provided with a large loading opening in the top of sufficient size to dump the entire contents of the container at one time. The trailers in use usually have sufficient capacity, and compaction devices, to dump 10 to 20 loaded containers before going to the disposal point. In the several cities where this type of combination equipment is in use, real economic advantages are being reported. It is interesting to note

FIG. 6-19. Equipment specially designed to dump large portable containers directly into large volume compactor type bodies. The units pictured are manufactured by the MB Corp., New Holstein, Wisconsin; and Dempster Bros., Knoxville, Tennessee.

that portable containers and hoisting units are being used in 113 of the reporting cities (Table 6-1).

Can-Carrier Trucks

In those cities where the containers are transported with their contents to the disposal points, special equipment must be provided. Usually this is done where the city provides a can exchange service, which also includes washing the garbage cans. This is a very desirable procedure from the sanitation or public health standpoint, but has generally proved to be an expensive method of refuse disposal service. Today, only a few cities provide this service. Fredericksburg, Virginia is an example. Two different types of vehicles are found where the can exchange method is used, rack-trucks and stake-body trucks. Both are relatively inexpensive because no hoisting equipment, end gates, or special mechanisms are needed, and they are usually locally fabricated by the city forces and shops. (The rack truck is simply an arrangement of shelves on which the garbage cans are placed during the collection and hauling operation.)

SUMMARY

The conditions and policies existing in any community will dictate which particular type and make of collection body is best suited for its service. Each community must make its own evaluation and selection.

In evaluating the different types available, diligent study should be given to the characteristics of each type, particularly those directly affecting the performance of the collection employees. These include:

1. Height of loading edge from the ground

2. Effective width of loading hopper (can only one, or more employees load simultaneously?)

3. The over-all loading space, including vertical clearance (does the upper edge of the hopper interfere with the ready unloading of containers?)

FIG. 6-20. Filled garbage cans are hauled on rack trucks to the incinerator at Fredericksburg, Virginia. Bags of rubbish collected at the same time are hauled in the rear compartment and on top of the body.

4. Time of loading and packing cycle, or how soon loading can again begin

5. Degree of compaction

6. Any inherent safety hazards, and location and ease of actuating controls

7. Ruggedness and ease of maintenance

8. Appearance

9. Cost (first cost as compared with long-range costs)

10. Adaptability of equipment for other work

11. Desirable turning radii (cab forward or cab over engine versus usual design)

12. Relative merit of compactor versus enclosed noncompactor or open-top vehicles

FIG. 6-21. Various route conditions can be most suitably met with trains. For instance: if the work loads become unusually heavy or more routes must be added, they may only require the addition of trains. Trains work equally well on all types of pick-up services, whether it be alley, curbside, carry-out, or estate collection. Trains shown in upper photo are currently being used in Norway, Michigan, while train in lower photo is used in Chicago.

chapter 7
PLANNING REFUSE COLLECTION SYSTEMS

Planning refuse collection systems consists of finding the most suitable combination of methods and equipment to meet local conditions. The preceding chapters have dealt with three factors: (1) local conditions influencing collection operation, (2) the refuse collection methods available for use, and (3) kinds of refuse collection equipment used in American cities. It is of course unwise to consider either methods or equipment without relation to local conditions, and equipment and methods are so interdependent that they must be planned together. Thus, it is apparent that all three factors must be correlated to arrive at an effective plan.

PROPER APPROACH TO PLANNING

The planning of refuse collection is essentially the process of evaluating the various ways of using men and machines to find the most efficient arrangement. As a preliminary requirement accurate data must be secured on numerous processes and certain norms of performance and cost must be developed. The determination of the best combination of methods and equipment involves a thorough understanding of local conditions, a wide knowledge of refuse collection activities, and the application of engineering economics. There are no real substitutes for such analytical planning, and short cuts may result in sacrifices costing many times the possible saving in planning expense. Determinations on the basis of estimates, guesses, or opinions are not satisfactory.

The following are factors which must be explored thoroughly to permit adequate planning:

1. The community refuse problem
   a. Types and quantities of refuse produced
   b. Responsibility for disposal
   c. Extent to which municipal, contract and/or private methods are used
   d. Collection frequency
2. Disposal methods
   a. Extent of separation required
   b. Location of disposal points
   c. Pollution control regulations

3. Material to be handled
   a. Weight of materials
   b. Compressibility
   c. Method of preparation and storage at origin of production
   d. Quantity
      1. Salvage potential
      2. On-site disposal
      3. Effect of method of financing
      4. Exclusions and service limitations
4. Type of equipment available or selected
   a. Capacity of units—compacting or uncompacting
   b. Single operator—or crew operation
5. Population density
   a. Number of service stops
   b. Quantity of refuse per service stop
   c. Multiple unit dwellings
6. Location of refuse for collection
   a. Curb
   b. Alley
   c. Backyard
7. Organization of crews
8. Work output in man-hours per ton collected
9. Physical layout of area
   a. Street pattern
   b. Topographic features
   c. Traffic patterns
      1. One-way streets
      2. Rush-hour problems
      3. Arterials
10. Climate
    a. Rainfall
    b. Severity of winter temperatures
    c. Snowfall
    d. Summer temperatures and fly-breeding
11. Type of zoning
    a. Residential—single family and multiple dwellings
    b. Business
    c. Industry

With data on the above factors at hand, actual layouts and route work can be started, or a computerized systems-analysis program begun.

Fixed Elements and Factors Open to Determination

The factors listed above may be segregated into two groups—those which are fixed by rigid policy or existing conditions and those wherein the administrators can exercise discretion. Fixed policy or existing conditions may include the following factors:

1. Type of refuse produced
2. Population density
3. Physical layout of area
4. Zoning
5. Climate

Factors open to determination are:
1. Responsibility for disposal
2. Disposal methods
3. Extent to which municipal, contract, and/or private methods are to be used
4. Materials to be handled
5. Type of equipment available or selected
6. Location of refuse for collection
7. Organization of crews

Statement of Policies

All policies fixed by the council, committees, or executives should be clearly stated in writing by the planning group, and they should be thoroughly understood by the administrator and his staff. This will define planning boundaries. It is rather difficult at times to get agreement on fixed policies, particularly those which have been informally adopted through custom. However, their precise definition serves to clear the air and enable the planner to see exactly what he has to start with and what determinations he must make.

Where it can be demonstrated that a change in policies is desirable, every effort should be made to correct the situation either immediately or as soon as it is feasible. Sometimes lack of funds or traditional habits have operated to establish the kind and extent of the service rendered. Sometimes poor service is due to faulty planning, unenlightened views of citizens, or conditions that no longer exist. Public education and the development of detailed supporting evidence will help to bring about the needed amendments. Such changes often require considerable time, however, and the analysis of the work to be done should not be deferred unless it is evident that the extent and kind of service may be radically changed in the near future.

Often the settled factors concern wage rates, hours of work, personnel specifications, overtime policies, and whether the compensation period of the employees begins at a garage or at the routes. In such cases, the planning agency need not inquire into the advisability of using a higher or lower grade of employee and need not investigate the desirability or economy of working shorter or longer shifts. Again, public sentiment or officials will dictate the selection of vehicles from an appearance viewpoint even to the extent of requiring completely enclosed bodies. Obviously, in these instances, the range of possible equipment is very limited.

The location of refuse containers for collection may also be predetermined. If it has been decided that householders must place the refuse on the curb, in the alley, on property lines, or at back doors, a large part of the field of inquiry is removed because the usable methods are drastically limited. For example, if the collection must be made from back doors, there are but two methods to compare: set-out and set-back by separate crews, or carrying the material directly to a waiting vehicle. Of course, there may be some variations in these practices which need investigation. Usually, the matter of refuse container location is continued on a "historical" basis, without considering the need for a change.

Whether or not the regulations governing the preparation of refuse for collection are enforced may make a substantial difference in the study of comparative methods. Freedom to designate the preparation procedures will permit the selection of a more effective collection method. Where satisfactory cooperation of householders cannot be secured, however, some of the most efficient methods may have to be omitted from consideration.

Limitations Due to Other Local Conditions

After all of the existing policies affecting the planning of a refuse collection system are clearly stated, it is necessary to appraise the other factors which are more or less fixed by local conditions.

FIG. 7-1. Small refuse collection vehicles usually prove economical where haul to disposal sites is short and where speed of collection is relatively slow. The unit pictured above has a 6-cubic yard capacity and is called the "alleycat." It is used in Philadelphia in areas having narrow alleys.

The kind of labor available for refuse collection work and the effect of labor unions may have an important bearing on methods. Also, the amount of money that can be spent may preclude the consideration of certain arrangements. The existence of alleys will vitally affect the planning work and in some cases will narrow the field of methods or equipment. For example, where there are numerous narrow alleys, vehicle size may be virtually established. Climate, topography, con-

dition of streets and alleys, and other factors may rule out some practices, procedures, or equipment that would otherwise be available.

This narrowing of the field of inquiry is the beginning of planning.
It is essential that the whole situation be reviewed in a systematic manner to eliminate needless study.

EFFECT OF DISPOSAL METHODS ON PLANNING

It has already been pointed out that it is necessary to determine the
methods of disposal before the collection system can be laid out. The
disposal plan depends, not on the collection system, but on the availability of suitable sites, the market for salvageable materials, the degree
of sanitation desired, and similar matters. The collection system must
be fitted to the requirements of the particular disposal processes. In this
discussion of planning collection systems, it will be assumed that the disposal processes have already been determined, and the influence of
these processes in the layout of the work will be examined.

Separations Determined by Disposal Processes

Local conditions may require the use of a particular disposal
method or large investments in existing plants may preclude a change.

FIG. 7-2. Large capacity vehicles such as this 20-cubic yard compactor are usually justified
where hauling distance to the disposal area is great and local conditions such as type of
terrain and size of streets and alleys permit their use.

Thus, one of the most important factors in the whole problem of refuse
collection may be beyond the control of the designer of a collection
system. The disposal method—however selected—virtually dictates the
kind and number of refuse separations. Garbage should be separated
from other refuse when it is disposed of by the hog feeding, reduction,

grinding processes. Combustible materials should be separated from
rtain noncombustible refuse for disposal by incineration. Putrescible
aterials should be segregated from refuse that is to be put in open
imps. No separations are necessary when the sanitary fill method is
ed. Separation requirements, in turn, fix many of the practices which
ouseholders must use in preparing refuse, influence the selection of
ollection methods, and affect the problem of determining the most
itable equipment.

Each class of refuse collected separately will require a method and
quipment different from those which would be used if another kind of
paration, or no separation, were employed. The kind of separation
ill also determine whether or not a topman should be used on open-
ody trucks. Ordinarily such employees are not required for separate
ollections of garbage or ashes. When rubbish is included in the col-
ction, however, it is often found that topmen are desirable.

The selection of disposal methods involves the determination of the
es for the necessary plants or dumps and the measurement of the
erage length of haul for each area or district as well as maximum
d minimum hauling distances. With the length of hauls known, a
und basis is provided for a study of the proper balance between load-
g and hauling time for each of the different methods considered. This
lance is an important factor in determining methods as well as for
termining what capacity of equipment is needed.

quipment Factors Determined by Disposal Processes

The methods of disposal may govern several very important aspects
the design or selection of collection equipment. Watertight bodies,
r example, may be required for certain separations of refuse. If gar-
ge is collected separately, and particularly if it is unwrapped, the
d gates and body seams must be watertight. Other classes of refuse do
t ordinarily contain free water and the collection bodies used for them
e usually not watertight.

The unloading conditions at the disposal sites may limit the selection
the type of end gates or the means of unloading the vehicles. Also,
e location of the disposal areas or plants may rule out the possibility
divided bodies for the collection of two different classes of refuse
the same time.

The decision as to the use of transfer stations and supplemental
ansfer equipment will be guided considerably by the length of haul.
here the hauls are very long, it may be necessary to use supplemental
quipment without further investigation, but ordinarily the type of
quipment found to be most suitable on the routes will also be a factor
such decisions.

SELECTION OF METHODS AND EQUIPMENT

After it is known just which refuse collection factors are fixed, it is
ssible to study the variable elements. The first task is to select the
llection method and collection vehicle, consistent with fixed policies

and existing conditions, which will do the collection and hauling wc
most efficiently. If it were possible, it would be much simpler to stu
separately the method of getting the refuse from the receptacles in
the vehicles, the method of organizing the crews, and the selection
equipment. They are interrelated to a great extent, however, and it
not feasible to treat them as separate inquiries. What is wanted is t
most efficient plan as a whole, and it may develop that the cheap.
equipment and the cheapest arrangement of crews will not combi
to give the most economical service.

The general method of approach to the problem is to examine s
tematically the several possible combinations of equipment type, equ
ment size, loading method, and arrangement of crews, and to determ:
for each combination the cost of collecting a unit quantity of refuse.
is obvious that there will be a great many possible combinations
study unless some of them are eliminated. The limitations imposed
public desires, by disposal methods, and by local conditions, all
which have been discussed, considerably reduce the number of separ.
analyses. An illustration may serve to make this clear.

Suppose it is found after a preliminary investigation of a munici
refuse system that the following factors are fixed:

1. *Wage rates.* Eight-hour day. High overtime rates make it inad
able to work over eight hours except in unusual circumstances.

2. *Place of reporting.* Shifts begin and end at the garage rat
than at routes.

3. *Point of collection.* Refuse is collected from back doors.

4. *Separations.* Sanitary fill disposal method, permitting all refuse
be collected together without separation.

5. *Hauling distance.* Disposal site is fixed and haul can be me
ured to any district. Average haul three miles.

6. *Loading point.* There are no alleys. Collectors must load
vehicles in streets.

7. *Frequency of collection.* Two collections a week all year.

8. *Containers.* Standard cans provided by householders. One n
can lift any receptacle.

9. *Vehicles.* Equipment must be attractive, but not necessarily
closed.

10. *Topography.* Relatively level. (It has been found that there
about a 15 per cent greater labor requirement in hilly refuse collect
than in collection on relatively level areas.)

Although it may seem that the design of a collection system is grea
restricted by these requirements, actually much study and analysis
necessary to complete the plan. The main points to be decided are:

Means of getting refuse to vehicles. The refuse can be brought out
set-out and set-back crews and loaded from curbs, or it can be tubl
out by collectors directly to waiting vehicles. Studies may include the p
sibilities of loaders setting cans out and back while trucks are en ro
to the disposal points, of loaders helping set-out and set-back crews,

loaders doing the set-back work only.

Method of organizing crews. Severe labor restrictions limiting the daily work period make several methods questionable. Unless the quantity of refuse produced is rather uniform throughout the year and from collection to collection, the daily route method, the single load method, and even the large route method and the relay method may be so unsuitable as to preclude their serious analysis. The various methods available for use are described in Chapter 5. Ordinarily no method should be automatically cast out unless it is clearly evident that it is inefficient.

Most suitable equipment. Many types of equipment are available for use. The size of chassis and body must be determined, as must the loading and unloading devices, enclosed or nonenclosed, compactor or non-

G. 7-3. The rate of collecting refuse is one of the important factors in determining the most economical plan. Where collectors carry rubbish and ashes from basements or from storage vaults on private premises to the waiting vehicles, the necessarily slow loading makes it desirable to keep the equipment expense per hour as low as possible.

compactor, and total cost. Before such matters can be determined, it is necessary to have basic information on the speed and cost of doing a unit of work for each kind of operation so that the different kinds of methods and equipment can be combined in various patterns and the cost of each combination arrived at for comparison with other possible arrangements.

Basic Data Required

Records of the operation of the refuse collection activities in any municipality may provide valuable data for the development of a new collection system or the study and adjustment of the existing plan. It is not likely, however, that such records will supply all the evidence needed. Where administrative records are meager, practically all the required information will have to be secured through special analyses, time studies, and spot surveys.

Among the more important data required are:

Weight of a cubic yard of the kind of refuse that must be handled. For

this purpose, average unit weight will ordinarily serve, but it is alwa
well to know something about the maximum and minimum unit weigh
and the districts or seasons in which they occur. It is usually satisfa
tory to measure the weight and volume of the refuse of a typical loa
from each route once a month. When a year's experience is not availab
it may be satisfactory to accept the measurements that can be obtaine
currently and estimate the variation from them.

Speed of travel to disposal points. This involves the total time requir
to haul a load from a district to a disposal site, dump the load, and r
turn to the route. Sometimes different sizes or kinds of equipment w
have to travel at different speeds. Ordinarily, however, traffic conditio
are the predominant influence. Usually it is necessary to make tin
studies of hauls from the different districts or routes and of dumpir
operations at the disposal points.

*Equipment rental rates for each kind and size of vehicle consider(
during the study.* The rates (unit cost of equipment operation) depe
in part on original cost and depreciation charges which must necessari
be determined from more detailed information on the design of the equi
ment. Many of the decisions as to the kind of unloading devices, e
gates, side doors, covers, mechanical loading, appearance, relati(
between chassis and body capacity, materials of construction, and tl
like should ordinarily be made after the disposal method is selected, b
before the collection plan is set up. Controlling fixed elements should
kept in mind at all times, of course. The cost of each kind and size
vehicle proposed for use or studied in connection with a collection a
rangement must be known or estimated rather accurately. Estimat
must also be made regarding the approximate amount each class
vehicle will be used and their economically useful life. Such data w
make it possible to calculate the rental rates per hour which must
charged against refuse collection operations to insure the coverage
all the costs involved in owning, maintaining, and operating the vehicl(

Speed of loading refuse. The time required to load a cubic yard or
ton of refuse from householders' receptacles into the collection vehicl
must be determined for each method studied. When set-out and set-ba(
service is included for study, it is ordinarily possible to treat this oper
tion apart from the loading data and find the time per cubic yard or p
ton needed for this work. Time studies on several variations of ea(
method may have to be made to provide sufficient information. Loadir
speed in areas of different densities of population may be neede
relative speed with different sizes of collection crews will be desirabl
as will the relative output of continuous loading of the relay plan (o
truck loading while the other is en route to disposal site) as compar(
with intermittent loading and resting. The speed of loading can, in ea(
case, be translated into unit cost of loading. Also the time required
fill a vehicle of known capacity can be easily computed.

Quantity of refuse produced. Detailed data on the production
refuse are needed primarily for the determination of routes. This is

later step in the planning of a refuse collection system, but because some of the information is helpful in making certain decisions on methods, it is included here. The total quantity, expressed in cubic yards or tons, that must be collected each day of the week during different seasons must be known with reasonable accuracy. In most cases it is helpful to know the rate of production in different districts, and not infrequently a block-by-block checkup is made to provide a basis for estimating cumulative quantities on the different routes. Sometimes simply the stops or families are counted; at other times the persons living in each building, or the standard containers provided, are enumerated as a basis for estimating.

Classification of complaints. It is helpful in some studies to make an analysis of citizen complaints by classifying them as to district, cause of complaint, or otherwise. Complaints originating with the collection forces should not be ignored in such a study because they will disclose some important clues to improvement.

It is usually not difficult to make time studies and spot checks of methods actually established in a community. Valid data on other methods and practices, however, may not be so easy to secure. To have much significance the tests of such methods and practices should be made in the municipality for which the study is being made so that differences in local conditions among cities will not cloud the results. This means that one or more crews will have to make collections in several different ways so that the required information can be gained. A word of warning may be needed here: If such trials are to be valuable, they must duplicate as nearly as possible the operations as they would take place with crews experienced in the specific routines and familiar with the location of containers and the sequence of collection. It is not satisfactory to test a green crew on an entirely new work routine. Also the tests must be continued long enough so that the ultimate efficiency of an average crew is approached.

The basic information outlined here is essential to any rational study of the refuse collection problem. The elements of the problem must be reduced to the simplest terms and the original data secured on that basis. Some examples of studies made by municipal refuse collection agencies may be helpful in illustrating the kind of data obtained and the manner in which they are recorded. These examples are given later in this chapter.

Time of Collecting Refuse

For most residential properties it does not matter what time of day daytime collections are made; in general, the convenience of the collection agency will determine the hour. Night collections in residential areas are not usually satisfactory because of the inevitable noise, but there is usually no objection to night collections in commercial areas. In cities that have traffic congestion in the business centers during the day, not only do collection operations add to inconvenience and danger; the collection work itself is seriously hampered. The opportunity to use the refuse equipment during two shifts is also cited as an advantage of night collection by some officials.

In some places it may be possible to make changes in the time of collection to realize improvements in effectiveness or economy without inconveniencing householders or property owners. The time of starting and stopping residential collections in 80 cities and commercial collections in 59 cities providing municipal or municipal contract service is shown in Table 7-1.

TABLE 7-1
Hours of Refuse Collection in Residential and Commercial Areas

Time of Day	Residential		Commercial	
	Number of Cities	Per Cent	Number of Cities	Per Cent
Start:				
5:00 A.M. or prior......................	7	8.8	16	27.1
5:01-6:00 A.M...........................	12	15.0	12	20.3
6:01-7:00 A.M...........................	45	56.2	18	30.5
7:01-8:00 A.M...........................	16	20.0	7	11.9
Other..................................	..	..	6	10.2
Total..............................	80	100.0	59	100.0
Stop:				
2:00 P.M. or prior......................	12	15.0	21	35.6
2:01-3:00 P.M...........................	14	17.5	4	6.8
3:01-4:00 P.M...........................	34	42.5	15	25.4
4:01-5:00 P.M...........................	12	15.0	7	11.9
Other..................................	8[1]	10.0	12[2]	20.3
Total..............................	80	100.0	59	100.0

[1]Seven cities reported "when complete"; one after 6:00 P.M.
[2]Four cities reported "when complete"; one after 6:00 P.M.

Analysis of Possible Variations

The actual process of selecting the collection plan is largely a mathematical analysis of the various combinations of methods and equipment feasible in a particular community. The first step, then, is to list the variables to be examined. These can be classified under three heads: (1) methods of getting refuse into vehicles, (2) kinds and sizes of equipment, and (3) methods of organizing crews.

An example of such a list of variables is as follows. (The items are not selected to represent the variables for any known city or even for typical community.)

A. Methods of getting refuse into vehicles
1. Set-out and set-back, with curb loading
a. Separate set-out and set-back crew
b. Separate set-out crew, collectors returning container while vehicle is hauling
c. Small set-out and set-back crew, collectors assisting while vehicle is hauling
2. Tubbing refuse directly to collection vehicles
B. Equipment possibilities
1. Compactor type trucks
2. Enclosed noncompactor trucks

3. Open trucks
C. Methods of organizing crews
    1. Relay method
    2. Reservoir route method
        a. Using five crews and six routes
        b. Using six crews and six routes

These are the only possible variations that exist in this hypothetical tuation if the size of the collection crew used is the most efficient for ıe particular size of truck investigated.

The first cost investigation would be made using the first entry in each ɾoup: separate set-out and set-back crew, curb loading, compactor ɾucks, and the relay plan of crew organization. The basic data previusly secured will provide the time required for loading under this ıethod, for hauling with this equipment, for finding equipment and ıbor cost and the number of loads. The result of the computation will e expressed in the unit cost of collecting and hauling a ton of refuse ɾor cubic yard if weight data is not attainable.)

The next combination must then be computed, using the first item of ıe first group, the first of the second group, and the second of the third ɾoup, to obtain the unit cost under this plan. It is apparent that in the bove example there would have to be 36 such analyses if all possible ombinations were to be investigated. However, the methods of loadıg designated as (b) and (c) under A-1 cannot be used under the relay ιlan because the crew will not be free to help with the set-out operations.

The object of this inquiry is to determine the particular combination ιf methods and equipment which will permit the work to be done at the east unit cost under the prevailing conditions. Hence, computations ınust be made for all the pertinent combinations. The results can usually ιe summarized in a single table. Sometimes it is desirable to carry hrough a series of computations at the same time, such as the costs for ·arious kinds or sizes of equipment in connection with one method. ۸n example of this type of analysis is presented in Tables 7-2 and 7-3.

TABLE 7-2
A Random Example of the Analysis of Unit Costs,[1]
Jsing Various Types of Equipment in Connection With a Constant Method
(Collection From Curb by Daily Route Method)

Type of Truck	Body Capacity (cu. yds.)	Loading Time (minutes)	Hauling Time (minutes)	First Load (A.M.)	Second Load (A.M.)	Third Load (A.M. or P.M.)	Fourth Load (P.M.)	Fifth Load (P.M.)	Total Tons Hauled
ompactor.......	12	90	30	7:30 9:00	9:30 11:00	12:00 1:30	2:00 3:30		16.0
nclosed ιoncompactor....	12	70	30	7:30 8:40	9:10 10:20	10:30 12:00	1:00 2:10	2:40 3:30	12.0
ιpen............	12	75	30	7:30 8:45	9:15 10:30	11:00 12:15	1:15 2:30	3:00[2] 3:30	9.5

[1]Separate set-out crew brings cans to curb for $1.10 per ton of refuse. This amount ınust be added to collection unit cost to arrive at total.
[2]Last load is not complete.

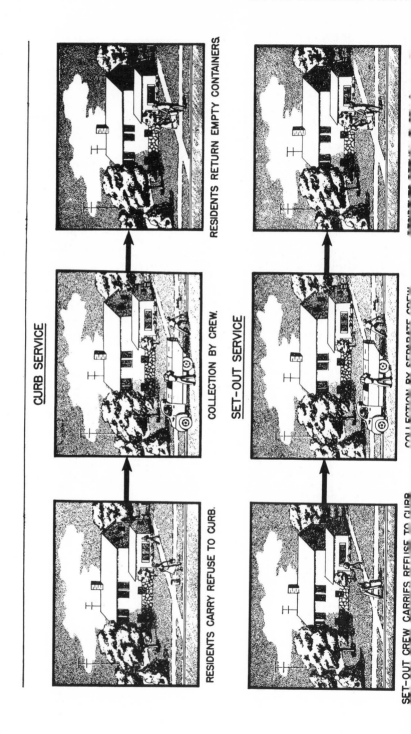

CURB SERVICE

RESIDENTS CARRY REFUSE TO CURB.   COLLECTION BY CREW.   RESIDENTS RETURN EMPTY CONTAINERS

SET-OUT SERVICE

SET-OUT CREW CARRIES REFUSE TO CURB   COLLECTION BY SEPARATE CREW

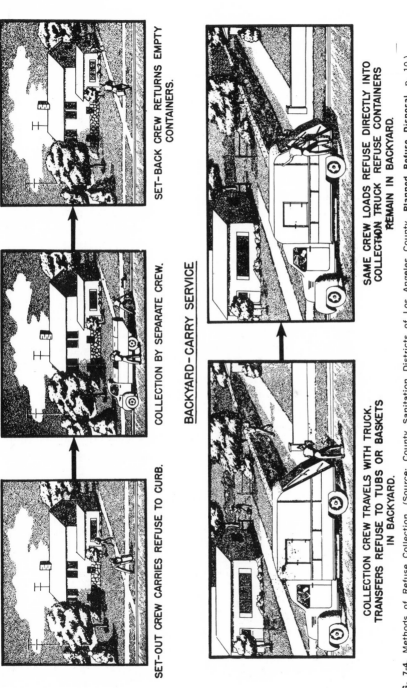

SET-OUT CREW CARRIES REFUSE TO CURB.

COLLECTION BY SEPARATE CREW.

SET-BACK CREW RETURNS EMPTY CONTAINERS.

BACKYARD-CARRY SERVICE

COLLECTION CREW TRAVELS WITH TRUCK. TRANSFERS REFUSE TO TUBS OR BASKETS IN BACKYARD.

SAME CREW LOADS REFUSE DIRECTLY INTO COLLECTION TRUCK REFUSE CONTAINERS REMAIN IN BACKYARD.

FIG. 7-4. Methods of Refuse Collection. (Source: County Sanitation Districts of Los Angeles County, Planned Refuse Disposal, p. 10.)

TABLE 7-3
Summary of Unit Costs
(Based on Data in Table 7-2)

Type of Truck	Number of Loads	Hours on Route[1]		Equipment Rate	Equipment Cost	Labor Cost	Total Cost	Cost per Ton	Tons
Compactor	4	7:30 11:30	12:00 3:30	$2.00	$16.00	$46.50	$62.50	$3.90	16.0
Enclosed Noncompactor	4+	7:30 12:00	1:00 3:30	1.50	12.50	46.50	58.50	4.80	12.0
Open	4+	7:30 12:45	1:15 3:30	1.32	10.56	46.50	57.06	6.00	9.5

[1]Crews' time begins at garage and ends at the routes. Crews consist of two loaders and one driver.

Here the only method considered is collection from the curb by a crew of two loaders and a driver who does no loading. The daily route plan is employed, and the crew rests while the vehicle makes the four-mile haul to the disposal site. The known data, as determined by time studies, special analyses, or policy stipulations, are first recorded. From the unit weight of the refuse (in this case, 400 pounds per cubic yard as presented by the householder), the volumetric capacity of the bodies can be related to the carrying capacity of the chassis. The loading speed with the above-mentioned crew has been timed for each type of equipment, so with a previously determined allowance for loss of time in starting and stopping, the loading time for each size body can be figured. The distance to the disposal site is known and the traveling speed and dumping time have been measured, so the total hauling period can be computed and recorded. The day's work is laid out on the basis that the crews begin work at the route at 7:30 A.M. After the number of loads is determined for each size vehicle, a second tabulation can be made showing the weight of refuse collected for each size truck, the predetermined equipment rental rate, the labor cost from known wage rates, and finally the total cost and the cost per ton.

The compactor truck is plainly the most economical under the conditions set out. It is emphasized, however, that some other methods of organizing the crews would undoubtedly show more economical costs. Also, different labor and equipment rates would change the results. Under other local conditions, a different size of crew might prove more effective. The set-out and set-back cost was previously measured at $1.10 per ton of refuse and this amount must be added if a comparison is made with other methods which call for bringing the refuse from householders' premises. A second summary can be added showing the difference that would result if the time that the crews start on the route is used instead of the time they leave the garage.

The value of comparative analyses of unit costs of collection may be made clearer if a second series of computations is made with the same basic data except that the method of getting the refuse into vehicles is changed. For instance, instead of using a separate set-out and set-back

crew followed by curb loading, suppose the refuse is to be carried from
back doors by the collectors to waiting vehicles. This analysis is shown
in Tables 7-4 and 7-5. The least cost under this plan also is shown to
result with the compactor truck at $7.20 per ton if time begins at the
garage. Note, however, that the comparative cost for set-out and set-back
with curb loading is $5.00 per ton after the set-out and set-back cost has
been added. It is apparent from this second analysis that the labor expense is very high in relation to equipment cost. This would lead to the
inference that results would be different if a method making more effective use of labor were employed. The relay method, for example, should
be analyzed in detail to see if the unit costs are less than those of the
daily route method given in the above analysis. Still other combinations
to be studied may disclose methods even more efficient.

Every reasonable combination of equipment and methods should be
explored; often the most efficient arrangement will occur with unexpected
groupings. Also, it should be kept in mind that some of the most astute
and experienced operators are quite unable to select efficient methods
by mere observation or judgment. *It should be repeated that there is no
acceptable substitute for careful factual analysis.* It may seem difficult
and time-consuming, but in the long run the savings will repay many
times the cost of the work and effort involved. Moreover, it is only
through such analyses that officials, taxpayers' committees, and citizens
can be convinced that the most effective and economical plan is being
used. The details and summaries of the studies constitute positive and
extremely valuable evidence.

TABLE 7-4
A Random Example of the Analysis of Unit Costs,
Using Various Sizes of Equipment with a Constant Method
(Collection from Back Doors by Daily Route Method)

					Time		
Type of Truck	Body Capacity (cu. yds.)	Loading Time (minutes)	Hauling Time (minutes)	First Load (A.M.)	Second Load (A.M. or P.M.)	Third Load (P.M.)	Total Tons Hauled
Compactor	12	180	30	7:30 10:30	11:30 2:30	3:00 3:30	8.70
Enclosed Noncompactor	12	130	30	7:30 9:40	10:10 12:20	1:20 3:30	7.50
Open	12	120	30	7:30 9:30	10:00 12:00	1:00 3:00	6.75

TABLE 7-5
Summary of Unit Costs
(Based on Data in Table 7-4)

Type of Truck	Number Loads	Hours on Route	Equip- ment Rate	Equip- ment Cost	Labor Cost	Total Cost	Tons	Cost per ton
Compactor	2+	8	$2.00	$16.00	$46.50	$62.50	8.7	$7.20
Enclosed Noncompactor	3	8	1.50	12.00	46.50	58.50	7.5	7.80
Open	3	8	1.32	10.56	46.50	57.06	6.75	8.50

DETERMINATION OF ROUTES

The purpose of routing is to subdivide the community into units that will permit collection crews to effectively provide an efficient sanitary service to the community.

The size of the community will determine the necessity for and the size of the division or districts for administration and supervision.

The number of routes per district will be determined by the amount of supervision to be exercised on the work of the individual crew by the man in charge of the district.

The size of each route will be determined by the amount of waste per stop, distance between stops, speed of loading, speed of truck, traffic conditions during loading time, etc.

Basically, the route should consist of a proper amount of work for a crew for the daily working period. The crew should service all proper ties eligible for this service in their area. Routes should, whenever practical, be compact, with a logical progression through the area. Unnecessary travel should be avoided. Traffic conditions on the route should be thoroughly studied to prevent lost time in loading, to reduce hazards to employees, and to minimize tying up of regular traffic movements by collection forces. Topographical and physical barriers and arterial streets should be used as route boundaries wherever possible to avoid lost time in travel.

Routes within a district should be laid out so that the crews start at the point farthest from the disposal area and, as the day progresses, move toward that area, thus reducing the length of the haul. When possible the work of the crews in a district should be parallel as they progress throughout the day, with routes finishing up within a short distance of each other. This enables the supervisor to be present when crews are completing their work and enables him to shift crews to trouble spots to complete the day's work.

Experience has shown that the principle of having established routes regularly serviced on the same day of the week will do much to secure public co-operation. The work load will tend to level out within the seasonal variation pattern.

Essentially, the process of laying out routes is one of trial and error. Starting at the meeting places of crews or certain other logical points for the beginning of routes, the designer lays out the course of travel for a crew. By using the production and collection speed data, the time of loading and hauling for each load can be computed and the progress along streets and alleys can be determined. After a day's or a week's work has been laid out, the area served can be outlined or shaded in color and another route begun in the same way. During this period of preliminary layout, it is not advisable to mark the working map on which the essential data are recorded, because the inevitable adjustments and erasures may soon obliterate the notations. One very satisfactory device is to use sheets of tracing paper over the working maps, on which only the outlines of the blocks and the names of streets have been traced. The

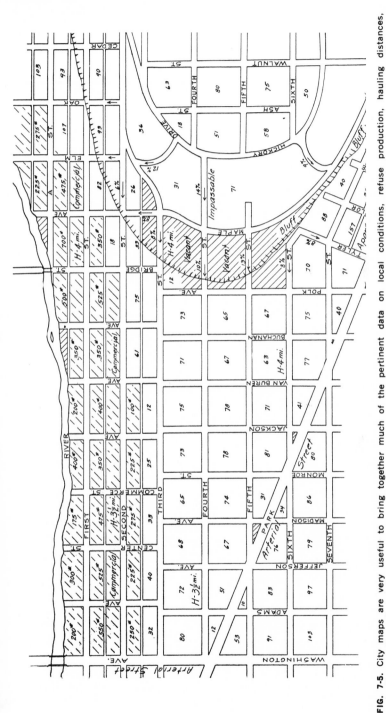

FIG. 7-5. City maps are very useful to bring together much of the pertinent data on local conditions, refuse production, hauling distances, and other matters that influence routing. This plat shows special areas, physical barriers, heavy traffic arteries, and average hauls. The production of mixed refuse is indicated by the average number of pounds per collection for each block in the commercial area and by the number of persons living in each block in residential districts. The original layout was made on a map drawn 400 feet to an inch.

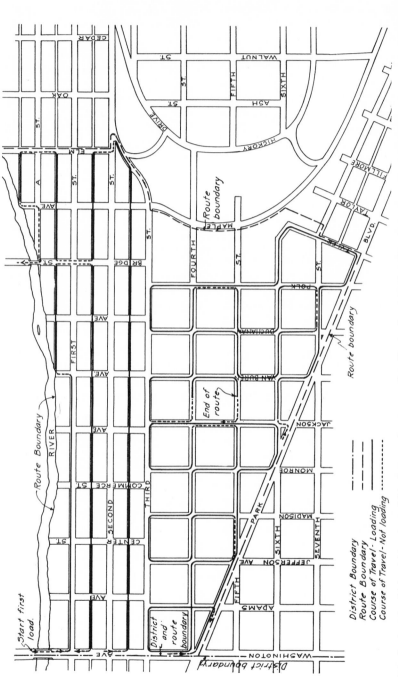

FIG. 7-6. Routes should be laid out on fairly large-scale maps, using the basic data that has been brought together on production, collecting speed, local conditions, and the points of beginning and ending of the collection work. Compare this layout with Fig. 7-5.

routes can be laid out and revised several times on such tracings without any impairment of the original data. If many alternative routes are studied, additional tracing paper sheets can be used.

Special routes should usually be laid out first. Those areas which must be collected at night, market districts, and commercial routes can be included in this class. In the remaining area, the layout should ordinarily start with the places where the time of collection has already been fixed. For example, some of the crews may start early in the morning in the business district and work out into the residential districts. The first load may be partly or entirely from commercial properties. The layout of routes should be continued until the city has been completely covered, using care to follow the special instructions recorded on the working map.

It cannot be expected that the first layout will include all properties of a district or finish the task without part of a route left over. It is more likely to be evident that a better start could be made, or that an entirely different plan should be adopted. A revised routing plan must be made in such cases and carried out in the same manner as the first trial. There should be no hesitation in making a second, third, or even fifth trial if necessary to secure a logical arrangement.

No definite principles can be laid down as to the best shape or formation of routes. In flat areas, the designers usually have a free rein, and can lay out routes along a single street or alley, or can shuttle back and forth on adjacent streets, or around one block after another. In hilly terrain, however, much more attention must be given to avoiding steep hills and natural barriers than to obtaining a regular pattern of routes. Route layout is easiest for long blocks where all the houses face east or west, or north and south. The refuse from an entire block can be collected during one passage through an alley or street (where traffic conditions and other pertinent factors permit). The situation is much more difficult where houses face in all four directions. The collection vehicles must usually traverse all sides of a block, which normally involves considerably more unproductive haul. Figure 7-6 illustrates route layout in both kinds of block arrangement. Sometimes it is possible to avoid circling a block by collecting the refuse of some corner properties from the side rather than the front, or by carrying containers from side street locations to the corner. The value of the latter practice can best be determined by time studies.

If the last routes are not quite complete or if small areas remain outside of routes after an otherwise successful layout has been made, adjustments can usually be made rather easily by distributing the excess or deficiency over several nearby routes.

The layout must take into consideration the method that has been adopted for organizing the crews into working units. When the relay method is used, for example, it is especially desirable for the whole day's route to be continuous. If the reservoir plan has been selected, the routes must be arranged in accordance with the number of crews that make up a working group. The methods that provide for weekly assignment require long continuous routes which cover completely entire areas with as few irregularities of outline as practicable.

Routes are occasionally laid out on a load basis rather than on a daily or weekly plan. This provides considerable flexibility in scheduling. A crew can work efficiently in two or more locations during a da where it may be desirable.

PREPARATION OF SCHEDULES

The assigning and grouping of routes must be coordinated with th general internal organization plans for administering refuse collectio work. Sometimes the collection districts are formed for the purpos of decentralizing the work for each day. In other cases, the arrangemer is made to divide the work into suitable administrative districts. Th assignment of routes to crews ordinarily is influenced considerably b the districts that are established. Sometimes cities are divided into two three, or more districts when the activities are too extensive to be super vised properly by one official. In such cases, it is customary to place supervisor or other official in immediate charge of each district. Nor mally, the division is made so that there will be full-time work, withi each district, for a definite number of collection crews. For example, collections are made twice a week, the number of routes in a distric should be divisible by three; in other words, six crews would serv eighteen routes. It may be rather difficult in some cities to make the dis tricts equal, particularly where a single crew may be assigned to five c six routes.

In some cases, districts are formed in order to concentrate all the co lection activities for any particular day within one section of a city s that a supervisor may more easily keep in close touch with all crew. The only objection to this plan is that all districts must contain th same number of routes so that the size of the collection force will n have to vary from day to day. To accomplish this, there may have t be sacrifices in efficiency which would overshadow the gain in bett supervision. Nevertheless, the plan is good where it can be applied with out necessitating radical adjustments in the size and number of routes c in the practices and procedures which have been decided to be best.

Where components of refuse are collected separately some officia prefer to have the individual crews collect all classes of refuse withi particular areas in order to fix complete responsibility. The collectio practices and the routes for the different classes, however, are no likely to be the same, and often different equipment will be neede Moreover, additional routines would have to be learned by the colle tion crews. It would appear that the disadvantages of having to us alternately different methods and vehicles would outweigh the benefi of having but one crew operate in an area.

Where the demands of organizational arrangements do not interfer it is desirable to assign adjacent routes to individual crews for the wor on successive days. This makes for ease in controlling the operations and for fixing responsibility.

The general principle that the work of a crew for any day should be in a compact or at least in a continuous area is not followed in some cities because of the difficulty in securing efficient use of equipment in routes located far from disposal plants. In such cases, the work may be

FIG. 7-7. In Los Angeles, a dispatcher working with illuminated master route-map controls operations of individual garbage collection crews.

divided, usually on a load basis, so that all crews may have their first loads farthest from disposal points and each subsequent one closer. This kind of an arrangement will sometimes prove economical, especially if supervision and control are of high grade.

The schedules should be recorded on a master map showing for each route the collection days and the assigned crews. These schedules can be reduced to tabular or list form for central office use. Usually it is wise to prepare maps of each route or maps of the areas assigned to each crew. These maps should show the starting and stopping points of routes and the precise course which the collection crew should take. Sometimes the headquarters and district offices as well as the central complaint clerk are supplied with tabulated information on routes, showing by street name and block just when the different classes of refuse are supposed to be collected and which crews are scheduled to do the work. Thus, any question raised by citizens on the collection service can be answered immediately and the responsibility placed on the proper crews. Furthermore, it will be possible to locate any crew within a very short time. A typical schedule is presented in Table 7-6.

TABLE 7-6

Typical Schedule of a Refuse Collection Route

Day		Route #	District	
On	From	To		Time
Delta	Erie	Observatory	Turn Right	7 A.M.
Observatory	Delta	Paxton	Turn Right	(Start at garage)
Paxton	Observatory	Erie	Turn Right	
Erie	Paxton	Delta	Turn Around	
Erie	Delta	Grace	Turn Left	
Grace	Erie	Observatory	Turn Right	
Observatory	Grace	Monteith	Turn Right	
Monteith	Observatory	Erie	Turn Right	
Erie	Monteith	Paxton	Turn Around	8 A.M.
Erie	Paxton	Duncan	Turn Left	
Duncan	Erie	Observatory	Turn Right	
Observatory	Duncan	Shaw	Turn Right	
Shaw	Observatory	Linshaw	Turn Left	
Linshaw	Shaw	Dead End	Turn Around, Left on Shaw	
Shaw	Linshaw	Erie	Turn Right	
Erie	Shaw	Monteith	Turn Right	
Monteith	Erie	Ashmont	Turn Right	
Ashmont	Monteith	Astoria	Turn Right	
Astoria	Ashmont	Dead End	Turn Around, Right on Shady Lane	
Shady Lane	Erie	Observatory	Turn Left	
Observatory	Shady Lane	Monteith	Turn Right	
Monteith	Observatory	Linwood	Turn Right	9 A.M.
Linwood	Monteith	Arcadia	Turn Left	
Arcadia	Linwood	Linwood	Turn Left	
Linwood	Arcadia	Observatory	Turn Left	
Observatory	Linwood	Michigan	Turn Around	
Observatory	Michigan	Morton	Turn Right	
Morton	Observatory	Dead End	Turn Around, Right on Observatory	
Observatory	Morton	Linwood	Turn Right	
Linwood	Observatory	Sarita	Turn Right	
Sarita	Linwood	Dead End	Turn Around, Right on Linwood	
Linwood	Sarita	Cryer	Turn Left	
Cryer	Linwood	Observatory	Turn Right	
Observatory	Cryer	Duncan	Turn Right	
Duncan	Observatory	Linwood	Turn Left	
Linwood	Duncan	Princella	Turn Right	10 A.M.
Princella	Linwood	Dead End	Turn Around, Right on Linwood	
Linwood	Princella	Halpin	Turn Around	
Linwood	Halpin	Paxton	Turn Right	11 A.M.
Paxton	Linwood	Observatory	Turn Right	
Observatory	Paxton	Meier	Turn Right	
Meier	Observatory	Griest	Turn Left, Back Down on Paxton	
Griest	Paxton	Grace	Turn Right	
Grace	Griest	Utopia	Turn Right	

TABLE 7-6 (Continued)
Typical Schedule of a Refuse Collection Route

Day		Route #		District	
On	From	To			Time
Utopia	Grace	Dead End	Turn Around, Right on Grace		12 Noon
Grace	Utopia	Linwood	Turn Around		
Grace	Linwood	Observatory	Turn Right		
Observatory	Grace	Kilgour	Turn Right		
Kilgour	Observatory	Springer	Turn Right		
Springer	Kilgour	Grace	Turn Left		
Grace	Springer	Griest	Turn Left		1 P.M.
Griest	Grace	Inglenook	Turn Right		
Inglenook	Griest	Dead End	Turn Around, Right on Griest		
Griest	Inglenook	Halpin	Turn Around		
Griest	Halpin	Kilgour	Turn Right		
Kilgour	Griest	Springer	Turn Right		
Springer	Kilgour	Delta	Turn Right		
Delta	Springer	Griest	Turn Around		
Delta	Griest	Erie	Turn Right		
Erie	Delta	St. Johns	Turn Right		
St. Johns	Erie	Avery	Turn Left		2 P.M.
Avery	St. Johns	Dead End	Back Out		
St. John	Avery	Observatory	Turn Right		
Observatory	St. John	Delta	Turn Around		
Observatory	Delta	Obs. Drive	Turn Right		
Obs. Drive	Observatory	Dead End	Turn Around, Right on Observatory		
Observatory	Obs. Drive	Wellston	Turn Left		
Wellston	Observatory	Dead End	Turn Around, Left on Observatory		
Observatory	Wellston	Obs. Place	Turn Left		
Obs. Place	Observatory	Avery	Turn Left		
Avery	Obs. Place	Dead End	Turn Around		
Obs. Place	Avery	Observatory	Turn Left		
Observatory	Obs. Place	Herschel	End		
					3:30 P.M. (End at garage)

Frequently the seasonal variations in the amount of refuse will make considerable difference in the plans for collection work. Some methods permit seasonal expansion and contraction in the size of crews according to variations in refuse production, particularly where the variation is not great and rather large crews are used. In some cities, however, the variation from one season to another is so great that attempts to vary the size of the crew accordingly would result in inefficient operation most of the time. In such cases it is usually desirable to formulate two different plans of operation—one for the period of relatively high production and one for the period of lower production. Garbage, for example, typically is produced in large quantities in the summer months. Often summer schedules go into effect about the first of May and continue to November. (Fluctuations in refuse production are discussed in detail in Chapter 2). When the double plan is used, a complete routing and scheduling system is usually adopted for each plan and separate maps and tabulations are prepared.

STUDIES OF REFUSE COLLECTION SYSTEMS

The University of California at Berkeley carried on a comprehensive study of the refuse collection systems employed in 13 California cities in 1950-1951. Much basic design criteria was developed through analysis of the data collected. This information was published in 1952 as Technical Bulletin No. 8 of the Sanitary Engineering Research Project, University of California at Berkeley, and titled *An Analysis of Refuse Collection and Sanitary Landfill Disposal*. It represented the first comprehensive effort to develop basic refuse collection system design criteria, on a broad basis, in almost three decades. Portions of this study are reproduced in Appendix C of this volume. Study of this data and analytical approach is recommended to the engineer responsible for the development or re-design of a community refuse collection system.

TYPICAL REFUSE COLLECTION PLANS

The following collection plans show how different municipalities have met particular situations. These cities were selected because they solved their refuse collection problems by carefully analyzing local conditions and applying the most effective methods to meet them. Another reason for selecting these particular cities was that they illustrate the application of totally different collection methods and practices.

Cincinnati, Ohio

Cincinnati, Ohio, has a population of 502,550 and covers an area of 77.6 square miles. The terrain is rolling for the most part but many very steep high hills lie within the built-up sections. The character of the community is typical of cities in this population group. The commercial and industrial areas are quite extensive. The poorer residential districts have many multiple-family buildings, but the other areas are predominantly of the single house type and are quite large.

The refuse from the residential areas is collected entirely by the city but in the commercial areas the city collects only garbage and dead animals. Private collectors are responsible for the hauling and disposal of ashes and rubbish from commercial buildings. Garbage from hotels, restaurants, and similar places may be collected by licensed private collectors if the owners or operators prefer it to city service. The responsibility for the city's share of refuse collection lies in the department of public works. A division of waste collection of this department has immediate charge of this activity. The city is divided into ten districts for the purpose of administration and control.

Collection methods. Combustible and noncombustible refuse are collected separately, although within any one district the responsibility for the collection of both classes of refuse is under a single supervisor. Garbage and combustible rubbish are collected once a week; ashes and noncombustible rubbish are collected once a week. All garbage must be drained and wrapped, and bulky rubbish must be reduced to an acceptable size and properly bundled. On the whole, suitable containers are provided by the householders.

All kinds of refuse are collected in the residential areas except rubbish from construction operations. There is no limit on the quantity of refuse that will be picked up at each collection. The average length of haul to the incinerators for combustible refuse or to the dumps for noncombustible refuse is about three miles. The refuse in residential areas is brought to the curbs by separate forces of set-out men about an hour before the collection crews arrive to load the material. The empty cans are returned to the curb and taken in by the householders. Fundamentally, the plan adopted for the collection of refuse is the relay method. Under this plan, a typical crew may consist of two trucks, two drivers, and two or three loaders. While one truck is hauling refuse to the disposal site and returning to its route, the collection crew is loading the other truck. In some areas the balance between loading time and hauling time is not suitable for this arrangement and other relay arrangements are made. Sometimes three trucks are supplied for two collection

FIG. 7-8. Loading garbage in Philadelphia. The garbage is picked up on the premises and transported to the collection vehicle using lightweight 32-gallon plastic butt cans.

crews when the hauling distance is fairly short. An attempt to use five trucks with three crews did not prove satisfactory and was abandoned. Ordinarily, the set-out work can be handled by one set-out for each collection crew.

Supervision. The supervisors maintain close contact with all the crews and keep a rather continuous check on comparative progress on the various routes. Toward the close of each day the crews which have completed their assigned task considerably before the regular quitting time are given further assignments in routes in the same district where work has for some reason been delayed. These additional crews begin at the end of the route and work toward the crew regularly assigned to the area. This inter-route relief plan is not a regular feature of the planned operations but is utilized when unusual conditions create abnormal amounts of work on particular routes.

Records. A modern system of records and cost accounting has been in effect for several years and is proving of inestimable value by providing the administrative control necessary for the proper management of this system. The department and division officials use the summary operating reports regularly to check on the efficiency of the various parts of the service and on the various crews. Immediate steps are taken to correct any weaknesses disclosed. Adjustments in routes, equipment, and crews are made on the basis of the record system. Incidentally, this system provides practically all information necessary for studying route layout and for determining or readjusting schedules. Spot checks are made as additional information may be necessary.

Hartford, Connecticut

The City of Hartford, Connecticut has a resident population of 162,178 according to the 1960 census. This represents a decrease of approximately 15,000 persons over a ten-year period, caused primarily by the physical changes that have occurred and still are occurring to the city through redevelopment, the building of super highways, and the movement of various segments of the population to the suburbs. The 18-square mile city still has approximately 57,600 family housing units to collect from, however, and 215 miles of streets to traverse in its daily refuse collection.

Department of public works forces collect refuse daily, six days a week, in the downtown business area and once a week on a five day a week basis in the residential areas. Commercial and industrial establishments are limited to ten barrels per collection and any refuse over and above the ten barrels must be handled and hauled by the concerns themselves or by a commercial hauler.

Collections by city forces begin at 7:00 a.m. in the downtown business area and involve the entire collection fleet of 12 20-cu. yd. packers and 85 men. It takes this force approximately 1¼ to 1½ hours to serve the downtown business area. The buildings and businesses in the six day a week downtown collection must put refuse out for curb collection, as must businesses given twice-a-week service in selected areas of the city. When the downtown collection is completed, the force divides to serve three residential routes. Once-a-week residential collection involves roll-out service, in which the city rolls all material out to the curb and returns the barrels just back of the street line or sidewalk.

The collection service is divided into three types: (a) regular packer truck collections, (b) large container service collections, and (c) bulk item collections.

Quantity of Refuse and Costs. The quantity of refuse to be disposed of has gone from a total of 99,750.4 tons (496,000 cu. yds.) in 1955 to a maximum of 159,078.31 tons (795,391 cu. yds.) in 1962. It dropped back to 149,971.04 tons in 1964 (749,827 cu. yds.), but in 1965 was again showing an increase. The increase up to 1962 was caused mainly by the large amounts of building demolition involved in redevelopment and in highway construction. The upswing in 1965 was due to both redevelopment and flood control work.

Of the 154,283 tons collected in 1965, city forces collected 57,848 tons, or just about 37 per cent, leaving the remaining 63 per cent to be collected by contractors or brought directly to the disposal facilities by residents and commercial concerns hauling their own wastes.

The monthly averages per year over the last eight years for city-collected material are as follows: (Years are fiscal years April 1 through March 31 and the year in the tables is the year ending March 31).

TABLE 7-7
Average Monthly Refuse Collected, Hartford, Conn.

	City-collected Monthly Average (Tons)	City-collected Yearly Total (Tons)	Yearly Total Private and City-collected (Tons)
1957............	4,577	51,969	116,012
1958	4,620	55,444	126,182
1959............	4,619	55,433	127,786
1960............	4,652	55,819	128,555
1961............	4,617	55,400	153,677
1962............	4,653	57,398	159,078
1963............	4,582	54,978	151,312
1964............	4,777	57,319	149,971
1965............	4,821	57,848	154,283

City-collected refuse is further tabulated by type of collection, that is, packer collection, container collection, and bulk collection for the past eight years and is as follows:

TABLE 7-8
Type of Collection by City, Hartford, Conn.

	Regular Combustible Packer Collection (Tons)	Container Collection (Tons)	Bulk and Non-Combustible Collection (Tons)
1958............	49,564.00	3,307.20	2,572.50
1959............	49,062.83	3,891.07	2,479.14
1960............	49,370.55	4,610.82	1,837.98
1961............	50,041.94	4,625.57	732.53
1962............	50,484.76	5,030.40	1,882.75
1963............	49,217.05	5,148.15	612.98
1964............	50,912.19	5,664.15	743.00
1965............	50,934.99	6,052.90	859.84

The weights per cubic yard for the three types of collection over the past five years are as follows:

TABLE 7-9
Weight, by Type, of City Collected Refuse, Hartford, Conn.

	Packer Collection (lbs./cu. yd.)	Container Collection (lbs./cu. yd.)	Bulk and Non-Combustible Collection (lbs./cu. yd.)
1961	384	165	511
1962	396	159	508
1963	427	153	507
1964	444	144	503
1965	466	130	560

The department of public works has through continuing review of its collection practice been able to realize the following cost of collection over the past seven years: (Note: Costs include all personnel, equipment operating and overhead, non-personal supplies, and department overhead expenses).

TABLE 7-10
Cost of Collection Per Ton, Hartford, Conn.

	All City-collected Refuse	Packer-collected	Container-collected	Cu. Yd.	Non-Comb. and Bulk	Per Capita
1958	$10.33 per ton	$10.55 per ton	$6.81 per ton	$2.44	——[1]	$3.08
1959	$10.76 per ton	$11.57 per ton	$6.82 per ton	$2.35	——[1]	$3.19
1960	$10.94 per ton	$11.97 per ton	$6.37 per ton	$2.45	——[1]	$3.29
1961	$10.85 per ton	$11.63 per ton	$6.67 per ton	$2.27	——[1]	$3.71
1962	$11.60 per ton	$11.81 per ton	$8.11 per ton	$2.05	$15.90[2]	$4.11
1963	$11.44 per ton	$11.35 per ton	$8.61 per ton	$2.11	$50.75[2]	$3.88
1964	$10.89 per ton	$10.90 per ton	$8.10 per ton	$2.02	$37.16[2]	$3.85

[1]Included in packer costs.
[2]Basically bulk collection since 1962. Dollars per ton.

Personnel and Equipment. The regular collection division, using packer trucks, is divided into three districts or routes, each route being assigned to a district foreman (Sanitation Foreman II) who is assigned the following men and equipment to carry out his collection assignment:

1 Sanitation Foreman I	(assistant working foreman)
4 Sanitation Leadmen	(packer truck drivers)
1 Heavy Truck Driver	(spare driver)
10 Sanitation Laborers	(assigned to loading or shaking barrels)
11 Sanitation Laborers	(assigned to rolling out barrels to the curb)

The equipment assigned to each foreman per route consists of one radio-equipped pick-up truck and four 20-cubic yard rear-loading packer trucks.

The three district foremen report to a refuse collection supervisor who heads the regular collection division of 85 men. This division has one radio-equipped supervisor's car, three radio-equipped foremen's pick-up trucks, twelve 20-cubic yard packer trucks on regular assignment and four spare 20-cubic yard packer trucks. Eleven sanitation laborers in each route are equipped with a hand truck for rolling out barrels and the division keeps an inventory of 40 hand trucks, 33 on assignment and 7 spares.

The regular collection division is worked on the route basis. The men go home when the day's route is complete and receive 40 hours pay for a five-day week, even if they put in fewer hours, and receive overtime only when the five-day route actually works a total of more than 40 hours for the week.

Every Saturday, one foreman, two packer trucks, two leadmen and four sanitation laborers are paid four hours overtime to collect in the downtown business district for the sixth day curb collection. The crews are rotated so a crew works one Saturday every six weeks.

Each packer truck makes an average of three trips per day carrying between five and five and one-half tons per trip. The average distance travelled for all trucks from collection route to the incinerator is four miles. The average time taken per truck for this round trip is about 45 minutes.

In 1961 the public works department was successful in getting a regular packer replacement program put into its budget and with the regular replacement of four packer trucks per year was able to realize a savings in parts, labor, and maintenance of $28,000 on a fleet of 20 packers in the first two years of the replacement program. The packer fleet now has a complete turnover every five years as compared to 8 to 10 years before regular replacement was instituted. The packer fleet has not been used for snow plow work to date, which is another factor holding down repair and maintenance costs.

The large container collection force is assigned to a supervisor who also is responsible for bulk item collections.

The personnel and equipment assigned to this service consist of five single hoist trucks, five heavy truck drivers, and one spare hoist truck.

The supervisor is assigned a radio-equipped pick-up truck and is charged with the responsibility of approving the box location and justifying the need of the property owner requesting large container service.

The force now services some 200 boxes, ranging in size from 6 to 12 cubic yards. Ninety per cent of the boxes are owned by the persons using the service, while the remaining 10 per cent are used by the city for its schools and municipal buildings and as spares.

The increase in demand for the large container service—from 12 boxes in 1950 to 202 in 1965—has allowed the public works department to reduce its more expensive packer collection force with resulting savings to the city.

While property owners must purchase their containers, the boxes are serviced and maintained by the city. This includes painting, cleaning, and deodorizing. Container service is not considered suitable where less than 30 regular barrels would be required or where a commercial or industrial concern is involved. It is specifically tailored for large residential units, insitutions, and schools.

Each of the five hoist units services an average of between 8 and 10 containers per day over a five-day week, with some containers requiring more than one emptying per week.

Bulk item collection is carried on by the same division that handles the large container service and is assigned to the same supervisor. This service is equipped with two large radio-equipped, metal body rack-type dump trucks with power tailgates. Each truck is manned by a crew consisting of one heavy truck driver and two sanitation laborers, making a total of six employees assigned to the bulk item collection service.

Each truck averages 30 to 40 pick-ups a day to collect items left at the curb and called in by the property owner or resident, or radioed in by the packer route foreman. Items picked up range from pianos to tires, but for the most part consist of furniture and appliances such as stoves, refrigerators, washers, sofas, bed springs, and mattresses. In some respects, the bulk collection service may benefit the furniture and appliance outlets as much or more than the residents, since very few dealers now haul away trade-in or obsolete units as they formerly had to as part of the sales contract for the new item. The public works department is constantly reviewing this service as it is an expensive one in terms of cost per ton hauled, as shown in the preceding tabulation.

The department has experimented with various methods of collection over the past 12-13 years and continues to investigate new procedures and methods as they develop. To date, however, it has been found that since manpower is the most costly item in a collection system, a new method or item of equipment must eliminate an equal or greater amount of manpower costs or it will not greatly improve the collection system or reduce its costs.

Pasadena, California

The City of Pasadena, with a population of 123,700 (as of July, 1965), encompasses an area of 22.6 square miles and has 330 miles of streets. There are approximately 50,000 family dwelling units within the city limits with many of the older single family buildings gradually being replaced with multi-unit residential construction.

By ordinance, the city provides once-a-week backyard pickup (combined combustible and non-combustible, including wrapped garbage) from all residential dwellings containing five families or less. Apartment buildings of five units or more, the large estate properties of over 20,000 square feet in area, and commercial establishments have a choice between private or municipal collection service. At the present time, approximately two-thirds of the residential refuse is removed by the city with the balance by private collectors. Most of the commercial establishments are serviced by a private collection service.

All refuse must be stored in covered, tapered containers of 15 to 45 gallons maximum size. Total weight of the containers when loaded is limited to 75 pounds to minimize employee back injuries due to excessive loads. Brush, newspapers, etc., if not in containers, must be tied in easily handled bundles. Each family is permitted up to 200 gallons pick-up once a week for which service they pay a specified basic monthly fee.

Approved fabricated metal containers from one to four cubic yard capacity are also serviced. These containers can be rented from the city if desired.

It is noteworthy that except for rates and special services available, the standards of equipment and refuse storage as stipulated in the ref-use ordinance of the city apply as well to private refuse collectors who must be licensed by the city.

The number of family units served each day by a single refuse collec-tion truck and crew varies with the nature of the terrain and the amount of bulky refuse, such as brush trimmings. In the hilly areas, with long steep driveways, a crew collects from 240 to 330 single family residences each day, or 1,340 families each week. Other routes vary to over 600 families a day, averaging 2,100 to 2,650 families each week.

The 15 collection routes vary from 11 to 16 tons of refuse collected each working day (Five days a week), occasionally with overtime. (Operation is based on task production with overtime only beyond 40 hours in one week). This averages to about four tons of refuse collected by each sanitation crewman. The annual tonnage for the combined collection is in excess of 50,000 tons.

Organization. Responsibility for the collection of refuse in the City of Pasadena lies with the engineering-street department headed by the city engineer-superintendent of streets, who reports to the city man-ager. Within the department, a director of sanitary service devotes a portion of his time to directing activities of the sanitation division. A sanitation superintendent supervises the entire field operatons, assisted by four sanitation foremen and three sanitation inspectors. The actual refuse collection is accomplished by fifteen sanitation crews, each gener-ally consisting of one truck driver in charge of three crewmen. Presently there are 19 truck drivers and 70 crewmen employed in the sanitation division. One of the foremen has been assigned as a health and safety instructor and meets regularly with each crew.

Method of Collection and Operation. Refuse collection in Pasadena is accomplished with large 50-cubic yard packer trucks served primarily by small three-wheel motorized "scooters". The scooter operators load all refuse from backyard locations into the $1\frac{1}{3}$-cubic yard dump body of the scooter for transport to the front-end loading 50-cubic yard pack-ers. The scooter load is discharged into the packer by means of a hydraulic actuated dump.

Each sanitation collection crew consists of a truck driver, two motor-ized scooter operators, and generally a third crewman who collects refuse from locations inaccessible to the scooters, using a hand-wheeled metallic container of $\frac{1}{2}$-cubic yard capacity.

Although the large packer trucks are of 50-cubic yard capacity, they are frequently required to make two trips per day to the landfill in order

FIG. 7-9. Pasadena, California uses three wheel scooters with 1⅓-cubic yard dump bodies to collect refuse from backyard locations. Refuse is then transferred to front-end loading 50-cubic yard packer trucks.

to complete the individual route collection. Under the same circumstances, smaller 16- to 20-cubic yard packer trucks would be required to make three or four, and sometimes five, trips per day to the disposal site. Consequently, wherever possible, the smaller trucks are employed in a relay operation as "switch trucks" to reduce the delays in collection time while the assigned route truck is enroute to the disposal site.

Radio communication between the sanitation office and the foremen in the field permits transfer of equipment and personnel where required. This is of considerable benefit in the event of equipment breakdown or of an unusually large volume on a particular route. It also permits prompt response to "missed pickups" that are telephoned in to the office.

There are 15 regular sanitation collection routes which encompass the city, including collection of many scattered street and park trash containers which are regularly served on a route basis. Some additional service is given as required.

Equipment. All motorized equipment is rented on a mileage basis from the city transportation division. Vehicles are maintained during the night shift to minimize down time. Fifty-cubic yard front-end loading packers are the mainstay of the operation, each averaging about 9,000 miles per year. They have a legal carrying capacity of about eleven tons. Four 20-cubic yard rear and side loading packers are used for operation in certain areas too confined for the larger vehicles. Several 16-cubic yard rear loading packers are used as switch trucks to keep

assign to a crew whose work load appears lighter than usual, a portion of an area assigned to a crew with a heavier than usual work assignment. The field supervisors operate radio-equipped vehicles and maintain contact with a central coordinator as well as with each other, thus permitting reassignment of crews from one supervisor's territory to another to meet any emergency condition.

Coordination and control. All refuse loads are weighed at the disposal sites. Time and mileage information is also recorded on a load basis. This basic information provides excellent source data for work programming and control procedures. The ability to measure the work performed and the time required permits supervisors to make necessary route adjustments, provide personnel training and counseling when and where indicated, and to program future operations. Over a period of many years, Los Angeles has manually processed operational source data. The value of this data on a timely basis has indicated the desirability of utilizing recent developments in the field of electronic data processing, with the added benefit of increasing the amount of needed data that can be expeditiously handled. Los Angeles has as an immediate goal the establishment of a management information system which will furnish various levels of refuse collection supervisors with prompt, accurate information—thus aiding in the steady improvement of performance.

College Park, Maryland

College Park, Maryland is a city of slightly over 20,000 persons, located on the northeast fringe of the Washington, D.C. metropolitan area and is the home of the University of Maryland. Refuse collection requirements are quite diversified in that collections are made on a regular basis from single family homes, duplexes, multi-family apartments, fraternities and sororities, and various business establishments. As a result of the foregoing, and in an effort to find a more efficient method of handling refuse in order to cut down citizen complaint, the Westvaco Papercan Refuse System[1] was adopted after suitable trial.

The container used in the Westvaco system is a single-ply product made of 100-pound Clupak extensible kraft paper, with stretch characteristics that enable it to absorb the impact of heavy loads without rupturing. In addition to their toughness, such Papercan bags, made of chemically treated paper, withstand rain, sleet, and snow for days on end. The seams of the container are sealed with water and grease-resistant glue and the bottom is secured with a sewn, tapebound closure. The container measures 43 inches in length with a face 15 inches wide and a gusset width of 12 inches. It holds about 40 gallons of refuse, nearly double the capacity of the average garbage can.

The containers hang from heavy-gauge steel holders with a rubber-ringed, hinged lid providing a convenient and highly sanitary cover. The bags fit over a circular metal sleeve and are held in place by a

[1]See April 1963 issue of *The American City.*

FIG. 7-10. College Park, Maryland adopted a paper container collection system after a trial period and a survey of citizen opinion.

simple clamp. The collector releases the clamp to remove the filled bag and places a fresh container on the holder.

The system provides both a bracket-type holder which can be fastened to the siding of a house, a wall, or other strong, vertical surface, and a portable stand-type holder which may be located in any desirable area near the rear of the house. A circular metal guard is provided as optional hardware to protect the bags from attacks by foraging animals where needed. To date, the guard has been needed in less than 10 per cent of the installations.

College Park provides twice-a-week back-door service for 3,550 single-unit dwellings, and 500 multiple dwellings, comprising 4,050 stops on 18 collection routes. Irregularities in the intervals between collections, the need for special pick-ups caused by breakdowns in the regular service, and the noise and litter caused by emptying cans into trucks were some of the problems facing the collection service.

Time studies showed that it took about one-third of the time to collect the same amount of refuse in paper containers as it did in conventional containers. Extrapolating these results for the entire city, the accompany-

ng tables compare the man-hour breakdown of the old system and the
Vestvaco system and offer a comparison for a week's operation expressed in terms of labor costs (based on the current hourly rate of
1.50).

TABLE 7-11
Time Requirements of Two Collection Systems

	Old System	Westvaco
ublic-works man-hours available per week..................	920	920
ssigned to refuse collection................................	679	384
ssigned to street sweeper and landfill......................	80	80
et for all other assignments................................	161	456

Labor costs represent only a part of the savings indicated under the
Vestvaco system. Experiments carried out during the trial period with
n open-bed truck loaned by the department of sanitation of the District
f Columbia proved that the paper containers make the use of this type
f vehicle feasible.

TABLE 7-12
Cost Comparison of Two Collection Systems

	Old System	Westvaco
ublic-works wages budget per week.......................	$1,380.00	$1,380.00
efuse-collection labor costs...............................	1,018.50	576.00
treet sweeper and landfill.................................	120.00	120.00
et for other purposes.....................................	241.50	684.00

It was already planned to replace three of the compactor-type units in
962. Thus, the decision to go to open-type vehicles was not as radical
s it might sound. Had it not been planned to replace the compactor
ucks, it is doubtful that the switch would have been made.

Comparing capital costs on the open-type trucks with compactor unit
osts was more eye-opening than imagined. Three G.M.C. Model LV-
009 trucks with power steering and all extra heavy-duty equipment and
ith specially built Gar Wood 20-cubic yard bodies were purchased for
14,298.21 or the equivalent of one 20-cubic yard compactor truck. The
vings are apparent.

The system worked, but how about public acceptance? To find out,
e University Municipal Technical Advisory Service was asked to con-
uct a survey in the trial area. Interviews conducted by the university
roup, working under the direction of the city, showed that:

90 per cent were willing to purchase either the paper containers or
a holder.

89 per cent favored the use of paper containers over the old system.

92 per cent felt that there was much less noise on collection days.

88 per cent felt that the litter had been reduced.

EXAMPLE OF TIME STUDIES AND ANALYSIS OF OPERATION

The following tables illustrate the kind of data that are secured by refuse collection agencies to provide the facts necessary for making detailed comparative analyses of the various possible combinations of methods and equipment. These examples do not show all of the information that may be needed for a particular investigation; neither do they indicate all of the ways that such information may be recorded and summarized.

TABLE 7-13

Time in Minutes Required for Average Man to Walk
1,000 Feet Carrying Various Loads and Stopping at
Various Regular Intervals[1]

Weight Carried (pounds)	Stops at Intervals of									
	10 ft.	15 ft.	20 ft.	25 ft.	30 ft.	40 ft.	50 ft.	100 ft.	150 ft.	200 ft
None........	4.71	4.39	4.21	4.08	4.00	3.89	3.82	3.70	3.65	3.61
12...........	4.79	4.45	4.26	4.15	4.07	3.96	3.92	3.78	3.75	3.72
25...........	4.86	4.53	4.35	4.24	4.15	4.05	4.00	3.85	3.82	3.79
50...........	4.92	4.60	4.43	4.30	4.23	4.12	4.05	3.92	3.88	3.85
75[2]........	5.02	4.68	4.50	4.39	4.31	4.21	4.15	4.00	3.97	3.92

[1]Studies made in Philadelphia, Pennsylvania.
[2]75 pounds was maximum weight that a man could carry consistently.

Some of the data may be useful to refuse collection officials, but it must be emphasized that they represent performance in a particular city under definite local conditions. They may not be valid under other conditions. It will ordinarily be necessary to make similar time studies, production analyses, and other inquiries in the communities for which the planning work is done.

Tables 7-13, 7-14, and 7-15 show some time study information for several individual operations which were considered in Philadelphia. The analysis of the time required for the entire collection from different points on premises in Philadelphia is presented in Tables 7-16 and 7-17 on pages 197 and 198.

TABLE 7-14

Time in Seconds Required for Average Man to Walk Up
Various Heights of Stairs Carrying Various Loads

Weight Carried (pounds)	Height of Stairs				
	4 ft.	6 ft.	8 ft.	10 ft.	12 ft
None...............................	3.00	4.20	5.60	7.15	9.20
25.................................	3.35	4.68	5.25	7.82	9.90
50.................................	3.82	5.30	6.93	8.70	10.80
75.................................	4.20	6.07	7.89	9.70	12.00

TABLE 7-15
Time in Seconds Required for Average Man to Walk Down
Various Heights of Stairs Carrying Various Loads

Weight Carried (pounds)	Height of Stairs				
	4 ft.	6 ft.	8 ft.	10 ft.	12 ft.
None.........................	3.00	4.00	4.95	5.90	7.40
25.............................	3.40	4.49	5.55	6.70	8.40
50.............................	3.85	5.12	6.57	8.00	9.95
75.............................	4.92	6.42	8.20	10.00	12.25

TABLE 7-16
Summary of Observations Made to Evaluate Ash and Rubbish
Collection from Cellars in Philadelphia, Pennsylvania[1]

Time Required in One Average House

	Load (pounds)	Distance (feet)	Height (feet)	Time (seconds)
Up steps.........................	None	...	4	3.00
Wait to enter...................	None	...	...	75.00
Through house to cellar door...............	None	30	...	7.20
Down cellar steps..........................	None	...	8	4.95
Walk to cellar window..................	None	22	...	5.41
Open and close cellar window..............	None	...	...	60.00
Walk to receptacles...........................	None	10	...	2.83
Lift and place 3 receptacles................	41	...	4	13.74
Carry 3 receptacles.........................	41	30	...	8.82
Return 3 receptacles.......................	10	30	...	8.57
Return to steps............................	None	12	...	3.39
Up steps......................................	None	...	8	5.60
Return to front door......................	None	30	...	7.20
Down steps.................................	None	...	4	3.00
Walk 20 ft. to next house..................	None	20	...	5.05
Total for one house...				213.76

Time Required to Carry Receptacles from Cellar Window to Curb

	Load (pounds)	Distance (feet)	Time (seconds)
Window 10 Feet From Curb			
Carry 3 receptacles.................................	41	30	8.82
Return 3 receptacles...............................	10	30	8.57
Walk 20 ft. to next house.........................	None	20	5.05
Total for one house, three trips......................................			22.44
Window 30 Feet from Curb			
Carry 3 receptacles.................................	41	90	22.80
Return 3 receptacles...............................	10	90	21.90
Walk 20 ft. to next house.........................	None	20	5.05
Total for one house, three trips......................................			49.75
Window 100 Feet from Curb			
Carry 3 receptacles.................................	41	300	69.66
Return 3 receptacles...............................	10	300	67.86
Walk 20 ft. to next house.........................	None	20	5.05
Total for one house, three trips......................................			142.57

[1]City of Philadelphia, *Report on Proposed Change of Refuse Collection Methods.*

TABLE 7-17

Summary of Obervations Made to Evaluate Ash and Rubbish
Collection from Side and Rear Yards
In Philadelphia, Pennsylvania

Time Required in One Average Yard

	Load (pounds)	Distance (feet)	Height (feet)	Time (seconds)
Carry to back yard............................	10	20	...	5.10
Empty 1½ receptacles into carrier...........	56	...	2	9.22
Return to gate..............................	56	20	...	5.35
Return to back door.........................	10	20	...	5.10
Empty 1½ receptacles into carrier...........	56	...	2	9.22
Return to gate..............................	56	20	...	5.35
Total.................				39.34

Time Required from Yard to Curb via Alley

	Load (pounds)	Distance (feet)	Time (seconds)
Carrying Distance 80 Feet			
Carry 2 carriers....................................	56	160	38.20
Carry 2 carriers back..............................	10	160	34.60
Total.................			72.80
Carrying Distance 130 Feet			
Carry 2 carriers....................................	56	260	62.10
Carry 2 carriers back..............................	10	260	56.24
Total.................			118.34

Time Required from Rear of Houses to Curb via Side Yard

	Load (pounds)	Distance (feet)	Height (feet)	Time (seconds)
Carrying Distance 60 Feet				
Carry 2 carriers..............................	10	120	...	27.94
Empty 2 receptacles...........................	56	...	2	18.44
Carry 2 carriers..............................	56	120	...	29.16
Walk 20 ft. to next house....................	10	30	...	5.10
Total.................				80.64
Carrying Distance 125 Feet				
Carry 2 carriers..............................	10	250	...	66.40
Empty 3 receptacles...........................	56	...	2	18.44
Carry 2 carriers..............................	56	250	...	58.80
Walk 20 ft. to next house....................	10	20	...	5.10
Total.................				138.74

A time and motion study for Rockville, Maryland called for each of the sanitation workers to go to the back of the houses, dump the household containers into a plastic tote can and carry the full tote can to the sidewalk. The full tote can is then left on the sidewalk and an empty tote can which has been placed there by the crew leader is picked up by the sanitation worker. The sanitation workers continue their operation as described, and at the same time the crew leader picks up the full tote cans, deposits them into the rear loading hopper, advances the truck to a point where the workers will bring full tote cans, empties the existing tote cans into the hopper, activates the packing mechanism, sets the empty tote cans on the sidewalk, and picks up full tote cans. A sketch (Fig. 7-11) of the proposed operation is included to show the operations of the various crew members.

From observations and studies the following average conditions were found in Rockville as shown in Table 7-18,

TABLE 7-18

Lot Frontage	75 feet
Distance from sidewalk to point of storage of household containers	80 feet
Distance from truck to back of sidewalk	30 feet
Number of household containers per residence	2 each

The following critical times of various operations, Table 7-19, were found to be average for this type of operation.

TABLE 7-19

Equipment yard to route	15 min.
Incinerator to equipment yard	15 min.
Dump at incinerator	8 min.
One round trip to incinerator	38 min.
Average walking time of worker	4 ft./sec.
Average time to empty one household container into tote can	8 sec.
Travel time between blocks	15 sec.

It was found by a Program Evaluation Review Technique (PERT) diagram that the crew leader can perform his duties in a manner that does not cause the sanitation workers to lose time in their operations. Since the time required for the performance of the duties of the crew leader were not critical, they are not included in the analysis of time required to collect the average household. The following analysis, Table 7-20, considers the action of one worker picking up refuse from a typical block with 10 houses on each side of the street:

This analysis considers the action of one worker only, with the assumption that the other worker would be collecting the same number of houses on the other side of the street in the same amount of time. Such factors as adverse weather, houses on one side of street, vehicle malfunctions, domestic animals, and fences and gates, will cause the operation to be slower. If one considers the 75.92 seconds as 100 per cent efficiency, it would seem safe to assume an overall rating of 85 per cent efficiency as the average time required to collect one house. Applying this factor, the average time to collect from one house for each

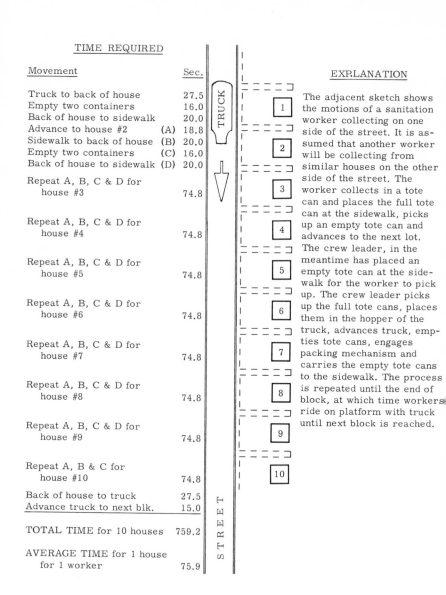

TIME REQUIRED

Movement		Sec.
Truck to back of house		27.5
Empty two containers		16.0
Back of house to sidewalk		20.0
Advance to house #2	(A)	18.8
Sidewalk to back of house	(B)	20.0
Empty two containers	(C)	16.0
Back of house to sidewalk	(D)	20.0
Repeat A, B, C & D for house #3		74.8
Repeat A, B, C & D for house #4		74.8
Repeat A, B, C & D for house #5		74.8
Repeat A, B, C & D for house #6		74.8
Repeat A, B, C & D for house #7		74.8
Repeat A, B, C & D for house #8		74.8
Repeat A, B, C & D for house #9		74.8
Repeat A, B & C for house #10		74.8
Back of house to truck		27.5
Advance truck to next blk.		15.0
TOTAL TIME for 10 houses		759.2
AVERAGE TIME for 1 house for 1 worker		75.9

EXPLANATION

The adjacent sketch shows the motions of a sanitation worker collecting on one side of the street. It is assumed that another worker will be collecting from similar houses on the other side of the street. The worker collects in a tote can and places the full tote can at the sidewalk, picks up an empty tote can and advances to the next lot. The crew leader, in the meantime has placed an empty tote can at the sidewalk for the worker to pick up. The crew leader picks up the full tote cans, places them in the hopper of the truck, advances truck, empties tote cans, engages packing mechanism and carries the empty tote cans to the sidewalk. The process is repeated until the end of block, at which time workers ride on platform with truck until next block is reached.

FIG. 7-11. Right hand portion of illustration explains and diagrams collection system analysed in Rockville, Maryland time and motion study. Findings are shown on left.

TABLE 7-20

Truck to back of house #1,	110 ft./4 ft./sec.	= 27.5 sec.
Empty two containers	2 x 8 sec.	= 16.0 sec.
Back of house to sidewalk	80 ft./4 ft./sec.	= 20.0 sec.
Advance to house #2 (A)	75 ft./4 ft./sec.	= 18.8 sec.
Sidewalk to back yard (B)	80 ft./4 ft./sec.	= 20.0 sec.
Empty two containers (C)	2 x 8 sec.	= 16.0 sec.
Back of house to sidewalk (D)	80 ft./4 ft./sec.	= 20.0 sec.
Repeat A, B, C & D for house #3		= 74.8 sec.
Repeat A, B, C & D for house #4		= 74.8 sec.
Repeat A, B, C & D for house #5		= 74.8 sec.
Repeat A, B, C & D for house #6		= 74.8 sec.
Repeat A, B, C & D for house #7		= 74.8 sec.
Repeat A, B, C & D for house #8		= 74.8 sec.
Repeat A, B, C & D for house #9		= 74.8 sec.
Repeat A, B & C for house #10		= 54.8 sec.
Back of house #10 to truck, 110 ft./4 ft./sec.		= 27.5 sec.
Move forward to next block		= 15.0 sec.
Total time for 10 houses on one side of street		759.2 sec.
Average time for 1 house for one sanitation worker		75.92 sec.

worker would be (75.92/.85) 89.32 seconds or 1.488 minutes. Using this figure as the amount of time required for two houses and two men and considering other necessary operations, a typical schedule, Table 7-21, would be as follows:

TABLE 7-21

Function	Time Req'd	Time of Day
Start..		7:00 A.M.
From equipment yard to route......................	0 hrs. 15 min.	7:15 A.M.
Collect one full load, 265 houses		
(1.488 x 265/2 = 197 min.)......................	3 hrs. 17 min.	10:32 A.M.
Round trip to incinerator...........................	0 hrs. 38 min.	11:10 A.M.
Lunch..	0 hrs. 30 min.	11:40 A.M.
Collect remaining 265 houses......................	3 hrs. 17 min.	2:57 P.M.
One way incinerator................................	0 hrs. 23 min.	3:20 P.M.
Incinerator to equipment yard, check in		
(route complete).................................	0 hrs. 15 min.	3:35 P.M.
Gas, oil, wash truck................................	0 hrs. 25 min.	
Vehicle servicing complete.........................		4:00 P.M.

It is seen from the above schedule that a route of 530 houses can be serviced by a crew leader and two sanitation workers using compactor trucks, tote cans, and back yard pick up service, in slightly more than an eight hour shift. Since the servicing of the truck can be accomplished by the crew leader or a sanitation worker, it appears that overtime pay for ½ hour would be due only to one man of the crew. Complaints regarding "skips" would be followed up by the assistant superintendent and appropriate action taken.

The above time schedule will vary from the "heavy collection" to the "light collection" days of the week, with the schedule representing the heavy days. The lighter collection days could be finished in a shorter period of time. It is felt that since the collection service will be on a task basis, the crews will be able to be their own efficiency experts

in order to finish as early as possible. Examples of some short cut
would be:

(1) The saving of approximately 20 seconds collection time per hous
by collection of two houses in one tote can, and,

(2) Leaving the sanitation workers on the route with burlap square
while the first load is taken to the incinerator.

SUMMARY

The effectiveness and economy of refuse collection operations depen
to a large extent on the care and intelligence exercised in developing
the plans for conducting the work. Where methods and equipmen
are selected and routes and schedules are determined on the basis o
exhaustive comparative analyses of sound basic data, the arrangement
can be demonstrated to be the best that can be secured for a particula
local situation. Any other approach to the planning problem will almos
certainly result in less efficient methods and costlier operations.

chapter 8

SUPPLEMENTAL TRANSPORTATION OF REFUSE

It is not always feasible or economical, and sometimes it is not even possible, to haul refuse in the collection vehicles direct to the disposal sites. The vehicles may be too small for efficient transportation or their speed may be too slow. If the disposal areas cannot be reached by highways, it may be necessary to use railroads or boats for conveying the refuse. In such situations, some kind of supplemental transportation is a necessary part of the system of collecting and delivering the refuse for final disposal.

THE PLACE OF SUPPLEMENTAL TRANSPORTATION

When collection vehicles were drawn by horses, it was common to use transfer stations and supplemental transportation whenever hauls from the collection routes to the disposal points were more than three or four miles long. Sometimes supplemental transportation was employed for even shorter distances when it was obvious that hauling by wagons was more expensive than by railroad, barges, or trucks. With the introduction of the faster motor trucks into the refuse collection services, the situation changed radically and many transfer operations were abandoned in favor of direct hauls to the disposal sites.

The selection of the best combination of methods and equipment to meet the requirements of the particular situation is largely a matter of cost analysis and engineering economics. For example, where collection operations are unavoidably slow, it may be uneconomical to buy and inefficient to tie up the large collection vehicles needed for long hauls. If investigation proves it is better to transfer refuse from small capacity vehicles, there should be no hesitation in adopting supplemental transportation methods. There are several potential savings to be gained from supplemental transportation where long hauls are involved. It is possible to transport more refuse per trip; crews have more time for actual collection work; and labor costs are cut since fewer equipment operators are needed to haul a few large, rather than many small, loads to disposal sites.

Sometimes when refuse is collected by one agency and disposed of by another, the material from the collection vehicles must be transferred to the vehicles of the disposal agency. Several cities in California, and

Washington, D.C., transfer garbage to private contractors' or farmers' trucks for hog feeding. However, in most cities refuse is hauled to incinerators or to final disposal sites by collection trucks.

Whenever refuse is to be transported by water, it must be transferred at suitable docks to the boats or scows. Ordinarily the material is dumped from the collection vehicles rather than carried in the vehicles or bodies onto the vessels. New York transfers refuse to scows and barges which are towed to the disposal sites. Some cities have been able to secure suitable dumping areas or disposal plant locations adjacent to railroad rights-of-way and rail haul may be the only or the most economical means of transport. Washington, D.C., transfers refuse to railroad cars.

ESSENTIALS OF A SUPPLEMENTAL TRANSPORTATION SYSTEM

As the connecting link between the collection service and the disposal process the supplemental transportation system must equal in capacity, sanitation, reliability, and adequacy, the standards of the other parts of the operation. It must afford the most economical means of delivery of refuse to disposal sites with facilities to handle the material without confusion, loss of time, or the creation of nuisances.

In considering the dependability of a transfer system, it must be recognized that a failure at the transfer station or in the hauling operation, may seriously disturb and delay both the collection and the disposal processes. There should be ample reserve facilities at the loading station and enough reserve hauling equipment to take care of any emergencies. Collection vehicles should have easy access to the unloading points and be able to discharge their loads and return promptly to the collection routes. Whenever it is necessary or desirable to remove refuse from a transfer station at a rate slower than that at which it is delivered, adequate storage capacity must be provided at the station.

METHODS EMPLOYED IN SUPPLEMENTAL TRANSPORTATION

The particular methods of supplemental transportation to use in any situation depend on local conditions. Among the more important factors to be evaluated are:

1. Character of the refuse to be transported
2. Special requirements of the disposal method used
3. Quantity of material that must be handled
4. Community attitude toward appearance and sanitation
5. Availability of suitable transfer sites
6. Collection methods that have been selected
7. Kind of collection equipment used
8. Particular conditions of transportation that may be encountered.

The kinds of transfer equipment currently used by American cities are described below and some indication is given concerning the more important advantages and disadvantages of each.

Large-body motor trucks. Some municipalities now use 5- to 10-ton trucks, with 15- to 30-cubic yard bodies, for the supplemental transportation of refuse. It would be difficult, in many situations, to demonstrate that these large transfer trucks really result in sufficient savings to compensate for the loading station expense, the lost time involved, and the somewhat greater reserve equipment costs. Nevertheless, when the hauls are over seven or eight miles long, when very small capacity collection vehicles are used, and when the operation can be conducted with a minimum delay to the large hauling units, it is possible that substantial savings can be made.

FIG. 8-1. Shown above is a 60-yard Hobbs Hyd-Pak transfer trailer, and below a Leach Packmaster trailer as used in Chicago.

The use of semi-trailers for transferring refuse from the loading or transfer stations to disposal points overcomes to some extent the disadvantages of large trucks. Because it is possible to leave such vehicles at the stations to be filled as the refuse arrives, the necessity of storing material is eliminated. In most cases, the operation can be conducted quite efficiently because the idle time expense of trailers is normally much less than that of large trucks, since no driver time is lost and fixed costs are lower.

It is customary to operate the hauling of refuse by semi-trailers on a shuttle plan. The tractor truck leaves an empty semi-trailer in position at a transfer station and then hauls a loaded semi-trailer to the disposal point. Usually the operations are planned so that a trip can be made while the empty semi-trailer is being loaded; thus the tractor truck is utilized full time. If the haul is very long, however, it may be necessary for greatest efficiency to operate two tractor trucks with three semi-trailers. Santa Monica, California uses semi-trailers into which the refuse is compacted with a stationary packing unit. Pay loads of 18 tons per trip

FIG. 8-2. The City of Pasadena, California, provides a backyard pickup for all residential refuse collections. Motorized scooters are employed in the backyard unit collections with each scooter effecting a mobile transfer of refuse by dumping its load into a 50-cubic yard, front-end-loading packer truck for ultimate transport to the sanitary landfill disposal site at Scholl Canyon.

are achieved, and Chicago uses them for supplemental transportation between the city's transfer station and the disposal point. The semi-trailers are 66 and 78 cubic yards in capacity with a conveyor type unloading bed.

The Sanitation Districts of Los Angeles County employ hauling units that consist of a truck-tractor pulling a semi-trailer, followed by a full trailer. Combined volume of the two trailers is 120 cubic yards, which results in a payload of about 20 tons.

Various methods of unloading trailers are employed. Side-dumping trailers are used at Beverly Hills, California, and Seattle. The "winch" type unloads by drawing the rear wheels to the tractor with a winch and prop, causing the body to raise. The "crane" type uses a separate crane to raise the front of trailer body which is hinged at the rear. The "hydraulic hoist" type usually has a smaller capacity and the body is raised by one or more hydraulic hoists. The "bulkhead" or "compactor plate" type employs a movable bulkhead not only to compress refuse in the process of being loaded but also to eject the load from the body at the disposal site. Usually one tractor truck and one semi-trailer is used in the hauling operation, although an extra trailer is available at the loading station to prevent the possibility of any delay to the collection crews.

FIG. 8-3. Los Angeles County Sanitation Districts' trailers permit maximum legal California gross vehicle weight and a payload of about 20 tons.

Water transport equipment. Barges, scows, lighters, and special freight boats are used to transfer refuse from collection vehicles to disposal plants, land dumps, or water dumps. Usually the vessels are towed by tug boats, but some of them are self-propelling. However, the use of this method of transportation is now limited to transfer operations; the disposal of refuse at sea is no longer practiced in the United States because of potential beach pollution and economic haul factors related thereto. In 1934, the practice of dumping at sea was discontinued by the city of New York because of an injunction obtained by New Jersey cities sustained by the U. S. Supreme Court.

One of the disadvantages of transferring refuse by water is that it may be impossible or impractical to move the boats during storms. If storm periods are extensive, it may be necessary to supply a large number of standby boats in which the collected refuse can be stored. In developing the facilities for transferring the refuse to vessels, consideration must be given to providing dock space for the loading operations as well as for the loaded boats and the empty reserve vessels.

Tug boats ordinarily are not city owned unless the operations are so extensive that they can be used full time in the refuse transfer service. Usually it is considered more satisfactory to contract for the towing service or to rent tug boats as necessary. Boats that are used are generally divided into compartments or bunkers into which the refuse is loaded.

New York, Boston, and Victoria, B. C., use large flat bottomed barges or scows to transfer refuse from water-front transfer stations. The New York barges are 37 feet wide, 150 feet long, and hold about 2,000 yards of material.

These boats are not self-propelled but are towed by tug boats from the transfer station to the disposal areas. In New York and Boston, the refuse is towed to land dumps outside the city limits. In Victoria, Canada, however, the refuse passes through a crusher and then to scows which are hauled to sea for dumping.

A study in Washington, D. C., on the advisability of transferring refuse by scows up the Potomac River to land dumps showed the plan to be impractical and uneconomical in that particular locality. Not only were river conditions unsuitable for the regular movement of scows, but the unit cost of the project was shown to be greater than that of some other available methods.

When refuse is transported by water to land fills, it is usually necessary to transfer the material twice, once from the collection vehicle to the boats and again at the disposal site from the boats to trucks or trailers for transport to the point of dumping. The extra cost involved in such operations is another major reason why water transportation of refuse has decreased considerably in recent years.

Railroad and railway cars. Railroad and railway facilities are utilized in a few communities for transferring refuse to disposal areas or plants. This method is not used as widely as it was in the past because of the development of large truck and trailer equipment which is more flexible and can be better adapted to operating conditions. Nevertheless, in some situations the method may be both economical and effective. The railroad cars now in regular use are almost always of the gondola type, although in former years both the hopper cars and specially built rotary dump cars were employed. The usual plan is to dump the refuse from the collection vehicles into cars at the transfer station (Washington, D. C.), or into pits at the transfer station and then reload by crane into cars. The transfer of refuse by street railway equipment has disappeared.

It should be remembered that the principles of balancing weight capacity and volumetric capacity apply in the case of railroad or railway cars as a means of supplemental transportation just as they do when trucks and trailers are used. It is certainly not in the direction of economy to provide body capacity of only 15 to 20 tons on railroad cars, when the carrying capacity of the car is 40 or 50 tons.

It may be a disadvantage that considerably more reserve equipment will be needed in the case of railroad transportation because the hauling agency and the movement of cars cannot be directly controlled by refuse collection officials. Inadequate track facilities, inadequate storage space, failure to meet train schedules, fires, unsatisfactory track maintenance, and the like, may result in costly delays at the transfer station as well as at the disposal point.

Washington, D. C., provides gondola railroad cars for transferring garbage from a central loading station to a landfill site about 30 miles from the city.

Shuttling

Oakland, California, collection trucks shuttle directly to a disposal site on San Francisco Bay which is approximately 12 miles from the city. Chicago uses a relay system for shuttling collection trucks. Trucks are brought to a central parking area after the last load of the day from where they are shuttled to the disposal site by a new crew of drivers. The round-trip averages approximately 50 miles.

Transferring refuse from the collection vehicle to the supplemental hauling unit can be accomplished at stations that can be constructed at convenient locations, or it can be done right on the collection route. One system of collection and haul presently finding favor in some communities consists of a train of collection containers towed by a jeep-type vehicle. A large "mother" truck accompanies several of these trains into the field and the filled containers are picked up and emptied into the truck by a lift device on the front of the "mother" truck. Collection continues with the train while the truck makes the trip to the disposal site.

TRANSFER STATIONS

It is more common, however, to provide transfer stations for removing the refuse from collection trucks and placing it in the long-haul vehicle. The terms "loading station," "transfer station," or "relay station" are used to describe such facilities. Among the more important considerations in planning and designing transfer stations are locations, types of stations and facilities, provisions for sanitation, and accessories to efficient operation. The use of a transfer station may also provide for a salvage operation to reduce the volume of refuse to be hauled by the transfer vehicles to the disposal site. Some data on transfer stations now in use are given in Table 8-1.

Location of Stations

For greatest efficiency, a transfer station should (1) be located as near as possible to the center of production of the collection area which it serves; (2) be convenient to the secondary or supplemental means of transportation; (3) be so placed that there will be a minimum of public objection to the transfer operations; and (4) be located at points where the construction and operation will be most economical. It is seldom that all the ideals can be met and frequently some sacrifice in efficiency must be made to meet local conditions such as zoning, and so on.

It is usually not very difficult to locate the theoretical centers of collection areas, from which there is ordinarily some latitude before there is a serious reflection in increased collection costs. As a starting point in the problem of locations, however, it is desirable to know exactly the best site in relation to the collection routes.

TABLE 8-1
Typical Refuse Transfer Installations
In Selected U.S. Cities

City	Number of Stations	Method of Transport	Type of Refuse Handled	Average Haul to Disposal Site miles)
Abilene, Texas..............	1	Truck	Combined refuse	7
Beverly Hills, California....	1	Truck	Combined refuse	10
Chamblee, Georgia........	1	Truck	Combustibles	15½
Chattanooga, Tennessee..	1	Truck	Combined refuse	4½
Chicago, Illinois............	1	Truck	Combined refuse	22½
Denver, Colorado..........	1	Truck	Combined refuse	12
Detroit, Michigan..........	2	Truck	Rubbish & ashes	19
Johnson City, Tennessee..	1	Truck	Combined refuse	6
King County, Washington..	7	Truck	Combined refuse	—
Los Angeles Co. San. Dists.				
South Gate, California..	1	Truck	Combined refuse	15
Orange County, California.	3	Truck	Combined refuse	16
New Orleans, Louisiana....	1	Truck	Combustibles	15
Pasadena, California.......	1	Truck	Comm'l garbage	40
Sacramento, California....	1	Truck	Combined refuse	—
	(pvt.)			
Santa Monica, California...	1	Truck	Combined refuse	8
Washington, D.C.	1	Truck & rail	Garbage & ashes	—

Note: Other cities reporting the use of transfer stations include: Huntington Beach, Long Beach, Los Angeles, Midway District, and Oakland, California; Wethersfield, Connecticut; Ocala, Tallahassee, and Winter Park, Florida; Calumet City, and Wilmette, Illinois; Council Bluffs, Iowa; Boston, Needham, Quincy, and Worcester, Massachusetts; Alpena, and Flint, Michigan; Reno, Nevada; Merideth, New Hampshire; Metuchen, New Jersey; Amsterdam, and New York City, New York; Bay Village, Bexley, Grove City, Marietta, New Philadelphia, and Shaker Heights, Ohio; Reading, and Shillington, Pennsylvania; Knoxville, Tennessee; Arlington, El Paso, and River Oaks, Texas; Spokane, Washington; Victoria, British Columbia.

When trucks or trailers are used for supplemental transportation, there is usually a rather wide range in the sites available to the main highways that must be used. However, it is desirable to avoid routing the equipment through residential areas or through congested business areas. Generally it is good policy to route the vehicles on thoroughfares where heavy truck traffic is already an accepted factor. When boats or railroad facilities are used, the available locations are much more limited because the transfer stations must be right at the water edge or immediately adjacent to the railroad tracks. In such cases, it is likely that the available areas within reasonable distance of the center of the collection areas will be very few.

The nature of the work of transferring refuse, involving as it does the concentration of collection vehicles and the shifting and storage of large masses of waste material, is such that violent objections are likely to be raised by property owners in the vicinity of a proposed transfer station. Even though the operation is carried out without public nuisance, free of odors, flies, dust, or noise, the idea of having such a plant nearby is repulsive to many citizens. It is usually not advisable to select locations in residential or commercial neighborhoods or even on vacant land which in time may be developed as a residential area. The most suitable sites are in industrial areas—not only to avoid public objection, but to comply with current zoning requirements or those which may be anticipated.

ECONOMIC ANALYSIS
OF
SUPPLEMENTAL TRANSPORTATION SYSTEMS

As part of an overall program of refuse disposal, the Sanitation Districts of Los Angeles County in 1958 opened a transfer station in the City of South Gate, California.

The Districts had a dual motive in establishing the station. First, there appeared to be a need for such a facility in the area due to a lack of nearby disposal facilities, and second, the station would provide a vehicle for experimentation and for gaining experience in an operation that seemed destined to play an increasingly large part in meeting the county's refuse disposal needs as the closer-in disposal sites were exhausted.

In line with the districts' policy, this station is open to the public and charges are levied for each load of refuse sufficient to cover the costs at the station, the costs of hauling, and the cost at the final disposal point. As a result of this open-door policy, the station has been subjected to the harshest economic analysis possible—the open market. It is unlikely that one would patronize the site unless it were economically advantageous to do so.

The most thought-provoking point of the experience gained at this station is found in the fact that by far the majority of the patrons at the site have only a small quantity of refuse to dispose of. The preponderance of loads accepted at the station are less than one ton in weight and loads of more than three tons are uncommon. The real service the station provides is to the small hauler, while the large commercial haulers have decided to direct-haul to the disposal site, the nearest one being 10 miles away.

In analyzing experience gained at the station, the districts developed the following method of comparing the cost of direct haul with a transfer and haul operation.

In any transfer operation, the costs of owning and operating the station itself are entirely unproductive and must be "earned back" by the greater efficiency of the haul vehicle being used. There also might be another unproductive expense incurred at the disposal site, inasmuch as the transfer vehicles will quite likely require a longer time than collection vehicles to unload at the disposal site. Using the South Gate station as an example, the unproductive costs are:

1. Station cost, including O & M, billing
   and accounting expense, etc. $1.13 per ton
2. Extra unloading time at disposal site.
   (Based on $15.00 per hour cost for
   transfer vehicle including driver,
   20-ton payload, and ¼ hour extra time)

$$\frac{.25 \text{ hr. x } \$15}{20 \text{ tons}} = \underline{\quad.19\quad}$$

Total unproductive cost $1.32

The total unproductive cost (in this case $1.32) is plotted at zero time on a graph such as shown in Fig. 8-4. The total cost of transfer and haul for any travel time is then represented by a line drawn through this point on a slope equal to the haul cost per ton per minute. At South Gate, the $15.00 per hour and the 20-ton payload results in a figure of $.0125 per ton per minute. With this line established, any direct haul vehicle can be compared with the transfer operation by drawing a line through the origin with a slope equal to the cost per ton per minute for the particular truck. Where this line intersects the transfer cost line is the point in total extra travel time beyond which it is more economical to transfer and prior to which it is cheaper to direct-haul. It is to be emphasized that this is additional time beyond that which might be required to make a round trip to the transfer station. As can be seen in the examples illustrated on Fig. 8-4 a $12 per hour truck with an eight-ton payload can travel for an extra 110 minutes round trip before it would be cheaper to patronize the South Gate Transfer Station. In the other example shown, a pick-up truck costing $4 per hour with the driver can spend only 11 minutes more in a round trip to the disposal site than to the transfer station.

Inasmuch as many collection trucks are being built that can spend an additional two hours in traveling directly to the disposal site, it appears that transfer stations should be more frequently thought of in terms of

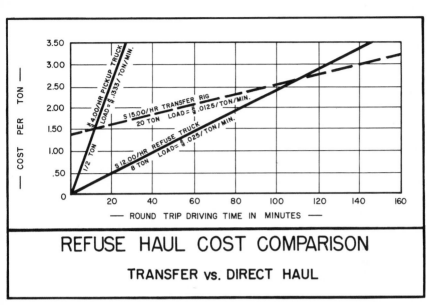

REFUSE HAUL COST COMPARISON

TRANSFER vs. DIRECT HAUL

FIG. 8-4. Experience at the South Gate Transfer Station of the Sanitation Districts of Los Angeles County indicates that, contrary to common conceptions, transfer stations are more useful to the small individual refuse hauler than to municipal trucks or large commercial haulers.

the small hauler than as part of a large municipal collection operation. It is interesting to note that this philosophy is contrary to the present practice of many communities where the small individual haulers are not even permitted to use the station and only large commercial haulers or municipal trucks are accepted.

Types of Transfer Stations

Although it would be possible to transfer loaded collection bodies to the long-haul vehicle, the prevalent practice is to transfer refuse itself. There are numerous ways of accomplishing this, but nearly all methods that have been used can be placed in the following categories:

1. Direct-dump transfer stations where the collection trucks dump directly into the long-haul unit through the use of a two-level arrangement of the station.

2. Storage-type stations where the refuse is dumped into storage or on a platform and then rehandled in some way to place it in the transfer vehicle.

In either of these types of structures, however, there are numerous variations in design, depending considerably on the emphasis placed on appearances, economy of operation and maintenance, and the avoidance of nuisances.

A simple type of transfer station is a platform from which the collection vehicles dump their loads directly into the bodies of the transfer

equipment. Such structures are normally of steel or concrete, and elevated to a height sufficient to permit easy and complete dumping.
Platforms are made by building concrete retaining walls around the
platform area, filling the enclosure with earth, and paving the surface.
If ramps are necessary, they are usually built the same way.

In some transfer stations refuse is lifted into elevated hoppers by
means of belt or bucket conveyors. The material is dumped from the
collection trucks into pits so shaped that the refuse falls by gravity to the
conveyor. The hopper is constructed high enough to permit the transfer
vehicles to drive underneath to be loaded.

A rather novel transfer arrangement is provided at the grinding
stations in St. Louis, where garbage is transferred to farmers' trucks.
The collection trucks are elevated by means of a compressed air lift

FIG. 8-5. The West 135th Street Marine transfer station operated by the Department of
Sanitation, City of New York.

similar to the equipment used in modern garages for raising automobiles.
From this elevated position the dump bodies are raised and their contents discharged directly into the transfer trucks below. While this
method is somewhat slower than direct dumping from platforms, both
equipment and operating costs are relatively low. Where the quantity
to be transferred is not great this type of transfer station has considerable merit.

Water-side stations for transferring refuse from collection trucks to boats are similar to platform structures. They are usually built much like piers and ordinarily the location can be selected so that the dumping floor is approximately at ground or street level, eliminating the need for long ramps. Usually these stations are entirely enclosed, both for the sake of appearance and to prevent the scattering of refuse or the dissemination of odors. The new transfer stations provided by New York are not only attractive but are designed and operated so that there is no opportunity whatever for the creation of nuisances. The entire dumping floors are enclosed by light, airy buildings, and ample space is provided so that the collection trucks can maneuver easily into dumping positions and quickly discharge their loads into the scows below. Curtains created by sprays of water reduce the dust escaping, and cause a downward current of air so that the dust will tend to be kept below the platform level.

Mechanical transfer of refuse. Several different types of plants are provided by American cities which transfer refuse by crane or derrick from the collection vehicles to the supplemental transfer equipment. Such transfer stations are usually enclosed, but where large boats are loaded by such methods the enclosing of the entire station is not feasible.

Capacity of Transfer Stations

The question of capacity involves not only storage facilities in the transport equipment, the amount of dumping space, or crane size, but especially is concerned with the easy movement of collection vehicles and supplemental transfer vehicles in entering, maneuvering, and departing. The capacity of a platform station where vehicles dump directly into waiting trucks, railroad cars, or boats, is normally determined by the length of the dumping platform or the number of vehicles that can be in a dumping position at one time. The quantity of material transferred may be considerably reduced, however, if the vehicles have to wait for each other or if considerable maneuvering is necessary to get into dumping position. At crane plants, the capacity is ordinarily determined by the speed and size as well as the number of cranes provided, but here again full capacity may not be realized if there is much confusion in maneuvering and dispatching the collection vehicles.

Most transfer stations are built large enough to handle peak loads so that there will be no delays to the collection vehicles. In some cases, however, it is the space required for the transfer equipment rather than for the collection vehicles which determines the size of the platforms and dumping length.

The main effort in design is generally directed toward balancing the facilities so that there will be no bottle-necks in the operation. At Flint, Michigan, the arrangements permit two collection trucks to dump at a time, and there is space for four transfer trailers to be in position to receive the garbage. A maximum of 13 garbage trucks are used in the collection service and 18,000 tons of material are handled annually.

FIG. 8-6. The transfer station in Washington, D. C., is located only a few thousand feet from the U. S. Capitol. The station is pleasing architecturally and specially equipped for dust and odor control.

Provisions for Sanitation

Transfer stations can be constructed and operated so that their objectionable features are reduced to a minimum. Under suitable conditions, it is possible to operate them without any nuisances whatever and without arousing complaints. To accomplish this, the stations must be kept as clean as possible at all times, the escape of dust and litter must be prevented, the dissemination of odors must be kept to a minimum, and the structures and premises must be kept neat and attractive.

The transfer structures, buildings, and ramps should be made of concrete, brick, or other material that can be easily cleaned. Moreover, the structures should be fireproof. In general wood is not satisfactory, not only because of the fire risk involved, but also because it is almost impossible to keep it really clean and sanitary.

Washington's transfer station is an excellent example of a modern station embodying all necessary sanitary and operating facilities. Its ventilation system has equipment for air treatment consisting of fans, dust cyclones, filters, carbon cannisters, and a discharge through the annular space of a 100-foot stack.

The station has enclosed stalls where three to four collection trucks in each stall can dump into semi-trailers facilitating the control of dust and odors.

Another area is provided for dumping into railroad gondola cars. Also included in the station are squad rooms, offices, wash racks, scale room, and garage space.

Careful operation is an important factor. Any spillage should be picked up immediately, and the greatest care should be exercised in the loading of transfer vehicles.

Transfer Station Accessories

As a rule there should be scales at all transfer stations to weigh the refuse as it is delivered in collection vehicles so that continuing records of the performance of each collection group can be compiled for administrative control purposes. Scales are frequently needed to weigh the refuse in the transfer equipment when it is sold to hog farmers or other persons, or when there are no weighing facilities at the disposal points. Scales are also a necessity when the station is open to the public and charges are levied based on the weight of refuse to be handled. Electronic or automatic recording scales are the most suitable, but in some cases the manually operated types may be satisfactory.

There should be some office space in every transfer station and telephone service should be available. When the transfer stations serve also as district headquarters or as dispatch points, more complete office arrangements will be necessary. Transfer stations are the logical points of contact between the central office and the field supervisory officers and crews for issuing special orders, calling attention to complaints, and periodic reporting. Also, it is desirable that there be facilities for telephone communication between the transfer station and the disposal units.

Insofar as transfer stations are used as meeting points or headquarters for the collection crews, they may be used to house facilities for the comfort and convenience of the workmen. Toilet rooms should be provided for the collection crews as well as for the station attendants, and locker rooms and shower baths can be installed to help in improving working conditions. It may be desirable to provide a room where the collection crews and transfer station employees can eat their lunches.

SUMMARY

In comparing methods of supplemental transportation with direct haul in collection vehicles, it must be recognized that the real purpose is to move a definite quantity of refuse a definite distance. Accordingly, in evaluating the different plans, the cost per ton mile of transport, with all overhead and fixed charges included, is the factor on which the economic selection should be based. The lowest cost per ton mile in transport, however, is not the only consideration. The whole operation must be dependable, sanitary, and must meet with public approval.

In comparing alternative methods of transportation, emphasis must again be placed on providing adequate reserve facilities to meet all

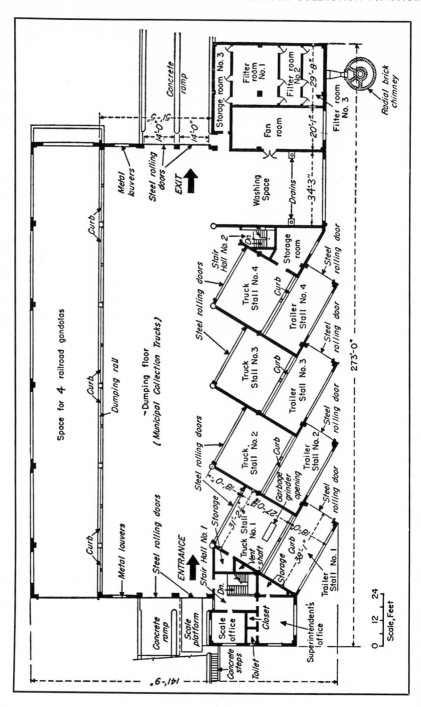

FIG. 8-7. Plan of refuse transfer station, Washington, D. C.

reasonable emergencies, and the cost involved in owning and maintaining such reserve equipment must be included in the unit cost of providing the service.

The necessity of providing transfer stations under some plans of transferring refuse may serve to make these operations less economical than the exchange of vehicles or refuse collection bodies. The advantages and disadvantages of each plan must be evaluated for the particular situation, in the interest of selecting not only the most efficient plan of procedure, but also the one which offers the least interference and annoyance to citizens.

chapter 9

SPECIAL REFUSE COLLECTION PROBLEMS

Almost every community faces special or seasonal problems in connection with the regular collection of refuse. Some of these have been discussed in preceding chapters, but others somewhat less closely related to routine operation are presented here. The control of scavengers and the regulation of private hauling of refuse are mainly administrative matters. However, the effectiveness of the administrative control influences collection operations and not infrequently the operating forces take some part in the actual enforcement of regulations. The disposal of special kinds of refuse such as market garbage and rubbish, Christmas trees, building materials, large furniture, hazardous materials, condemned food, dead animals, and street cleaning accumulations affects particular routes or special crews rather than the regular service. Also, annual or semi-annual rubbish collection is sufficiently different from normal routine operation to justify special treatment.

CONTROL OF SCAVENGERS

Scavengers, unless carefully controlled, cause some particularly irritating problems in connection with the collection of municipal refuse. As results of their uncontrolled operations, the contents of refuse containers are scattered over streets and alleys, cans and covers are damaged or lost, and collection officials and employees may be unjustly blamed for insanitary conditions and depredations.

Scavengers are usually very poor or unemployed persons who pick over refuse to salvage articles and materials that can be sold to junk dealers or to glean food or supplies that can be used in their homes. They are not private collectors, as the term is used in this volume, because they are not operating under instruction or even with the permission of the business concern or the householder. Changes brought about in recent years tend to eliminate the old-fashioned scavenger to a great extent. The horse and wagon and the familiar pushcart have practically disappeared from the city streets and alleys. Persons who might now be classified as scavengers are ones who own a truck and who collect more or less on a business-like basis. The chief item now collected by private individuals is paper in all forms. Bundled newspapers, cardboard cartons, etc. have a ready sale, and regular routes can be established by these individuals. The majority of cities allow individuals, under constant and efficient supervision, to make regular pickups of paper, especially in the downtown area. This relieves the city of considerable bulky refuse collection and makes salvage material a source of income which would not be possible if these materials are placed in regular refuse collection trucks.

No major city now allows uncontrolled or unauthorized scavenging by individuals. Where this practice is still in effect, the operations of the scavengers vary widely, depending on the location of the householders' containers between collections and the set-out practices on collection days. The scavengers are prohibited from trespassing on private premises, but once the refuse is placed in alleys or streets, they feel free to explore it and take any part of it. When the householders place the containers at the curbs or at street or at alley property lines on designated collection days, the activities of the scavengers are necessarily limited to those particular days. While it is more expensive to make collections from the backyard, one advantage is that it eliminates scavengers from rummaging through and scattering the contents of containers used by the householders.

Under their police power or ordinances of the department in charge of refuse collection, cities have the right to prohibit any interference with the refuse placed by business firms or householders for collection, and they have the authority to enforce the prohibition and to inflict penalties for violations. The great majority of cities have ordinances which specifically forbid disturbing any container or removing any part of its contents. The ordinance in effect in Miami is typical:

> Section 12. Paragraph (g) *UNLAWFUL ACTS*
> It shall be unlawful to molest, remove, handle or otherwise disturb the container or containers or other materials which have been placed on City property for servicing by the refuse collectors; provided that this paragraph does not apply to the owner, occupant, lessee or tenant of the residence, dwelling or business establishment from which the container and contents or material are removed.

Many cities have much longer sections to their ordinance. They go into details specifically mentioning containers and materials not to be taken. They also include penalties for violations.

The great majority of all cities now enforce their ordinances in regard to scavengers and to licensed private collection agencies. This change has been brought about by the demand of citizens for a clean city and through the efforts of beautification committees that have been formed in the majority of cities. The demand for change and for enforcement of ordinances dealing with this practice was brought about by the serious abuses of unrestricted scavenging. The carelessness of scavengers frequently left streets and alleys littered with refuse. The covers of the containers were removed and not replaced.

Those cities that do allow limited salvaging usually give supervisory authority to the Director of Sanitation or of Public Works to issue licenses to the scavengers or private haulers. This official is also given the authority to revoke the license for violation of rules or regulations adopted. Before licenses are issued, it is customary to make sure that the licensed individual is familiar with the rules and regulations relative to transporting salvaged materials, protecting citizens' property, littering streets and alleys, and replacing covers on containers. Usually the individual is required to designate the area or route on which he will operate so that infraction of rules or responsibility of complaint can be more readily determined.

The value of licensing depends largely on effective enforcement to make sure that the scavengers actually secure licenses and that licenses are revoked when the rules and regulations are violated. The active cooperation of the police force is usually necessary, although foremen, supervisors, and other refuse collection employees are frequently deputized as police officers either in addition to, or in lieu of, police assistance. Police supervision and control is preferable if it can be secured.

There is a marked reluctance, however, on the part of most Police Departments to enforce the ordinances of Sanitation Departments. In line with this feeling, a great number of cities have added sanitarians and sanitary police to the personnel of the Sanitation Departments. These employees are provided with police uniforms and a badge and have police powers to enforce the ordinances of the Sanitation Department. Philadelphia, Baltimore, and Miami are among the cities that have found it particularly advantageous to have a group of uniformed employees working directly under the head of the department responsible for sanitation. These employees not only enforce the ordinance but are of great value in educating the citizens as to the purpose of the ordinances.

PRIVATE HAULING OF REFUSE

Commercial and industrial establishments that are not given municipal collection service frequently haul their refuse to disposal points instead of employing private collectors. Typically, they use their own delivery or service vehicles and employees, although in some cases special equipment may be provided where garbage or produce waste must be hauled or where great quantities of rubbish must be moved. There is no fundamental objection to this means of refuse hauling, but municipal officials generally recognize that it must be controlled so as to avoid the development of nuisances or increased cost to the city for street cleaning, dump control and maintenance, or disposal plant operation. This control is usually much more difficult than the similar regulation of private collectors because the companies are much more powerful financially and politically and to some extent because it is harder to detect violations.

Most municipalities have the statutory right to control the use of streets and other public ways. They may prohibit all private hauling of refuse, may limit the transportation to municipal forces or licensed private collectors, or may issue permits to private companies or individuals to haul their waste materials in accordance with specific rules and regulations. All of these methods are used, but the most common practice is to permit either licensed private collectors or authorized individuals or companies to haul the refuse that is not collected at public expense.

Practically all cities have regulations for handling garbage, wastes from food processing plants, produce waste, and other putrescible material, and, for the most part, these regulations are rigidly enforced. Such material must be placed in watertight, metal, tightly, covered containers or must be carried in vehicles with watertight, all-enclosed bodies. Much less attention is given the hauling of ashes or rubbish, and in many communities little or no control is exercised. It is not unusual to find ashes or rubbish being moved to disposal points in vehicles that permit much of the fine dust and dirt to sift on to pavements. Loading and handling practices also are often inadequate, with the result that quantities of rubbish are dislodged from overloaded trucks or are blown from the vehicles by the wind.

A great number of cities are turning their attention to the problem of ash and rubbish hauling and are acquiring modern equipment that eliminates the littering of streets with this material when it is being transported to disposal areas. New, all-enclosed, metal, packer-type trucks have been perfected for the removal of incinerator ash and cans. Less expensive all-enclosed trucks are available for the hauling of ash from homes and business places. All-enclosed, packer-type equipment is available for rubbish collection. Open trucks that are still being used in rubbish collection are equipped with tailgates and a net to prevent blowing of rubbish when being transported over the city streets. While there are still individual or small outfits engaged in private refuse collection work, most of this work is accomplished by large, well-organized companies that are equipped to handle refuse collection in an efficient and adequate manner. Most of these private collection companies have modern equipment and work with the cities in which they are located. Some cities are antagonistic to the private collection firms, but the majority find there are certain types of material that can best be collected by the private haulers. When a cooperative plan can be agreed on by the municipality and the private collector, it is advantageous to the city.

Satisfactory control of refuse hauling involves both the approval of the equipment proposed for use and the insistence on proper loading and handling practices. Some ordinances empower a public works official or some other city employee or agency to establish and enforce rules and regulations for both trucks and procedures. Others simply authorize such employees to condemn vehicles unsuitable for hauling waste through the streets. In either case, the burden of discovering the defective vehicles or faulty practices is on the municipal officers. Too often these officials are hampered by insufficient forces or funds or are restricted by political pressure to such an extent that only the most flagrant violators are made to change their methods. Better results are secured from a more positive plan of regulation under which any individual or corporation desiring to haul refuse over city streets must first secure a permit which stipulates acceptable methods and practices.

The formal application for such a permit should include information as to the kind of materials to be hauled, the approximate amount, and a description of the equipment proposed for use. Before the permit is granted, the equipment is examined to see that it meets the local requirements for the kind of refuse produced. Any violation of the stipulations, or the use of equipment other than that specifically approved, may cause immediate revocation of a permit. Usually the permit is free, but a small charge to defray enforcement expense may be justified. The permits may be valid until revoked or it may be provided that they must be renewed annually.

Some cities have an ordinance which provides that it is unlawful for any person, firm, or corporation to transport combustible or noncombustible waste produced by such person, firm, or corporation over the streets of the city unless a permit to do so is first secured from the Director of Public Works. If the Director of Public Works is satisfied that an applicant has suitable vehicles for hauling such wastes and that he is willing to comply in all respects with existing regulations, he then issues a permit which is valid until revoked.

The refuse hauled by private individuals or companies is ordinarily accepted at regular municipal disposal points, although sometimes certain kinds of materials, particularly industrial waste products, must be taken to private dumps. Some municipalities charge for disposing of refuse brought by private persons or companies; some charge only for industrial refuse, while some accept any reasonable quantity without charge. A few cities charge for disposing of all refuse from commercial or industrial properties.

Some industries and processing plants have particularly objectionable waste materials to haul to disposal sites. Considerable difficulty is experienced with canning plants, fisheries, and the like. For example, one city received complaints about the transportation through the city of shells, hulls, and other waste from shrimp and crab meat canning plants. A solution was found by enforcing the deodorizing of this refuse before it was hauled through the streets. Another solution found to have merit is for fish and meat processing plants to keep waste in air-conditioned enclosures until collection is made.

MARKET REFUSE COLLECTION

Market refuse storage and handling is only a problem when it is allowed to become or remain a problem. Strict regulations for storage handling and disposal must be enforced.

Probably more refuse is produced in public market areas than in any other kind of municipal district. Large amounts of spoiled or unsalable fruits and vegetables, banana stalks, vegetable tops, husks, pods, poultry waste, and similar organic materials are discarded daily and will create serious aesthetic and public health problems unless the material is properly handled and collected frequently. In addition, a large volume of combustible rubbish such as crates, cartons, boxes, and miscellaneous wrapping and packing materials accumulates in such areas.

The housekeeping habits of the public market areas have undergone drastic changes in recent years. This change was brought about by:

1. Demands of citizens for a cleaner market place.
2. Recognition by the market authorities that cleanliness means better business for them.
3. Improved equipment for storing and handling market refuse.

The advent of large, covered metal containers that can be located throughout the area of the market and large front-end loaders with ability to load and pack the contents of the containers has provided the public markets with the solution to their refuse problem. Since this modern equipment answers the problem of disposal of market refuse, it is comparatively easy to enforce the rules and regulations in regard to refuse storage and removal at these locations.

Unrestrained littering and careless handling of refuse materials are not at all necessary in market areas. With competent supervision and proper regulation, the refuse collection work is not materially different from other areas where large quantities of refuse are produced.

HANDLING OF CONDEMNED FOOD

Food or produce that has been condemned by local, state, or federal health officials as unfit for sale for human consumption still belongs to the wholesaler, jobber, shipper, or merchant who is usually held responsible for its disposal. The materials deemed to be unsatisfactory must, under most health ordinances, be promptly removed by the owner and destroyed in a manner approved by the health officer. The provisions of the Toledo ordinance are typical:

> The Division of Streets shall not collect any abandoned, condemned or rejected product, by-product, manufacturers' waste materials, or stock of any wholesale dealer, as for example eggs, fish, pickles, fruit, or vegetables, and which shall be regarded as trade waste, but all such material shall be conveyed to one of the incinerators, destructors, or dump of the Division of Streets by and at the expense of the consignee or owner of such materials, and there destroyed at his expense.

Often the owner or hired private collectors will haul the condemned food to incinerators, reduction plants, or landfills for disposal with other municipal wastes. In this connection it should be pointed out that there is some danger in charging condemned canned food into incinerators. If the contents are fluid, as soup or syrup, the producer should be required to punch holes in cans and drain the material into sewers. If the contents are partly solid, the cans should be punched at the expense of the owners before they are put into the furnaces.

Unsatisfactory situations sometimes arise because of the demands for immediate removal and disposal. The health officials usually insist on witnessing the destruction of the spoiled food to make sure that it is not again offered for sale, or that it is disposed in such a manner as to prevent salvaging by individuals for consumption. Because it is not always possible for the dealers, shippers, or merchants to arrange for prompt hauling of the material, much of the inspector's time is lost, and unpleasant relations develop between the health officials and the food handlers. Appeals by the health departments to municipal refuse agencies to remove condemned food immediately often have resulted in improving this situation. Sometimes such collections have been made even in cities where no commercial service whatever is rendered. In such cases, the owner of the spoiled food is usually expected to reimburse the municipality for the cost of the work, although occasionally cities accept such removal as a legitimate public expenditure in the interest of public health.

COLLECTION OF DEAD ANIMALS

The collection of dead animals, although normally a part of the activities of a municipal refuse collection agency, must be considered separately from routine operations because of the emergency nature of the work and because special equipment is needed for handling large carcasses. If refuse is collected regularly as often as once a day, it is sometimes possible for the crews to pick up small dead animals as a part of routine activities, but horses, cows, mules, and other large animals must be removed by special crews or by contractors. In the last 25 years there has been a great reduction in the number of large dead animals to be disposed of by the average city. This reduction has now reached the point where the problem is non-existent in a great number of cities and is classed as a minor problem to the balance.

Citizens universally insist on the prompt collection of dead animals whether they are found on public or private property. The objections are based on aesthetic grounds as frequently as on public health and sanitation reasons. It is not generally understood that private ownership in animals does not terminate with their death or that the owners are granted by law a reasonable time to sell or otherwise dispose of the remains before they can be confiscated by government authorites. Public demand for immediate removal of animal carcasses is so great, particularly in the more densely populated areas, that most cities have established emergency collection services to insure that the removal is accomplished within twenty-four hours. In most instances, the collection is made within two or three hours of the notice to the responsible agency.

The great majority of all cities use special crews for collecting and removing dead animals particularly in the larger cities. Prompt collection is required, and it is ordinarily neither effective nor economical to interfere with routine collection operations by having regular crews leave their duties to make casual emergency collections. A small enclosed-body-truck, often ½- or ¾-ton, is the typical equipment for collecting dead dogs, cats, and other small animals. The driver normally does the loading. He keeps in regular communication with his headquarters so that the locations of dead animals can be obtained soon after they are reported.

Los Angeles, for several years has equipped its dead animal collection trucks with two-way radios to permit quick transmission of pickup requests to its collectors in the field. This has made possible prompt collection without excessive back-tracking of the collection trucks, and frequent commendations from citizens that their request was taken care

FIG. 9-1. Special crews are usually assigned to the work of collecting small dead animals such as dogs and cats. The operations are handled on an emergency basis so that the removal may be completed within a short time after the location of such dead animals is reported. This truck is one used in this work in Los Angeles.

of "almost before they hung up the telephone." The intelligent use of the equipment has created numerous admirers of the city's collection service.

Most municipalities undertake to collect dead animals by their own forces due to the emergency service required. If a city operates an incinerator, small animals are sometimes collected with combustible refuse and then burned, but it is generally agreed that the collection of small dead animals is best done by special crews assigned to this work. These special collection personnel can take the animals to the location of the combustion chambers where the animals can be placed and completely cremated. This is by far the best method for disposing of small dead animals. Some of the newer incinerators, such as those in New York, have special facilities for handling and burning large animals, but in most cities, the large animals are disposed of in other ways. Where garbage is disposed of by the reduction method, all dead animals are usually collected and hauled to the reduction plant. In those cities that have incinerators, it is usual for veterinarians who have dog and cat hospitals to contract with the city for the disposal of their dead animals.

Large dead animals are seldom disposed of on landfills even when all other municipal refuse may be dumped, although small animals may be so handled. Officials and citizens do not approve of dumping animals and usually some other disposal means are adopted. Even burial of large animals at dumps is not advisable unless burial at a depth of six feet or greater is assured, because certain diseases, such as charbon or anthrax, are transmittable from vegetation growing in areas where infected diseased carcasses are buried in shallow graves.

If there is a rendering plant in the vicinity, arrangements can usually be made for the destruction of the dead animals there, although often they are interested in only the large carcasses, the processing of which yields saleable by-products such as grease, fertilizer, and hides. Typically, the contracts with the rendering companies specify the methods and equipment for collecting and hauling the animals and state the amount of compensation for the service. Where the city forces collect the animals and deliver them to the rendering plant, the company usually pays from one to five dollars for large animals. It is customary, however, for the rendering companies themselves to collect the large animals because they have the special equipment for loading and hauling the bodies. Some cities pay the company an annual lump sum or a fixed unit price; some simply give the animals to the company to compensate for the work of collection.

Complaints or notices of dead animals are usually routed to refuse collection headquarters from central complaint offices or from the police or other departments. At night the notifications are ordinarily given to police officials and they send them to the proper office early the following morning.

COLLECTION OF STREET CLEANING REFUSE

In smaller cities, street cleaning refuse is generally collected and hauled by the regular refuse collection crews. Often such work is limited to emptying litter boxes and baskets, but in some cases, the sweepings collected by handbroom men or "white wings" are hauled from the cleaning routes. In isolated instances, refuse collectors may load piles of sweepings left by gang sweepers or deposited by street sweeping machines where it is not feasible or economical for the stree cleaning agency to provide special collection equipment.

Major cities with large street cleaning sections find that it is advantageous to separate all street cleaning operations from regular refuse collection crews. Sweepings deposited by the street sweeping machines are usually collected by a truck equipped with a front-end-loading attachment. These trucks are routed to follow the street sweeping machine so that the pickup of street sweepings can be made shortly after it is deposited on the streets. The use of litter containers has grown to the extent that special attention must be given to the emptying of their contents. This is particularly true in those cities that utilize a large number of pole litter containers. Since these pole litter containers are small, it is necessary that they be emptied at frequent intervals. This cannot be done as a sideline by other crews, but it must be scheduled and worked by men and equipment who are responsible for this operation.

The street dirt picked up by "white wings" is often placed in metal cans or in canvas, paper, or burlap bags, and temporarily stored in out of the way places near the street cleaning routes. Many cities in striving for cleanliness find that the metal cans, drums, or loaded bags are unsightly and objectionable to their citizens. One solution to the problem is to provide large litter containers in each block with liners made of canvas in which the "white wings" can deposit sweepings from their carts. The contents of these containers would have to be collected daily. Another solution is to provide a truck and driver to the downtown area which would meet the "white wings" at regularly scheduled locations to collect the contents from their carts. The use of all-enclosed, compactor trucks facilitates collection work. The type and size of this equipment makes it possible for cans of street sweepings to be more readily emptied into the truck hopper, and less trips are required each day to the disposal area, saving much travel time for cleaning operations.

OTHER SPECIAL PROBLEM REFUSE

Large Branches and Christmas Trees

Almost all cities, even the very small ones, have purchased enclosed refuse compactor trucks for the hauling of garbage and household trash. This equipment has improved efficiency and reduced to a minimum the loss of refuse and need for tarpaulins or nets.

The problems of collecting large branches after storms, bundles of brush or hedge trimmings during the summer, and Christmas trees after this holiday have led some municipalities to find supplementary equipment to reduce bulk and the number of loads trucked to the disposal areas. A number of cities, especially in Florida and California because of climatic conditions, must collect large quantities of yard rubbish throughout the year. While some compactor trucks can be successfully and efficiently used, these cities find that they must maintain a sizable fleet of open-bodied trucks for rubbish removal. Large-bodied open trucks equipped with a chain bed for dumping answer the need of these cities. Some restriction must be placed on the size and weight of the material to be transported by these trucks. The ordinance of the City of Miami states, "Tree trunks or other branches of trees or shrubbery shall be cut into lengths of five (5) feet or less and no single piece shall exceed fifty (50) pounds in weight." All cities handling large amounts of yard rubbish have this restrictive clause in their ordinances.

Many cities now use wood-chipper machines—attached to open-bed trucks with canvas covers—or types of compactor trucks to reduce Christmas trees, small branches, and hedge trimmings to chips. Chipper machines reduce the bulk of the material so it can be disposed of by incineration if desired.

FIG. 9-2. Wood chippers have been found to be useful in reducing large branches to chips which can be easily collected and disposed in an incinerator or landfill. The wood chipper pictured above is medium-sized and handles up to four inch diameter limbs. (Asplundh Chipper Company)

Hazardous Materials

Many cities have found that hazardous materials have increased to the point where they have to prohibit their collection by municipal collection services and require the producer, owner, or his agent to dispose of them under conditions prescribed by the Director of Public Works. Hazardous materials include such things as cleaning fluids, crankcase oils, cutting oils, paints, plastics, explosives, acids, caustics, poisons, drugs, radio-active materials, and fine powdery earth.

Radio-active materials, drugs, poisons, and like substances should be required to be disposed of under the supervision of the Director of the Health Department.

The handling of material that is dangerous to the collector is recognized by all cities as a problem. Materials have caused serious injury to collectors and have caused much absenteeism. Many city ordinances demand that "all dangerous material, such as broken glass, light bulbs, razor blades, fluorescent tubes, etc. shall be deposited in an open, *disposable container* and placed alongside the regulation container for disposal."

Building Materials

Many cities do not consider it their job to collect materials left over from rebuilding or remodeling. Other cities limit the size and weight of building materials they will collect and also specify that such building material must originate from work done by the owner or tenant. If the work is done by a builder or contractor, the waste building materials must be removed by them. Certainly, all building materials from demolished buildings must be removed by the contractor. These materials usually have to be disposed of at the municipal refuse disposal area.

Large Furniture

Many cities do not collect large furniture, refrigerators, or stoves as part of the municipal refuse collection. On the other hand, many other cities do provide that all refuse from dwelling places and even small commercial establishments should be picked up by the municipal collection agency. With the large proportion of refuse trucks of the compactor type and with many mechanical incinerators, collection of large furniture does not ordinarily fit into the combustible refuse collection pattern. Several cities have found it necessary to provide for special pick-up of bulky items including large furniture.

One city has converted old refuse collection vehicles for use on street cleaning work and has assigned one open truck and a crew of three men to pick up divans, refrigerators, bedsprings, stoves, and old pianos. It was found that this procedure was most economical of equipment and manpower. When not needed for furniture pick-up, the open truck went on regular street cleaning detail, cleaning gratings over catch basins and heavy accumulation of dirt, sand, or leaves from gutters.

The majority of cities that do not collect large furniture, refrigerators, stoves, etc., on a regular schedule do accept and remove this type of material on annual or semi-annual clean-up drives.

Oil Containers

Since many cities do not pick up any commercial refuse, the oil cans from garages are usually taken by the owner or private collector to a landfill area.

For the cities that do pick up refuse from commercial establishments and have incinerators, the presentation of oil cans at garages may be a significant problem. Most garages wish to return the one or five-quart oil can, when emptied, to the carton in which it was received and then put it out for collection. However, it is desirable that oil cans be separated at the garage, compressed by some means, and put out in a regulation container for collection with noncombustible refuse. When this has been done the paper cartons can be broken down and tied in bundles for collection as combustible refuse.

ANNUAL OR SEMI-ANNUAL RUBBISH COLLECTION

Many cities collect at public expense only garbage or garbage with combustible rubbish, expecting householders or property owners either to remove the other refuse themselves or to employ licensed private collectors to dispose of it. Unfortunately, under this system, some people will allow large quantities of ashes and rubbish to accumulate in alleys, backyards, and basements so that large sections of the city become littered and disorderly in appearance and fire hazards are created. Municipal officials have these choices: (1) Enforce the ordinances prohibiting nuisances, insanitary conditions, or littering. (2) Provide regular collection service for ashes and rubbish. (3) Collect such material once or twice a year. Because enforcement is usually difficult and unpopular, numerous cities designate certain periods as "clean-up weeks," during which time refuse is collected free by special forces.

FIG. 9-3. Huge quantities of rubbish may accumulate at properties in communities that do not give regular removal service. Only annual or semi-annual collections are made in some of these cities. The usual practice during the clean-up weeks is for the refuse collectors to collect everything that is placed at curbs or alleys by the householders.

It is not to be inferred that all "clean-up weeks" are compromises between complete refuse service and littered communities or between complete service and adequate enforcement of laws and regulations. For many cities, particularly the smaller ones, annual or semi-annual collection of ashes and certain rubbish provides a suitable or desired standard of service. Also, there may be other municipalities where the majority of the citizens dispose of all or a large part of their refuse regularly and clean-up periods are used to correct conditions in relatively small areas. Refuse collection officials point out, however, that the lack of regular rubbish or ash collection may lead to conditions as expensive to correct as the provision of adequate service. Promiscuous dumping of refuse on vacant property, on streets and alleys, in manholes and catch basins, and in other prohibited places cannot be entirely controlled even when rigid enforcement is attempted. Street littering is increased by the careless transportation of refuse by individual householders, resulting in added street cleaning expense. The cost of supervising dumping areas is increased when many citizens haul their own refuse to dumps.

Several years ago the consequence of incomplete collection service was strikingly revealed by a study in Pittsburgh. At that time, garbage and rubbish were collected regularly but ashes were picked up only once a year during a spring clean-up campaign. The total cost of making the annual ash collection, of removing ashes from vacant properties, streets, catch basins, and sewers, and of collecting the ashes illegally concealed in garbage and rubbish containers was computed to be $225,000, whereas the estimated cost of providing weekly collection for this class of refuse was $256,240.

Tremendous quantities of ashes and rubbish are hauled away during annual collections, but the total amount in any community is certainly much less than would have been picked up if regular service were given. Much of the combustible rubbish is probably burned in furnaces or trash burners as it is produced and considerable quantities are more or less regularly hauled away by the householders or private collectors. Nevertheless, it has become rather usual in some cities for householders to store until late in the spring all the ashes and noncombustible rubbish produced in the fall and winter months.

The different practices in storing large quantities of rubbish and ashes depend in a large measure on the points at which the material will be accepted for collection. Private collectors will carry the refuse from any place it is kept, and often tub it from basements, from garages, or other outbuildings, or from storage vaults anywhere on the premises of the householder. Their fees depend on the difficulty of collection and the total amount of work involved. Municipal agencies, however, usually require the householders to place the refuse at curbs or in alleys for spring or fall collections in order to keep the expense at a minimum. Where there is an alley, the householder usually stores the material near the alley property line, and sometimes in the alley itself, to avoid having to rehandle it during the clean-up period. He may place it in open piles, in barrels, in boxes, or in other receptacles, or in concrete or brick storage vaults. Often the accumulation overflows the containers provided.

If collections are made from curbs, the residents must carry all of the stored material to the streets. Some cities insist that it be placed in some kind of container, but others permit it to be piled in lawn strips, on sidewalks, or even in the gutters. There are some cities in which the municipal collectors will carry the refuse from back doors, from storage vaults in backyards, or from buildings.

Because it is ordinarily not feasible to have the regular garbage collection forces participate in spring or fall clean-up activities, it is necessary to organize special crews and to provide additional equipment. Usually, the facilities of other municipal departments and agencies are used to the greatest possible extent. Typically, employees and suitable equipment which can be temporarily released from street, sewer, water, and street cleaning departments are employed in clean-up collection activities. Where necessary, dump trucks are rented from contractors or hauling companies, and temporary helpers are hired. The severe load placed on the city at such times is similar to loads after hurricanes, ice storms or heavy snowfall.

FIG. 9-4. Yard rubbish constitutes a large part of the refuse collected in Miami. The use of a clam shovel bucket and crane to load the yard rubbish from the curb has been found to be more economical than hand labor.

Householders and property owners must receive adequate notice of a clean-up collection so they can prepare the refuse and place it for collection at the proper time. Newspaper advertisements and articles are usually used for this purpose but some cities also distribute notices or have the regular refuse collection employees notify each householder

In addition to the time of collection, information is given on the proper location for collection, kinds of materials that will be accepted, and suitable preparation of the refuse. Ordinarily no quantity limitations are imposed upon householders during clean-up weeks.

PASSAGE OF COLLECTION VEHICLES ON PRIVATE PROPERTY

As a general rule it is better for municipal vehicles to use public right of way for passage. This is particularly applicable to modern refuse collection vehicles because of their size and weight. For example, residential driveways are usually not designed to support heavy vehicles and maneuvering collection vehicles in areas with restricted passage on a routine basis lends itself to accidental damage or destruction of property.

In many cities it is much more convenient to the private citizen or businessman for the refuse to be placed so that the collection vehicle will have to travel over private rights of way. In New York City, such a situation is handled by requiring the home or business owner concerned to specifically request such service and sign an agreement releasing the city from all liability for personal and property damage resulting from the provision of this special service.

There have been a number of cases where the municipality has been sued for injuries inflicted by the alleged negligent operation of a refuse collection truck. Generally, in the absence of a statute, the city is not considered liable for an injury inflicted by the negligent operation of a refuse truck in the performance of a *governmental function*. However, the municipality may be held liable if at the time of the accident the vehicle was being negligently operated in the performance of a *corporate or proprietary function.*[1]

In Massachusetts, for example, it has been ruled that the removal of ashes by a city from private premises is a public duty and the city is not liable for negligence.[2] The California Vehicle Code and the Ohio Statutes, however, are examples where municipalities are rendered liable for injury to person or property as a result of negligent operation. The courts are not in complete agreement on the question of whether the collection of refuse is a governmental or corporate or proprietary function.[3] Therefore, it is very important that such matters be discussed thoroughly with the municipal attorney before any decision relative to vehicular use of private thoroughfares is reached.

[1] Eugene McQuillin, *The Law of Municipal Corporations* (3rd ed.; Chicago: Callaghan and Co., 1949-51), Vol. 18, p. 261.

[2] *Haley v. Boston*, 191 Mass, 291, 77 N. E. 888, 5 L. R. A. (N. S.) 1005.

[3] O. C. Peterson, "Public Liability in Public Works," *Public Works Engineers' Yearbook* (Chicago: American Public Works Association, 1955).

chapter 10

MUNICIPAL, CONTRACT OR PRIVATE COLLECTION OF REFUSE

Should the community's refuse be collected by municipal forces, by contract from the municipality, or by private collectors? Is there some combination of these methods which would be more advantageous to the community? These are questions which are frequently being raised because of dissatisfaction with the existing collection service, demands for increased service, pressure from private firms or individuals or unions interested in various phases of refuse collection and disposal, or because of general agitation to reduce the cost of operations. The issues are also raised when public officials, elected or appointed, find it necessary to introduce proposals for changes in, or expansion of existing refuse collection services, regulations or fees, new landfills, incinerators or other collection or disposal facilities.

In general there is good evidence that municipal collection and disposal of refuse gives the most satisfactory results in most American and Canadian communities. It must be strongly emphasized, however, that no categorical answer can be given as to the best plan or combination of plans to employ. The factors which must be taken into consideration by the officials responsible for decisions in these matters, vary so greatly that comparisons between communities are most difficult and frequently misleading. Unfortunately, decisions are too often made without proper detailed consideration of the total volume of all classes of refuse generated in the community, how these are stored, collected, delivered to the disposal point, and the problems encountered in their collection and disposal. Before adopting or changing methods of refuse collection and disposal, comprehensive analyses must therefore be made of all pertinent factors as they pertain to or are affected by local conditions.

DEFINITION OF MUNICIPAL, CONTRACT, AND PRIVATE COLLECTION

It is desirable to define the terms used to designate the three types of collection service because somewhat divergent meanings have been implied in writings on this subject and in ordinances. The distinctions observed in this discussion are as follows:

"Municipal collection" involves the performance of the collection operations by city employees and equipment under the supervision and direction of a regular municipal department or official, just as such public functions as street cleaning, sewer maintenance, or pavement repair are conducted.

"Contract collection" consists of the engagement by cities of private companies under formal agreements and definite specifications to collect and haul municipal refuse, for which the contractors are paid from general public revenues or service fees collected by the city. Usually the contracts are awarded on a competitive basis to the lowest responsible bidder, and contractors must furnish suitable performance bonds.

"Private collection" involves the collection by individuals or companies of refuse materials from private properties, the arrangements for which service are made directly between the owner or occupier of the premises and the collector. Often such collections are as regular and as systematic as municipal and contract operations, but in some cases the private collector conducts his business on the basis of individual orders, much as a hauling company. Private collectors usually operate under city licenses or franchises. Municipal regulation may be extensive or may be confined simply to enforcing general public health and nuisance ordinances. The amount of the charges for private collection service is in some cases fixed by ordinance, but usually the collectors are free to make independent agreements with their customers.

Where an individual collector or company is granted an exclusive privilege to conduct the refuse collection business for an entire city and has a formal contract or franchise with the municipality, there is some confusion as to the classification of the services. The significant point of distinction is not that a contract or franchise is in force, but that the collector is paid by his customers—not by the city—for the service rendered. These collectors with exclusive privileges are actually private collectors as that term is used in this discussion.

It is difficult at times to differentiate between contract and private services in cities where arrangements are made for individuals or companies to collect municipal refuse for its value as hog feed or fertilizer or for its salvage value. Since neither the householder and commercial or industrial firms nor the cities make money payments in such cases, the service category in a theoretical analysis would depend on whether the refuse used for payment belongs to the householder and firms or to the cities. The practices, however, conform more nearly to those of private collectors and consequently such operators are designated here as private collectors even though they may operate under formal agreements.

This category must also include private truckers and haulers who, incidental to their hauling and delivery contracts with commercial and industrial firms, also undertake to haul the wastes from such firms. Furthermore, firms frequently have their own fleet of trucks and may haul their own refuse.

The main points of distinction may thus be summarized as follows:

Municipal: city pays employees; operation by city departments.

Contract: city pays contractor for doing collection work.

Private: citizens, or firms, individually, or in limited groups pay collectors or private operating agencies.

PRESENT USE OF THE THREE SYSTEMS

In most cities and communities there is usually a combination of methods of collecting the various forms of refuse. A study of any community's methods would not be complete, however, unless consideration has been given not only to the collection but also to the methods and facilities employed in disposal. Information gathered from other cities may therefore often be incomplete and must be used with caution. Table 10-1 shows the numbers of cities, grouped by population, reporting the use of municipal, contract or private methods of collection and the relative number that have various combinations of these methods.

Table 10-1
Type of Collection Agency Used in 995 Cities in 1964

| Method | Population in 1000's | | | | | | | | |
	5-10	10-25	25-50	50-100	100-1000	1000 and more	Not Stated	Total	Per Cent
Municipal	116	172	92	34	29	—	3	446	45
Contract	54	70	30	13	7	—	1	175	18
Private	49	43	20	12	3	—	3	130	13
Municipal and Private	15	46	27	22	34	4	3	151	15
Municipal and Contract	1	10	12	8	1	—	1	33	3
Municipal, Contract, Private	3	4	6	1	1	1	—	16	2
Contract and Private	8	14	12	7	3	—	—	44	4
Totals	246	359	199	97	78	5	11	995	100

Forty-five per cent of the cities reporting have complete municipal service and 65 per cent have complete or partial municipal service. There is a noticeable indication that the larger cities incline toward combined municipal and private collection and 44 per cent of the cities over 100,000 fall in this category. A further 34 per cent of this group have municipal collection whereas only 8 per cent have contract and 6 per cent have private collection.

TRENDS

In general the usual process of development of refuse collection systems has been as follows: At first if the community had no organized service, private collectors or private collection enterprises established businesses for the purpose of removing refuse from the premises of those who were able and willing to pay for the service. The next step involved public financing of the collection activity and the extension of the service to all residential and other properties, often by contract under performance specifications. Then as the city grew, as administrative facilities improved and as the standards of sanitation and service developed still further, the main part of the service was conducted as a municipal function by city employees, private haulers perhaps continuing to collect from many of the business and industrial firms.

There is no doubt that this pattern of development has been followed in many cities, but the question of the relative merits of private and contract operation compared to municipal operation can hardly be dismissed as simply an evolutionary tendency, for many large cities still operate successfully under the contract plan or under the private collection arrangement.

The factors which have probably contributed most to the trend for municipal or partial municipal collection are the age of cities; the increasing emphasis on sanitation; the increasing demand and willingness to pay for better service; the "glamorization" of the refuse collection industry; and the trend toward increased efficiency and better management in municipal administration.

The following tabulation shows a comparison of the types of collection agency used by cities surveyed in 1939, 1955 and 1964. Certain trends

Table 10-2
Type of Collection Agency Used by Cities in 1939, 1955 and 1964

Collection Agency	A 1939 Survey Number of Cities	%	B 1955 Survey Number of Cities	%	C 1964 Survey Number of Cities	%
Municipal..................	105	55	494	55	446	45
Contract..................	34	18	134	15	175	18
Private....................	20	11	95	11	130	13
Mun. & Private............	20	10	51	6	151	15
Mun. & Contract..........	4	2	72	8	33	3
Mun., Con., Private........	—	—	26	3	16	2
Contract & Private.........	7	4	21	2	49	5
Total..................	190		893		995	

are indicated but because of the possible variances in the methods of reporting and the number of cities which replied in the years shown, care should be exercised in drawing conclusions. This is further substantiated by the fact that there are certain compensating trends which no doubt tend to distort apparent trends. Most noticeable is the decrease by 10 per cent in the percentage of cities having municipal collection only and the corresponding increase by 9 per cent in those having combined municipal and private collection. At the same time the percentage of cities using combined municipal and contract collection has decreased by 5 per cent and the percentage of cities with either municipal or partial municipal collection has decreased by 7 per cent from 72 per cent to 65 per cent since 1955.

MUNICIPAL RESPONSIBILITY FOR REFUSE COLLECTION

It is generally accepted that refuse collection is a governmental function in the sense that public interest is so greatly affected that cities must take positive action to see that adequate service is available or that the householders and other producers of waste materials handle and dispose of their refuse without endangering or annoying other citizens. It has been held by the courts that "in disposing of its garbage and in letting a contract therefore, a municipality acts in its governmental capacity and not in its corporate or private capacity."

Although cities are responsible for the proper handling, collection, and hauling of municipal refuse, they are generally unrestricted in deciding how the work shall be done. In the last analysis, public desires and standards will control the methods employed, at least in the long run. The attitude of the citizens dictates the extent to which collection service will be provided from public funds and determines its character. Where public confidence in government operation is lacking, contract operation will be demanded.

Regardless of the method adopted for conducting the actual collection operations, it is generally accepted that municipalities have definite responsibility for seeing that the collection and hauling work is done in a sanitary manner and that nuisances are not created through the storage or handling of the refuse. The amount of municipal control over the actions of citizens and collectors on matters of handling waste materials varies widely among communities, both as to the extent of the regulatory provisions in ordinances and administrative rules and as to the extent to which these regulations are enforced. General legislation, however, is normally adopted for the following:

1. Controlling the handling and storage of refuse materials on private properties, including the kind of containers that may be used, length of time of storage and provisions against littering of private premises.

2. Controlling methods and equipment employed in collection and hauling of refuse.

3. Prohibiting the littering of streets or other public areas and the dumping of refuse in such places or on private properties, unless specifically approved for such purpose.

4. Empowering health, police, fire or public works officials to enforce the prohibition of any practices which may endanger public health, create insanitary conditions, or cause nuisances.

5. Setting up schedules of fees, charges and penalties.

IS REFUSE COLLECTION A PUBLIC FUNCTION?

The use of the private collection method cannot be entirely due to an unwillingness to finance the operations from public funds because cities can, and do, provide municipal service and charge service fees similar to the charges made by private collectors. It is more likely that the individualistic attitude is still strong enough in some cities to prevent the acceptance of refuse collection as a public function or the expenditure of any public funds for this purpose. That this attitude is rather widely held is evidenced by the general tendency of cities to provide only partial collection service at public expense. As we have seen, many cities even yet leave all or a considerable part of the collection work to private collectors.

REVIEW AND ANALYSIS OF COLLECTION METHODS BY REFUSE ADMINISTRATION

The collection and disposal of the community's refuse represents one of its major and costliest problems and those public officials who administer these services must provide at the lowest cost and with minimum nuisance, the level of service desired by the citizens served. Demands for changes are usually being made on such officials because of dissatisfaction with existing services or as a result of proposals received from various persons or groups. Officials who are unable to meet such demands with up-to-date, thorough and factual data for all aspects of their operations, and knowledge of trends elsewhere, often either allow or are forced to accept changes which in the long run are not in the interest of the community. There is therefore a definite responsibility for refuse administrators to periodically make comprehensive analyses of their collection and disposal operations and where necessary or desirable, to either introduce changes themselves or offer factual support or opposition to proposals put forward by others. Proposals involving changes in collection methods are often originated and promoted by persons whose intentions are not in the best interests of the people served. They are often introduced when it is known they will receive considerable attention because of public dissatisfaction with existing service or because of current political activities. The size and complexities of the refuse problem demands that officials meet such proposals with a sound, analytical approach and proven techniques instead of rules of thumb, guesses, partial estimates and prejudiced opinions.

As a result of a noticeable trend toward organization and expansion of the private refuse collection industry, and in some cases a willingness to pay for better service, many communities are receiving proposals for increased or improved service through contract or private collection and disposal. The analysis and report on such proposals by the officials concerned often involves the preparation of detailed specifications or regulations and comparisons with existing services. This alone may be the first important step from a poorly run or out-of-date municipal operation to a good one and if taken advantage of, may lead to improvements which may preclude going to contract or private collection.

When reviewing collection methods and operations or analyzing proposals, officials concerned should include possibilities of making better use of services, facilities and techniques which may be available in other sections of the city service. An ailing municipal refuse operation may, for example, be upgraded by arrangements with other departments or sharing or pooling of the use of manpower, equipment, yard and storage areas, repair and service facilities and of the services of accounting, billing, personnel, pay roll and other sections.

COST COMPARISONS FOR MUNICIPAL, CONTRACT, AND PRIVATE COLLECTION

It is obvious that if valid cost comparisons are to be made between methods of collection, refuse officials and administrators must insist that an equitable basis of comparison be established and that some recognized form of cost analysis such as total annual cost be used. The pros and cons of various proposals involving the three methods will, when analyzed, have considerable bearing on decisions but in the long run total annual cost must remain the most important deciding factor. It follows that poor decisions will be reached if attempts are made to compare total annual cost of schemes in which elements such as the level of service are unequal. The annual cost of a poorly supervised municipal service with old, worn-out equipment should not, for example, be compared to a proposed contract system which would be required to give better service with more modern equipment. Proper analysis may prove that the most economical approach can be achieved by reorganization and up-grading of the municipal system to provide the desired level of service which the contract method would have to meet.

COMPARISONS BETWEEN CONTRACT OR PRIVATE SPECIFICATIONS AND MUNICIPAL REGULATIONS

It has often been said that if as much care could be taken in the preparation and enforcement of rules and regulations for municipal refuse collection as there is in the preparation and enforcement of detailed specifications for contract or private collection, there would be far more successful municipal operations. Specifications defining a contractor's or private collector's duties and responsibilities and stipulating the conditions of the agreement are essential and exceedingly valuable, for if properly prepared they provide a clear statement of policies, methods and procedures. Many municipal agencies would be in a much better position if they had as clear a code of practice and policy, if they made sure it was kept up to date and if they devoted as much effort to its inspection and enforcement.

POLITICAL INTERFERENCE

In the democratic society it is essential and desirable that elected political bodies make decisions and formulate policies which will enable them to exercise proper control over the public functions within their jurisdiction. After such policies have been established and as decisions are made, the administrative details must become the responsibility of the appointed officials. Whereas political control and decision are necessary and proper, political interference with the administrative function is undesirable and improper and invariably leads to dissatisfaction, poor administration and inefficiency.

Unfortunately, political interference is prevalent in the refuse collection systems in many cities. The refuse collection service is particularly attractive to political bosses because of the great number of employees that must be hired to drive trucks, collect and dispose of refuse. Many politicians believe that anyone can fill such positions satisfactorily, although this notion has been positively disproved in numerous cities and municipalities that have operated under good and bad personnel administration. Such experience has proven that it is not true for operators and helpers and that it is far less true for inspectors, foremen, supervisors and superintendents.

Political interference in personnel and other matters such as the purchase of equipment, union activities, and the award of contracts relative to collection or disposal almost invariably results in demoralization of the administrative staffs, favoritism, inefficiency and irregularities and inequities in the level of service provided. The result can only be poor service and unnecessary high cost to the taxpayer. Furthermore, it is not only municipal refuse collection and disposal systems that are subject to the activities of the political machine. Contract and private systems are also affected, perhaps by more subtle means, but with the same highly undesirable results to the citizen.

Obviously the ability of senior officials and administrators to cope with the problem of political interference in such matters as refuse collections and disposal may be somewhat limited but it should be the ultimate objective of all levels of the administration to eliminate political interference entirely from such operations. It follows that careful consideration and analysis of this factor must be included in studies involving municipal, contract and private refuse collection.

MUNICIPAL COLLECTION OF REFUSE

Under sound, nonpolitical management, municipal operation is economical, satisfactory to householders and citizens, beneficial from a public health standpoint, and a credit to the community. In other circumstances it may be less efficient and less desirable than possible alternative arrangements. For good municipal operation there must be a desire on the part of city officials to provide honestly and efficiently the kind of service wanted by the citizens, and a sound, modern administration to secure it. This implies capable management, qualified personnel, adequate equipment, and freedom from the meddling of politics. With such administration, it can be said fairly that municipal collection is more likely to promote effective and economical service than either of the other plans.

Non-Profit Service

Because it does not have to earn a profit nor pay income tax, municipal collection has a substantial initial advantage in a comparative evaluation on a cost basis. To provide the same service a contractor must be able to do the work at sufficiently less cost to make up for the profit he must gain, plus the municipal expense of supervising his operation, and the expense of his license. In addition, contractors and private collectors must include taxes and interest on capital in their costs—items which municipalities do not have to meet, unless funds for purchasing the equipment or other plant and facilities are raised by borrowing. Most cities are able, through quantity purchasing, to provide equipment, gasoline, oil, parts, tires and other supplies at costs considerably lower than contractors would have to meet. Relative security of employment, pension plans, etc., provide more incentive for city forces than is usually available from contractors. Furthermore, cost advantages and better service are usually available to a municipal agency which uses the city's central facilities for equipment service and repair, accounting, billing, personnel, payroll and similar functions.

In view of these advantages it is not difficult to understand that some cities are able to operate municipal services at a considerable saving to their citizens. Valid cost comparisons are difficult, however, unless the standards of service in each case are very carefully defined. In city collection systems it is sometimes difficult to keep the standard from creeping upward so that the service provided becomes much better and more extensive than would be given by contractors or private collectors.

Emphasis on Sanitation and Appearance

Municipalities operating their own refuse collection service are motivated by the desire to protect public health, prevent insanitary conditions, and improve community appearance. Because of their direct responsibility to the people, municipal employees often provide numerous extra services and exercise greater care in handling and loading refuse than is expected or realized from contractors or private collectors. The operators of collection businesses as a rule do as little as possible to improve community conditions, for to them such extra services mean decreased profits. As is natural under the circumstances, they are more inclined to increase production speed by doing the minimum required to meet the contract requirements.

Under municipal operation it is much easier for city officials to respond to legitimate requests of citizens for improved community appearance. Extensive efforts can be more easily made to reduce the amount of littering by citizens and by the collection forces and in many places the unsightliness of the collection service and equipment has thus been eliminated. It is notable that the increase in the use of attractive and enclosed collection vehicles and in the uniforming of employees has occurred most in municipally conducted services.

Response to Complaints

Courteous and prompt response to citizen complaints is one of the more outstanding characteristics of municipal service. Most municipal officials take advantage of the opportunity to improve public relations by immediate investigation of all complaints and by correcting any undesirable condition caused by the operation of the collection system. Nuisances and insanitary conditions or other conditions not the responsibility of the refuse service can easily be referred to the department responsible. To provide the same level of complaint service for contract or private collection a city would have to employ many more inspectors and special pick-up vehicles and in most cases would be unable to pass the charges on to the collection company.

Co-operation of Citizens

If refuse collection operations are to be successful in terms either of economy or effectiveness of the service, the active co-operation of citizens is essential. The proper handling and storage of refuse, regularity in the placing of containers for collection, and restraint in littering are all essential to efficient operations. Experience has proven that the good will and assistance of householders and property owners can be more readily secured under good municipal management. Comparable levels of co-operative spirit have rarely been developed under contract or private operations because it is difficult to convince people that they have anything to gain by making the work easier for the private enterprises. Furthermore, contractors do not have adequate police power to enforce regulations, and city officials seldom are ready to give them aid.

Relative Cost of Municipal Collection

The cost of municipal refuse collection service may be much less than that of contract or private operation or it may be decidedly greater, depending in large measure on the character of the management. In almost all cases of abandonment of municipal collection systems the main reason has been the high costs that accompany poor administration. Not all of these failures, however, have been caused by incompetent supervision and direction, for political interference and shortsighted policies on the part of city councils have often thwarted able and conscientious managers. Regardless of the reasons, however, it is obvious that cost of service is the most important single factor in judging the success of any of the methods, or combination of methods, of collection. It is equally obvious that if proper use is made of the advantages available to the municipal method of collection, cities can compete effectively in this field by adopting sound principles of administration, progressive management methods and up-to-date equipment.

Refuse handling costs are much higher than they need to be in many communities because of miserly policies, buying equipment on a lowest first cost basis, and the emphasis on cheapness (unwillingness to spend adequate sums of money), rather than on overall efficiency. Undoubtedly there are many sincere officials and administrators who, in the belief that they are serving the best interests of the taxpayers, have prevented effective and economical management and operation by adherence to such shortsighted policies. It is most unfortunate that such mistaken and uninformed attitudes should still prevail in this relatively large and important area of municipal operation. Though they have sometimes resulted in the abandonment of inefficient and costly municipal operation, they have often led to the adoption of contract or private operations which have proven to be even more unsatisfactory and more costly to the taxpayer.

More progressive cities and administrators have realized that basically there is very little difference between municipal refuse collection systems and comparable private enterprises insofar as their requirements for the efficient co-ordination of large numbers of men and many units of expensive equipment are concerned. It is to their credit that by adopting modern business and administrative techniques and procedures they have been able to periodically analyze parts or all of their operation, determine areas of high cost or inefficiency and introduce changes and improvements to produce a less costly and more acceptable service.

To keep the relative costs of municipal collection down, it is necessary to critically examine at regular intervals all aspects of the operation and to employ work study, recording and costing methods which will produce reliable information on which to base recommendations for improvement. Details of factors involved and the techniques employed are discussed elsewhere in this manual but the following is an indication of the type of questions which must be examined in detail:

How many hours and minutes of effective work does each man do in a shift or a week and how can this be increased? How much time is required for each crew to travel to and from each route, between pick-ups, from route to disposal point? How many cans, cubic yards or tons of refuse are handled by each crew each day and how does this compare with other routes? Would more or better supervision produce a lower overall cost? By providing larger or different collection equipment can the number of men be reduced, or the daily volume per crew increased or the travel time reduced? Should the frequency of pick-up, number, size or type of containers be changed to increase efficiency?

Advantages of Municipal Operation

1. Profits do not have to be earned. Therefore the collection work can be less expensive by the amount of the profit, or additional service can be given.

2. Municipalities, particularly those of large size, can usually purchase collection trucks, gasoline, oil, tires, and other operating supplies at a price advantage not available to contractors or private collectors.

3. Since municipal operations do not involve profit, they are not subject to state or federal taxes, hence these costs are not passed on to the citizens.

4. Requests and complaints by citizens are usually given more prompt and more courteous attention and more uniform interpretation and enforcement of regulations results.

5. Sanitation and the protection of public health are the primary aims.

6. There is greater probability of obtaining qualified employees under modern municipal merit systems. Better selection and training of workers are possible.

7. Though higher wages and fringe benefits may be paid, actual

operating costs for similar kinds of service are less than those of contractors or private collectors if the municipal operations are ably and properly administered.

8. Management and policies are continuous over a long period, making it possible to profit from experience and training. Long-range plans can be developed.

9. Greater flexibility in operations can be secured by transferring employees and equipment to and from municipal refuse agencies. Likewise, the facilities of these agencies can be used effectively on emergency activities such as snow removal and clearing after storms.

10. Continuous records can be maintained over a long period of time and these are invaluable in the efficient management of the collection activities.

11. Citizens co-operate more readily and more effectively under municipal operation than under privately controlled enterprises.

12. Operations are more flexible than under the contract method. Adjustments and corrections can be made when necessary.

13. All details of control and administration remain with the responsible agency.

14. Detailed work studies may be made as required and systematic records set up as a guide to changes in policies or methods.

15. Advantage can be taken of the integration of services and facilities with other municipal departments.

16. If the administration is progressive, changes may be introduced at any time to take advantage of technological improvement of methods, equipment, accounting, etc.

Disadvantages of Municipal Operation

1. The entire collection service may be demoralized, service may be poor and costs too high when operations are subjected to political interference. Employees appointed on a political basis are usually unqualified and inefficient and their loyalty is to the political machine rather than to the community and its administrative officials.

2. Many councils and officials favor cheapness instead of economy in administration. Inadequate salaries for supervisory positions make it impossible to secure qualified administrators. The failure to replace equipment that has served its economically useful life results in inefficient operation.

3. The tendency to provide unreasonably extravagant service to complainants beyond that given to the majority of citizens results in excessive cost.

4. The failure of municipalities to provide adequate retirement plans for their employees often results in the retention or transfer to the refuse collection service of aged workers and those with disabilities, with the inevitable results of ineffectiveness and higher cost.

5. In general in municipal service it is more difficult and takes longer to remove inefficient employees.
6. Costs may be higher because of failure to use the labor force most effectively. In many cities actual working time is less than on comparable private jobs and direct work incentives are not generally accepted in municipal service.
7. Because the major emphasis is on sanitation and appearance and because municipal governments are not in a position to risk public funds on salvaging materials for which there is a fluctuating market, municipalities often cannot take advantage of salvaging methods employed by contractors and private collectors.

CONTRACT COLLECTION OF REFUSE

Before reaching a decision on whether to use or continue the contract method of refuse collection a number of factors should receive very careful analysis by public officials and administrators. These factors vary considerably with existing local conditions and the problem is therefore one of honestly, impartially and thoroughly analyzing (costwise and otherwise) the advantages and disadvantages of each.

It is usually found that a great deal of lobbying, promotion and political influence are generated by proposals involving contract collection Unfortunately such proposals are often advanced when the administration is in difficulty over dissatisfaction with existing service, or with the introduction of changes to collection and disposal methods. Under these circumstances, when local officials find it difficult to ensure that all factors are being properly recognized, analyzed and fairly presented serious consideration should be given to engaging qualified consultants to handle the problem.

The claim that there is greater economy in performing the work is usually the strongest argument presented by proponents of the contract method of refuse collection. This is widely accepted by those with the somewhat biased opinion that any activity can be conducted at less cost by private enterprise than by cities or municipalities because of superior management policies and methods. Arguments are also advanced that contractors will render satisfactory and effective service simply because it is good business to do so, that the profit incentive is a strong motive for efficient management, that contractors make more effective use of labor and equipment, and that there is less political interference.

Those opposed to contract collection point to examples of failure of this method in other cities where dissatisfaction with the service has led citizens to demand changes or where it is evident that the contractor has not used acceptable business methods. They also cite examples where contracts do not provide for adequate wage rates or acceptable working conditions, where agreements are made on the political rather than on the competitive basis, where once established the costs have risen unreasonably or the grade of service has declined.

It must be abundantly clear that all the arguments for and against the contract method of collection may be substantiated to a lesser or greater degree by evidence and opinions from many sources. The real problem is to analyze and cost all relevant arguments and factors as they are affected by existing local conditions. Advantages of contract collection in one community may be disadvantages under conditions prevailing in another community, and vice versa.

Political Interference and Contract Collection

In some cities collection operations under contract may be free from the political interference to which a municipal operation would be subjected. The duties and responsibilities of the contractors as set out in the agreements and specifications should therefore prevent special favors or extra services being given as political rewards. The contractor has to provide a specified service at a definite rate or for a definite amount of money. With no political interference the amount of his profits will be determined by his ability to select employees carefully according to their ability to do the work, to use equipment best suited to the particular operation, and to employ the best management principles in the conduct of his business.

If contracts are not awarded strictly on the basis of honest, open competition but are granted in reward for political services or loyalty, or for donations to party funds, the benefits inherent to the contract plan may disappear. The payments to contractors in such circumstances are often much larger than they should be and the collection jobs and equipment purchase orders may be improperly awarded to party workers. In extreme cases the collection system may be to all practical purposes operated by the political machine. Thus, even though the actual work of collecting refuse may be done efficiently, most of the advantages and benefits will accrue to the political organization and not to the people of the community.

Length of the Contract Period

Refuse collection contracts must be of sufficient duration to make it feasible for the contractor to purchase and amortize the equipment and facilities necessary to provide effective service. Usually several months are needed to install and adjust a contract system for the first time. Many contracts are made for five-year terms although the period may be as short as one or two years or as high as ten years, depending on local circumstances. Five years is considered a reasonable time for amortization of vehicle costs but such a period is considered too short to recover the capital investment in transfer facilities, disposal plants or garage facilities. Many cities are unwilling to let contracts for more than five or seven years because of the probability of important changes in conditions, many of which cannot be foreseen at the time the negotiations are conducted. Sometimes cities will either arrange to provide certain buildings and other facilities or, where the contractor has provided them, to take them over at previously agreed upon depreciated amounts, in the event of termination of the agreement.

It is quite unlikely that in any community there will be many individuals or companies experienced in the operation of large refuse collection enterprises. Consequently there will not be many responsible persons willing to compete for a contract which requires such large capital outlay and detailed technical experience, unless the contract is long enough to make it possible to recover from the initial period of high costs involved in experiment, adjustment and familiarization. It may be doubtful if five years is enough time for a previously inexperienced organization to achieve the most efficient operation and to iron out all the weaknesses and problems that inevitably develop in setting up a contract collection system for the first time. These factors would tend to make the average costs over the beginning of the contract period much higher than over the latter part of the period. Of course if, after public tenders have been called, subsequent contracts are being negotiated with the same contractor the advantages of experience, technical study and adjustments should lead to lower costs to the contractor and the possibility of lower contract prices to the community.

In practice, contracts lapse more often than they are renewed, with the result that cities may be faced with successive periods of adjustment to new contractors. Furthermore, the 1964 survey indicated that of the cities using the contract method, 78 per cent employed only one contractor. Unfortunately no tabulation was made of the period of contracts involved but these factors, together with other considerations discussed, have tended to establish the five-year period for the majority of contracts.

Effective Use of Labor by Contractors

It is often said that contractors are able to use labor more effectively than municipal agencies. Such a general statement should not be accepted as an argument in favor of contract refuse collection until it has been established by careful analysis that such is actually the case if all relative conditions in the community being considered are taken into account. No doubt the statement is true in many cases but this should not rule out the possibility of criticism of this aspect of a contractor's operation, nor of improvement in the same aspect of a municipal operation in that community. Some contractors (and some cities) have adopted modern methods of personnel management to increase production and employee earnings through work incentive plans whereby the workers are able to earn, in proportion to output, somewhat more than the prevailing daily wages. Objections have been raised to the piece-work type of incentive plan in refuse collection operations because they encourage dishonest scale operation, load padding, dissatisfaction amongst some employees and objections from unions. Contractors make more use of incentive plans than do cities, but a noticeable trend toward more progressive personnel management and labor relation policies and an interest in work measurement and work standards in municipal administration will tend to increase productivity of municipal forces.

The contract method of operation has been severely criticized on numerous occasions for the exploitation of labor, extremely low wages, long hours and unsatisfactory working conditions. In some cases contractors have taken advantage of local conditions or unemployment periods to reduce wages below subsistence levels. This objection to the contract method is not as important now as in past years because labor is better organized in most parts of this continent and cities have stipulated in their contracts and specifications the minimum wages that contractors can pay for the various kinds of work. It is often very difficult to detect and prove actual violation of such clauses.

Salvage or Use of Refuse by Contractors

The prodigious amount of waste of everyday materials in cities on this continent as compared to other parts of the world would seem to justify attempts to use salvage as a means of offsetting collection costs. Where contractors are able to use or dispose of some of the collected material profitably, such as by sale of garbage to hog farms or by salvage and sale of selected materials, they may be able to submit somewhat lower bids. Proposals for contract collection of refuse are frequently accompanied by over-promotion of the idea of salvage or use of part of the material and this may appeal to some as an apparent means of reducing collection costs. The record indicates that with very few exceptions, most cities have found that salvage operations are not aesthetically nor economically practicable. Proposals from contractors who offer low prices because of their intention to use or salvage part of the collected materials must therefore be investigated with caution.

Specifications for Contract Operations

Before a contract can be let for refuse collection, detailed specifications must be drawn up so that all who are interested can bid on an equal basis. Specifications are the heart of any contract. They cover the obligations of both parties and describe the service to be rendered. It is manifestly impossible to forecast exactly the work to be done in this type of a service contract, so various means have to be devised to prescribe or measure performance. Before the specifications are drawn up, the conditions under which a contractor will operate must be fully analyzed. Careful estimates must be made of all costs which the contractor and the city will incur, and contingencies and emergencies must be planned for. The specifications, the contract, and the regulations governing the services to be provided, should be spelled out so that the municipality and the contractors understand them. Public health, sanitation and convenience must remain the most important considerations.

It is often desirable to provide in the specifications, tender forms or contract documents for proposals from the contractor which would combine certain basic requirements specified by the city with other features proposed by the contractor. This gives the contractor more scope

FIG. 10-1. Contractor's truck for collecting residential rubbish. Note the front overhead loading hopper to overcome disadvantage of high loading height.

within the essential controls imposed by the city. There may be more problems in subsequent analysis and comparison of bids received but there may be benefits in service, tendered prices or both.

The contract should provide that the city has control over labor practices; provisions for wage increases should be stated in the contract on the basis of a predetermined scale; wage kickbacks from employee to employer should be prohibited and penalties set; and provisions on discrimination because of race, creed, color and union affiliations should be included. There should also be provision for increased or decreased payments to the contractor to take care of increased or decreased operating costs, and variations in the amount of refuse to be handled, as well as provision for controlling the salvage or use of refuse.

Contracts and specifications should include carefully worded clauses defining penalties if the contractor fails to perform the services contracted for, or if he performs them inadequately. Provision must be made for inspections, the handling of complaints, breakdowns in service, and the procedure for enforcing penalties on the contractor.

Normally, regulations for the kinds and locations of refuse containers, for the ways in which refuse or certain classes of it are to be separated, and for sanitary conditions with which householders and businesses must comply, will be drawn up and enforced by the city. The city is also usually responsible for informing the public of the regulations. These provisions should be carefully defined in the specification and contract, together with the responsibilities of the city and the contractor with respect to reporting infractions and enforcing the regulations.

The basis of payment to the contractor may vary considerably in accordance with local conditions and other requirements such as the method of disposal. In one city a contractor's remuneration may be based on the quantity of material collected, at a fixed price per ton with a minimum guarantee; in another, the payment may be made on a lump sum basis with force account payments allowed for extra services not covered in the specifications; or payment may be based on population of the city, with stipulated methods of estimating the yearly change in population. When the city operates the disposal facilities and adequate provision is made for weighing at the disposal sites, incinerators or transfer stations, payment based on the actual tonnage collected is probably the most equitable and acceptable.

That some cities have operated contract systems with economical results and satisfactory service, indicates that such a service contract can be effective when conditions are right and when specifications and contracts are adequately drawn. The integrity of the contractor, the co-operation of the public, and the proper inspection and control by the public officials concerned, must also be recognized as important factors in the success of such operations.

Specifications for contract refuse collection operations are given below in check list form, as a guide. The items are only suggested, all of them may not be needed in any contract and there may be important additional items required in some agreements. It should be noted that the list of items is a useful guide in preliminary studies and preparation of cost estimates by municipal officials in connection with proposed contract operations.

1. Definition of terms used in specifications and contract
2. Classes and kinds of refuse to be collected
3. Separation into classes and the number of separate collections
4. Hours of collection (for different districts)
5. Frequency of collection (for different districts and various classes of refuse)
6. Holidays on which collection is not mandatory
7. City to enforce the use of proper containers
8. Contractor to report on violations of sanitary laws by citizens
9. Kinds of properties to be served
10. Area to be served (defined completely)
11. Contractor to establish routes; furnish maps of routes to city and keep them up to date
12. Provision for extending service to new properties
13. Location of containers for collection; replacing containers
14. Kind of vehicles to be used (bodies enclosed, watertight, maximum allowable capacity)

15. Contractor to furnish adequate amount of equipment
16. Loads to be covered with tarpaulins or otherwise
17. Equipment to be maintained in good condition, painted uniformly
18. Equipment to be numbered and labeled as specified
19. Method and frequency of cleaning the vehicles
20. Equipment not to be overloaded
21. Scattered refuse to be collected (broom and shovel on each truck)
22. Direction and supervision of work must be satisfactory to city
23. Office with telephone to be provided for receiving complaints
24. Agent for contractor to be designated for receiving notices and orders
25. City may appoint inspectors who are to have access to contractor's equipment and property
26. Employees of contractor to meet local citizenship requirements
27. Minimum wage rates for various kinds of workers
28. Employees to be courteous; incompetent or disorderly workers to be removed when so ordered by city
29. Employees to wear numbered badges
30. Complaints to be answered courteously and promptly
31. Collectors not to trespass unduly on private property
32. Collectors to follow pedestrian walks, not cross from one property to another
33. Vehicles not to interfere unduly with traffic
34. Certain kinds of streets not to be used for hauling to disposal sites
35. Loaded vehicles not to be left standing on streets
36. Collectors' vehicles shall be parked in suitable off-street parking areas overnight
37. Collection to be quiet, not to create nuisance
38. Service not to be interrupted because of closed streets
39. Refuse to become property of contractor (or to be delivered to specific locations)
40. Description of disposal methods to be used (including location, operation, and control of disposal sites)
41. Care of disposal sites or plants
42. Disposal methods and locations may be changed
43. Contractor to furnish city reports of operations and complaints
44. City to control contractor's operations outside city in traveling to disposal sites, caring for dumps, or operating disposal plants
45. Basis of payment for contract work
46. Payments to contractor
47. Approximate amount of refuse; guaranteed minimum
48. City to prohibit collection by scavengers or private collectors
49. Contractor to abide by all state, county, and local laws and regulations
50. City to be free of any liability
51. Contractor to carry liability and compensation insurance

52. Bond to be furnished; equipment and facilities pledged as part of bond
53. Contractor not to assign contract or dispose of property without permission of city
54. Duration of contract
55. Termination of contract on six months' notice
56. In case of breach of contract, hearing to be held before Council or city officials
57. City may conduct operations with contractor's equipment in case of failure by contractor and bondsmen
58. Right to reject all bids
59. Sum to accompany bid
60. Liquidated damages specified for various violations of specifications, such as:
    (a) Failure to clean up spillage
    (b) Overloading vehicle
    (c) Failure to answer complaints
    (d) Using improper vehicles
    (e) Failure to clean vehicles
    (f) Failure to keep vehicles closed
    (g) Loaded vehicles left standing on streets
    (h) Unabated nuisances at dumps or disposal plants
    (i) Failure to park vehicles overnight in off-street facility
61. Penalties

Advantages of Contract Collection

Disadvantages of the municipal operation will usually constitute advantages of the contract system, and advantages of municipal plans will ordinarily be weaknesses of the contract arrangement. Only the very important arguments are repeated here and these should be considered along with the items listed on pages 246-248.

1. There may be more comparative freedom from political influence in the management and operation of refuse collection by contractors and in the awarding of contracts, but this will depend on local conditions.
2. Contract collection in a particular city may be more economical than private or municipal collection because of generally more competent management, better planning of operations, and more effective use of labor and equipment. However, contract collection may be more costly than municipal collection because of profit increment, less favorable purchase of equipment and supplies, and the need to pay certain state and federal taxes.
3. The necessity of a comprehensive statement of the precise duties to be performed and the responsibilities to be assumed, prevents the development of extravagant services and encourages a standard of equitable or required service to all properties.
4. Providing the contract so requires, the costs of collection work are

known fairly accurately at the beginning of a fiscal period and this is advantageous to municipal budgeting and financial planning.

5. In the event that reliable and acceptable means are available for the salvage or use of collected material by the contractor, more favorable contract prices may result, though this factor may be very hard to properly assess.

Disadvantages of Contract Collection

1. Changing from the municipal to the contract method of collection usually involves a commitment for a fairly long period and during that time the means of accurately determining municipal costs for comparison purposes may be lost.

2. Once established, there is a tendency to perpetuate the contract method, even though it may not be the best solution.

3. The granting of contracts in reward for political support, rather than on the basis of competency and costs, may defeat at once any advantage that may accrue through the contract plan.

4. There is a tendency to sacrifice sanitation and public health considerations to profits.

5. Contractors are generally reluctant to answer complaints promptly or to correct conditions, beyond the stipulated requirements of the specifications and contract. This leads to strained relations between the contractor, the public, and the municipal administration.

6. Contract operations must be continuously inspected by competent city officials and employees, adding substantially to the total cost of the collection work.

7. The limited duration of some contracts makes it necessary to absorb amortization costs in a period shorter than the normal economically useful life of equipment, thereby increasing the cost of the service. This may be more of a problem in contracts involving disposal as well as collection, or the provision of buildings and similar facilities by the contractor.

8. The difficulty in anticipating changes in labor rates makes it necessary for contractors to increase their bids, particularly if unions are involved.

9. It is very difficult to develop comprehensive and fair specifications which will adequately control unforeseen occurrences.

10. Contractors who get into financial difficulties or who are faced with termination of contracts, will cut corners wherever an opportunity develops, with the result that the standard of service is liable to be reduced and the cost of control increased.

11. Specifications and contracts usually presume a definite disposal method for the entire period. Should necessity dictate a change, negotiations with the contractor may prove costly to the municipality.

12. Except in rare circumstances the number of reliable contrac-

tors available to bid competitively is very limited and if renego-
tiation of a contract should be the solution it may prove costly.

13. Any savings resulting from technological improvements mean increased profit to the contractor and are not passed on to the
public.

14. If all collection is by contract it is difficult to establish bases of
comparison and to assess the quality or the level of service.

PRIVATE COLLECTION OF REFUSE

The private collection of refuse fills an important need where no
publicly-managed or financed system is in operation or where municipal or contract collection service is not provided for certain kinds of
properties or certain classes of refuse. When the operations are conducted under conclusive privileges or when collectors are assigned to
particular districts, the service is often fairly efficient but on the whole

FIG. 10-2. Truck wash-down operation by private collectors in San Francisco. Effective
municipal supervision of regulations is necessary to achieve desired standards of sanitation.

it is an expensive means of refuse collection.

There has been a noticeable increase in the use of this method of collection. The 1955 survey indicated that 11 per cent of the cities surveyed
employed this method exclusively and a further 11 per cent used
some combination of the private method with either municipal or

contract collection; whereas in the 1964 survey 13 per cent of the cities surveyed used private collection exclusively and a further 21 per cent used some combination of private collection with either municipal or contract collection. Most noticeable was the increase from 6 per cent to 15 per cent for cities employing municipal and private collection.

The increase in private refuse collection operations can be attributed to a number of factors, including a trend toward organization of the private refuse collection industry into local, state and national associations, 'glamorization' of the industry through increased advertising and public relations programs, increased control through licensing and other regulations and the easier acquisition of landfill disposal sites by private enterprise. Undoubtedly there has been a resulting improvement in the level of service provided by many private collectors but unfortunately there has been no tabulation of data to indicate that expansion in the use of this method can be attributed to lower relative costs to the community. It may be that despite evidence of higher relative costs, an increasing number of communities are willing to encourage private collection of refuse, providing the level of service is acceptable to the customers served.

The extent of private refuse collection operations in a community, especially the larger cities, is sometimes very difficult to determine, particularly where the city does not operate or control all disposal facilities. If, however, the city has the majority of the disposal facilities, it is much easier to record and analyze the quantities and nature of material delivered by private haulers. This information is very necessary in comprehensive analyses of a community's total problem of refuse collection and disposal.

Private refuse collection on a completely optional community-wide basis is not considered satisfactory from a sanitary and public health point of view, because such service seldom extends to all properties of a community. Presumably each property that is served may get the kind and extent of collection service that is desired but almost invariably there will be areas in which numerous properties are not served and therefore become littered, unattractive and liable to other nuisances. There is a tendency for many private operators to be selective in their clientele because there is more profit in collection from certain types of premises.

Exclusive Private Collection Privileges

Private collection may prove very satisfactory where a single business enterprise is granted the privilege of conducting a refuse collection service for an entire community. In such cases the collection businesses are very similar to privately owned public utilities operating without competition under franchise, as there is no control such as would be provided by competition. The prices charged and the kind of services given by these collection firms should be regulated by municipal ordinances. An agreement between a city and a collection enterprise usually stipulates the methods, rates, equipment and operating practices and normally the Department of Public Works or the Department of Public Health is made responsible for supervising the collection work, to see that the provisions of the agreement are fulfilled. Not infrequently the license fee or franchise fee is fixed at the amount needed to pay for municipal regulation but in other communities it may be considerably more. When properly controlled, the rates charged for service may not be excessive but because of the private enterprise nature of the operation, the charges for average residences are usually more than they would be under municipal operation.

Assignment of Private Collectors to Districts or Routes

In an effort to eliminate the inefficiency and confusion of unrestricted competition and to provide collection service to all areas, some cities assign private collectors to specific districts or routes. Under this arrangement the municipal control of services and rates must be about the same as that given an exclusive enterprise. The collection firms or individuals are licensed and specific ordinances or regulations govern the collection work. It is undoubtedly harder and more expensive to supervise several such collection enterprises than it is to oversee a single company but in some respects the collectors under this plan are more amenable to control, because if they fail to give satisfactory service there will usually be others ready and willing to take over the district or route involved. This is not so under the exclusive arrangement, however, since it is improbable that another company would be readily available with the management experience, equipment and personnel to provide service in case that collector defaults.

Probably the most outstanding example of private collection by a system of routes or districts is in San Francisco. Associations of collectors are given permits by the city and are assigned to specific districts. Normally there is only one association in an area but in a few densely populated districts, two may be designated. A comprehensive system of charges is established by ordinance so that rates are uniform for similar service throughout the city. The voters of San Francisco, when given a chance at the polls, elected to continue the operation of the private system in preference to municipal or contract collection financed from tax revenues. The City Health Department investigates complaints about charges and character of service and settles disputes.

Unrestricted Competition Among Private Collectors

In general, the larger the city the less the tendency to control the operation of private collectors by fixing the prices chargeable or by establishing routes or areas for their operation. The private collectors are therefore free to solicit business anywhere and to make their own arrangements with their customers as to the kind of service and the compensation. In many cities they are licensed and their operations are controlled only by the regulations of the Public Health or Public Works Departments. In many cities no control whatever is exercised except that

provided by general ordinances governing public health and nuisances
A popular impression is that unrestricted competition between severa
private collectors may have some advantages of better service and lowe
costs but the inevitable result is a duplication of labor, equipment and
supervision, resulting in inefficiency and increased overall cost to the
community.

Extent of Political Control

Undoubtedly some municipal officials have concluded that under con
ditions prevailing in their administration, it is better to leave the col
lection of refuse in the hands of private businesses than to have munici
pal or contract collection under selfish political control. Such a conclusior

TABLE 10-3
San Francisco, California Refuse Collection Rates

Monthly rates from residences and flats for one container of not exceeding thirty-two
gallons. Made from ground floor:

No. Rms.	Collections Per Week			
	1	2	3	4
1-4	1.25	2.50	3.75	5.00
5	1.30	2.60	3.90	5.20
6	1.35	2.70	4.05	5.40
7	1.45	2.90	4.35	5.80
8-12	1.60	3.20	4.80	6.40

Monthly rates from residences and flats for one container of not exceeding thirty-two
gallons. Made from second floor, one stairway above ground floor or basement:

No. Rms.	Collections Per Week			
	1	2	3	4
1-4	1.35	2.70	4.05	5.40
5	1.40	2.80	4.20	5.60
6	1.45	2.90	4.35	5.80
7	1.60	3.20	4.80	6.40
8-12	1.70	3.40	5.10	6.80

Monthly rates from residences and flats for one container of not exceeding thirty-two
gallons: Made from third floor, two stairways above ground floor or basement:

No. Rms.	Collections Per Week			
	1	2	3	4
1-4	1.45	2.90	4.35	5.80
5	1.55	3.10	4.65	6.20
6	1.60	3.20	4.80	6.40
7	1.70	3.40	5.10	6.80
8-12	1.80	3.60	5.40	7.20

Monthly rates from residences and flats for one container of not exceeding thirty-two
gallons. Made from fourth floor, three stairways above ground floor or basement:

No. Rms.	Collections Per Week			
	1	2	3	4
1-4	1.60	3.20	4.80	6.40
5	1.65	3.30	4.95	6.60
6	1.70	3.40	5.10	6.80
7	1.80	3.60	5.40	7.20
8-12	1.90	3.80	5.70	7.60

Monthly rates from apartment houses:

Table 10-3, continued

No. Rms.	6	4	3	2	1
		Collections Per Week			
10	4.75	3.75	3.40	3.05	2.80
20	8.95	7.65	6.90	6.05	5.35
30	12.30	10.05	9.20	8.10	....
40	15.25	13.55	11.50	....	....
50	17.65	15.95	13.55	....	....
60	19.45	17.95	....	....	....
70	21.55	20.10	....	....	....
80	23.50	21.90	....	....	....
90	25.40	23.70	....	....	....
100	27.35	25.30	....	....	....
110	29.65	....	....	....	....
120	31.85	....	....	....	....
130	34.00	....	....	....	....
140	36.20	....	....	....	....
150	38.25	....	....	....	....
160	40.45	....	....	....	....
170	42.55	....	....	....	....
180	44.75	....	....	....	....
190	46.80	....	....	....	....
200	49.00	....	....	....	....
210	50.70	....	....	....	....
220	52.75	....	....	....	....
230	54.65	....	....	....	....
240	56.65	....	....	....	....
250	58.60	....	....	....	....
260	60.60	....	....	....	....
270	62.45	....	....	....	....
280	64.50	....	....	....	....
290	68.35	....	....	....	....
300	70.30	....	....	....	....
310	72.20	....	....	....	....
320	74.20	....	....	....	....
330	76.25	....	....	....	....
340	78.05	....	....	....	....
350	80.10	....	....	....	....
360	81.90	....	....	....	....
370	84.00	....	....	....	....
380	86.15	....	....	....	....
390	88.20	....	....	....	....
400	90.25	....	....	....	....
410	92.05	....	....	....	....
420	94.25	....	....	....	....
430	96.40	....	....	....	....
440	98.75	....	....	....	....
450	100.65	....	....	....	....
460	102.85	....	....	....	....
470	105.05	....	....	....	....
480	107.20	....	....	....	....
490	109.30	....	....	....	....
500	111.45	....	....	....	....
510	113.65	....	....	....	....
520	115.80	....	....	....	....
530	117.85	....	....	....	....
540	120.00	....	....	....	....
550	122.20	....	....	....	....
560	124.40	....	....	....	....
570	126.55	....	....	....	....
580	128.65	....	....	....	....
590	130.80	....	....	....	....
600	132.70	....	....	....	....

Rates for residences and flats shall be increased for more than one container of a maximum of thirty-two gallons by 70 cents per additional container per month.

may be justified, providing it is true that the officials concerned are in fact unable to circumvent politics in the operation of an adequate municipal collection system. It is probable that a well-operated and controlled private system has some advantages over other methods conducted extravagantly or inefficiently.

Of course, not all private collectors remain free from political interference, even though this was the case when they established their operation in the community. It often occurs that licenses are issued only to those who enjoy political favor, particularly if the collection operations are satisfactory and profitable. In general, political control is liable to be exercised to a greater degree where considerable municipal regulation is in effect and it has been the experience that because of political considerations, elected officials are reluctant to curtail the activities of private collectors, once they have become established.

All Properties Not Served by Private Collectors

In communities which rely entirely on optional private collection, many properties do not receive adequate collection service, either because the householders are unwilling to pay the fees charged or because it is not profitable for the collectors to work in some districts. In this respect such private service is unsatisfactory for a modern municipality, because of the unwholesome and insanitary conditions created where refuse is not regularly collected. These may endanger the people living in these areas and in large measure are a detriment to the whole community. The efforts made in some cities to require all properties to use the private collection facilities have been fairly successful but many cities are not willing to undertake the comprehensive program of enforcement and education needed to induce citizens to use the service available. Extensive and continuing sanitary inspection of properties and impartial insistence on the abatement of nuisances may help to extend the collections in congested and poorer areas, but it will not aid materially in sparsely settled districts where it is not economical for private collectors to operate.

Supplemental Private Collections

Actually, careful analysis would indicate that there are very few cities which do not have some form of private refuse collection. Where complete service is not provided by municipal or contract collection methods, either as a free service or on a fee basis, private collection may be either allowed or encouraged. Frequently certain commercial or industrial properties with unusual types of waste or unusually large volumes of material will be denied regular municipal or contract service and they may have to resort to some arrangement for private collection and disposal. A relatively large number of cities provide for municipal collection of only one or two classes of refuse, or alternatively collect only from residential properties. In such cases the remainder of the collection service is provided by private operators and the householders or property owners involved have no choice but to pay the higher collection fees which are usually involved. Under these circumstances there is an apparent responsibility on the part of the refuse officials and administrators involved to more carefully investigate the possibilities of extending the municipal or contract collection facilities.

Licensing Private Collectors

Considerable control is necessary to prevent bad practices that are almost certain to develop when private collectors are left free to choose any kind of equipment and methods to dispose of the refuse in the easiest way. Officials in many cities that have not adequately licensed or otherwise regulated private collectors, have found that nuisances and littering have caused so much trouble and complaint that strict regulations and enforcement become essential.

A private collector must usually make a formal application to a city official such as the Director of Public Works or the Director of Health, for permission to conduct a collection business. A rather complete investigation is usually made of the equipment he proposes to use and the arrangements made for disposal. In addition the applicant ordinarily must state the districts in which he plans to operate and the methods and practices he intends to adopt. Frequently he must sign a statement to the effect that he will abide by the laws of the state, county and city and will conform to the rules and regulations established by the department in charge of the regulation of collectors. The amount of preliminary investigation appears to range from perfunctory examination of the completed application form, to intensive inquiries and field inspections, depending to a large extent on whether the licensing procedure is used primarily as a means of raising revenue or as a means of regulation and control. When the officers responsible for the supervision of private collectors are satisfied that the equipment and the disposal arrangements are suitable and that the applicants are willing to comply with the regulations, licenses are issued on payment of the required fees. Several cities issue permits for which no fee is charged, while others require specific licenses for each employee or each piece of equipment, in addition to a general permit to operate.

It is usually necessary to explain all regulations in considerable detail to each private collector granted a license and to periodically inspect his operation, to ensure that he is complying with the conditions under which he was granted a license to operate. It is desirable that copies of all regulations be provided to and acknowledged by the licensee. Listed below are a few of the matters usually included in such regulations. Reference should also be made to the check list of items shown under "Contract Operations" (see Pages 253-255).

1. Kind of equipment that must be used
2. Covers for vehicles
3. Maintenance, painting and identification of equipment
4. Cleaning equipment, frequency, and methods
5. Hours of collection for specific districts

Form 787—1200 Sets—12-56

DEPARTMENT OF PUBLIC WORKS
City of Los Angeles
BUREAU OF STREET MAINTENANCE
STREET USE INSPECTION DIVISION
ROOM 604, CITY HALL — BU 5211, STATION 635

150

APPLICATION FOR

PERMIT TO HAUL COMBUSTIBLE RUBBISH AND MARKET REFUSE

Last Name .... First Name .... Middle Initial

Firm Name ....

Street No. .... Street .... City .... Zone .... Phone No. ....

Make of Truck .... Year .... License No. ....

Check kind of material to be hauled: Combustible .... Market Refuse .... Both ....

I HEREBY CERTIFY

(1) that all of the statements made hereon are true and correct to the best of my knowledge.

(2) that I understand and will conform to and obey all of the requirements of the Los Angeles Municipal Code and all regulations of the Board of Public Works relative to permits and to the removal, disposal, and conveyance of combustible rubbish and market refuse.

(3) that any other person or persons permitted to drive the truck described above will be instructed to comply with said rubbish regulations.

Date .... 19........

....
Applicant's Signature
(Owner)
(Agent)

PERMITS ARE NON-TRANSFERABLE. PERMIT EXPIRES DECEMBER 31.

NOTE: READ CAREFULLY THE ORDINANCE REQUIREMENTS PRINTED ON THE REVERSE SIDE HEREOF.

PERMIT FEE $12.00	Received and reviewed by:	
	.... 19........	Permit No. ....
	Date .... 19........	Permit No. ....
	(Street Use Inspection Division) 19........	City License No. ....
	Do Not Use This Space	

ORDINANCE REQUIREMENTS—"HAULING OF COMBUSTIBLE RUBBISH AND MARKET REFUSE"
(REFERENCE: L. A. MUNICIPAL CODE, ORD. 77000, SEC. 66.00 TO 66.30, ETC.)

a. All trucks shall have tight sides when used for hauling combustible rubbish, or a water-tight tank for hauling market refuse. The entire load shall be confined within the body of the truck.

b. All trucks shall be covered at all times while transporting combustible rubbish or market refuse.

c. This permit to haul combustible rubbish or market refuse shall be in the truck at all times while it is being used to transport such material.

d. The permit-number plates shall be fastened securely, one on each side of the truck. Plates shall be located in the center of the body, half way between the truck floor and the top of the sides.

e. If this permit is suspended or revoked, then the truck which is described herein is restricted from further engaging in the rubbish business in the City of Los Angeles during the period of suspension or revocation.

f. No market refuse or rubbish shall be conveyed in or through the Central Traffic District between the hours of 7:00 A.M. and 6:00 P.M. of any day.

g. All rubbish (exclusive of salvage) shall be disposed of only at legal dumps or incinerators.

h. This permit does not allow the picking up or conveying of garbage upon or along any public street, alley, or any other public place in the City of Los Angeles. (GARBAGE is defined to be all animal and vegetable refuse from kitchens and household waste that shall have resulted from the preparation of food.)

FIG. 10-3. A form for application for a private collector's license of Los Angeles. The ordinance provisions and the department rules and regulations are printed on the back of this form.

Director of Health   *Sanitary Engineer*

DAVIDSON COUNTY DEPARTMENT OF HEALTH

NASHVILLE 3, TENNESSEE

Permit No..................................

APPLICATION FOR PERMIT

TO COLLECT AND DISPOSE OF REFUSE

TO THE DIRECTOR OF HEALTH OF DAVIDSON COUNTY, TENNESSEE.

The undersigned hereby make application for a permit to engage in the business of:

☐ Collection and Disposal of Kitchen or Market garbage.

☐ Collection and Disposal of mixed refuse (exclusive of night soil).

☐ Collection and Disposal of night soil.

It is agreed that the above operations will be conducted in accordance with the requirements of Chapter 372 of the Private Acts of 1947, State of Tennessee and pertinent rules and regulations adopted by the Davidson County Board of Health June 25, 1947.

Name of Applicant:..
Owner or responsible operator of Business.

Business Location:..

Mailing Address:...........................Tel. No.........................

Section of Operations:...
(For example: Belle Meade, Woodbine, Inglewood, etc.)

VEHICLES:

Number	Make	Model (year)	License No.	Type of Body	Final Inspection		Approved	
					Date	By	Date	By
1.								
2.								
3.								
4.								
5.								
6.								

....
Signature of Applicant.

By:...

DO NOT WRITE IN THIS SPACE

LICENSE FEES:

Number of Vehicles...................................

Amount per Vehicle.................................

Total License Fees.................................

ACKNOWLEDGMENT OF RECEIPT OF LICENSE FEES:

License Fees of $............................

Were received by me on...........................
AND receipt therefor issued to the Applicant.

Signature...

Title...

FIG. 10-4. In Davidson County, Tennessee, application for a private collector's permit is made to the County Department of Health. Each vehicle must be inspected for conformance with county regulations and approved before a permit is issued.

6. Prohibition against littering
7. Shovel and broom on each vehicle, to clean up spillage
8. Interference with traffic
9. Specified routes for hauling to disposal sites.
10. Parking loaded vehicles on streets
11. Overloading restrictions
12. Reporting customers' violation of sanitary ordinances
13. Practices at dumps or disposal plants
14. Up to date lists of customers to be furnished to city officials
15. Maintaining office or telephone communications
16. Use of disinfectants
17. Compliance with all ordinances and laws
18. Period of renewal of license
19. Salvage practices
20. Penalties
21. Handling of complaints

Although penalties are usually specified in ordinances establishing the licensing procedure and are available for use in controlling private collectors, much more effective regulation can be secured through the power to revoke licenses for persistent violation of rules and regulations. Usually satisfactory control can be maintained if licenses are revoked promptly when circumstances justify this procedure. The city should always be ready to fill in the gap when a license is revoked, either by its own forces and equipment or with those of another private collector.

SUMMARY

It is obvious from the foregoing discussion of collection systems that no plan will guarantee good results. The success of any arrangement depends on good personnel, sound, progressive management, efficient modern equipment, adequate ordinances, and a minimum of political interference. The optimum conditions for economical and effective refuse removal service are realized when one agency conducts all of the work of removing all kinds of refuse from all properties. In the interests of maintaining responsibility, control and operation within the proper area of government activity of the community, it should be the objective of such government to provide the desired service adequately and at the least possible cost to individuals and the community as a whole. Any division of operations among two or more agencies, part municipal and part private, constitutes at least some duplication of equipment, labor, supervision, overhead and control and usually leads to inefficiency, confusion and higher costs. If these objectives can be achieved and a high grade of management maintained, the advantages of municipal collection stand out favorably in comparison with the other two plans, because of better community sanitation and appearance, better relations between the people and their government, more complete service, and lower cost.

Refuse collection and disposal has become one of the largest operations in most cities, both in terms of the number of employees and the annual expenditures. Fortunately in many cities the standards of collection have been rising steadily in quality and in extent of service, as the demand for such service has increased. Cities are taking more pride in the efficiency of their refuse collection services and in the appearance of their collection force and equipment. Quite properly, the service is regarded as the one in closest continual contact with the public and must therefore be a suitable example of municipal efficiency. As the stature of the activity has been raised, higher competence has been required of the employees, supervisors and administrators.

The contract system, which has many advantages, has been employed by many cities and municipalities, especially small ones, largely because they have been unable to achieve or maintain the level of administrative efficiency required to provide adequate municipal collection services. The cost of contract refuse collection services should certainly be less than for similar operations under mediocre public administration, but this does not constitute proof of a widespread belief that contractors' management methods are superior.

Private collection, though normally more expensive, is a desirable alternative where conditions are such that neither municipal or contract service can be established under reasonably favorable circumstances. Private collection also plays an important role in supplementing other methods when these do not offer complete collection.

It must be recognized that none of the collection methods—municipal, contract, or private—can be made free of the disadvantages of political interference, if it is the will of those in power to use the service for political advantage. It must therefore be the ultimate objective of officials and administrators to remove all political interference from this very important phase of the community's operation. To this end they must, from time to time, make thorough studies and complete analyses of the total refuse collection and disposal problem and present thoroughly and impartially, the facts and estimated costs necessary to support recommendations for improving the refuse handling service.

Two trends are discernible: the movement toward at least partial municipal operation may be explained by the general improvement in the techniques of administration of many municipal governments; the tendency to provide more complete service and better collection service may be, in part, a result of more extensive municipal operation or simply a response to public demand for cleaner and more healthful communities. An emerging problem faced by many cities is the demand or need for furnishing of complete municipal service to all properties.

chapter 11

FINANCING REFUSE COLLECTION OPERATION

What methods are available to provide the necessary funds to meet the cost of refuse collection services required by the community? How can such costs be equitably distributed? These are difficult and often perplexing questions which must be answered by city officials when establishing, revising or extending refuse collection services. The planning of the collection system or combination of systems, consists of evaluating the various ways of using men and machines to find the most efficient arrangement to meet local conditions and, as discussed in other chapters, usually involves analysis of many complex factors. The selection of the best means of financing the desired operation, however, may be even more complex.

Most cities and municipalities experience an ever increasing demand for more sanitary and more complete refuse collection service and in many cases this cannot be provided from general property tax revenues without unduly curtailing other essential activities. Several different plans of securing the funds needed for refuse operations have been tried and these plans are discussed in this chapter in sufficient detail to show the advantages and disadvantages of each.

SOURCES OF FUNDS

The principal methods of financing refuse collection may be briefly summarized as follows:

General Property Taxes

Regular appropriations are made from general revenues obtained from annual property taxation, state-collected, locally-shared sales taxes, or similar sources.

Separate Property Taxes

This involves levying separate ad valorem taxes, usually on the same basis as general property taxes, for a specific purpose such as refuse collection.

Service Charges or Fees

These are established charges made to householders and other producers of refuse, on the basis of the measured, estimated, or presumed amount of waste removed.

Can and Container Rental Charges

These are established rates or charges made to provide householder and other refuse producers with municipally owned, standard refuse cans, bulk containers or other receptacles, including paper or plastic bags, and to cover the cost of emptying, servicing, maintaining, and replacing such containers.

Special Assessments

These are similar to service charges except that assessments are made against the properties benefited, whereas service charges are usually made to the persons receiving the service.

Miscellaneous Revenues

These may include proceeds from fees for private collection licenses, fees for salvage privileges, sale of salvaged material, sale of collection privileges, etc.

PRINCIPLES INVOLVED IN FINANCING REFUSE COLLECTION

It is generally accepted that municipal functions performed for the good of a whole community should be financed from general taxation, while those conducted for the particular benefit of certain individuals or organizations should be supported by charges or fees against the persons or properties benefited. There is little question but that each person who receives refuse collection service is benefited by having the waste materials regularly removed from his premises, thereby relieving him of the annoyance and inconvenience of disposing of them himself. The community concern is apparent at once, however, if an individual fails to handle his refuse properly and permits his premises to become unsanitary and untidy. The dangers to health are not confined to the premises of the negligent party, nor are the nuisances created harmful only to the offender. Neighbors who are disposing of their refuse properly may be equally affected and the influence may be felt over a rather wide area. Because community sanitation and attractiveness have properly been emphasized in most municipal refuse collection operations, the use of general revenues to pay for a basic service to all householders has traditionally been authorized in most communities. Every municipality would probably use this method of financing its basic service, if adequate funds could be raised within existing authority. Financing of the portion of the refuse collection service which is of particular benefit to the individuals served becomes somewhat more difficult and usually involves the collection of separate fees or charges based on the quantities of materials removed.

The adequacy of funds available to finance all the community's services is the major consideration in the choice of methods to be adopted for financing refuse collection service. In many communities, appropriations from general revenues have been adequate to provide satisfactory and reasonably complete collection service for residential areas. In some municipalities, however, the funds made available from

this source have been so small that an effective basic service could not
be given, or some kinds or classes of refuse could not be collected at all.
Moreover, the amount of the appropriations has often fluctuated considerably in some cities, being sufficient in prosperous times but wholly
inadequate in recession periods. Where appropriations are not adequate to give citizens the kind of collection service they want, this
means of financing would appear to be quite unsuitable unless it is supplemented by other methods.

It is often difficult to determine the amount of funds that must be made
available for different kinds of service, and the relation between various levels of service. A tabulation of per capita expenditures in accordance with the level of collection service provided is presented in Table
11-1 only for purposes of demonstrating the wide range in such figures.
The significance of this tabulation lies not so much in the actual per
capita amounts, as in the great differences in the cost of the various
levels of service. The tabulation may otherwise be very misleading,
because no consideration has been given to the amount of work performed or the frequency or extent of service given, and a wide variation
in each class is inevitable because of great differences in wage rates,
population densities, collection methods, length of hauls, and other factors.

TABLE 11-1

Range in Per Capita Costs
For Refuse Collection of 38 Public Agencies
in 1960, by Type of Service

Extent and Character of Service	Number of Cities	Maximum	Median	Minimum
Complete residential and commercial service. (All classes and almost all kinds of refuse collected.)	25	$7.40	$5.02	$2.04
Complete residential service only. (Some small commercial establishments may be included.)	6	3.72	2.57	0.64
City-wide service, but some kinds of refuse not collected or one or two classes omitted from business area.	4	4.58	4.01	2.25
Only one class of refuse collected in residential area or business area or partial service throughout the city.	3	3.25	2.78	0.24

Complete service may cost as much as one hundred per cent more
than partially complete collection and three or four times as much as a
limited collection. Such differences help to explain the inability of
cities to obtain sufficient funds from general revenues to finance adequate collection service. Because of the tax limits imposed in some
states, it would be quite impossible for some cities to double or treble
their present appropriations to provide for extended refuse collection
service without seriously robbing other activities which probably are
already under-financed.

1964 SURVEY OF METHODS USED TO FINANCE REFUSE COLLECTION

Table 11-2 is a tabulation of the replies received in 1964 from 857 Canadian and American cities showing, by method of collection, the methods used to finance their refuse collection services.

TABLE 11-2
Methods Used to Finance Refuse Collection by 857 Cities in 1964

Method of Financing	METHOD OF COLLECTION								
	M	M & C	M & P	M & C & P	C	C & P	Total	%	% in 1955[1]
General tax	209	25	81	20	68	26	429	50	67
Service charge	149	24	37	4	74	11	299	35	33
Tax & Service charge	69	10	29	4	8	4	124	14	—
Other	2	1	0	1	1	0	5	1	—
Totals	429	60	147	29	151	41	857		
%	50	7	17	4	17	5			

[1] In the 1955 survey the replies from 849 cities were tabulated under only two methods of financing (general tax, service charge) and by only two methods of collection (M-municipal, C-contract, P-private).

In Table 11-2 the figures indicate the number of cities which finance the municipal and contract portions of their collection service only, by the methods shown. Cities which reported private collection only have not been included. There may be some discrepancies between the 1955 and 1964 surveys, but the figures indicate a significant trend toward more use of the service charge method of financing. Approximately one-half of all cities reporting finance their refuse collection service with funds from general taxation alone, whereas approximately one-half of all cities reporting derive all or part of the funds required from service charges.

ADVANTAGES OF GENERAL REVENUE FINANCING

a) Complete refuse collection service benefits the entire community and should be financed the same as other public health activities.

b) The cost of a collection operation is distributed more nearly on an ability to pay basis, than under any other commonly used plan.

c) All properties receive collection service, insuring the safe disposal of all waste materials.

d) Special bills do not have to be issued or paid and tickets do not have to be presented. This saves a great deal of inconvenience to the individuals served and it also avoids considerable added overhead expense and decreased efficiency within the operation.

e) If financing of the refuse collection service is by this method exclusively, then all refuse may be collected by municipal or contract forces, a more efficient operation results, and the number of complaints can be minimized.

DISADVANTAGES OF GENERAL REVENUE FINANCING

a) Since most cities have relied heavily on a general property tax as a major source of revenue, it has in recent years provided a decreasing share of required local revenue. This trend, together with the tax limits imposed in some states, has resulted in many cities being unable to provide sufficient funds to carry out a reasonable minimum program of refuse collection. In such cases the advantages of public financing may be partially or wholly lost.

(b) It is not practical, nor fair to provide complete collection from commercial and industrial properties at public expense because of the great quantities of refuse produced by some businesses and because the amount varies so widely among properties. Either special charges for extra service must be made or private collectors must be employed to collect everything over a reasonable maximum amount. This leads to duplication, less efficiency and overall increased cost to the properties served.

(c) If some properties are exempt from general taxation, these individuals or properties will get free service while others will have to bear an undue burden.

(d) The assessed value of a property may have no relation to the amount of refuse that must be collected from that property, or to the comparative cost of providing the service.

(e) Because of their limited and restricted tax sources, cities have a difficult time financing local services in times of depression and inflation alike. During a depression the revenue from the property tax often declines sharply and during an inflationary period the cost of labor, materials, and equipment outruns the ability of the cities to get enough dollars to pay for them. Furthermore, in good and bad times alike the extent of municipal services, including refuse collection, steadily increases.

USE OF SEPARATE PROPERTY TAXES TO FINANCE REFUSE COLLECTION

A few cities raise part or all of the funds needed for providing municipal refuse collection and disposal service by levying separate ad valorem taxes, usually on the same base as the general property taxes. From the viewpoint of an administrator of a collection service, there is no fundamental difference between such financing and the general fund method, except in the control of the revenues and the determination of appropriations. All of the advantages and weaknesses listed for financing refuse service from general revenue apply also to separate taxes on property. In addition, there is somewhat less flexibility in the administrative control.

The usual purpose of making a separate levy for refuse collection is to ensure the segregation of enough money to provide the kind of service wanted and to prevent the diversion of the funds to other activities or functions. In effect such levies are similar to special appropriations and generally are not considered within the sphere of budget operations. Actually, separate taxes and separate funds for the refuse collection function are not desirable. The revenues are neither more uniform nor more certain than those from general funds. There is no assurance that greater appropriations will result and usually the control of expenditures is less satisfactory. The amount of separate levies stipulated by law is ordinarily permissive rather than mandatory and often only a maximum limit is prescribed. In the last analysis, a local governing body almost always determines the amount of the revenues, whether in the form of tax rate or budgetary appropriation.

USE OF SERVICE CHARGES TO FINANCE REFUSE COLLECTION SERVICE

Service charges or fees are periodical charges by municipal governments based on the measured, estimated, or presumed amount of waste material removed. The charges are established as nearly as practicable according to the amount and kind of service rendered and in proportion to the benefit derived by individuals and businesses, in contrast to general property taxes which may be levied more nearly on the ability to pay basis. For the most part the inability of cities to provide adequate appropriations from general funds for the standard of collection service required has been responsible for the adoption of the service charge method. However, some cities use the plan so that one agency can do the collection work for an entire community, thus providing for the possibility of maximum efficiency. Others use it because they believe that the cost of refuse collection should not be paid from general public revenue but do not want the confusion and ineffectiveness of the usual private collection arrangement.

There is undoubtedly much interest in the service charge method in many cities and there are definite indications that now it is being used more widely than in the past, as shown in the following table:

TABLE 11-3
The Decade of Adoption of Service Charges
For Refuse Collection in 79 Local Governments[1]
In the United States and Canada

Decade of Adoption of Service Charges	Per Cent of 79 Local Governments
1910-1919	1.3
1920-1929	6.3
1930-1939	8.9
1940-1949	44.2
1950-1959	34.2
1960	5.1
	100.0

Source: Data extracted from a 1961 survey by the Municipal Finance Officers Association of the United States and Canada (Lennox L. Moak, "Refuse Collection and Disposal Service Charges", Chicago, 1961)
[1] The 79 local governments levied a charge for each type of refuse collection service performed.

The change of attitude toward, and increased use of this method is probably accounted for by the unquestioned successes of cities using the method and by the evidence that some of the former objections to the plan are being overcome. Service charges augment the funds available from general taxation and provide the means of financing required in the trend toward a higher proportion of municipal collection.

Advantages of Service Charges

(a) They provide an additional means of raising municipal revenue.

(b) Either general property taxation may be reduced by the amount used for refuse services, or such revenues may be employed for other municipal activities.

(c) More complete municipal or contract service may become available to all properties at reasonable cost, where formerly certain classes of refuse were not collected at public expense and citizens had to use more expensive private collection service or do without.

(d) Commercial and industrial refuse varies so greatly that free municipal or contract service cannot be equitable. Under a service charge system payment can be made proportional to the cost of removing the waste material.

(e) There is more assurance that adequate funds can be obtained to conduct a more desirable and efficient collection and disposal system.

(f) All individuals and all properties may be treated on an equitable and impartial basis; each gets the extent and kind of service paid for.

(g) More accurate analysis of quantities and costs involved results from more accurate measurement.

(h) Under this plan the cost of service to ordinary residential properties is not likely to be very much different than for service financed from property taxes, provided a low cost billing and service charge collection procedure is followed.

(i) There is increased incentive for householders to keep the amount of refuse within reasonable limits.

(j) Periodic review and updating of the charges or fees for certain kinds of service becomes possible.

(k) This method lends itself to setting up rates for new or experimental methods of collection such as containerization.

Disadvantages of the Service Charge Method of Financing

(a) Refuse service charges levied according to the benefits received are regressive. The amount of refuse does not vary with the ability to pay taxes; poor families may have more refuse per capita than wealthy ones.

(b) Actual benefits from refuse collection accrue more to the community than to individuals, in the same way that benefits from water and sewerage service are community-wide to a great extent.

(c) Additional costs are involved in measuring and keeping track of quantities involved and the administrative costs of billing and collection may be fairly high. Furthermore a certain number of accounts may not be collected. All of these represent additional costs which must be borne by citizens.

(d) Individuals may register numerous complaints over the rates charged or the quantities involved, particularly under some kinds of rate structures where the administrative officials determine the charges made.

(e) Poor families and other individuals may refuse to purchase the refuse service on the grounds that they cannot afford it, or that they can dispose of their own wastes in a manner satisfactory to them. The result may be unsanitary conditions and littered communities and sometimes the city may have to make collections from such properties without payment in order to prevent such conditions. This problem, however, has been overcome by many communities by requiring all properties to use the municipal collection service.

(f) The cost of sanitary inspections and the enforcement of public health and nuisance ordinances will be increased greatly when the use of the service is optional and the number of properties that do not have collection service are increased.

(g) There may be more fluctuations in the nature and volume of materials collected on individual collection routes with a resulting loss of efficiency.

(h) There is more encouragement for private collectors to extend their operations, to cut rates, or to provide better individual service. This results in more stops, starts, and fluctuations in established municipal or contract routes.

City Experience with the Service Charge Method of Financing

Without doubt there is evidence to support each one of the merits and weaknesses of the service charge plan. It is essential to know, however, to what extent the advantages have been realized and the weaknesses have been overcome in actual practice.

Surveys conducted by the APWA in 1955 and 1964 indicate that the minimum number of cities known to be using the service charge method of financing all or part of their refuse collection service increased from 350 to 425. The current status of financing refuse collection in communities of various sizes are shown in the following table.

The data show that the smaller communities tend to rely more on service charges than do the larger communities.

As might be expected, refuse collection by contract more frequently is financed by straight service charges than municipal collection. Municipal collection services, on the other hand, use more frequently a tax and service charge financing combination.

It should be noted, however, that the method of financing refuse collections through general tax revenues is employed to an almost equal degree in municipal as well as contract collection systems. Financing collections through service charges, and general tax plus service

TABLE 11-4
Methods of Financing Refuse Collection Services,
By Size of Community, 1964

Population Size of Community	Total No. of Communities in Sample	Per Cent	Distribution of Financing Methods			
			General Tax	Service Charge	Tax and Serv. Chg.	Other
5,000-9,999	180	100.0	47.2%	39.0%	13.4%	0.6%
10,000-24,999	307	100.0	46.0	38.0	16.0	0.0
25,000-49,999	190	100.0	51.5	32.7	14.2	1.6
50,000-99,999	93	100.0	58.0	28.0	12.9	1.1
100,000-999,999	74	100.0	59.5	27.0	13.5	0.0
1,000,000 and over	6	100.0	66.6	0.0	33.4	0.0
Total Sample	850	100.0	50.1	34.9	14.4	0.6

charge arrangements, is found in 47.6 per cent of the communities removing refuse by contract.

Cities have adopted many different methods of measuring refuse collection service, some of which are based on the estimated or average cost of conducting the collection and disposal work, and others on the benefits received by the individuals or properties serviced. Most of the rate structures are relatively simple and in many cases it has been contended that the rates are so simplified that they do not provide a very accurate measure of either cost of service or benefit. It is significant, however, that the actual charges are often too small to justify the greater expense and overhead cost of applying more accurate but much more complex measures. The number and extent of local factors involved will vary considerably in each community.

It is interesting to note in this context that some local governments exercise their rights to regulate private refuse collector operations. Data from 268 local governments reveal the following information.

TABLE 11-5
Regulation of Private Collector Operations
by Local Governments, 1964

Type of Regulation	Yes	No	No Answer	Total
Set Rates............................17.1%		78.7%	4.2%	100.0%
Issue franchises.....................22.4		71.6	6.0	100.0
Limit number of licenses...........19.8		72.8	7.4	100.0

Bases for Rate Structures

The following are among the bases of measurement of service employed by cities in setting refuse collection service charges. Sometimes a single base is used but it is more common to combine two or three different measures. Not infrequently the bases or combinations used in the residential and commercial or industrial districts are different. Detailed information on refuse collection and disposal service charges in

380 American and Canadian communities is contained in an 87 page survey published by the Municipal Finance Officers Association of the United States and Canada in 1961.

Uniform charge for each service. The uniform charge for each residential household or each service is the simplest rate structure. The assumption is that the benefit is equal for all properties or that the cost of service is the same for each stop. When the rates are low, a uniform charge is satisfactory for very small communities or for residential districts which contain predominantly single family or two family dwellings.

Number of rooms. Rates based on the number of rooms may approximate in a very rough way the benefit derived or the difference in the cost of making collections. It is more likely, however, that such a measure is designed on the ability to pay principle to favor poor families. Such a rate plan is usable only in residential districts or, in some cases, for office buildings.

Number of dwelling units or apartments. "Type-of-property" rate structures provide a general classification for differential flat rates in accordance with average benefits or average collection cost for various kinds of businesses and for multiple or single dwellings. Such presumptive measures serve to eliminate most of the extreme inequalities. In many cities, it is used for residential rates, to separate single family residence charges from those for apartments or duplex units.

Number of containers. Using the number of containers as a basis for refuse collection charges provides a reasonable estimate of the quantity of the material removed and therefore may be a good index of benefit. If collection conditions are relatively uniform among properties served, the rates may measure the cost of service fairly accurately. Usually the maximum size of containers is specified by ordinance and the tendency is for all householders to provide the largest can allowable. This kind of rate structure has been, or is used currently in St. Petersburg, Florida; Albuquerque, New Mexico; Laramie, Wyoming and Fergus Falls, Minnesota.

Size of containers. The size of containers permits a fairly accurate measure of the quantity of refuse collected because citizens may provide receptacles of the size best suited to their average needs. Both the number of containers and the size of containers are satisfactory bases of quantity measurement, in commercial and industrial as well as residential areas. Among the cities that use or have used this method are Montgomery, Alabama; Spokane, Washington; and Tacoma, Washington. Many cities which employ the bulk container method of refuse collection use this basis of measurement of service.

Measured volume of refuse. This provides a fairly accurate measure of quantity but a rate structure based on such a measure does not take into account any of the possible differences in collection conditions. The volume may be measured in the householders' containers or the refuse may be transferred to tubs or baskets of known capacity. Usually the rates are established for each property on the basis of measurements made during a series of three or four collections. This method is used extensively to determine the amount of regular charges to commercial properties. Some examples include Traverse City, Michigan; Wheeling, West Virginia; Laramie, Wyoming; Detroit, Michigan; Cheyenne, Wyoming; and Edmonton, Alberta.

Time consumed in making collections. This provides an accurate base for charging according to the cost of service but it may not be at all suitable for measuring benefit unless the time is limited to loading time and excludes the travel time between stops. It is probably most useful in communities where the collection conditions vary widely among properties. Tuscaloosa, Alabama; Little Rock, Arkansas; Grand Forks, North Dakota; and Spokane, Washington use, or have used this method to fix rates for commercial properties. In most cases the average time consumed in making several successive collections is determined in order to establish the regular charges.

Floor space of buildings. The amount of floor space in the building served is used to approximate the extent of service rendered. This plan is effectively combined with the "kind-of-business" method in Fort Worth, Texas.

Frequency of collection. This is usually a supplemental measure of benefit or cost of service that is applied in either residential or commercial districts when there is some option as to the number of collections that will be made in a stated time, such as a week. Some cities offer service for one, two, or three collections a week, or daily collection throughout the community at the option of the customers. Such cities include Berkeley, Fresno, Redwood City and Roseville, California and Paducah, Kentucky. Numerous cities employ the plan for commercial properties.

Distance from collection vehicles to containers. The distance of containers from the loading point is an auxiliary measure, that may be effectively used where there are great differences in the distances that collectors must walk to pick up the refuse. The same idea is used in setting higher rates when collectors must go into basements or to the second floors of buildings to make collections. Spokane and Tacoma, Washington use this device.

Topography. This may affect the cost of collection work substantially and rate structures may be established to take this factor into account. Usually such a base is adopted when some properties are on steep hills or where collectors have to ascend or descend steep walks or steps to make collections. Normally such adjustments in rates are applied by districting the communities according to the difficulty in making collections, as in Berkeley, California.

Class of refuse. Where different classes of refuse are collected separately it may be well to have different rate schedules for each class, because of different frequency of collection or because the cost of collection and disposal for the two or three classes is not the same. In some cases only one class of refuse may have to be collected from some properties. Topeka, Kansas and Morgantown, West Virginia have different rates for different collections.

Readiness to serve. Such charges are included in some rate structures in much the same manner as they are employed by utility companies. They are particularly justified in commercial areas where the quantity of refuse produced at certain properties varies unreasonably.

Service Charge Rates for Residential Properties

Residential refuse collection fees tend to be highest in private collection systems and lowest in municipal collection systems. The fees for refuse collection by contract tend to be in the middle. This is shown in the following table.

TABLE 11-6

Residential Collection Fee Per Month for One-Family Unit
By Type of Collection System, 1964

Collection Fee	Municipal	Contract	Private
(Number of Survey Communities)...............	(234)	(92)	(42)
$0.01—$0.99....................................	6.4%	7.6%	2.4%
1.00...	21.4	11.9	4.8
1.01— 1.25....................................	16.2	23.9	9.5
1.26— 1.50....................................	35.4	21.7	28.6
1.51— 1.99....................................	7.7	20.7	21.5
2.00...	9.0	4.3	11.9
2.01— 2.99....................................	3.0	6.5	14.3
3.00 and over..................................	0.9	3.4	7.0
	100.0	100.0	100.0

In evaluating the foregoing data it must be kept in mind that private collection systems are financed almost exclusively from private sources. This is not the case for municipal and contract collection systems as was pointed out earlier.

The main characteristics of the rate structures now in effect for residential properties in typical cities have been tabulated and are presented in the following three tables. The primary purpose of the tabulations is to show the methods of establishing service charge rate structures and caution must be exercised in the use of the information for any other purpose. Any conclusions reached by analysis of the actual rates shown will obviously be of very limited value because there is no indication of the multiplicity of local factors which have been involved in arriving at the individual rates.

Charges set without regard for quantity. Rates established without regard to the quantity presented for collection have been adopted for residential areas in numerous cities. Some of these cities have flat rates and some use flat rates in combination with other bases of measurement, such as the number of rooms or apartments or the kind of material collected. Some examples are given in Table 11-7.

Quantity as a Basis for Charges. Rates based primarily on the quantity of refuse normally set out for collection in residential areas are shown in Table 11-8.

TABLE 11-7

Examples of Residential Rates Charged for
Collection of Unrestricted Quantities of Refuse

City	Service Charge Period	Single Unit Rate	Each Added Unit in Building
Little Rock, Arkansas....................	Year	$12.00	—
Camden, Arkansas......................	Year	9.00	—
Burbank, California.....................	Month	1.00	0.75
Compton, California....................	Month	1.00	—
Pomona, California.....................	Month	1.50	0.50
Alhambra, California....................	Month	1.35	0.50
Fort Collins, Colorado...................	Year	5.00	—
Springfield, Illinois.....................	Quarterly	4.50	—
	Semi-Annually	8.00	—
	Annually	14.00	—
Perry, Iowa............................	Month	1.50	—
Salina, Kansas.........................	Month	1.50	—
Monroe, Louisiana......................	Month	2.50	—
Sidney, Nebraska.......................	Year	18.00	3.00
Albuquerque, New Mexico...............	Year	21.00	12.00
Grand Forks, North Dakota..............	Month	1.55	1.30
Warren, Ohio...........................	Quarter	4.50	—
Oklahoma City, Oklahoma..............	Month	2.50	2.50
Shawnee, Oklahoma....................	Month	1.00	0.75
Corpus Christi, Texas...................	Month	1.35	—
Midland, Texas.........................	Month	2.00	2.00
Rock Springs, Wyoming.................	Quarter	2.25	1.50
Quebec, Quebec, Canada...............	Year	9.00	9.00

TABLE 11-8

Residential Rates Based Primarily
on Quantity of Refuse Collected

City	Where Collected	First Container[1]			All Over Base Amt.		
		Cap.	Rate	Per.	Ea. Addl.	Rate	Per.
Santa Clara, Calif............		30 gal.	1.25	Month	30 gal.	.45	Month
St. Petersburg, Fla.[2]........	Alley, rear house line	30 gal.	2.25	Month	30 gal.	.40	Month
Sterling, Colo..............		20 gal.	1.00	Month	20 gal.	.25	Month
Spokane, Wash.............	Alley or 25′ from curb	30 gal.	1.25	Month	30 gal.	1.00	Month
	25′ to 125′	30 gal.	2.00	Month	30 gal.	2.00	Month
Tacoma, Wash.[3]............	25′ or less	30 gal.	1.10	Month	30 gal.	.80	Month
	25′ to 75′	30 gal.	1.50	Month	30 gal.	1.05	Month
	75′ to 120′	30 gal.	1.85	Month	30 gal.	1.25	Month
	Over 120′	30 gal.	2.20	Month	30 gal.	1.50	Month
Edmonton, Alberta.........	Alley	1 cu. yd.	Free	Week	cu. yd.	1 00	Week

[1]The first container, or the basic quantity, is usually charged at a higher rate in order that certain expenses, such as readiness to serve and route travel time will not be duplicated.

[2]Second 30 gallons, 65¢ per month.

[3]25¢ added for each flight of stairs.

Frequency of Collection and Quantity as the Basis for Charges.
Some cities offer residential properties an option of two or more different frequencies of collection, usually varying from once a week to daily. Typical rate structures involving both frequency of collection and quantity bases, are shown in Table 11-9.

TABLE 11-9
Monthly Residential Rates Based on Quantity and Frequency
of Refuse Collection

City	Quantity or Size of Container	Collections per Week				
		1	2	3	5	6
Berkeley, California[1]	30 gallons	$ 1.00	$ 2.00	$3.00	—	$ 6.00
	40 gallons	1.10	2.20	3.30	—	6.60
	50 gallons	1.75	3.50	5.25	—	10.50
Fresno, California[2]	30 gallons	19.20	33.00	—	—	73.20
	30 gallons	13.80	17.40	—	—	61.20
Eugene, Oregon	1 can	1.60	3.20	4.20	—	—
	2 cans	2.75	5.50	7.50	—	—
	ea. addl. can	1.00	1.00	1.00	—	—
Paducah, Kentucky	96 gallons[3]	1.00	3.40	6.00	—	—

[1]For District No. 1. Other districts slightly higher.
[2]Per year.
[3]Three cans.

Service Charge Rates for Commercial Properties

Commercial rate structures are usually more complicated than residential ones because of the greater variation in the service needed and in the kind and quantity of refuse produced. Recent developments in more specialized equipment and methods of handling, particularly in the containerization field, have also necessitated more involved rate structures. The main characteristics of various rate structures for commercial properties are discussed hereunder in seven main groups and tabulation of typical cities included under each group follow the discussion.

Commercial rates based on quantity. A few cities base their commercial collection rates almost exclusively on the actual or average quantity, volume, or weight presented for collection at business properties. If a city has standardized on a specific size of container the establishment of regular rates is accomplished merely by counting the number of receptacles. Usually, however, various sizes of containers are set out and the quantity must be established by estimating the average quantity. Rate structures for typical cities are shown in Table 11-10.

TABLE 11-10
Commercial Rates Based Primarily
on Quantity of Refuse Collected

City	First Container		Second Container		Ea. Added Cont.		Period
	Capacity	Rate	Capacity	Rate	Capacity	Rate	
Coral Gables, Florida	60 gal.	13.00	—	—	30 gal.	6.50	Quarter
Rochester, Minnesota	32 gal.	0.50	32 gal.	0.40	30 gal.	2.00	Month
Tacoma, Washington[1]	30 gal.	1.50	30 gal.	1.15	30 gal.	1.00[2]	Month

[1]Stairs, 25c per month per flight extra.
[2]Third can no charge. $1.00 for each can over three.

Frequency and Quantity Base for charges. Many cities have commercial rates for different collection frequencies combined with quantity variations. The different frequencies may be established by districts, by option of the individual customers, or by the decision of municipal officials. Typical rate structures are shown in Table 11-11.

TABLE 11-11

Monthly Rates for Commercial Collection Based on Quantity and Frequency

City	Quantity, Number or Size of Containers (Gallons)	Collections per Week						
		1 Rate	2 Rate	3 Rate	4 Rate	5 Rate	6 Rate	7 Rate
Berkeley, Cal.......	30 gal.	$ 1.00	$ 2.00	$ 3.00	$ 4.00	$ 5.00	$ 6.00	$ 7.00
	40 gal.	1.10	2.20	3.30	4.40	5.50	6.60	7.70
Fullerton, Cal.......	1st cu. yd.	2.00	2.00	3.00	....	....	4.00	....
	Ea. addl. cu. yd.	1.00	2.00	3.00	....	....	....	....
San Angelo, Tex....	5 cu. yd.	....	....	4.00	....	....	6.00	....
Eugene, Oregon.....	1 can	1.75	3.25	4.75	5.50	7.75	9.00	....
	2 cans	3.10	5.50	7.50	9.00	12.50	14.50	....
	3 cans	4.25	7.50	9.75	13.00	17.75	20.00	....
Longview, Wash.....	1 cu. yd.	5.35	8.80	10.40	....	....	18.40	....
	2 cu. yd.	8.85	14.40	17.40	....	....	31.00	....
	3 cu. yd.	10.95	18.90	23.00	....	....	41.50	....

Charges estimated by city officials. This kind of rate structure gives municipal officials the responsibility for estimating the average quantity of refuse collected. Because of the difficulty of fixing definite rates that will be equitable for all commercial properties, some cities empower their city managers, directors of public works, superintendents of refuse collection, or some other official to estimate the time, quantity or cost of providing service to various properties.

Sometimes a provision is included in the rate ordinance to the effect that the rates for each premise should be not less than the actual cost to the city. or as nearly as practicable, equal to actual total cost. Various means have been devised by refuse collection officials for making field measurements of time or quantity. Table 11-12 shows some of the means

TABLE 11-12
Bases Used by Four Cities to Compute Commercial Rates for Refuse Collection

City	Rate Terms
Tuscaloosa, Alabama.........	1 minute or less to collect per week, $3.00 per month
	1— 3 minutes, 7.50
	3— 8 minutes, 15.00
	8—20 minutes, 22.50
	20—30 minutes, 37.50
	Over 30 minutes, 60.00
Little Rock, Ark..............	$12.00 per truck hour
Birmingham, Mich............	5¢ per cubic foot in excess of 90 gallons per week
Grand Forks, No. Dak........	Stop watch time for collection. Application of $1.50 cost per minute of crew per week. $2.00 per month minimum.

used. When time is measured as an index of the cost of collection, the route travel time is ordinarily not included. Often four or more collections in sequence are measured to obtain a fair average rate. Regulations ordinarily provide for all estimated rates to be reviewed periodically in order to identify changes in conditions and amounts.

Charges based on kind of business. Some cities have established rates on the basis of the kind of business, primarily to obviate the measurement of the extent of service or the arbitrary establishment of rates by city officials. These rates are generally less accurate than those determined by other means, unless auxiliary methods are also provided, but they have the advantage of being fairly definite. Typical rates are given in Table 11-13.

Commercial charges based on square footage. Fort Worth, Texas has developed a rather complicated plan that takes into account both the kind of business and the size of the business, but it produces a rather accurate basis of charging for commercial collection service. The principle of this rate structure is illustrated in Table 11-14.

Flat rates. Flat rates in commercial areas are not common but some examples are shown in Table 11-15.

Commercial rates for large container service. Service charges by cities providing large container service are shown in Table 11-16.

TABLE 11-13
Commercial Rates for Refuse Collection Based on
Kind of Business, 1961

Vero Beach, Florida	Monthly Charge
Restaurants, daily collection	$ 7.50
Theaters, daily	8.00
Retail and Wholesale establishments, daily	8.00
Grocery stores, daily	15.00
Supermarkets, daily	75.00

Westerville, Ohio			Monthly Charge
Churches and lodge halls			1.50
	large	medium	small
Retail food	35.00	20.00	5.00—10.00
Restaurants	30.00	20.00	10.00—15.00
Mercantile	35.00	20.00	5.00—10.00
Drug stores	15.00	20.00	7.50
Industrial	40.00	25.00	5.00—10.00
Auto service stations & commercial garages			7.50
Barber shops, beauty salons, laundries, funeral homes			5.00
Hospitals, clinics, nursing and rest homes			15.00
Theaters, bowling alleys, skating rinks, billiard parlors			10.00
Schools, libraries, public buildings			10.00

Oklahoma City, Oklahoma	Monthly Charge
Restaurants	4.50- 45.00
Hot tamale and ice cream stands	4.50- 15.00
Drug stores	4.50- 40.00
Hospitals and sanitariums	6.00- 60.00
Butcher shops	4.50- 30.00
Retail grocers	4.50- 60.00
Retail fish stores	4.50- 20.00
Wholesale grocery stores	10.00- 60.00
Retail poultry stores	4.50- 20.00
Wholesale poultry stores	10.00- 60.00
Wholesale fish stores	10.00- 60.00
Hotels	6.00-100.00
Miscellaneous establishments	4.50- 60.00

Shawnee, Oklahoma	Monthly Charge
Grocery stores	2.00- 30.00
Drug stores	2.00- 10.00
Restaurants	2.00- 10.00
Shoe, clothing and department stores	2.00- 30.00
Barber shops	1.00- 2.00
Garages	2.00- 25.00
Self-service laundries	
a. 1st 5 machines, per machine	.25
b. 2nd 5 machines, per machine	.15
c. 11 or more, per establishment	2.50
All other	1.00- 75.00

TABLE 11-14
Collection Rates on Square-foot Basis in Fort Worth, Texas

The collection of refuse from commercial premises is divided into 16 classes.

Six collections per week		Three collections per week	
Class	Monthly Charge	Class	Monthly Charge
I	15.00	Ia	7.50
II	10.50	IIa	5.25
III	7.50	IIIa	3.75
IV	6.00	IVa	3.00
V	5.25	Va	2.65
VI	4.50	VIa	2.25
VII	3.75	VIIa	1.85
VIII	3.00	VIIIa	1.50

Each of the classes has its own active business area value, and these vary according to their general occupancy class, i.e., commercial buildings, such as garages.

Class I and Ia	100,000 sq/ft
Class II and IIa	70,000 sq/ft
Class III and IIIa	50,000 sq/ft

or, in case of hotels, the areas are computed at ½ those of "commercial" buildings.

TABLE 11-15
Flat Rates Charged for Refuse Collection from Commercial Properties

Billings, Montana.................		$60.00 annually, each place of business
Topeka, Kansas...................Inside	Fire Dist. #1—Garbage	$2.00 a month
Outside	Fire Dist. #1—Garbage	.75 a month
Outside	Fire Dist. #1—Trash	1.00 a month

TABLE 11-16
Rates Charged for Refuse Collection by Large Container Service[1]

	Rate Terms
Tuscaloosa, Alabama..	More than once daily, 8 cubic yards, $37.50 per month
	Not more than once daily, 8 cubic yards, $22.50 per month
	Not more than once daily, 6 cubic yards, $15.00 per month
Paducah, Kentucky....	10 cubic yards
	1 day a week, $26.80 per month
	2 days, $35.45
	3 days, $45.10
	4 days, $52.75
	5 days, $61.00
	6 days, $70.00
	8 cubic yards
	1 day a week, $22.80 per month
	2 days, $31.45
	3 days, $40.10
	4 days, $48.75
	5 days, $57.00
	6 days, $66.00
	6 cubic yards
	1 day a week, $18.80
	2 days, $27.45
	3 days, $36.10
	4 days, $44.75
	5 days, $53.00
	6 days, $62.00

[1]Service consists of transporting large detachable refuse containers to disposal sites for emptying. Full container is replaced with an empty one at time of pickup.

Billing Service Charges

Billing procedures vary considerably because each city has to establish its own methods to meet local conditions or departmental or other organizational needs, and the billing arrangements established for other municipal functions. Data on the billing procedures used in various cities are shown in Table 11-17.

TABLE 11-17

Methods Used by 41 Cities to Bill Service Charges For Refuse Collection in Residential Areas

City	Billing Period (Months)	Method of Billing	Issuing Agency	Billed in Advance	All Property Assessed[5]
Montgomery, Ala.....	3	Separate bill	Sanitary Department	Yes	...
Tuscaloosa, Ala......	1	With water bill	Water Works Department	Yes	Yes
Little Rock, Ark......	3	With water bill	Water Department	Yes	Yes
Berkeley, Calif.......	3	Separate bill	Refuse Collection Department	Yes	No
Burbank, Calif.......	2	With electric bill	Public Service Department	...	Yes
Fresno, Calif..	2	Separate bill	Waste Disposal Department	Yes	...
Glendale, Calif......	2	With water bill	Public Works Department	...	...
Pomona, Calif........	2	With water bill	Water Department	...	...
Redwood City, Calif...	...	With water bill	City Collector	No	Yes
Richmond, Calif......	3	Separate bill	Contractor	...	...
Riverside, Calif......	2	With water bill	City Light & Water Department	...	...
Roseville, Calif.......	1	With water bill	Utility Department	Yes	Yes
Santa Monica, Calif..	2	With water bill	Public Works Department	...	...
Farmington Township, Conn.............	12	Separate bill	Town Manager	Yes	Yes
St. Petersburg, Fla....	1	With water bill	Department of Finance	No	Yes
Twin Falls, Idaho....	2	With water bill	Water Department	...	Yes
Rockford, Ill........	3	With water bill	Water Department	...	...
Winnetka, Ill........	2	With water bill	Finance Department	Yes	No
Topeka, Kans........	1	With water bill	Water Department	...	Yes
Paducah, Ky.........	1	With water bill	Water Company	No	Yes
Somerset, Ky........	1	Separate bill	City Clerk	...	...
Traverse City, Mich...	1	With water bill	Utility Department	No[1]	No
Fergus Falls, Minn....	...	...	Water & Light Department	...	Yes
Albuquerque, N.M....	...	With water bill	Fiscal Department	...	Yes
Clovis, N.M.........	3	Separate bill	City	Yes	...
Fargo, N.D..........	3[2]	With water bill	Water Department	...	...
Grand Forks, N.D....	1	With water bill[3]	Waterworks Department	No	Yes
Marion, Ohio........	3	Separate bill	Department of Public Service	Yes	...
Middletown, Ohio....	3	...	Finance Department	Yes	No
Enid, Okla..........	...	With water bill	Water & Sewer Division	...	...
State College, Penn...	3 & 12	...	...	Yes	No
Rapid City, S.D.......	3	With water bill	Water Department	Yes	Yes
El Paso, Texas.......	1	With water bill	Water Department	No	Yes
Fort Worth, Texas....	1	With water bill	Water Department	No	Yes[4]
Temple, Texas.......	1	With water bill	Comptroller	...	Yes
Spokane, Wash.......	4	With water bill	City Utility Division	...	Yes
Tacoma, Wash.......	2	With water bill	Light Division	No	Yes
Morgantown, W. Va..	3 & 12	Separate bill	Sanitation Department	Yes	Yes
Wheeling, W. Va.....	...	With water bill	Water Department	...	Yes
Cheyenne, Wyo......	3, 6, or 12	With water bill	Board of Public Utilities	Yes	Yes
Laramie, Wyo........	12	Separate bill	Engineering Department	Yes	Yes

[1]City manager may require advance payment or deposit.
[2]Monthly billing for properties without water service.
[3]Separate bill for properties without water service.
[4]95 per cent assessed.
[5]Properties are charged whether they use service or not

Billing periods range all the way from a month to a year. Also, it is quite common for cities to combine refuse bills with water or other utility bills to reduce the overhead expense. In detail, the billing practices in municipal and contract collection systems are as follows:

TABLE 11-18

Incidence of Billing Periods and Methods in Municipal and Contract Refuse Collection Systems, 1964

Billing Methods and Periods	Municipal Collection	Contract Collection
(Number of Survey Communities)........	(255)	(96)
Joint billing with utilities.................	67.5%	39.6%
Monthly.............................	61.2	35.4
Quarterly...........................	5.9	4.2
Semi-Annually.......................	0.4	0.0
Separate billing.........................	25.1	53.2
Monthly.............................	7.0	24.0
Quarterly...........................	13.0	23.0
Semi-Annually.......................	2.4	0.0
Annually............................	2.7	6.2
Other billing..........................	7.4	7.2
Total	100.0	100.0

Ticket systems, which involve the purchase at city offices or from city officials of books of tickets and the surrender of the tickets as the refuse is collected, were formerly popular because they eliminated the necessity for billing. None of the 41 cities reporting their billing practices to the APWA however, used this plan as a basic method of billing for residential service. Probably the annoyance of householders at having to pass out tickets each collection day and of purchasing ticket books offset the advantages.

Of the 41 cities reporting, refuse collection bills were issued by the water or utility department in 23; by public works or sanitation operating units in seven; by finance or other similar departments in seven; by the city manager or clerk in two; and by the refuse contractor in one.

Collection of Service Charges

The success of the service charge method of refuse collection depends in large measure on the ability to collect the charges regularly and inexpensively and to avoid the necessity of interrupting collection service to properties. Cities use numerous devices and methods to collect charges regularly and to enforce the payment of delinquent accounts. Some of the practices are shown in Table 11-19.

Table 11-17 showed that 28 cities bill refuse service charges with water or other utility statements and normally it is not permitted to pay the accounts for the two services separately. Citizens pay these bills promptly to ensure continuous water supply, whereas they might in some cases try to get along without refuse service.

The collection of fees in advance has proved to be a very successful

TABLE 11-19
Methods Used by 36 Cities to Collect Delinquent Refuse Collection Accounts

City	Length of Time Service Continued to Delinquents	Action on Delinquent Accounts	Penalty
Montgomery, Ala.	30 days	Refuse service discontinued	. . .
Tuscaloosa, Ala.	30 days	Refuse service discontinued	Full fee required to restore service
Little Rock, Ark.	30 days	. . .	50¢ penalty each bill; legal action
Berkeley, Calif.	6 months[1]	Refuse service discontinued	. . .
Fresno, Calif.	30 days	Refuse service discontinued	. . .
Glendale, Calif.	None	. . .	Legal Action
Redwood City, Calif.	. . .	Refuse service discontinued	. . .
Richmond, Calif.	6 months	Refuse service discontinued	. . .
Riverside, Calif.	60 days	Refuse service discontinued	Personal visits to collect
Roseville, Calif.	. . .	Refuse service discontinued	Misdemeanor for letting refuse accumulate
Farmington Township, Conn.	. . .	Refuse service discontinued	. . .
St. Petersburg, Fla.	Indefinite	Water shut off and refuse service discontinued	. . .
Twin Falls, Idaho	. . .	. . .	Turned over to private collection agency
Rockford, Ill.	Not fixed	Refuse service discontinued	. . .
Winnetka, Ill.	30 days	Refuse service discontinued	. . .
Topeka, Kans.	30 days	Refuse service discontinued	Legal action
Paducah, Ky.	. . .	Refuse service discontinued	Health Department acts at once
Somerset, Ky.	30 days	Refuse service discontinued	
Traverse City, Mich.	Reasonable time	. . .	Lose 10% discount
Fergus Falls, Minn.	30 days	. . .	10% added after 10 days
Clovis, N.M.	. . .	. . .	$5 to $100 fine
Grand Forks, N.D.	Continuous	Lien placed on property and water shut off	All properties must pay for service
Marion, Ohio	30 days	Refuse service discontinued	50¢ added after 10 days; plus 30¢ a week; 50¢ to renew
Middletown, Ohio	14 days	Refuse service discontinued	
Enid, Okla.	Indefinite	. . .	Collection no problem yet
State College, Penn.	[2]	Refuse service discontinued	$1 to $25 fine
Rapid City, S.D.	[2]	Water shut off and refuse service discontinued	City Manager may use other collection methods
El Paso, Texas	30 days	Refuse service discontinued	File police complaint for illegal disposal of refuse
Fort Worth, Texas	10 days	Refuse service discontinued	. . .
Temple, Texas	Indefinite	Water shut off and refuse service discontinued	. . .
Spokane, Wash.	. . .	Lien placed on property	. . .
Tacoma, Wash.	60 days	Refuse service discontinued	50¢ added after 60 days
Morgantown, W. Va.	30 days	. . .	Police court; account paid in lieu of fine
Cheyenne, Wyo.	Indefinite	Lien placed on property and water shut off	$2.50 maximum charged for collecting delinquent account
Laramie, Wyo.	Indefinite	. . .	$2.50 maximum charged for collecting delinquent account
Edmonton, Alberta, Canada	60 days	. . .	Court Action

[1]Commercial, 3 months.
[2]May discontinue at once.

collection device. It is probably used wherever it is legally possible or practicable. Sixteen of the 41 cities reported collecting all fees in advance. If the bills are not paid by the designated time, action is normally started at once to collect the account or stop the collection service. Discounts for prompt payment also have proved effective. Penalties for failure to pay bills on time have a similar effect.

The current trend is definitely in the direction of continuing regular refuse service rather than stopping it for non-payment of charges. In such cases the collection of delinquent accounts is enforced by other legal means. For example, Table 11-19 shows that 12 cities shut off water service, place a lien on the property or take other punitive action, but continue refuse removal service. Seven cities continue service for indefinite periods, depending on the official view of the conditions surrounding each case. The authority to stop removal service is frequently permissive rather than mandatory and the tendency is to apply all other pressures before stopping service. One city discontinues service after 10 days of delinquency, one after 14 days, eleven after 30 days, three after 60 days and two after 6 months.

Cities use various means of collecting delinquent accounts before they resort to stopping the refuse service. Some use department employees to call on delinquent customers and others use regular collection agencies. If the collection service has been stopped, full payment plus any penalties is usually required before service will be renewed. Eventually, practically all cities may use such means as are available to collect money due the city, with or without stopping the collection service. Ordinance penalties may be invoked or suits may be instituted. Some cities make both the property owners and tenants responsible for the payment of refuse charges.

A few cities have required customers to sign orders or agreements before removal service will be started in order to have adequate evidence to support collection suits to recover overdue accounts. This procedure is similar to that used by some privately owned utility companies and even by some municipally owned utilities. However, no city reported this procedure in the APWA survey and it may be assumed it is not used as much as in earlier years.

The collection of delinquent accounts, one of the big problems in the earlier days of the service charge plan, no longer is regarded as a serious problem. There are, of course, some uncollectable accounts—involving transient customers particularly—but losses are usually kept at a minimum through sound administrative practices.

Adequacy of Revenue from Service Charges and Fees

Despite the fact that service charges are applied to their whole collection systems, many cities find that refuse service charges are inadequate to finance all expenses of the collection and disposal system, including operating and overhead costs and debt service. Other sources of funds must then be used to finance the operation or the level of service must be curtailed.

Several of the ordinances establishing the service charge system definitely state that the intention is to finance the collection and disposal service without making a profit. Sometimes it is made the responsibility of the officials in charge to revise the rates as may be necessary to keep the whole operation or designated portions of it, self-supporting.

Large and small communities are included in the number of cities which finance their refuse collection by service charges exclusively. This is shown in the following table:

TABLE 11-20

Population Size and Service Charge Income in Communities Financing Their Refuse Collections by Service Charges Exclusively, 1960[1]

City	Popula-tion (Thousands)	Annual Income from Refuse Collection Service Charges (In Thousands of Dollars)	Year Service Charges Were Levied Originally
Tuscaloosa, Alabama...	63	168	N.A.
Anchorage, Alaska......	43	287	N.A.
Ketchikan, Alaska.......	6	75	1940
Sacramento, Calif.......	190	909	1922
Santa Monica, Calif......	83	612	1949
St. Petersburg, Fla......	180	1,289	1948
Dade County, Fla........	935	2,101	1951
Council Bluffs, Iowa.....	54	148	1935
Perry, Iowa.............	6	30	1959
Wichita, Kansas........	255	519	1944
Salina, Kansas..........	40	111	1960
Billings, Montana.......	55	391	1940
Minot, No. Dakota.......	31	115	1952
Westerville, Ohio........	7	48	1950
Oklahoma City, Okla.....	324	2,246	1925
Oil City, Pa..............	18	120	1946
Fort Worth, Texas.......	356	1,935	1943
Wichita Falls, Texas.....	104	572	1941
Eagle Lake, Texas.......	4	15	1950
Tacoma, Washington....	148	815	N.A.
Richland, Washington...	24	138	1959
Wheeling, W. Va.........	53	213	1947
Kamloops, Br. Col.......	10	43	1930
Quebec, Que.,..........	240	526	N.A.

Source: Municipal Finance Officers Association of the United States and Canada "Refuse Collection and Disposal Service Charges" by Lennox L. Moak, 1961

[1]Does not include all cities relying completely on service charges to finance their refuse collection.

Public Approval of Refuse Charges

Public opinion of the refuse service charge system and of the rate charged is of considerable importance in appraising the success of this means of financing. Several of the reporting cities stated that the public attitude was favorable and none indicated public displeasure. Usually such charges are introduced along with proposals for updating, extending, or improving the service and there is, therefore, more chance of acceptance by the public.

Equitable Distribution of Cost

Distribution of the cost of refuse collection and disposal operations among the citizens is considerably different under the service charge method of financing than under the general property taxation method. The amount of difference depends to a large extent on the completeness of municipal service in both residential and business areas. Normally, poor families paying for this essential service as an occupancy or utility tax, will be compelled to pay substantially more than on any ability to pay basis. This may be held to be a serious disadvantage, as undoubtedly it is, when offsetting corrections cannot be made at other points in the tax plan. However, it is not proper to criticize the effects of one tax, particularly a small one, without considering the consequences of all tax levies combined. The objective should be to achieve equitable distribution of the total costs of government among the citizens of a municipality. The suitability of refuse service charges must be appraised on the basis of their effect on citizens in relation to other possible methods. The general approval expressed by officials in cities using this plan would indicate that service charges for refuse removal can be fitted satisfactorily into taxation plans in most communities.

One of the most significant changes that has taken place in the refuse collection field in the past twenty years is the much greater insistence on complete collection service throughout the entire community, including both residential and commercial areas. This is of particular interest in a discussion of service charge financing, because the strongest argument that has been leveled against the plan over the years has been incomplete service due to the optional element and the inability of all families and businesses to pay for the collection.

As indicated in Table 11-17, numerous cities now require all properties to use the municipal collection service. Of 28 cities reporting whether all property is assessed, 23 of them require all residential properties to use the service and actually make universal charges, and 5 indicated that service is optional. Eighteen cities require all commercial properties as well as all residential properties to use the municipal service and to pay the standard charges. Compared with previous data this is a remarkable advance and gives some indication that the service charge plan may become more widely used in the future.

Most modern ordinances that require universal charges provide some means of appeal from rates that are considered to be too high, or from paying for service that is not needed or received. They also include some machinery for adjusting inequities.

Service to Properties Outside of the City

Some cities accept customers outside the city limits and normally offer the same service as is given to their citizens. If no organized collection service is available to such outside properties, undesirable refuse disposal practices may seriously affect the public health of the entire area or may cause nuisances.

Often municipal refuse collection rates are set somewhat higher for outside customers to compensate for possible longer hauls or greater travel distance between pickups. Four cities reported that outside properties are regularly served and their outside rates are compared with the regular city rates in Table 11-21. Ordinance provisions in other cities give the operating officials the power to set rates for unusual conditions.

TABLE 11-21

Rates Charged by 4 Cities for Refuse Collection
Service Outside City Limits, Compared with City
Rates

City		Rates
Montgomery, Alabama........		Rates slightly higher outside city
Roseville, California...........	Outside:	$1.75 a month for 30 gallons collected once a week. Each added 10 gallons, 40¢
	Inside:	$1.00 a month for 30 gallons collected once a week. Each added 10 gallons, 15¢
Traverse City, Michigan.......	Outside:	$1.25 a month for 1st dwelling unit. 70¢ added units
	Inside:	$ .95 a month for 1st dwelling unit. 50¢ added units
Marion, Ohio..................	Outside:	$5.25 a quarter for 10 gallons of garbage and 3 bushels of rubbish collected once a week. Excess at commercial rate
	Inside:	$3.75 a quarter for 10 gallons of garbage and 3 bushels of rubbish collected once a week. Excess at commercial rate

Efficiency of a Single Refuse Agency

The optimum conditions for economical and effective refuse removal service are realized when one agency conducts all of the work of removing all kinds of refuse from all properties. In the interests of maintaining responsibility, control, and operation within the proper area of the government of the community, it should be the objective to provide the desired service adequately and at the least possible cost to individuals and the community as a whole. The division of operations among two or more agencies, part municipal and part private, inevitably leads to the inefficiencies of duplicate equipment and duplicate supervisory forces. Frequently the forces of the different agencies work side by side in the same area. Such conditions automatically develop in communities which, for one reason or another, collect only from certain kinds of properties or pick up only certain classes of material. The refuse not picked up by city forces must be disposed of by the producers or by private collectors; in either case the cost is substantially greater than if it were all removed by a single agency.

When service charges are used to finance refuse collection work it is easiest to take advantage of the savings of conducting all work by a municipal agency and at the same time to secure all the other benefits that accrue from complete collection.

Administrative Expense of Service Charges

The cost of collecting service charges and other extra administrative costs involved in enforcing public health and sanitary ordinances represents additional expense to cities and this cost must be taken fully into account in appraising this method. Experience in several cities where modern utility systems of separate billing and collecting are employed, indicates that the administrative expense is between 10 and 13 per cent of total operating cost. Such amounts cannot be considered at all excessive but they are nevertheless extra costs that must be paid by the citizens. Many cities have succeeded in eliminating a part of this overhead cost by one means or another, but sometimes they have thereby been forced to adopt more arbitrary rate structures than would otherwise be selected. Cities that issue combined refuse and water or other utility bills are able to reduce the amount of overhead expense considerably.

COMBINING GENERAL REVENUE AND SERVICE CHARGE FINANCING

Numerous cities require refuse producers to pay part of the cost of collection, in an effort to combine the advantages of the general revenue and service charge methods of financing as previously indicated. In some cases the idea is to provide service uniformly to all properties at public expense but to charge for all removal above that considered to be normal or reasonable. The difficulty lies, of course, in defining accurately the point at which free collection should stop and charges should begin.

Another plan is to give unrestricted collection at public expense for residential properties but to charge for all service in the commercial areas or for certain classes of refuse.

The cities that have established partial service charges ordinarily do not make it mandatory for producers to use municipal removal facilities. Unfortunately, the attitude of the officials in some of these cities is to discourage the development of the service charge part of their activities and they are quite content to have private collectors do the work instead of city forces. In a few cases it is evident that high service charges have been established to force the employment of private collection agencies.

It is quite possible that some combination of publicly-financed and producer-financed refuse removal service may give better results in some communities than either plan alone. The distribution of the cost may be more equitable and adequate funds may thus be made available.

Under any such combination the overhead expense would be greatly decreased because it is probable that the great majority of properties would be served at public expense, leaving only a small number to which billing and collection costs would be applicable. The ticket system in such a case may be quite feasible, whereas under a complete service charge plan it may be less desirable.

FINANCING BY SPECIAL ASSESSMENT

The use of special assessments for financing municipal refuse collection service has been very limited in the United States, even though cities in numerous states have the authority to employ this method under their general police power, either in the abatement of nuisances or in providing a municipal service. General opinion opposes the idea of financing recurring current expenditures by special assessment, particularly where, as in the case of refuse collection, there is considerable general benefit involved. There is no legal or economic basis for such opinion and actually there may be some advantages in the distribution of the cost of regular services by special assessment. The arguments cited for service charges apply in the most part to special assessment. In reality, special assessments for refuse removal are very similar to service charges, except that assessments are made against the properties benefited whereas charges are usually made to the persons receiving the service.

Atlanta, Georgia is the only city on which data are available that uses the special assessment method regularly. Street cleaning and refuse collection and disposal are financed from a sanitary tax levied on a special assessment basis. The combined annual rate for residential properties is $4 for each 25 front feet, plus a flat sum of $6 for each property, except that the maximum fee for a property occupied by a single residence is $22. The commercial rates are $24 for each 25 front feet or fraction. The difference in the rates is based primarily on the frequency of street cleaning and refuse collection. These rates are currently financing only about one-half of the total cost of the services provided and are expected to be revised in the near future.

Delinquent extra charges for refuse collection in Fargo, North Dakota, are assessed against properties in the same manner as are charges for sidewalk repairs. This limited use of the special assessment device represents a means of collecting delinquent service charges as property liens.

SUMMARY

The two principle means of financing refuse collection operations are general revenues and service charges. Everything considered, it is better to provide the removal service at general public expense in those communities which are able and willing to appropriate enough to make possible complete collection from all properties. Complete collection means the removal of all garbage, ashes, and rubbish from all properties in all districts. If such appropriations cannot be made, it is far more desirable to establish service charges for all or part of the work rather than to fail to provide complete service throughout a municipality. Under the service charge plan the increase in cost for billing and collecting will normally be but a fraction of the difference between municipal operation and the sometimes more expensive private collection service. The benefits of the increased efficiency of a single refuse collection agency in comparison with any combination of municipal, contract, or private agencies has generally been given far too little attention by city officials.

The distribution of the cost of refuse collection operations is normally more equitable when the service is financed from general revenues, except insofar as the removal of abnormally large quantities is concerned. The relatively low cost of refuse collection, however, makes financing by service charges a very acceptable substitute when adequate funds cannot be provided for complete service from general funds. Numerous cities have found that the service charge plan can be incorporated successfully in their taxation systems.

chapter 12

ORGANIZATION

The goal of organization is a working arrangement through which a group of men can achieve a common purpose in the most effective manner with the least effort and friction and with the greatest satisfaction to all employees. To management as well as to all employees, the common purpose of the refuse collection service is the removal of refuse from households, commercial establishments, and public buildings—in a safe, sanitary, and economical way—and in accordance with the policies established by the representatives of the people. The group is comprised of the refuse collectors and their helpers, truck drivers, collection foremen, supervisors, and administrators as well as the members of the clerical, engineering, and auxiliary forces who have a part in the task. For easy administration, the whole task should be divided logically into workable parts such as divisions, districts, or sections; the personnel should be allocated to units and to specific positions; definite authority and responsibility should be assigned to each; and the several parts should be adequately coordinated.

No uniform pattern or common form of structure is possible for all refuse collection agencies. Policies are not the same, methods are different, conditions are dissimilar, and the groups vary widely in size. Equally important, the employees making up a group differ from each other and from the employees of other groups. Nevertheless, in determining the most suitable plan for a particular situation, the principles of organization structure and the organizational experiences of similar groups will be of assistance. Some of the more important principles of organization as they apply to refuse collection activities are enumerated in this chapter, and information is given on arrangements that have proved successful in various municipalities.

BASIC FACTORS IN ORGANIZATION

Listed below are some organization principles that are particularly important in developing a plan for conducting refuse collection operations effectively and harmoniously.

1. Clear and definite lines of authority should be prescribed to enable each employee to know precisely his place in the structure, to whom he is immediately responsible, what units and positions

are under his supervision, his duties and responsibilities, and his relationships with other employees and with other units of the service. The total responsibility should be so distributed that overlapping duties and responsibilities are reduced to a minimum.

2. Each employee should be given authority commensurate with the responsibility of his position. Such authority and responsibility should flow directly from higher positions to those immediately subordinate.

3. Separation of the work into divisions, bureaus, sections, or districts should be based on complete information as to the nature of the work, the methods and kinds of equipment to be used, and the distribution of the group throughout the municipality. Logically, the broad organization plan should not be formulated until the technical planning of methods, routes, and schedules, described in Chapter 7, is completed.

4. Division of the work according to purpose, area, time, or process should be based on a careful analysis of the work to be done and should follow the detailed planning of operations.

5. The number of subordinates reporting to an officer should not be more than he can supervise competently.

6. Each employee of officer rank should be engaged full time in supervisory work, but he should not become so involved in work details that he has no opportunity for general appraisal of progress or activity or for broad planning of the operations for which he is responsible.

7. Supervisory employees should control an area small enough so that they can devote their time to actual operations rather than to traveling between crews. In large cities, geographical division of the work is usually essential.

8. When the kinds of services to be performed vary widely as to the skill, technique, knowledge, or equipment required, the work should be divided so as to group together the positions requiring abilities and facilities.

9. Adequate provision should be made for specialized staff and auxiliary services. Such services may be a part of the internal organization of a refuse collection agency, or they may be furnished by another department or division.

THE PLACE OF REFUSE COLLECTION
IN THE MUNICIPAL ORGANIZATION

The place assigned to refuse removal service in the municipal organization has an important bearing on the effectiveness of day-by-day operations as well as on long-range plans for improvement and extension. The allocation is governed to some extent by the form of the municipal government. Other factors that influence the placing of the function are size of the community, the attitude of officials, the prestige of the function, the funds available, and special local conditions. Not infrequently, the capacities or preferences of department heads are taken into account.

TABLE 12-1
Allocation of Refuse Collection Service
to Major Departments by 637 Cities in 1964

Major Department	Number of Cities	Per Cent
Health	19	1.2
Sanitation	85	12.5
Streets	50	7.2
Public Works	361	56.6
Refuse, Waste, Garbage	12	5.2
Public Service Utility	38	5.3
Highway	2	1.0
Other	55	1.5
Not stated	15	9.5
Total	637	100.0

Allocation to Major Departments

Table 12-1 above shows where 637 cities place responsibility for refuse removal work.

Refuse collection is most frequently placed in a public works, sanitation, public service, or some other department that has responsibility for operating functions that involve engineering supervision. Although the service is essentially a public health function, operations are unlike those of other health activities. Formerly, the function was often conducted by private collectors or by contract, and public health departments of cities frequently supervised the removal service. The tendency in recent years, particularly in the larger cities, has been to conduct the service with municipal employees and to place the supervision of the actual collection work in public works operating units, but to leave in the public health departments the basic responsibility for enforcing the sanitation laws governing the storage and handling of refuse.

In extremely large cities there is the greatest freedom of choice. The operations are so extensive that it may be satisfactory to create separate departments of sanitation or to assign the work to public works or other operating departments. A refuse agency in a large city may contain its own research, planning, engineering, sanitation, public relations, and enforcement branches or specialists. In a very small municipality there may be a very limited choice of position. The service may be supervised by a department head or even directly by a city manager, mayor, or council committee.

Allocation within Major Departments

The refuse removal activity is grouped with other municipal services in various arrangements in the divisions, bureaus, or sections of major departments. An effort is usually made to bring together agencies that require similar supervisory knowledge and techniques, relate to a single function, employ like equipment or facilities, operate in the same areas, or exchange employees. A seemingly logical grouping of activities may

not always be practical because executive officers would have too much
or too little to handle efficiently or because of personalities, expediency,
or local tradition. The subordinate divisions in which the collection
activities of 637 cities are placed are shown in Table 12-2.

TABLE 12-2
Allocation of Refuse Collection Service
To Departments and Branches by 637 Cities in 1964

Department	Number	Branch	Number
Health	19	Health	1
		Sanitation	9
		Refuse, Waste, Garbage	3
		Not stated	6
Sanitation	85	Sanitation	21
		Public Works	4
		Refuse, Waste, Garbage	8
		Public Service, Utilities	1
		Other	1
		Not stated	50
Streets	50	Health	2
		Sanitation	12
		Streets	5
		Public Works	1
		Refuse, Waste, Garbage	8
		Other	2
		Not stated	20
Public Works	361	Health	2
		Sanitation	192
		Streets	18
		Public Works	23
		Refuse, Waste, Garbage	61
		Public Service, Utilities	1
		Highway	3
		Other	7
		Not stated	54
Refuse, Waste, Garbage	12	Sanitation	3
		Streets	1
		Public Works	1
		Refuse, Waste, Garbage	3
		Public Service, Utilities	1
		Not stated	3
Public Service, Utilities	38	Sanitation	12
		Streets	2
		Public Works	1
		Refuse, Waste, Garbage	11
		Public Service, Utilities	3
		Other	1
		Not stated	8
Highway	2	Not stated	2
Other	55	Health	1
		Sanitation	27
		Streets	4
		Public Works	5
		Refuse, Waste, Garbage	7
		Other	2
		Not stated	9
Not stated	15	Sanitation	4
		Streets	3
		Refuse, Waste, Garbage	1
		Not stated	7
Total Branches	637	Total	637

The most common arrangement is to group refuse collection, refuse disposal, and street cleaning together (1) in a sanitation department; (2) in a sanitation division of a public works, street, public service, or health department; or (3) in a unit of a street or other division of a major department. Refuse disposal is normally combined with refuse collection because of the inevitable and frequent contacts of the working forces of the two activities and because each influences to a considerable extent the operations of the other. Street cleaning is often combined with refuse collection because the two services have many personnel and equipment problems in common. All three activities require engineering supervision.

Sometimes, however, refuse collection and disposal form a division or bureau, with street cleaning either a separate division or combined with street or sewer maintenance. In Cincinnati, for example, the Division of Waste Collection includes both collection and disposal. Even when the three are combined in a single branch, the first division of work is likely to be made on the basis of activity—separating street cleaning from refuse collection and disposal and sometimes separating all three parts into operating groups at the same level. In Los Angeles, for example, the Bureau of Sanitation of the Department of Public Works has four divisions: (1) Refuse Collection and Disposal, (2) Sewer Maintenance, (3) Sewage Treatment, and (4) Research and Planning. Hartford has similar arrangements. Nevertheless, in some instances a geographical division of work is made before refuse collection is separated from one or more other activities. In New York City the Department of Sanitation is responsible for the collection of *all* garbage and domestic refuse. In addition, it is responsible for the disposal of *all* refuse (domestic, municipal, commercial and industrial) generated within the city, and for the cleaning of streets free of dirt, litter, and snow and ice. These responsibilities, except for the *disposal* of refuse, are carried out by its Bureau of Cleaning and Collection through eight Borough Commands which are subdivided into 57 semi-autonomous Sanitation Districts, each further splintered into four or five Sections. The refuse collection and street cleaning functions are under undivided control until they reach the Section level where they may be separated between two foremen, but even then with some overlapping of responsibilities for practical day to day reasons. In Toronto, Canada, the responsibility of refuse collection and street cleaning is not separated until it has been divided into three geographical divisions.

Many other arrangements exist; refuse collection is combined with other activities and is separated from them at various levels. The patterns of organization in six cities are shown on Table 12-3. Figures 12-2 to 12-7 at the end of the chapter show the organizational setup in Cedar Rapids, Iowa; Cincinnati, Ohio; Midland, Texas; Los Angeles, California; Richmond, Virginia; and New York City.

TABLE 12-3

Typical Public Works and Sanitation Department Organizational Arrangements[1]

	Main Department	2nd Echelon	3rd Echelon	4th Echelon	5th Echelon	
Cincinnati, Ohio	**Public Works**	**Div. of Waste Collection**	**Waste Collection Div.** 2 other geographical divisions Incinerator Division Garage Division	**4th District** 3 other districts in Division (Foreman)	**Crews**	
Fort Worth, Texas	**Public Works**	**Waste Disposal Div.** Administration Sec. Engineering Garage Building Light & Signal Street	**Collection Section** Incinerator Sec. San. Fill Sec.	**Crews**		
Hartford, Connecticut	**Public Works**	**Deputy Director** Highways Administration	**Waste Collection** Waste disposal Street Cleaning	**South District** 2 other districts	**Crews**	
Los Angeles, California	**Public Works**	**Bureau of Sanitation**	**Refuse Collection and Disposal Div.** Sewer Maint. Div. Sewage Disposal Div. Research & Planning Div. Administration Div.	**Collection Operation** Equipment Maintenance Division Officer	**South Central District** North Central District Western District East Valley District West Valley District	**Residential Combined** Commercial Garbage Animal Carcasses
New York, New York	**Sanitation Commissioner**	**Director of Operations**	**Bur. of Cleaning and Collection** Bur. of Motor Equipment Bur. of Waste Disposal Bur. of Plant Maintenance	**Borough Office— Manhattan West** 7 other Borough Offices	**District 5** 5 other Dist. in Borough Office—Manhattan West (Similarly for other Borough Offices.)	**Section** 3 other Sections in Dist. 5 (each dist. subdivided into 4 or 5 sections)
Richmond, Virginia	**Public Works**	**Bureau of Operations**	**Div. of Street Sanit.**	**Refuse Collection Sec.** Refuse Disposal Street Cleaning	**Crews**	

[1] Each city's department is divided into its main echelons. The organizational pattern through each echelon is underlined.

COOPERATION AMONG DEPARTMENTS AND DIVISIONS

At least four kinds of processes are involved in the conduct of a refuse system; (1) engineering supervision of operations and planning; (2) public health control of sanitary aspects; (3) police enforcement of regulations; and (4) public relations counseling. In addition, equipment, personnel, purchasing, accounting, and other services must be provided —often by units outside the collection agency. While local emphasis on one or another of these processes may decide the place of the refuse agency in the organization structure, there still must be coordination with other units. For example, if refuse collection is made a part of a public works or engineering department, the help of the public health authorities may be needed because of their greater powers to enforce sanitary laws. Police assistance may be necessary or desirable to enforce ordinances and regulations. The necessary legal, purchasing and accounting services are usually located in other departments. There is good reason why the several departments should aid each other by performing the services they can do easiest and best, and it is the task of management to see that such cooperation is made possible.

INTERNAL ORGANIZATION

The internal organization of an agency responsible exclusively for refuse collection services must be fitted to the collection methods that are selected and depends to some extent on such factors as the frequency of collection, the length of hauls, and the number of operations required. In large cities, the first division of work is likely to be a geographical one in order to limit the area under a single foreman or supervisor to that which he can effectively control and manage.

Before a plan of internal organization can be intelligently developed, most of the details of service and methods must be known, and the basic number of crews, trucks, and routes determined. The various methods normally used in collecting refuse were discussed in detail in Chapter 5, and suggestions for estimating the personnel and equipment requirements were made.

The objective in organizing the service is to arrange and utilize the manpower, equipment, and materials to achieve effective, expeditious, and economical conduct of the work. The organization plan must provide for a smoothly running machine, free of bottlenecks or obstructions. When emergencies arise, there should be reserves or resources to cope with them—whether in personnel, equipment, or other necessities for operation. However, the backlog of reserve equipment, maintenance forces, or other resources should not be so great as to cause an undue financial burden; it, too, should be in balance. Where seasonal fluctuations in work load are pronounced, the organization must be flexible enough to permit the necessary adjustments without loss of efficiency.

The Refuse Collection Administrator

The head of a refuse collection agency is now recognized as an important municipal administrator, while as recently as 15 years ago, cities required little more than the ability to control gangs of laborers. Several factors have influenced the change. Both labor and equipment costs have increased significantly, bringing a recognition that sound business management is essential to effective and economical service. Refuse collection has become one of the largest operations in most cities, both in terms of the number of employees and in annual expenditures. Furthermore, the standards of collection have been rising steadily in quality as well as in extent of service. Cities are taking pride in the efficiency of collection services and in the appearance of the force and equipment. Quite properly, the service is regarded as the one in closest continual contact with the public and must therefore be a suitable example of municipal efficiency. As the stature of the activity has been raised, higher competence has been required of administrators.

The rank of the head of a refuse collection agency varies considerably with the size of a community and with the character of the removal service offered. In a municipality of 10,000 population the operations may be supervised by a foreman in charge of several crews. He would report to a director of public works, city engineer, or other officer who necessarily would assume much of the responsibility for the planning, technical supervision, and management of refuse collection in addition to his other duties. The operation of a large city usually justifies the appointment of an administrator to assume full charge of all phases of the management of refuse collection and devote his entire attention to the work. Often he may provide both the administrative and technical skill needed to conduct the work effectively. Metropolitan city operations such as those found in Los Angeles permit the employment of a director to administer the activity and to coordinate the technical and production branches. In New York City the Director of Operations coordinates the work of the four Bureaus responsible for production. He correlates such work with the staff work of the several offices as occasion demands.

The officials responsible for refuse collection activities have various titles, depending on the type of organization and the size of the operations. A sanitation department or division is often headed by a director, superintendent, or engineer of sanitation—particularly if refuse disposal, street cleaning, or other activities are included. The person in charge of a refuse collection unit in such a department or division is frequently given the title of supervisor or superintendent of refuse collection, or in a smaller municipality, general foreman or simply foreman of refuse collection.

Provision for Line Activities

The term "line" activities refers to the things that are done to actually carry out the collection work. "Staff" activities deal with the various facets of administration. Line officers and supervisors form a continuous chain of command from the top executive down to the lowest supervisor. For example, the line of authority in a department of public works might start with the director of the department, flow to the head of a bureau of sanitation, to the superintendent of a refuse collection division, and then to district supervisors, and on to foremen. In such an organization, a staff unit like a personnel office might be attached to the department head or to the bureau head but it would not be in the line or chain of command.

The problem of organization is essentially one of providing adequate and competent supervision. The number of districts or other geographical divisions depends upon the area that can be effectively controlled by one supervisor. Considerable information on the operation should be available before final decisions on organization structure are made. Some essential data are: the number and size of crews, the number of routes, the collection method, and for each general area the time for collecting a load, the area serviced in collecting one load, and the length of haul. The distance between crews is also a significant factor since every supervisor should be able to visit each of his crews at least three times daily to investigate difficulties and carry out other administrative duties.

Route arrangements will influence the number of supervisory areas that should be created. If the collection plan provides for several crews on adjacent routes in a compact area on one day, and then for those crews to operate similarly in another compact area the next day, a supervisor can obviously be assigned more crews than if the crews are scattered throughout the city. Also, a supervisor can direct more crews if the activities for a day begin at the outer points of routes and work toward a central point, since this means crews will converge toward the end of the day when more frequent supervisor-crew contact is necessary.

In larger cities, several districts with a supervisor in charge of each may be needed. If the number of districts does not exceed eight or nine, each supervisor would typically report to a superintendent or other officer having city-wide responsibility. If more districts are needed, further geographical organization is desirable. Customarily, from four to nine districts are assigned to such a division over which a division superintendent or similar official is in charge. Each division superintendent would report to the official having city-wide reponsibilities.

The internal organization plan of the Refuse Collection and Disposal Division of the Los Angeles Bureau of Sanitation is adapted to a very large operating area. (See Figure 12-5). The collection operations are separated from refuse disposal, equipment maintenance and repair, and office activities at the first echelon and placed under a refuse collection superintendent. A geographical division is made at once into five districts. Within each district, the first division is made according to the kinds of materials collected: (1) residential combined refuse, (2) commercial garbage, and (3) animal carcasses. Each of these units in a district has its own office staff and control center for its collection crews.

Separate collection operations for different kinds of refuse often require special organizational arrangements. Generally, the frequency of collecting each class of material is different and different equipment may be used, justifying the use of crews continuously on one operation or the other. Washington D.C., for example, requires three separations of refuse. Each class of refuse is collected separately and the crews are organized under a superintendent who reports directly to the head of the Sanitation Division. The Trash Collection Section is divided into ten districts, the Garbage Collection Section eight districts, and the Ash Collection Section into three districts. Some smaller cities on the other hand, successfully use the same crews to collect two classes of refuse by assigning them to garbage collection four days a week and to trash collection in essentially the same areas on the other day or days.

FIG. 12-1. The use of two-way radio communication equipment helps the collection supervisor locate and correct trouble spots quickly. He can analyze the need and initiate corrective measures immediately.

The various possible arrangements are so numerous that all cannot be discussed separately. The important point, regardless of the service pattern, is to assign to a supervisor no more work than he can handle properly. The importance of adequate, positive, supervision has already been discussed. Any error should be on the side of too much supervision rather than too little.

One of the most difficult decisions faced by administrators is the question of the level at which geographical division should be made or a separation of activities accomplished. Usually, for example, street cleaning is separated from refuse collection relatively high in the structure, but sometimes the two activities are kept under the same supervision through one or more geographical divisions in the internal organization In some cases, refuse collectors do street cleaning work while trucks travel to and from the disposal plant.

The details of administrative control within the organization should be clearly understood by all of the line officers, even to the foremen and subforemen who may direct the work of a small number of employees.

Provision for Staff Activities

Refuse collection is too often considered to be purely a "line" activity, either because the staff work is largely ignored or because it is performed by the line officers. However, each refuse collection agency must plan and program its work, make studies of methods and equipment, plan and conduct educational campaigns, obtain suitable personnel, procure supplies and equipment, keep records and cost accounts, and provide equipment services. These staff and auxiliary functions must be provided for. Some of the advisory supervision or special service may originate within the organization of a refuse collection branch, either as a part of the line arrangement or as separate staff or auxiliary bureaus or sections. Some, or even all, may be outside the refuse collection organization proper and be provided for whole departments or for the entire municipal government.

The technical work of planning, programming, and conducting research, for example, may be done by the head of a refuse collection agency or jointly by him and the heads of his main subordinate divisions. It may be performed by a staff unit within his organization or by an engineering or research unit attached to his superior's office elsewhere in the organization structure. Only the very large cities make formal organization arrangements for staff units. In the New York City Department of Sanitation, for example, separate staff units immediately under the Commissioner of Sanitation are provided for engineering including management planning, investigations, labor relations, public relations (including sanitary education), medical services (including clinic and field service), and legal services. The auxiliary services in New York are mostly allocated to a separate Bureau of Administrative Services in the Department of Sanitation. (See Figure 12-7.)

In the Los Angeles Bureau of Sanitation almost all the needed staff and auxiliary services are provided by a Research and Planning Division, and an Administration Division. (See Figure 12-5).

Somewhat smaller cities almost always provide for the engineering and planning service to be done mainly by the line supervisors as a part of their management duties, although special studies may at times be made by engineering or other units of other departments, or personnel for such work may be loaned. Such cities as Hartford, Richmond, and Cincinnati do not have special staff service units within their refuse collection organization but place the responsibility for planning, programming, and research in the line positions.

Personnel, procurement, accounting, and legal services are frequently furnished on a city-wide basis to all departments, although in some cities departments, and occasionally even divisions, must undertake to provide some of these services for themselves. Equipment service on the other hand, is centralized in relatively few cities. Usually such services are provided for entire public works, public service, or sanitation departments to the component operations. Sometimes, however, refuse collection equipment maintenance is a direct responsibility of the collection agency itself.

Organization Charts

A clear line of command should be established and observed from the top down to each supervisor at the lowest level and through him to those employees for whose supervision he is responsible. The flow of authority can best be understood by all concerned when it is graphically presented, and each department or agency should chart its organizational structure. An organization chart for a refuse collection agency primarily should portray lines of authority. However, in identifying each unit in the organization, the name of the unit and the title of its head should be included. If the functions of units are not evident from the names, a statement of functions in each unit box is helpful to a satisfactory understanding of the management plan.

Organization charts should at all times reveal the actual lines of authority and the currently authorized unit names and titles. Charts that show an ideal plan or one contrary to facts serve no purpose and may be misleading.

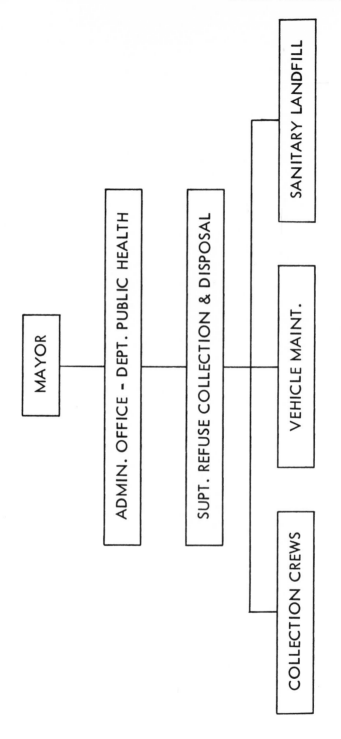

FIG. 12-2. The City of Cedar Rapids, Iowa, with a commission form of government, places responsibility for refuse collection in one division of the Department of Public Health.

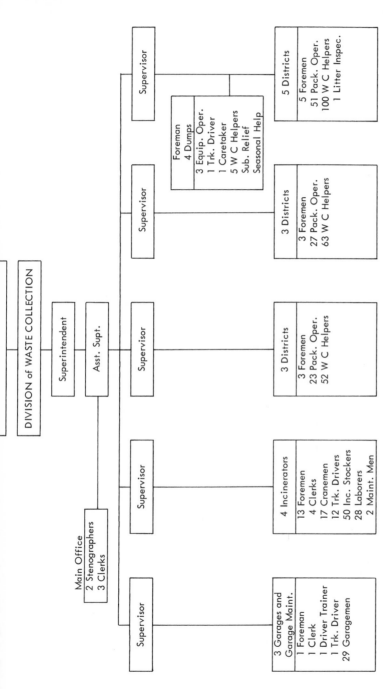

FIG. 12-3. The collection and disposal of refuse is assigned to the Department of Public Works in Cincinnati, Ohio, and made a separate division under the direction of a superintendent. The collection work is divided into three geographical areas, each headed by a waste collection supervisor, and further divided into districts in charge of foremen.

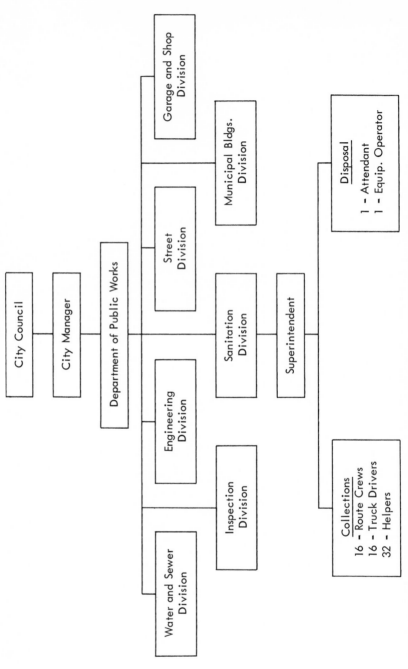

FIG. 12-4. Refuse Collection and Disposal Branches make up the Sanitation Division of the Department of Public Works in Midland, Texas.

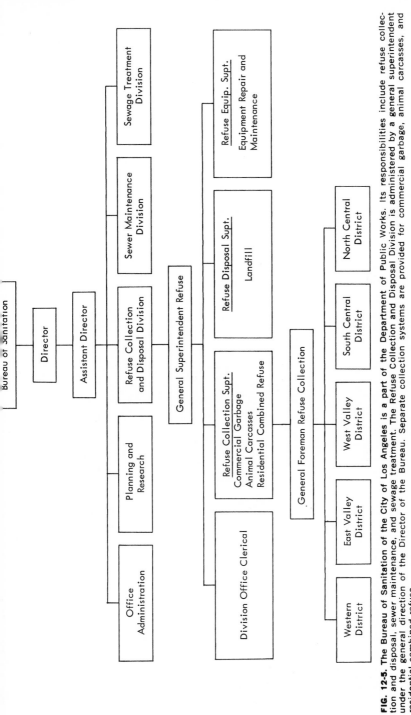

FIG. 12-5. The Bureau of Sanitation of the City of Los Angeles is a part of the Department of Public Works. Its responsibilities include refuse collection and disposal, sewer maintenance, and sewage treatment. The Refuse Collection and Disposal Division is administered by a general superintendent under the general direction of the Director of the Bureau. Separate collection systems are provided for commercial garbage, animal carcasses, and residential combined refuse.

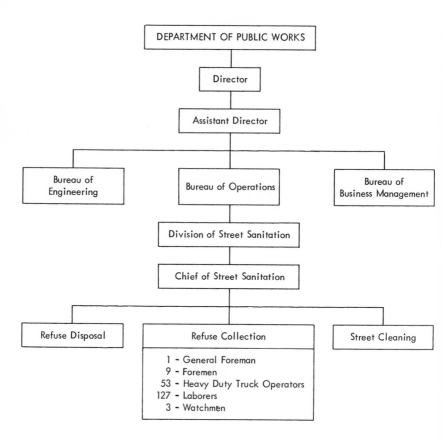

FIG. 12-6. In Richmond, Virginia, responsibility for refuse collection is in the Division of Street Sanitation of the Department of Public Works. A Chief of Division is in charge of collection operations.

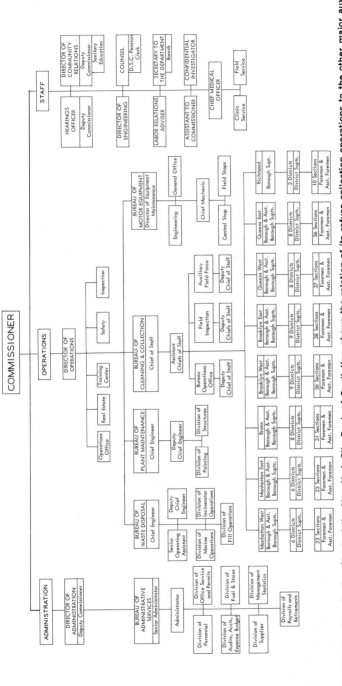

FIG. 12-7. The Organization Chart of the New York City Dept. of Sanitation shows the relation of its refuse collection operations to the other major auxiliary services such as the disposal of refuse, maintenance of its physical plant (incinerators, garages, transfer stations, etc.), and maintenance of automotive equipment. It also shows the district operation of the administrative function, budgets, payrolls, procurement of supplies, etc.) and the several specialized staff functions. The latter comprise Planning and Engineering, Legal, Medical, Public Relations, Safety and Labor Relations.

chapter 13

PERSONNEL

Successful administration of refuse collection operations depends in large measure on the way employees are selected, supervised, and trained and how their efforts and abilities are utilized. Competent, loyal workers and supervisors are needed for the satisfactory conduct of the refuse removal service. Thus, personnel administration and practices are especially significant in a refuse collection agency because of the great importance of securing qualified employees who are willing to make a career in this branch of public works. Public personnel policies will not be discussed in great detail in this book. The attitudes and policies of the central municipal administration determine, to a large extent the character of the management of the several departments and divisions of which the refuse collection agency is but one. Within the existing framework of a municipal government, however, refuse removal administrators can accomplish much by applying sound management principles.

Many refuse collection administrators find that they still have to emphasize continually the close relationship between the qualifications of their personnel and the efficiency of the service. There has been a great improvement in personnel policies and practices in the past twenty years. However, a strong tendency still exists to fill refuse collection positions without the use of civil service procedures or their equivalent. Insistence on accepting and maintaining the best personnel policies is the surest means of achieving a qualified loyal, well-trained group of workers who are happy in their jobs and who want to make a life work in this activity. The purpose of personnel administration is to recruit, to train, and to keep such workers.

The hope of progressive improvement in the refuse collection service lies primarily in capable management of the operations. In the first place, competent managers and supervisors must be placed in charge if the procedures and practices outlined in the first part of this book are to be effectively employed. Secondly, these officials can conduct the work effectively only by building a loyal force of able, trained workers. Competent personnel administration lies at the root of the whole effort to secure efficient conduct of the service.

Wages and salaries usually account for from 60 to 80 per cent of the cost of refuse collection. Sound personnel practice is desirable not only because of the volume of employment and of the amount of personnel service expense, but also because of the repetitive and regular nature of the work. Any saving, great or small, in the refuse collection service is repeated day after day. Of course the converse is also true. One inefficient or otherwise unqualified employee causes increased cost and reduced production day after day.

Also the need for enlightened personnel administration is desirable in the refuse removal service because of the intimate day-by-day contact of the workers with the householders and the general public. The service is one of the main functions of the municipal government, and it exerts a powerful influence on the public relations of the entire administration.

ESSENTIALS OF SOUND PERSONNEL MANAGEMENT

Personnel management has two fundamental objectives. The first is to see that all employees are capable, industrious, loyal, happy in their jobs, and cooperative with the management. The second is to see that wages, hours, and working conditions are equal to the best standards of the locality and elicit corresponding cooperation from the workers. These objectives may be realized by:

1. Attracting to the refuse collection service thoroughly able and qualified persons at all levels on the basis of fair dealings, competent management, and good working conditions.
2. Insuring equal opportunity for all qualified persons to compete for all positions in the service under impartial and competent examination procedure.
3. Establishing a career service that is satisfying, dependable, relatively stable, easily understood, and offers opportunity for promotion, increased compensation, and eventual retirement.
4. Providing remuneration appropriate to the service and assuring continued fair compensation in relation to similar work in private industry.
5. Training employees to do their work easily and properly and to prepare them for advancement in the service.
6. Having a workable means of separating from the service for cause, but protecting the incumbents against discharge for trivial, arbitrary, or personal reasons.

EFFECT OF EXISTING PERSONNEL POLICIES

The policies of municipal governments relating to the selection, control, retirement, and compensation of employees influence the kind of management that can be secured and the limits of effectiveness and economy that can be realized. A serious handicap is placed on every operating department when the value of sound personnel administration is not recognized and fostered by municipal legislators and executives.

It should not be inferred that most cities have failed to recognize the importance of good personnel practices or that they have done nothing about it. On the contrary numerous cities have placed all refuse collection positions under civil service or merit systems and have taken steps to see that able workmen are secured and are assured good and safe working conditions and more or less permanent jobs. Some municipalities have secured well qualified supervisors to direct and manage refuse collection operations, although many still fail to recognize the need for more than a boss of common labor to direct the services. A few cities have even adopted regular training programs to improve the character of the work and to prepare employees for advancement in the service.

Of the 637 cities that reported on civil service status in the 1964 survey, 154 have placed all positions in the refuse collection agency under civil service. The distribution, by size of municipality, is given in Table 13-1.

TABLE 13-1

Civil Service Status of Refuse Collection Employees
in 637 Cities in 1964

Population Group	Number of Cities Reporting	All Positions Under Civil Service		Not Stated
		Yes	No	
1,000,000 and over	5	5	0	0
100,000 to 1,000,000	69	37	32	0
50,000 to 100,000	66	27	37	2
25,000 to 50,000	134	41	89	4
10,000 to 25,000	227	37	181	9
5,000 to 10,000	124	5	116	3
100 to 5,000	6	0	6	0
Not stated	6	2	4	0
Total	637	154	465	18

More than a fourth of all the cities reporting have brought refuse removal employees under civil service protection, and the percentage with total coverage is very much higher in the larger population groups. The adoption of a civil service system does not in itself guarantee sound personnel management. However, improvements are continually being made in the administration of civil service systems, and they still offer the best hope for obtaining and retaining competent employees for government service.

In some cities modern personnel management techniques and policies have been instituted even though there is no legislative basis or legal protection for them. Merit systems which provide reasonably permanent, trained, and competent working forces have been established more or less informally. For the most part they serve to protect the various branches of municipal government from political patronage and rapid turnover of personnel, and may even include formal training or retirement programs. However, they usually provide no safeguards to protect the plan from being destroyed by an administration which is intent on using some unit such as the refuse collection agency for its own political ends. Many cities without formal civil service systems have established modern compensation and classification plans.

PERSONNEL PRACTICES IN REFUSE COLLECTION ORGANIZATIONS

Because refuse collection is essentially a labor service, the personnel problems encountered are somewhat different than those of many other government agencies. Some of the special aspects of these problems are discussed in the following sections.

Recruitment

Every well conceived merit plan for personnel administration provides for the selection, training, and promotion of refuse collection employees solely on the basis of their demonstrated capacity and qualifications to perform the collection tasks effectively. It provides for absolute impartiality in examination and other recruitment processes, particularly without regard to politics or political beliefs. Until recent years, the demand of some refuse collection supervisors for a free hand in hiring and firing collection employees was often acceded to in the belief that complete loyalty to the immediate boss would result in high efficiency and a low turnover rate. Two factors, however, prevented widespread success of the plan—the inability to select really fit and able workmen, and the absence of any real incentive for employees to make a career of the service. On the other hand, guarantees of tenure alone have succeeded only in enforcing the continued employment of many incompetents. The emphasis must be placed upon the very careful selection of personnel to whom tenure can be given with confidence.

It is becoming generally recognized that truck drivers and laborers should be selected on the basis of physical examinations; tests for physical strength, agility, and endurance; and capability tests. Because supervisory officers or even entire departments are not ordinarily in a position to conduct the examinations properly or economically, this part of the selection process usually must be handled by a central agency. The testing is not necessarily complicated or expensive. Usually all applicants must register at a central personnel office. Under civil service procedure, examinations are prepared and given under the direction of the regular examining staff. Municipalities not having civil service systems adopt various means. Sometimes personnel departments of cities do the necessary recruitment and examining even though the collection force is not in the classified service or not subject to any central personnel control. Under these circumstances, the qualified applicants are usually certified to the department in the order in which they are tested and approved. In smaller municipalities, the examination of candidates and the selection of employees may be done by a personnel officer or some other official, but often will be left to the operating department concerned. Such departments can, and should, adopt the same impartial and sound examination and selection procedures that are used by central personnel agencies.

The recruitment of supervisory officers is still unsatisfactory in many cities because the importance of having qualified people in these positions is not fully recognized. Cities with civil service systems generally secure better supervisors than do other municipalities. However, even in such cities, the lack of suitable job specifications and the use of inadequate recruiting and testing methods often result in the employment of people not properly equipped for the work. The greatest success to date in providing qualified foremen and supervisors has been achieved through intensive training of drivers, collectors, and others for promotion to higher positions.

Wages and Hours

Wages and hours of work for municipal refuse collection laborers and truck drivers are usually based upon prevailing rates for comparable work in commercial organizations and other municipal departments as well as upon policies and standards determined by city officials. For example, in Hartford, Connecticut, the municipal wage scale is oriented to the third quartile of wages paid for comparable work in the Hartford area by private employers. However, wages are often equal to the highest paid in private work. Typically, municipalities now establish regular work weeks and compensate employees for overtime for any service beyond the basic period. Most cities pay refuse collection employees full time for the basic period unless they are absent without leave. The variation in hours per regular work week reported by 896 cities is shown in Table 13-2. The largest cities predominantly have adopted a 40-hour basic week, as have many of the smaller communities.

TABLE 13-2
Basic Work Week for Refuse Collection Crews
in 896 Cities in 1964

Population Group	Municipal or Contract	Number of Cities Reporting	Hours worked per week							
			36	36-39	40	41-43	44	45-48	48	Not stated
1,000,000 and over	M	5	0	1	4	0	0	0	0	0
	C	1	0	1	0	0	0	0	0	0
100,000 to 1,000,000	M	69	0	0	50	1	6	11	1	0
	C	13	0	0	8	0	0	3	0	2
50,000 to 100,000	M	66	0	0	51	2	3	7	3	0
	C	29	1	1	13	0	2	7	0	5
25,000 to 50,000	M	134	2	0	82	3	18	19	8	2
	C	54	0	1	27	0	4	10	4	8
10,000 to 25,000	M	227	0	0	119	9	41	37	17	4
	C	88	4	0	37	1	7	17	7	15
5,000 to 10,000	M	124	2	2	50	2	30	24	14	0
	C	67	3	1	21	0	7	8	1	26
000 to 5,000	M	6	0	0	4	0	0	2	0	0
	C	6	0	0	2	0	0	1	0	3
Not stated	M	6	0	0	3	0	1	2	0	0
	C	1	0	0	0	0	0	1	0	0
Total	M	637	4	3	363	17	99	102	43	6
	C	259	8	4	108	1	20	47	12	59
Overall total	M & C	896	12	7	471	18	119	149	55	65

The wide daily fluctuations in the amount of refuse collection work make it difficult in many cities to arrange the operations so that each crew can work exactly eight hours or whatever the normal work period happens to be. Some of the prevalent methods provide for stopping the collection work at quitting time regardless of the progress made. In some places the routes are laid out so that workers will average a full day's work of 8 hours each day over a month or a year, but the crews are expected to work until the assigned task is finished. Some days they may work as little as five or six hours; on other days as much as nine or ten hours. By exercising close supervision and keeping fully informed on the progress of each crew, some administrators are able to make adjustments for variations so as to reduce irregular hours to a large extent. Others have organized the crews so that most of the daily and seasonal variations are equalized.

Task System

A number of cities such as Cedar Rapids, Waterloo and Dubuque, Iowa, have programed their garbage and rubbish collectors on a task basis, sometimes called the incentive system.

A time study is made of each route during average weather conditions, establishing a daily starting and stopping point. The study starts at the time the crew leaves the garage and ends at the end of an eight-hour day when the crew returns to the garage and parks the truck. Allowance is made for rest periods and lunch time.

The 40-hour week is divided into five separate routes of eight hours each. The crew is then responsible for collecting all garbage and rubbish at every collection point on the assigned daily routes. Because weather conditions and amount of waste material to be handled will vary at individual stops from week to week, the elapsed time for completion of each daily route will also vary.

Under the task system the crew is allowed to go home after full completion of the assigned task, which under ideal conditions could conceivably be in as little as 6 hours, or under adverse conditions more than the 8 hours, but they are paid for 8 hours work each day. It is found that the obligation of serving each householder has been met and that a hard and fast schedule can be maintained.

In event of a paid holiday during the work week, setting the route back one day following the holiday and working on Saturday to complete the week's work, the schedule is only interrupted for that week in which the holiday occurs.

The ability to set a firm schedule is appreciated by the citizen, particularly if curb collection requires the setting out of material by the householder.

The advantage to management is that the householder is assured regular service and that the trucks are off the streets and out of traffic within the shortest period of time. Management also benefits in that employees require less supervision and no overtime pay must be budgeted. It also avoids the concentration of units at disposal points and garages at the end of the day.

The wages paid by municipalities vary widely, depending upon the size of community, the section of the country, and the general economy of the area. The actual basic and maximum wage for foreman, truck driver, and loader positions reported by 669 cities for 1964 are given in Table 13-3. Various information received since these reports indicate a continuing upward trend in municipal wage scales.

TABLE 13-3

1964 Hourly Wage Rates for Refuse
Collection Employees for 669 Cities

Hourly Wages		Drivers		Collectors		Others	
		Minimum	Maximum	Minimum	Maximum	Minimum	Maximum
Under $1.00	Municipal	4	3	15	7	2	1
	Contract	0	0	0	0	0	0
$1.00 to $1.24	Municipal	48	13	90	37	11	6
	Contract	2	1	4	0	0	0
$1.25 to $1.49	Municipal	78	48	89	80	11	7
	Contract	13	6	19	12	2	1
$1.50 to $1.74	Municipal	102	75	106	74	17	13
	Contract	15	6	25	9	1	0
$1.75 to $1.99	Municipal	100	92	92	84	26	17
	Contract	15	9	17	13	4	0
$2.00 to $2.24	Municipal	94	72	89	65	22	17
	Contract	23	11	17	12	1	2
$2.25 to $2.49	Municipal	68	70	39	67	12	13
	Contract	16	11	6	4	0	0
$2.50 to $2.74	Municipal	41	63	21	48	9	9
	Contract	9	10	8	9	1	1
$2.75 to $2.99	Municipal	12	34	6	16	1	7
	Contract	8	14	5	6	3	3
$3.00 and up	Municipal	5	18	2	8	6	18
	Contract	16	10	12	7	2	2
Total—	Municipal	552	488	549	486	117	108
	Contract	117	78	113	72	14	9
Grand Total—		669	566	662	558	131	117

The problem of allowing the collectors to accept tips or gratuities from householders is a very troublesome one. In the interest of good public relations and effective enforcement of regulations most cities do not allow refuse collectors to request gifts or even accept them. The City of Los Angeles, for example, has adopted the following regulations:

Only those services which are authorized under existing ordinances or rules shall be performed. Whenever a crew is contacted by a citizen requesting service of a type not ordinarily provided, the crew should advise the citizen to contact the local district office of the division. Employees shall not solicit presents or tips of food, goods, or money; and they shall not receive any presents or tips for rendering unauthorized services. Service shall be up to a high standard without any special or extra compensation. An employee who makes an agreement with a second party whereby such party is to pay him in food, goods or money for rendering special services shall be subject to discharge.

It has become traditional in some cities for each householder to give his refuse collector a gift or gratuity at Christmas time. Sometimes such a recognition of service by citizens is entirely voluntary, but in other cases the collectors go from house to house requesting donations which householders may be virtually forced to give so that they will get good service. The trend is to discourage such gifts.

Making payments so that they will remove material that the municipality would otherwise not collect is still a more or less common practice in some cities. This practice should not be tolerated under any circumstances because the employees and equipment, provided at municipal expense to do a particular job, are diverted to the personal gain of the collection crew. In extreme cases it has been discovered that the crews were soliciting business from merchants and others who were not eligible for city service, with the result that the effectiveness of the regular operations was considerably diminished and the cost to citizens increased.

Fringe Benefits

Physical conditions of employment and various types of "fringe benefits" representing indirect remuneration (other than salary and wages) are assuming more and more relative importance. Fringe benefits include such things as vacations and leaves, retirement systems, uniforms, safety practices, sick leave, and group insurance coverage.

Retirement Systems. Retirement plans or pension systems have been adopted by many cities within the past ten years, and more and more municipalities are finding that such plans are necessary to compete successfully with private industry for qualified workers. Usually cities include their refuse collection employees within their retirement plans. The failure of many cities to provide for retiring and pensioning employees, however, continues to have a particularly harmful effect on refuse collection services. To keep aged employees on the pay roll long after they have lost their full strength and ability decreases over-all efficiency in any organization. But because refuse collection operations require strong men with more than usual endurance, the failure to replace incapacitated persons is particularly serious, slowing down entire crews and unduly increasing costs. In some cities, older workers can be assigned or transferred to white wing crews for street cleaning or highway maintenance where the tasks are not so strenuous as for refuse collection. A transfer practice which is not good, however, is sometimes practiced by cities that do not have a retirement plan. They reassign aged employees to refuse collection agencies on the assumption that anyone can lift and carry refuse cans. As a result, some collection organizations have so many older workers that the tempo of the whole operation is reduced. Furthermore, a service with no retirement plan offers a much less attractive career to qualified workers and supervisors.

Vacation and leaves. In most cities, supervisory officers of the refuse collection agency are permanent employees and are given regular vacations and leaves. In numerous municipalities, truck drivers, loaders, and other collection employees have been appointed as permanent employees and, regardless of whether they are paid on an annual or hourly basis, are entitled to regular vacation and sick leave benefits. Other cities, however, still pay their drivers and loaders only for actual time worked.

Sick leave. Many cities now grant an allowance of 10 to 15 days sick leave per year, with accumulation rights for any sick leave not used to a maximum total of 60, 90 or 100 days. This has been a big help to the municipal employee who has been faithful and regular for many years and then has a severe illness that lasts a month or more, during which he would otherwise lose his pay at a time when he may be faced with heavy medical expenses.

Group hospitalization insurance. Group hospitalization insurance for municipal employees is now nearly universal. Often employees must pay the full cost of this protection. Some cities contribute the cost for an employee but the cost for insuring the rest of his family must be borne by him.

Group insurance has also been an added feature of protection of recent years in many cities. Frequently, this insurance can be broad enough to cover injuries and death benefits.

Workman's compensation. Many states now require compensation for employees injured on the job. Usually, such compensation pays all medical expenses, and an income after the first or second week. Several larger cities finance their own compensation payments. They usually pay full compensation without any waiting period. A good supervisor or manager of the compensation system, coupled with adequate municipal medical service, can forestall any possible abuses and make this system beneficial to the employee at less cost to the city.

Earned leave time. Another benefit now being included in many businesses and in a few governmental agencies is leave known as "earned time". Granting a day off for each 50 working days or two months with no tardiness or absences is given as recognition of faithful service.

Other benefits. In some cities employees receive such other benefits as social security, annual increases of pay up to the maximum rate, seniority, opportunity for advancement within the organization, uniforms furnished by the city, discounts for purchases at certain stores for municipal employees, municipal credit union organizations from which city employees may borrow money at low interest rates to be paid back automatically through payroll deductions, or in which employees may deposit their savings and receive better than normal interest; also arrangements to pay Community Chest, employee organization dues, and Federal Savings Bond purchases by payroll deductions.

In some cities, employees who do not have the opportunity for further advancement receive longevity increases for being on the job 10, 20, 30 and even 40 years. Such increases, frequently 2.5 percent for each 10-year period, give additional compensation and recognition to those who cannot qualify for advancement but who, with long experience, provide a better service than is otherwise possible when frequent turnover is the rule.

Working Conditions and Safety

Much emphasis has been placed on improving working conditions in refuse collection agencies and increasing the safety of operations. Among the things that have been especially effective are assembly and locker-room facilities, provision of uniforms, development of safety practices, comfort arrangements, and provision of protective clothing for bad weather.

Assembly and locker-room facilities. Cities of all sizes commonly provide comfortable and protected places for employees to assemble for work and to eat their lunches. Sometimes separate rooms are made available at garages, incinerators, or transfer stations. In larger places, where such structures may not be within reasonable distance of some working areas, separate buildings are provided. In addition to assembly quarters, many of these buildings are equipped with lockers for the collection employees so that they can change their clothes if they wish and can keep their belongings safe. Shower baths are sometimes installed.

FIG. 13-1. Clean, light assembly buildings are provided in each organization section of New York for the refuse collection and street cleaning crews. Locker, shower, and lunch room facilities are provided in each area. The section supervisors also have offices in these buildings.

In many cities the meeting, locker, and shower rooms are attractively arranged with plenty of light and are kept spotlessly clean. In New York the men meet for roll call at the beginning and end of each shift and for the noon recess at a separate section building in each operating district. Each man has his own locker and many of the employees change to their uniforms before work starts and at night take a shower and change back to street clothes before going home. There is little question that comfortable, pleasant quarters are appreciated by the workers. Los Angeles has separate buildings for its men in several districts.

Provision of uniforms. Most cities still do not require refuse collection employees to wear uniforms. Of the 637 cities replying to the 1964 survey on this, 213 reported that uniforms are worn by collection employees. Of interest is the fact that 165 cities indicated they furnished a uniform free of charge. Another 25 cities helped in various ways to defray the costs of uniforms. If the employees must both buy their uniforms and keep them clean, some increase in wages is usually given to compensate for the added expense. Ordinarily two clean uniforms must be provided each week, but the men are expected to be neat and clean at all times.

FIG. 13-2. A section of a modern locker and shower room for refuse collection employees in Los Angeles. Such facilities, when kept clean and attractive, do much to make the work of refuse removal more pleasant and attractive for qualified workers.

There are at least four good reasons for uniforming the personnel engaged in providing refuse collection service: (1) identification of municipal employees, (2) safety, (3) increased morale, and (4) rendering the service more attractive. Almost invariably the employees are pleased and proud to wear uniforms, and public reaction is nearly always enthusiastic. Many cities require the employees to wear numbered badges for identification.

In view of the demonstrated success of uniforming employees, it is surprising that more cities have not adopted the practice. The expense is not great, and it is probable that the return through greater efficiency and improved morale is worth several times the cost.

Comfort of employees on routes. Refuse collectors often remain all day on their collection routes without going to disposal sites, garages, or shelters. They may carry their lunches on the trucks and take their noon recess wherever they happen to be at the time. In good weather this practice may not be objectionable, but on cold or rainy days the men find it extremely difficult to find a place where they can be comfortable and protected. In some cities the crews are transported relatively long distances to incinerators, garages, or transfer stations; in others, section or shelter houses are built for the purpose.

The lack of toilet facilities causes difficulty on some routes. Rest rooms of filling stations or garages may be available, but some administrators have found that the operators of such places object to their habitual use by refuse collection crews. Part of the work of supervision in a well managed organization is to see that reasonable and proper facilities are available for the comfort of the employees. It is not satisfactory to require the men to make their own arrangements. If it is impossible to provide separate buildings for district headquarters, it may be practical to rent space, suitable facilities or to compensate owners of garages or other business establishments to permit the use of rest rooms.

Protective clothing for collectors. To keep municipal refuse collection operations on schedule, collectors often must work while it is snowing or raining and during cold weather. Usually, the workers provide their own protection against the cold, but it is impractical for them to carry raincoats, boots, and other protective clothing every day so as to have them available in case of rain or snow. Consequently, many cities furnish raincoats and rubber boots and sometimes rain hats so that the men will be protected and operations can continue during adverse weather conditions. The clothing may be kept at district headquarters, shelters, or section houses, where the crews can go when they need it. Foremen and supervisors will sometimes get the articles and take them to the men at work. Some equipment is designed so that these items may be carried in a special compartment in the cab or under the body of the truck.

Development of safety practices. While not a hazardous occupation, refuse collection has numerous perils and dangers for workmen who are not alert or well trained. Collectors spend a large part of their day carrying loads into streets, sometimes through heavy traffic. They often have to ride the trucks from one location to the next. It may be necessary to lift exceptionally heavy loads and to handle defective refuse containers with sharp rusty edges. If they have to handle the refuse itself there is always the danger of being cut by glass, razor blades, or tin cans.

To protect the workmen and keep up efficiency, progressive administrators provide regular instruction to develop safe operating practices. There are both safe and dangerous ways to lift and carry refuse cans. The safest way is often the easiest, but many workmen will never learn it by themselves. In a collection organization that neglects safety instruction there are often numerous cases of hernia caused by lifting loads incorrectly and many accidents from carrying cans improperly. Street accidents, too, occur unless the best practices are followed.

The truck drivers also need safety training. Not only must they habitually use safe driving and operating methods; they must also protect the collectors from accidents while they are on the vehicles or while they are loading or consolidating the refuse.

Employee Training

Formal training for supervisors, collectors, and truck drivers has been instituted in numerous cities, but most refuse collection agencies provide some instruction to collectors in the course of their regular work. New York City has successfully conducted a regular training program for several years, with schools for supervisors and foremen as well as for truck drivers. All employees are encouraged to prepare themselves for promotion in the service. Of 621 municipalities reporting on employee training in 1964, only 102 (16.4 per cent) have organized training programs.

Several cities give routine demonstrations to new employees to illustrate easy and safe ways to perform their duties. Often new workers are systematically started with experienced crews, not only to train them in actual duties but also to give them an insight into the spirit of the organization and show them the benefits of effective teamwork.

Rules and Regulations

Definite rules and regulations have been formulated by several well administered refuse collection agencies. In addition to general information on the organization and the plan of operation, the rules cover such matters as hours, wages, vacations, leaves, accidents, retirement, and similar matters. They also deal with the conduct of the work, pointing out the methods of operation, the required practices, and the forbidden procedures. They are usually printed or mimeographed. Los Angeles, New York, and Cincinnati, are among those cities that have developed regulations.

Numerous cities operating under civil service or other merit system procedures have developed complete and definite rules and regulations defining proper and improper conduct of refuse collection employees. Often the compilation is called a "code of discipline," or "service guide." The codes of the New York City Department of Sanitation and the Refuse

FIG. 13-3. Staff conferences, both of the heads of the several divisions and of the employees in each unit, are important training devices. Pictured above is a briefing session for supervisory personnel at the Sanitation Training Center of the New York Department of Sanitation.

Collection and Disposal Division of the City of Los Angeles represent good examples of complete regulations. The codes usually identify the rules that call for penalties or discipline for offenses and define the extent of such penalties. Other information for the guidance or instruction of employees is often included. Typically the department head imposes all discipline and penalties. Hearings are sometimes a part of the department procedure and frequently are held by the civil service authorities.

Employee Suggestion Systems

The refuse collection employee is closest to the job and frequently is aware of needed improvements in the collection system. Programs to encourage employee suggestions have been found to be very helpful. Many cities have Employee Suggestion Award Committees. Annual, or semi-annual, and in larger cities, monthly awards are made to employees for good suggestions.

Many suggestions may come from the employees who do the work. Their suggestions may make the daily task easier, provide for safer operations, or result in better service to the taxpayer at no additional cost. Some suggestions may create better public relations or better personnel

FIG. 13-4. An employee incentive award ceremony. Employee incentive is an important part of a program designed to increase employee interest in the effective performance of his job to enable more economical and better accomplishment of the refuse collection agency's task. Awards should be made by the department head in a special ceremony to achieve maximum effectiveness.

relations. The worker should be encouraged to study his job and make suggestions for improvement.

Ideas for improving the refuse collection system to benefit the city, the public, or the worker, should be explained thoroughly by supervisors and foremen. If changes are made without explaining the reasons to employees, opposition may be expressed through slow-down, delays and attempts to make the change ineffective and unprofitable.

The worker should be asked to study the change and to make suggestions as to whether the change is good or whether there are details that should receive further study. He should be made to feel that he is part of the study and that his ideas will be considered along with those of the management. Each man needs to know that he is a part of a system of which he can be proud, and if he contributes his best efforts will have a chance for recognition or advancement.

Service Ratings

Many cities that operate under merit or civil service systems require supervisors to prepare a service rating report on each employee once or twice a year. Such reporting plans, if wisely conceived and carried out, are valuable aids in guiding promotions or other actions and in calling the attention of employees to less than satisfactory activity or conduct.

It has been found that a complete and detailed "personal" file for each employee is very valuable. Letters of commendation and reports of service ratings, truck cleanliness, rule violations, irregularities in attendance, and so on, are placed in the employee's personnel file.

In Los Angeles a deficiency notice is issued when violations of regulations have been noted or when any action inconsistent with proper operating practice has been charged. This form is shown in Figure 13-6, and may be issued by any supervisor. For minor infractions, no further action may be taken, but a copy is made a party of the employee's civil service file and repetitive violations may result in disciplinary action.

Complete records on employee conduct and performance will help the supervisor to support his position before civil service personnel or review boards when action is appealed by an employee. A supervisor who does not discipline or discharge incompetent employees often attempts to justify his nonaction because of cross-examination at a review hearing. The presentation in evidence of reports in writing prepared at the time of the offense or offenses, with copies to the employee will do much to relieve the supervisor of "pressure" at such hearings.

Employee Organizations

During recent years municipal employees have been organized to assist in bringing alleged grievances more effectively to the administrator's attention. Such organizations usually take one of three forms:

1. A general municipal employees' group or association represents all employees of the city or town. This type of organization is local only and does not have any state or national affiliation.

2. A municipal employee union represents the employees of a department or division where there is no national organization and there is a minority representation of a relatively small cross-section of the working force.

3. A local of a national labor union represents a group of municipal employees.

Of 896 cities reporting on employee organization in 1964, 631 (more than 70 per cent) indicated that their employees did not belong to a union. In the 229 cities where the employees were unionized, by far the greater number, 205, were affiliated with a national union.

TABLE 13-4

Employee Organization in 896 Cities in 1964

Are employees unionized? If yes, is the union nationally affiliated?	Municipal Number of cities	Per cent	Contract Number of cities	Per cent
Yes—qualified	7	1.1	5	1.9
Yes and affiliated	158	24.8	47	18.1
Yes and not affiliated	11	1.7	1	0.4
No	449	70.5	182	70.3
No answer	12	1.9	24	9.3
Total	637	100.0	259	100.0

26-S

CITY OF CINCINNATI

PERFORMANCE REPORT

(FORM A: To be used in rating employees working for ONE supervisor during rating period)

EMPLOYE ____________ TITLE ____________ PROBATIONARY REPORT ____________

DIVISION ____________ DATE ____________ ANNUAL RATING ____________

BEFORE MAKING ANY RATING, PLEASE READ THE RATING MANUAL

RATING FACTORS	UNSATIS-FACTORY	CHECK IN THE PROPER COLUMN: SATISFACTORY — Improvement Needed	GOOD	VERY GOOD	OUT-STANDING
1. **QUALITY OF WORK**—Accuracy, completeness, thoroughness, neatness of work.					
2. **QUANTITY OF WORK**—Amount of work done.					
3. **KNOWLEDGE**—Knowledge of methods, materials, objectives and other fundamental information, skill.					
4. **LEARNING ABILITY**—Speed and thoroughness in learning procedures, rules and other details, alertness, perseverance.					
5. **WORK HABITS**—Organization of work, care of equipment, safety, industry.					
6. **RELATIONSHIP WITH PEOPLE**—Ability to get along with the public and other employes.					
7. **DEPENDABILITY**—Degree to which he can be relied upon to do the job without close supervision.					
8. **ATTENDANCE**—Frequency and nature of absences and tardiness.					
9. **ATTITUDE**—Interest in the work, willingness to meet job requirements and accept suggestions, loyalty to the organization, ethical conduct.					
10. **PERSONAL FITNESS**—Physical capacity, appearance, personal habits.					
11. **JUDGMENT**—Soundness of decisions, common sense.					
FOR USE IN RATING SUPERVISORS ONLY: 12. **SUPERVISORY SKILL**—Planning and assigning work, making decisions, training, instructing and evaluating employes, leadership, fairness, interest in employe welfare.					
13. **OVERALL RATING**—Should reflect the above ratings.					

COMMENTS: Comments help support and interpret ratings. "UNSATISFACTORY," "IMPROVEMENT NEEDED" and "OUTSTANDING" ratings must be explained in this space.

RATER ____________ TITLE ____________ I have seen this report:

REVIEWER ____________ TITLE ____________ EMPLOYE'S SIGNATURE ____________

REVIEWER'S COMMENTS: ____________

THIS SECTION TO BE USED ONLY WHEN THE REVIEWER DOES NOT AGREE WITH THE OVERALL RATING SHOWN ABOVE:

I do not agree with the overall rating shown above for the following reasons: ____________

My overall rating of this employee is: ______UNSATISFACTORY ______IMPROVEMENT NEEDED ______GOOD ______VERY GOOD ______OUTSTANDING

CIVIL SERVICE COPY

FIG. 13-5. Service ratings serve as a basis for counseling employees regarding the improvement of their performance on the job. To help accomplish this it is necessary to use a prescribed procedure, not only to formalize the periodic review but also to provide a record of the review of the employee's performance. The employee performance report used by Cincinnati is an example of the type of form that may be used.

Form Gen. 78—2500 Sets—3-64 (K-41)

NOTICE TO CORRECT DEFICIENCIES

Date..

Name..

Class..

Department...Division..

....

....

....

....

The purpose of this notice is to call the above deficiency to your attention, and give you an opportunity to correct it. A copy of this notice will be placed in your personnel file and may be considered in future disciplinary actions.

I received a copy of this notice.

....
                Employee's signature   **Supervisor**

Copies: 1. Employee (White)   ....
         2. Civil Service (Pink)   **Approved**
         3. Employing Department (Blue)

FIG. 13-6. The City of Los Angeles serves a notice on an employee advising him that a note of the conduct in question is being made a part of the record. Thus, the employee is officially notified that repetition or continuation of his action may result in future disciplinary measures. The notice is forwarded through the supervisor and must be signed and returned by the employee.

The administrator of a refuse collection system must be alert to employees' rights to organize and to select a representative to speak for them. In many cities the administrator has set up a time and place to hear grievances as presented by either organized or unorganized employees.

Discussions of labor union activities inevitably turn to the question of the rights of employees to strike.[1] Anti-strike laws have been adopted in some localities but generally have proved to be ineffective. Public opinion is probably a more potent restricting force as is evidenced by the fact that some unions have voluntarily given up any rights they may have had to strike against the government. Some strikes, however, do occur despite prohibitory laws or the weight of public opinion. Since strikes do not as a rule occur in cities employing progressive personnel policies, there may be something to be said in defense of the employees if the strike is used as a last resort in securing a living wage or other decent conditions of service. There is less agreement with respect to the lobbying of employees with city councils; the sponsoring of salary increases or other emoluments through initiative ordinances, state legislation, or charter amendments; the use of threats or other compulsory methods to prevent dismissals for cause; or the extent to which the principle of collective bargaining should be carried. In this connection, it has been sug-

[1] The discussion on labor unions is taken from *Municipal Public Works Administration* (Chicago: International City Managers' Association, 1957) pp. 104-105.

gested as a principle to govern management-employee relationships in the public service that management meet collectively with employees on matters of general policy and over-all regulations, but reserve to itself the privilege of individual action in the specific application of the policies and regulations, that is, with respect to grievances resulting from disciplinary action involving individuals and not the whole group.

Because of the dearth of experience in dealing with labor relations these problems will involve much trial and error. Officials need constantly to bear in mind that there are two sides to every question and that many compromises are inevitable in harmonizing issues in which management employees, and the public often appear to have conflicting interests With a tolerant, conference-table approach these interests may generally be adjusted to the advantage of all concerned.

Experience proves that better employer-employee relations will be very beneficial to all parties concerned. It will help in the development of an atmosphere of mutual respect and confidence, improved efficiency a raised level of performance, fair labor standards and peaceful and harmonious relations between the management and the employees Public officials will find a reservoir of ability and understanding in their employees. It will probably be necessary to have such employees understand that municipalities operate by regulations, laws and ordinance which are not easily brushed aside to meet employee's demands. It is therefore well for public officials to discuss in good faith with employee or employee representatives all matters which are clearly within their power to determine. On other matters they might reach tentative agreements and submit these agreements to the proper legislative body for review and necessary action.

Labor-Management Relations

Many times, in the course of work, an employee compares himself and his job to other laborers and other workers, such as policemen and firemen, and he usually sees the bad things about his job and the good or favorable aspects of someone else's job. Then he starts to complain Unless those grievances are settled satisfactorily, efficiency of operations will probably suffer. An outline of a grievance procedure is presented below: [2]

The thinking and experience of persons who have worked out successful procedures with employees indicate that there are a number of exacting requirements for success in handling grievances. An employer who is thinking of setting up a grievance system, or reviewing an existing system, should check against these requirements:

1. An organization must have definite and fair personnel policies and these must be effectively communicated to all employees and all members of management.

[2] Quoted from Robert E. Sibson, "Handling Grievances Where There Is No Union." *Personnel Journal*, June, 1956, pp. 56-58, with permission.

2. Management at all levels must sincerely believe in the importance of solving grievances and they must vigorously support the grievance system.
3. The system must expressly and formally handle all questions and complaints which may arise.
4. Employees must have complete confidence in the sincerity of management and the effectiveness of the grievance procedure.
5. The grievance procedure should not undermine the effectiveness of line management, interfere with line management responsibilities in personnel matters, or align managers against each other.
6. The system must recognize in a straightforward manner that management is always the final arbiter of grievance of employee problems.
7. The grievance procedure should be a positive tool in human relations.

Written personnel policies are absolutely necessary to the success of any grievance procedure in a non-organized shop. For the employees, they set forth top management's position on important personnel matters. For members of management, they provide a yardstick for deciding specific questions and grievances which occur during day-to-day operations, rather than each following his own ideas.

Management support of the grievance system requires that it must be willing to:

1. Seek out employee grievances.
2. Accept reversal of decisions as a result of grievance handling.
3. Stand ready to adjust and modify policies.

It is also very important that all questions or complaints be handled by the grievance procedure. New problems brought up through the grievance procedure should be a major source of suggested improvements in written policy. If complaints and questions are handled as they arise, there will be no problem of small grievances growing into major complaints because of neglect or unnecessary delay.

Another requirement for success in grievance handling is that employees have complete confidence in the effectiveness of the procedure. This requires an aggressive but low-pressure selling program on the part of all members of management. Administrators must emphasize that it is important to the organization as well as to the employees to have questions and complaints solved satisfactorily. They must convince employees of the soundness of the system. They must impress employees with their sincere desire to solve problems quickly and fairly.

Employees will gain confidence in the grievance system only through experience. If management is going to demonstrate to employees that the system will satisfactorily resolve their problems, they must make sure that the following four requirements are met:

1. *No fear of reprisal:* There can be no fear of reprisals on the part of employees. If employees believe that by submitting a grievance

they might expose themselves to any type of reprisal on the part of their immediate supervisor, they will not use the system. All members of management must exercise self-restraint and good judgment in dealing with employee grievances.

2. *Employees understand system:* The grievance system must be formalized and reduced to writing. Employees must know how to present a grievance, where they should do it, when they should do it and exactly what will happen, step by step, when they do it. Uncertainty in their minds will surely tend to discourage the use of a grievance system.

3. *A problem solving atmosphere:* Grievances must be handled quickly. The grievance system which eliminates all unnecessary legalism and which is geared to solve problems in the shortest practical time encourages a problem-saving atmosphere.

4. *No skill disadvantage:* The employee should not be at any disadvantage in handling grievances because of lack of skill in presenting his case. Grievances involve questions of interpretation, motive, intent or opinion. The average employee is generally at a disadvantage in obtaining facts, expressing views, etc.

Management must be careful not to weaken the effectiveness of management or pit various members of the management group against each other.

Generally speaking, the grievance procedure should be designed so that line supervisors handle first-step grievances. The personnel department should only handle appeals from the decision of line management.

Grievances can, however, provide management with the opportunity of determining the causes of employee unrest. Armed with such information, management can initiate such policies and procedures as are necessary to eliminate or at least reduce employee dissatisfaction before it occurs. In this way, the grievance procedure in the non-union shop can serve as a means of "fire prevention"—a positive tool in a sound human relations program.

In the case of organized employees, complaints frequently are heard first by a foreman and passed on to his immediate supervisor. If action is not taken quickly, it may end up as a formal grievance by an employee representative. Because of the type of organization, such a grievance may take many days or months to correct, and many conferences to settle a dispute.

Each municipality of any size should designate an official to hear complaints by employees or by their representatives at a regular pre-determined time. The complaints should be presented in writing and the answer should be made in writing so that each side will clearly understand the other. In case the complaint has to be carried further to the Personnel Department, or to the Chief Administrator, a clear concise statement of the discussion to date will be available.

These findings as they are written up should be filed both with the employee organization and the department for future reference. Especially if an agreement is made to look into the matter, a written report should be made on the findings. The report, favorable or unfavorable, should be filed with the original discussion, with the employee organization, and the department.

In each case, final disposition should be reached on each matter one way or another. As has been stated before, it is not always possible to reach a decision favorable to the employee. But, if a favorable finding is made that cannot be consummated at the time, recommendation should be made by the department head to the management, personnel department, or to the council that consideration be given to reaching a favorable adjustment at an early date.

If the decision is unfavorable to the employee, the reasons should be given so that the employee can see for himself why such a decision was reached.

Happy employee relations should be the goal of each employer, whether it be a private or municipal organization, because a satisfied worker can do a better, more efficient job and his relations to the public will be more pleasant as he goes from door to door in his appointed task.

SUMMARY

Coordinating the abilities and efforts of refuse collection employees and providing capable, loyal, and cooperative supervisors and workers are perhaps the most necessary tasks of management and probably the most rewarding. Unless these tasks are properly done the operations cannot be entirely satisfactory or economical. The personnel aspects of administration deserve much more serious attention than they get in the majority of cities. The returns from capable personnel management are well worth the effort and cost.

chapter 14

EQUIPMENT MANAGEMENT

The effective management of motor equipment is essential to the efficient operation of refuse collection systems. There must be enough trucks or other vehicles to do the work; they must be kept in good operating condition to minimize breakdowns; ample reserve equipment must be on hand ready for use; idle equipment time must be kept within reasonable limits; and the total cost of owning, maintaining, and operating the vehicles must be as low as is consistent with sound operating policy. Managing refuse collection equipment is not materially different from managing the equipment of other public works agencies, but special consideration must be given to the regular cleaning of the vehicle bodies and to the maintenance of mechanical devices peculiar to refuse vehicles —elevators, compressing apparatus, doors, end gates, and body drainage systems.

Cities that have adopted sound methods have clearly demonstrated that they result in immediate and substantial reduction in equipment cost and that practically all difficulties brought on by haphazard operation and control can be eliminated.

ORGANIZATION FOR EQUIPMENT MANAGEMENT

The equipment maintenance organization may have a different degree of centralization from city to city, depending on the policy of the city administration. However, its goals are the same. The organization may function as a top level department responsible for all city equipment or it may be merely a sub-bureau of a major department. The main difference, however, is in scale of operations rather than type. The responsibility of the equipment organization, even as a division of an operating department, is to furnish the most efficient equipment to the operating organizations at lowest cost. The equipment organization generally includes maintenance; furnishing of licenses and insurance, if necessary, at minimum. It may also include storage, furnishing operators, purchasing, and dispatching.

An alternative is for the organization to serve in a dispatching capacity, have the maintenance performed by private firms, and the rest of the functions performed by the operating department. This method is used mostly by small municipalities or where equipment is decentralized to the extent that each operating department has a relatively small group of vehicles. Some of the disadvantages of this latter method, however, are that a profit must be paid to the private firm; a rigid quality control must be maintained; control of the vehicle whereabouts and availability is lost during the maintenance period; downtime may be increased; and the advantages of large-scale overhaul and specialization of maintenance work may be lost.

This chapter will treat the equipment organization as a separate organization performing all the functions mentioned above. If this organization is part of a larger organization, or if some of the functions are delegated to an operating organization, the principles involved remain the same and must be assumed by the other organization.

MANAGEMENT AND OPERATION

Management of municipal equipment is so specialized a task that it can be handled better as an auxiliary municipal service. If it is handled by each operating unit, maintenance and servicing of vehicles must necessarily be a subordinate task. A refuse collection agency, for example, is interested first in removing the refuse materials and in maintaining established collection schedules. Under the pressure of performing this primary function, proper equipment maintenance and operation may be sacrificed, and operating costs may be higher than necessary.

Moreover, a single operating agency or even a department may have too few vehicles for equipment maintenance to be conducted on a sound basis. The volume of work may be so small that it is not feasible to employ competent managers and mechanics. In such cases, refuse collection officials, although usually not trained or experienced in motor vehicle maintenance and operation, are required to assume full responsibility. On the other hand, if all of a municipality's equipment is controlled by one agency, it is usually possible to employ competent supervisory, clerical, engineering, and technical personnel. The largest cities may find it impractical to administer all equipment at one location and may divide the work geographically or by departments and still have units large enough to make it desirable to provide full-time managers and competent maintenance employees. For example, in addition to the central station, some large cities have outlying stations where only preventive maintenance work is performed.

FUNCTION OF EQUIPMENT ORGANIZATION

The equipment organization should be set up in such a manner that it is reimbursed for its activity. This is necessary in order to control costs and to determine accurately the cost of equipment as part of the total operating cost of an operating department. This billing is generally handled either like a private garage, where the operating department is billed directly for the specific work or it may be handled by an equipment rental plan which charges a flat rate per period of time for use of the motor truck, similar to the method of private truck leasing companies. In either case the billing should include all expense factors, such as fixed and variable expenses, materials, etc. A simple method of doing this is to break down the cost of operation of any department to an hourly basis and charge this for the time spent on the unit. Where the trucks are owned by the equipment organization, the rental should also include a depreciation charge.

Maintenance work should be performed mostly by the organization shop. Sometimes it is practical to farm some of the work out to private firms during peak load periods, though this is a practice to be discouraged for the reasons mentioned above. One of the advantages of centralizing is that by handling a large fleet the maintenance shop can afford specilization by trades to a greater extent. Men who are ignition specialists, hydraulic system specialists, etc., may be acquired. This can be accomplished to a greater or lesser degree depending on how much work is handled.

The shop load should be kept under close observation and control at all times. In smaller shops, this may be a duty of the foreman; in larger shops, a special dispatcher may be required. This function should not be overlooked and merits considerable scrutiny since it can save a great deal of time, money, and aggravation if properly planned and controlled.

PURCHASING EQUIPMENT

Procurement of satisfactory refuse equipment can only be accomplished when there is complete understanding, agreement, and coordination between the operating, equipment, and purchasing organizations.

The operating organization is interested in purchasing equipment which will yield the lowest cost per ton to refuse collected. Thus, this department should be in a position to determine and furnish data on optimum capacity with respect to loading and traveling time and load weight for the particular district and type of collection route for which the trucks are to be furnished.

The equipment organization is interested in obtaining the units which will have minimum maintenance and downtime and accessibility for easy servicing. Past records are an indication of maintenance costs. However, their evaluation in terms of new equipment should be considered with discretion since improvements in design, materials, and construction are developed continuously by manufacturers to meet the needs of customers and maintain an edge on their competitors. The equipment organization must not lose sight of the goal of the operating department in terms of those costs which it is expedient and desirable to incur to achieve the aims of the departments. This will be determined by the municipal administration policy, financial position, locality, type of disposal, type of city, size of city, and many other factors.

Experience has shown that, though maintenance may be quadrupled, frequently the savings to the operating department may be doubled, and, therefore, due to the tremendous difference in magnitudes of maintenance and operating costs, a large net saving results. (For example, compare the cost of maintaining an open dump truck and a mechanically loading enclosed refuse truck with their respective efficiency on a many-stop route.) Downtime should also be considered. Elimination of approximately 250 shifts of downtime per year would be equal to the addition of a unit to the fleet.

The purchasing organization's goal is to procure the highest quality equipment, meeting specifications as outlined by the operating and equipment departments, at the lowest price. To attain this, the specifications must be adequate to insure quality and efficiency and yet be broad enough to be equitable to a number of bidders. It may sometimes be necessary to sacrifice a small margin of quality and efficiency to increase the competition among bidders.

Equipment specifications should be sufficiently complete to enable all bidders to make their proposals on exactly the same basis and to identify without question the equipment or machinery wanted. When standard equipment is being purchased, greatly detailed specifications are usually unnecessary, but the specifications should list clearly the extra or optional accessories desired, should stipulate the time, place, and conditions of delivery, and should state the tests, if any, to which the equipment will be subjected. If the chassis and bodies of trucks or machines are to be purchased from different companies, the responsibility for the assembly, delivery, and performance should be definitely fixed.

Some of the larger cities follow the practice of purchasing equipment by the use of evaluation formulas.

"It is almost universally true that where bids are invited on equipment, no two makes are exactly equal. They may differ slightly in capacities, speed of operation, horsepower, revolutions per minute, torque, design, storage capacity or on patented features. Functionally they may do substantially the same thing, some at rates slower than others, they may require varying numbers of persons to operate the equipment, power and fuel consumption may be somewhat different, maintenance costs may differ widely, service may or may not be available for some equipment, salvage values at the end of their useful life may not be constant, technological advances in the industry may yield varying rates of obsolescence, some may have dual abilities while others may be special purpose units, others may be more durable (which may or may not be a desirable feature). All these factors and many more must be reflected in a specification.

"When quality is established by the buyer with detailed specifications as to gear ratio, engine displacement, design and physical dimensions, then performance responsibility rests with the buyer. When specifications are based on performance, it is generally presumed that the performance rests with the seller, and when you have a combination of the two basic types of specifications, it is one of the important duties of the purchasing agent in preparing and handling the commercial aspects of the specifications and contracts, that the areas of responsibility be clearly defined.

"Specifications must be of such nature as to provide yard sticks of evaluation that can be measured without misunderstanding when inspections and acceptance take place. Such descriptions of quality of performance should be so selected as to be reasonably determined without costly procedures or tests.

"The evaluation formula must be free of ambiguities to safeguard against later cries of discrimination when the bids are in and evaluated. If constants are employed, as they usually are, they should be clearly stated. If prequalification tests are to be used to determine some of the factors in the formula, the method of tests and their evaluations should be clearly set forth, so that the formula and the answers that will be derived after the bids are in can be calculated by all interested parties and the successful bidder . . . unmistakably.[1]"

There are some obvious advantages in having equipment from as few manufacturers as possible. A smaller supply of repair parts will be required; the mechanics and operators will have fewer types with which to become familiar; and more uniform appearance is presented. Too great insistence upon standardization, however, may result in unduly high costs because of the lack of suitable competition. Many cities have been able to limit the makes of trucks and automobiles to two or three without sacrificing materially on price. One of the best means of securing the most favorable prices and at the same time obtaining some standardization is to purchase equipment in quantity. It is not always possible to buy equipment in this manner because of financing difficulties or because equipment requirements are not sufficiently great, but if several pieces of one kind of equipment are to be secured in a year, it will usually be found that more satisfactory vehicles or machines can be obtained at lower prices if they are all purchased at one time.

TRUCK CHASSIS

Usually, the motor truck chassis is particularly the province of the equipment organization. However, the relative merits of the various types and makes are of concern to the operating department in regard to driver comfort, maneuverability, idle time due to road breakdowns, and any need for special design—for example, attachability of snow plows or ease of access to cab where the driver helps the loaders.

Inasmuch as most modern refuse collection trucks are large enough to be classed as heavy duty equipment, the specifications writer has a great deal of latitude with regard to choice of chassis component design. The motor truck manufacturers offer enough variations and options at each size rating that with few exceptions they can all compete in any range. Therefore, it behooves the municipality to select the type of truck most economical and efficient. For over-all design criteria S.A.E. truck ability prediction procedures[2] are a valuable guide for the selection of a chassis. The procedures provide a systematic means of evalu-

[1]Richard B. Berry, "Procurement," *Public Works Engineers' Yearbook 1955* (Chicago: American Public Works Association), pp. 49-53.

[2]*Truck Ability Prediction Procedures*, TR-82, Society of Automotive Engineers, 485 Lexington Avenue, New York.

ating power needs as related to such local factors as road conditions, topography and load weights and thus permit proper selection of engine, transmission, and axle ratio combinations. Use of this method permits chassis manufacturers the possible use of a number of combinations of engine, transmission, and axle ratios to achieve required performance. Experience in Chicago has shown that a maximum gradability of 25 per cent and maximum speed of approximately 35 miles per hour, with a five-speed transmission, provides a simple economical, easy-to-maintain unit for that city's operation (even with landfill type disposal). Where there is a long haul to and from the disposal site and higher speeds are desired, it may be advantageous to add a more complex two-speed axle. For landfill operation, radius rods on the rear should be mandatory and may be desirable for the front axles in terms of spring wear and axle and wheel alignment.

Tires should be kept as small as possible for economy and low loading height. 10:00 x 20 tires with 5,000-pound ratings have performed satisfactorily for gross vehicle weight of up to 32,000 pounds. Frames should be heavy duty with the section modulus x yield point equal to the maximum bending moment x safety factor. The safety factor should be commensurate with the dynamic loading of a truck frame. Frame selection is of great importance as it has a direct bearing on the operation and wear of engine, cab, transmission, axles, and indeed all other major components. A broken frame can be grave enough to make junking a serious alternative.

With the variety of options on the equipment, the buyer should review the drive system components to assure that the manufacturer has selected them with adequate torque input capacities, especially if there is any departure from standard models.

If cab-over-engine models are selected, the particular make should be carefully inspected as there are many things manufacturers are able to change to make for better maintenance. Attention should be paid to cab items such as hardware, door gasketing, etc. These can be eternal maintenance problems if not selected or attached properly.

Power options such as power steering, clutches, automatic transmissions, etc., should be employed judiciously and selected with care as they may be troublesome maintenance items. Since a motor truck is only as good as its economic usefulness, this should be one factor in determining whether such extra "gingerbread" is warranted or desirable.

CONTROL OF EQUIPMENT

Modern equipment control methods are well standardized, essentially the same plan being used by all large fleet operators, contractors, and municipalities. Failure to adopt them constitutes extravagance on the part of an agency operating several vehicles.

It is not proposed to present a complete discussion of equipment control here, but simply to state the essential parts of the system and to point out their special application to refuse collection equipment. It should be emphasized that the following control functions should be under the jurisdiction of the equipment group and not the operating groups.

Identification of Equipment

A simple scheme of numbering equipment should be adopted to make it easy to identify individual vehicles on the streets, in records and reports, and in control plans. License numbers are inadequate because of periodic changes, and motor or manufacturers' numbers are too long and meaningless. The numbers may be simply assigned in consecutive order or in each class.

The numbers are usually painted or stenciled conspicuously on the sides and back of vehicles for easy identification by foremen and supervisors.

Inventory Control

As a part of the city's property control system, a complete record should be kept of every vehicle in the refuse collection service. This record should give the details of the purchase, a complete description of the vehicle, and the number assigned. Often such records are combined with permanent operating records which show current value, estimated life, depreciation rate, rental rate, estimated annual use, and similar data.

Equipment Rental Plan

Equipment rentals provide a simple and accurate means of charging equipment expense to the operating units, districts, class of work, accounts, and appropriations. When the vehicles are centrally controlled and used by different agencies, rentals charges are essential, but the plan is also valuable for equipment managed by the operating departments.

Charges for gasoline, oil, repairs, tires, storage, insurance, and depreciation are made to the individual pieces of equipment. Equipment charges to operating accounts are made on the basis of rental rates, the amount for an hour or a mile depending on the class of vehicle. These rates are so established that the total annual rental receipts for a class of equipment are about the same as the total cost of owning, operating, maintaining, servicing, and storing all the vehicles of that class. Thus, the only charges that must be made to districts, routes, accounts, or appropriations for refuse collection operations are the rental amounts based on the actual use of equipment as shown on field reports.

The essential point is that, by this simple means, the total equipment cost is accurately included in all operating accounts. Other means of charging equipment costs to operations involve estimates, guesses, and approximations which at best are makeshift and at worst are erroneous. Sometimes only fuel and repair costs are included in operating statements and in operating costs. In many cases, depreciation, overhead, insurance, and storage are omitted entirely from refuse collection reporting and cost accounting. Such records are of little or no administrative value.

A 1956 survey of 305 cities of over 10,000 population[3] revealed that only 13 per cent financed motor equipment replacement by depreciation reserves accumulated through equipment rental charges. Most of the cities (76 per cent) financed such replacements by direct appropriations to the operating department. (It was also found that eight per cent of the cities made appropriations directly to the centralized equipment bureau, while three per cent of the cities use a combination of these methods.)

Assignment of Equipment

Usually, refuse collection vehicles are purchased to fit the particular requirements and conditions of the removal service and are expected to be used primarily on such operations. Consequently the vehicles in regular use as well as the reserve units are assigned permanently to the refuse collection agency. Nevertheless, when the number of vehicles needed fluctuates widely from day to day or from season to season, it may be advisable to use idle equipment on other municipal operations. Also, during emergencies it is usually necessary to use refuse vehicles on special work such as plowing snow, hauling snow, and clearing streets.

Under a central control system vehicles can be used wherever they can be of greatest effectiveness in the municipal service, but while released from their regular assignment the rental charges are made to the department operating the equipment.

Plant Facilities

Garages where maintenance work is performed should be selected very carefully. Servicing heavy motor trucks has many peculiarities not comparable with other types of equipment. When planning such a shop, one should be very familiar with the problems involved. Much of the equipment presently available is for automobile shops and is worthless for a truck shop.

Consideration should be given to centralized grease, motor oil, air, heavy duty electrical and drain oil lines with taps at strategic locations in the shop. Hoists of various types and floor loadings should be of adequate capacity to handle the heaviest equipment in the fleet, fully loaded. Ceiling clearance should be adequate to raise the longest dump bodies to full height. The shop should be designed for minimum aisle space and movement within the building. An ideal layout would allow trucks to enter and leave any shop bay from the outside without disturbing any other truck in the building. To accomplish this the building would be constructed with two rows of shop bays facing each other. Shop benches and equipment would be down the center, and the two outside walls would have overhead doors for their entire length. Bridge cranes could then be installed to run the entire length of the shop and cover any part of the floor.

[3]"Central Municipal Garages," *The Municipal Year Book, 1956* (Chicago: International City Managers' Association), p. 334.

FIG. 14-1. One of the storage garages for refuse collection equipment of the New York Department of Sanitation. For greatest efficiency the vehicles must be kept in garages when they are not being used on removal operations so they will be protected from the elements and can be regularly inspected and serviced.

Truck storage can be very complex. Certain rules and alternatives should be evaluated for each specific case. It is usually desirable to locate storage areas so as to minimize interruption of local traffic. As the trucks are large, noisy and, at best, not very attractive, they should be parked and stored away from residential neighborhoods.

Indoor versus outdoor storage should be weighed in terms of whether the added cost of buildings and the like can be justified by lengthened life and reduced maintenance. There is no way to determine this accurately without long years of comparative experience in a specific operation. Indoor versus outdoor parking, therefore, becomes a rather academic question when considered strictly on its own merit. Other factors which may or may not be decisive are:

1. Building costs.

2. Availability of unused space in existing buildings.

3. Availability of temporary or portable buildings and whether they are acceptable to all parties concerned.

4. Administrative policy with regard to public relations insofar as appearance of trucks and lots is concerned.

5. Importance of geographical distribution of the trucks relative to operating costs.

Preventive Maintenance

Poor performance and even breakdowns of equipment are often caused by improper maintenance and are preventable. To improve operating efficiency, automotive engineers have developed a plan of "preventive

FIG. 14-2. Often, vehicles must be parked in outside areas. This is a sanitation parking area of the Philadelphia Department of Streets. Note the neat orderly appearance of both the equipment and grounds.

maintenance" which has been shown conclusively to reduce equipment operating costs sharply.

Too often, vehicle control is entrusted to persons who have mechanical ability but lack maintenance foresight. It is common practice to repair trucks as quickly as possible when they cease to function and to restore them to productive service at once. Little consideration may be given to the cause of the failure or to the fact that it might have been avoided through timely preventive treatment.

The essence of preventive maintenance is the regularly scheduled inspection of each piece of equipment by qualified mechanics (usually every 1,000 miles or every 30 days on low mileage vehicles), and the immediate correction of any weakness or incipient failure that may be disclosed by such examinations. Daily servicing of the equipment is also part of the plan.

All preventive maintenance should be done at night in order to make units available during the regular daytime working hours. Since the work may be the equivalent of adding trucks to the fleet the additional expense is justifiable.

The operation of one well-known preventive maintenance system embraces two important phases of scientific maintenance:

FIG. 14-3. Modern equipment is essential to an effective and economical preventive maintenance program. This electrical diagnostic equipment is in use in one of Chicago's Department of Streets and Sanitation garages.

1. Performance of required maintenance operations at specific mileages accomplished with:

a. A series of mechanical work sheets prescribing services to be performed. Work to be done is no longer left to the judgment of the individual mechanic. Each man receives the same guiding charts to govern his procedure.

b. A preventive maintenance service schedule through which maintenance is planned in advance, eliminating the "peaks" and "valleys" of shop work which in itself is an economy.

2. Accumulation of operating and maintenance data made possible by:

a. The fleet maintenance record which contains the maintenance

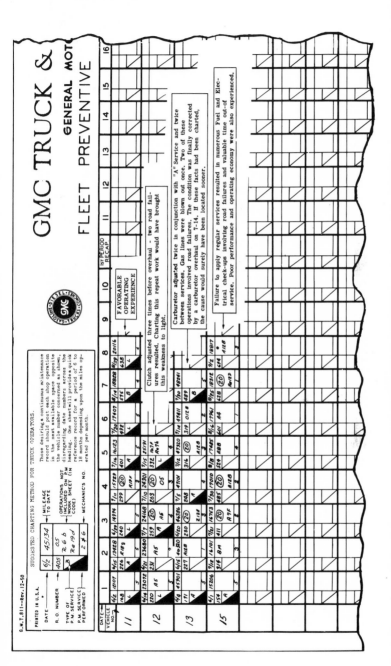

FIG. 14-4. The fleet preventive maintenance service record used in the General Motors Truck and Coach Company plan of preventive maintenance permits ready interpretation of all shop activity. Abuse in operation, ineffective repairs, chronic ailments, and frequency of maintenance work are brought to the attention of the equipment managers so that corrective measures can be taken promptly.

GMT 200 REV. 3-55
PRINTED IN U.S.A.

GMC PREVENTIVE MAINTENANCE WORK SHEET
GASOLINE ENGINE EQUIPPED TRUCKS

"A" SERVICE	"B" SERVICE
Suggested Mileage - 1000 to 3000 Miles	Suggested Mileage - 10,000 to 20,000 Miles
Suggested Time Interval - 3 to 6 Weeks	Suggested Time Interval - 3 to 6 Months

☐ ← ▬ INDICATE SERVICE TO BE PERFORMED ▬→ ☐

DATE_____   MODEL &
                                  CHASSIS NO._____

OWNER_____   TRUCK NO._____

ADDRESS_____   R. O. NO._____ MILEAGE_____

(√) OK   (X) ADJUSTMENT MADE   (O) NEEDS ATTENTION

"A" Service   "B" Service

CHASSIS SERVICE

1. **PITMAN & STEERING ARMS, DRAG LINK & TIE ROD** - Inspect for looseness.
2. **STEERING GEAR HOUSING** - Inspect. Tighten steering gear housing bolts.
3. **KING PIN DRAW KEYS** - Tighten.
4. **CLUTCH LINKAGE** - Examine clutch linkage for any abnormal condition.
5. **BRAKE MECHANISM** - Inspect hoses, lines, chambers, etc., for leaks - tighten connections. Examine cross shaft, cables, linkage, slack adjuster, etc., for abnormal wear. Inspect for oil and grease on drive line type parking brake.
6. **MASTER CYLINDER** - Examine fluid level and correct if necessary. Inspect brake pedal free travel and report.
7. **HYDROVAC** - Inspect and oil hydrovac.
8. **AIR TANKS** - Drain.
9. **TRANSMISSION(S)** - Inspect for leaks. Tighten rear bearing retainer cap screws.
10. **CENTER BEARINGS & BRACKETS** - Inspect for looseness.
11. **UNIVERSAL JOINTS AND FLANGES** - Inspect for looseness.
12. **PINION BEARING** - Inspect for looseness.
13. **DIFFERENTIAL HOUSING** - Inspect for lubricant leakage around differential housing and pinion oil seal. Tighten.
14. **REAR AXLE BREATHER** - See that Breather exterior is free from dirt.
15. **REAR AXLE BREATHER** - Remove, clean thoroughly and re-install.
16. **"U" BOLTS (Front & Rear)** - Tighten.
17. **SPRINGS** - Inspect shackles for looseness and wear and leaves for breakage or misalignment.
18. **TIRES** - Inspect for unusual wear.
19. **FRAME & BRACKETS** - Inspect for loose or broken members.
20. **MUFFLER** - Inspect condition of muffler, tail pipe & brackets.
21. **CAB HOLD DOWN BOLTS** - Tighten as necessary.
22. **LUBRICATION** - Lubricate chassis according to lubrication chart.
23. **DOOR LOCKS, HINGES & WINDOW REGULATORS** - Inspect for wear and proper operation - Lubricate
24. **PAINT & SHEET METAL** - Inspect for general appearance.
25. **SAFETY DEVICES** - Is vehicle equipped with the following: Turn Signals_____First Aid Kit_____Reflectors_____Jack_____ Clearance Lights_____Flares_____Fire Extinguisher_____
26. **LIGHTS** - Test all lights. Inspect lenses.
27. **FRONT WHEEL BEARINGS** - Inspect for looseness and report.
28. **KING PINS** - Inspect for looseness.
29. **WHEEL NUTS** - Tighten all wheel nuts.
30. **AXLE FLANGE NUTS** - Tighten to torque specifications.
31. **WHEEL BEARINGS** - Clean, repack and adjust all wheel bearings - replace grease retainers. Inspect brake lining, anchors, locks, springs, wheel cylinders and drums. Blow out drums and shoes, lubricate shoe anchors.
32. **TOE-IN** - Adjust if necessary: Before Adjustment_____After adjustment_____

GASOLINE ENGINE SERVICE

33. **BATTERY** - Take hydrometer reading each cell. 1. (Pos)___ 2.___ 3.___ 4.___ 5.___ 6. (Neg)___ Fill with distilled water.
34. **BATTERY** - Remove cables at battery - clean terminals - re-install cables and coat with petroleum jelly. Test voltage of each cell. 1. (Pos)___ 2.___ 3.___ 4.___ 5.___ 6. (Neg)___
35. **RADIATOR CORE** - Inspect for leaks. Inspect mounting.
36. **WATER PUMP** - Inspect for leaks. Inspect condition of belts.
37. **RADIATOR & HEATER HOSES & CONNECTIONS** - Inspect for leaks, cracks and deterioration. Tighten if necessary.
38. **CYLINDER HEAD** - Inspect for evidence of coolant loss.
39. **RADIATOR** - Examine coolant level - add water if level is low or tag steering wheel if level is low and antifreeze is used.
40. **WATER PUMP PULLEY** - Loosen belt and check pulley for looseness.
41. **AIR COMPRESSOR** - Tighten mounts - Adjust belts if necessary.
42. **ENGINE SUPPORTS** - Inspect condition of insulators.
43. **ENGINE** - Inspect for external oil leaks. Examine outside oil and fuel lines for chaffing and kinks.
44. **FUEL FILTERS** - Clean all - Clean fuel pump screen and bowl. Replace gasket.
45. **FUEL PUMP** - Test and record pressure_____and capacity_____
46. **STARTER AND GENERATOR** - Inspect commutator and brushes. Tighten connections.
47. **SPARK PLUGS** - Remove, inspect, clean and gap. Replace with new gasket.
48. **ENGINE COMPRESSION** - Test and record on each cylinder: Dry 1___ 2___ 3___ 4___ 5___ 6___ 7___ 8___ Wet 1___ 2___ 3___ 4___ 5___ 6___ 7___ 8___
49. **DISTRIBUTOR** - Inspect points - set point gap.
50. **DISTRIBUTOR** - Remove wires from cap - Inspect contacts for corrosion and cap for cracks. Inspect condition of wiring.
51. **IGNITION TIMING** - Set timing with light.
52. **CRANKCASE VENTILATOR VALVE** - Remove and clean.
53. **OVERHEAD OILING SYSTEM** - Inspect to see that proper oil flow is taking place.
54. **CYLINDER HEAD** - Tighten cylinder head bolts to torque specifications with torque wrench.
55. **VALVES** - Adjust valve lash. Replace cover gasket.
56. **MANIFOLDS** - Tighten nuts. Inspect for leaks.
57. **CARBURETOR** - Adjust idle with vacuum gauge.
58. **ENGINE OIL** - Change oil. Inspect engine oil for water and fuel dilution.
59. **ENGINE OIL FILTER** - Replace filter element.
60. **CARBURETOR AIR CLEANER** - Clean.
61. **CRANKCASE BREATHER AIR CLEANER** - Clean.
62. **AIR COMPRESSOR AIR CLEANER** - Clean.
63. **HYDROVAC AIR CLEANER** - Clean.
64. **GOVERNOR AIR CLEANER** - Clean.

OVER

FIG. 14-5. Front and back of work sheet for preventive maintenance service of gasoline engine trucks under the plan developed by the Service Division of the General Motors Truck and Coach Company. These instructions are the same for each vehicle and each mechanic, making it necessary for individual workers to determine the repairs or adjustments that should or should not be made. A similar sheet has been developed for diesel engine trucks.

			ROAD TEST				70.	POWER TRAIN - Report on operation.
		65.	STEERING WHEEL - Inspect steering gear play at steering wheel.				71.	BRAKES - Test operation of service brakes and parking brake.
							72.	OIL PRESSURE - Record at idle_____and maximum_____
		66.	WINDSHIELD WIPERS - Inspect operation of wipers and condition of blades.				73.	INSTRUMENTS AND ACCESSORIES - Inspect operation.
		67.	HORN - Test operation.					
		68.	HYDROVAC - Before moving vehicle make hydrovac operating test.					
		69.	CLUTCH - Test operation of clutch and report if free travel is ½″ or less.					

EXPLAIN IN DETAIL ALL ITEMS MARKED "O"

_____

LIST ITEMS HERE WHICH ARE NOT LISTED ON THIS FORM BUT FOUND TO BE IN NEED OF ATTENTION.

_____

SIGNED_____

FIG. 14-5. (Continued)

experience of each individual vehicle in a concise manner, revealing operating facts at a glance.

b. The fleet history record, which reflects the safe economic mileage life of all important units of the vehicle, permits repairs, and replacements to be made prior to failure by *fact* rather than by *guess.*

Under this plan, there are four mechanical inspection services:

A Service: This service is rendered every 1,000 miles throughout the life of the vehicle, or its equivalent in operating hours, or, on low mileage vehicles, every 30 days. It includes the adjustment of units affecting operating economy and, of course, a thorough lubrication and general inspection. Timing is checked, carburetor adjusted, spark plugs cleaned and spaced, etc.

B Service: This service is suggested at 5,000 mile intervals. All "A" Service items are included, plus many others requiring attention at this mileage. For example, wheel alignment is checked, grease retainers and bearings checked, brakes inspected and adjusted, the crankcase ventilator is cleaned, and the generator checked and charging rate adjusted.

C Service: This service is suggested every 15,000 miles or yearly. It includes all A and B items and involves arbitrary replacement of inexpensive minor parts which have served their economic usefulness. Certain concealed units are opened up, examined and adjusted to prevent abnormal wear and costly failure. The cooling system is thoroughly cleaned, valves are ground and springs replaced and the fuel pump overhauled or exchanged. Distributor points, rotor, condenser, and high tension wires are arbitrarily replaced.

D Service: This service is suggested at 30,000 miles. It includes A, B, and C items, together with an exacting examination of all major units. The thoroughness of this service insures continued satisfactory performance and reliability at a mileage which normally introduces an era of uncertainty. The transmission and differential are removed, cleaned, inspected and adjusted; spindle bolts, bushings and tie rod ends are replaced; the clutch is disassembled and discs, linings, etc., replaced. Universal joints and center bearings are overhauled; wheel bearings washed, inspected and repacked; brakes relined and brake mechanism overhauled, a general check and reconditioning of the engine takes place —pistons and rods are removed, bearings and cylinder walls checked, valves ground and parts replaced where necessary.

In addition to the above, it may be desirable to have an engine oil analysis program for detection of faulty engines or poor servicing. There are laboratories which specialize in this type of testing and can provide very worthwhile information on fleet condition.

Routing sheets are prepared so that vehicles may be brought to repair garages systematically. Special effort is made to stagger the service dates so that the maximum number of vehicles may be in operation and there is an even flow of work through the shops.

City of Los Angeles
Bureau of Sanitation
REFUSE COLLECTION & DISPOSAL DIVISION

DRIVER'S DAILY VEHICLE PREVENTIVE MAINTENANCE REPORT

I.   Driver's Responsibility:
Servicemen and Mechanics cannot do the whole job of preventive
maintenance. A great share of it must be done by the equipment
driver. Driver's responsibilities include:
1. Proper operating and servicing knowledge of his
   assigned equipment and its components.
2. Ability to properly operate the equipment, including
   its engine, transmission and auxiliaries.
3. Understanding of the maintenance services for which
   he is responsible and how he is to perform them.
4. Reporting of every 2,500 speedometer miles to his
   foreman. (When actual speedometer miles agree with
   mileage on sticker ON SPEEDOMETER.) This is reported
   on this form below and is used for scheduling P.M..
5. Reporting of trouble symptoms to his foreman by proper
   use of this "Driver's Daily Vehicle Report".
6. Follow all rules and regulations in "Service Guide".

Driver must meet these responsibilities to have an effective
preventive maintenance program.

II.   Driver's Daily Check List:
Drivers perform, under Collection Foreman's supervision, the
following daily Preventive Maintenance items:

O.K.	NEEDS REPAIR	
		BEGINNING OF SHIFT
		1. Check oil, water, and fuel. (Truck and auxiliary engines).
		2. Check for proper positioning of oil, water, and fuel caps.
		3. Visual check under truck for oil, water and fuel leaks.
		4. Check tires (For flats and tread).
		5. Close air-tank valves.
		6. Start and warm up engine.
		7. Check instrument gauges and warning lights.
		8. Check: clearance; turn; head; tail; and stop, lights.
		9. Check windshield wipers.
		10. Check horn.
		11. Check mirrors and seat belts.
		12. Check hand brake.
		13. Make rolling brake check, before leaving yard gate.
		14. Uncorrected defects will be reported to foreman before moving truck.
		END OF SHIFT
		1. Clean out cab.
		2. Hose off exterior and interior of truck per local foreman's instructions.
		3. Drain air-tanks and leave valves open.
		4. Check tires for flats and breaks by kicking.
		5. Report all defects to Collection foreman under "Daily Vehicle Report" below.
		6. Check Packer oil level.

III. **Driver's Daily Vehicle Report:**

I certify that I have made all of the above
checks and reports.   TRUCK NO._____

TRUCK OPERATOR:_____ DATE:_____ MILEAGE: _____
TIME REPORT RECEIVED FROM DRIVER:_____ RECEIVED BY:_____
FORM NO. M & S 65-41

FIG. 14-6. Driver's Daily Vehicle Preventive Maintenance Report emphasizes driver's responsibility in keeping maintenance costs to a minimum.

Historical records of all maintenance work are kept for each item of equipment. Usually codes are used so that all pertinent data may be shown on a single chart. Daily service of equipment is just as important as the mechanical inspections. This work is usually performed at the storage garage during the night or whenever the vehicles are not in operation. Such servicing includes checking crankcase oil, radiator water, tire pressure, windshield wipers, lights, and horn. Often the cabs must be cleaned and the windows washed. The gasoline tanks are filled so that the vehicles are ready for immediate use.

The continuous examination of the operating records and the maintenance history charts will assist in the discovery of unsatisfactory conditions. Operating abuses are usually disclosed and unsatisfactory parts or accessories are indicated.

FIG. 14-7. An automatic washer which can wash two trucks at the same time is used by the City of Philadelphia to maintain good appearance of refuse collection vehicles.

Cleaning the Equipment

Refuse collection equipment must be cleaned frequently to prevent the dissemination of objectionable odors and to increase its life. In some cities that collect unwrapped garbage, the vehicles are washed after each load is dumped. If garbage is carefully wrapped it is usually satisfactory to clean vehicles thoroughly at the end of each day. Vehicles used exclusively for ash or rubbish collection should be washed after each day's operation and should be cleaned thoroughly at least once a week.

The bodies are ordinarily washed by streams of water from large hoses that supply considerable pressure. The washing should be thorough enough to remove all particles of refuse. As a rule, the entire vehicle is washed, but sometimes the hose flushing is limited to the inside and outside of the bodies, the wheels and the chassis. Because hose washing will not remove grease, other methods must be used periodically to keep the equipment clean and to protect it from deterioration. The simplest way is to wash with soap and water. It has been found that in certain instances ordinary household detergents are as economical and effective as other methods. Another method is the use

FIG. 14-8. In Los Angeles, the bodies of garbage collection vehicles are cleaned after each load has been collected and dumped. A water supply line is attached to the front of the body and the water is introduced into the body by means of internal high-pressure rotating nozzles.

of a jet of live steam, into which liquid soap is introduced, and applied through a hose with considerable pressure. Care must be exercised, however, that the paint is not removed by this method.

Retirement of Equipment

An important part of an efficient equipment control plan is the orderly and systematic retirement of each vehicle when it has served its economically useful life. Inexperienced equipment managers may be greatly tempted to try to extend the use of old equipment and thus delay the purchase of replacements, but such a policy results usually in higher rather than in lower equipment costs.

The objective of an equipment manager is to secure the lowest possible unit costs of operation—not just low depreciation or outlay expenditures, or even the lowest maintenance expenses. One of his most important tasks is to determine when the point of diminishing returns is reached or, in other words, when a piece of equipment reaches a condition in which the unit cost of operation is higher than that of a new vehicle. While this time cannot be precisely determined, it can be estimated very closely by continuous study of operating records and by examination of the historical data on similar vehicles. Large fleet operators usually have enough experience and records to enable them to predict with some accuracy the hours or miles of use that can be secured most economically, and some of them replace equipment on this basis alone. Others combine this procedure with careful study of the maintenance cost of each vehicle. If a large number of experience records are not available, more dependence must be put on a study of month-to-month maintenance costs and the maintenance records for each piece of equipment.

TRAINING AND EQUIPMENT OPERATION

Low equipment costs depend as much on proper operation of the vehicles as on wise selection and adequate maintenance. Incompetent and careless drivers can defeat the best plan of equipment maintenance and care. To prevent the misuse of vehicles, drivers should be trained to handle the equipment safely and carefully, and supervisors and foremen should also be educated in its efficient use.

Much difficulty can arise out of the conflicting attitudes of equipment and operating personnel. The equipment group want the drivers to safeguard the vehicles from damage and abuse; the operating group want the drivers to complete the work quickly. The drivers are usually under the control of the operating supervisors, and, unless proper coordination is secured, the protests of the equipment people may be unavailing.

Some cities have established regular training for all drivers of refuse collection vehicles so that the equipment is operated properly and safe driving rules are followed. Usually, no instruction in equipment maintenance is given because the drivers are not permitted to make adjustments or to attempt repairs. This is particularly true where all repair and maintenance work is done by the mechanics of a central garage. Usually the drivers are not trained mechanics and they may cause considerable damage to expensive collection vehicles. The drivers, however, trained or untrained, are a valuable source of information on vehicle operating condition. Immediate attention to driver complaints and suggestions will help keep vehicles in top operating condition and also help promote high morale in the ranks of operating personnel.

Trained equipment operators mean increased efficiency and consequent saving of time and money. Trained operators also require less

Property of

_____

_____

Telephone_____

Chauffeur License_____

Payroll Number_____

_____

CITY OF MINNEAPOLIS
ENGINEERING DEPARTMENT
EQUIPMENT DIVISION
1308 Currie Ave. N.

_____

TELEPHONE

Dispatcher - - - ATlantic 1591

Stockroom - - - ATlantic 0948

Shop - - - - - ATlantic 0732

City Engineer - - BR. 7611

Police - - - - MAin 1361

Fire - - - - - MAin 1391

Ambulance - - .- MAin 1361

If you find this book please call Dispatcher

GENERAL INFORMATION

Seniority — After having satisfactorily served the probation period as prescribed by Civil Service Rules, you become a certified Civil Service operator and are entitled to consideration in seniority as such. However, bear in mind, that seniority entitles you to work only. You have no preference on different kinds of equipment or jobs over any other employee. You will perform such work as is assigned to you.

Care of Equipment—It is the duty of all operators before leaving the Garage, to see that gas, oil, water and tires are all alright. Also test the hoist and brakes to see that they are O.K. Drivers are not required to drive a piece of equipment with faulty brakes. Any accident due to this fault will be held against the driver. Fill out an Operator's Mechanical Report on each piece of equipment when you pull in regardless of whether anything is wrong or not. Call the Dispatcher's Office for motor or tire trouble during the day time. At night call the shop.

Riders—There shall be no passenger in or on any piece of equipment, who is not a duly authorized employee of the City or the Job the equipment is working on. There will be no exceptions to this rule and violations merit suspension.

Children—Do not permit children near your equipment at any time. If you find it necessary to call the Police to chase them

FIG. 14-9. The Equipment Division issues a guide to refuse collection drivers in Minneapolis. Care of equipment, which is the responsibility of the driver, is carefully outlined; the balance of the pamphlet is set up to serve as the driver's record of operation.

supervision and are essential in a program to reduce maintenance costs and realize life expectancy of equipment.

In-service training programs and apprenticeship courses are conducted by many cities. Instructional aids are available from a number of sources such as the automotive equipment manufacturers. Also, the manufacturers sometimes conduct local classes for mechanics and garage employees and several have special schools at their factories or training centers. In-service training programs include driver training on safe operation of equipment, limited field servicing of equipment, and reporting on equipment defects and accidents.

RENTING PRIVATE EQUIPMENT

Instead of buying refuse collection vehicles and storing and maintaining them, some cities rent equipment from private owners, usually with a driver. There are many objections to this practice, but if it is not feasible to purchase and manage equipment on a sound basis, rental may prove to be advisable.

One of the most important difficulties in renting equipment is that it may be impossible to obtain vehicles suited to the work. It has been pointed out that economical collection can be secured only when the equipment is selected to fit the collection methods used and proportioned to the unit weight of the refuse that will be handled. Ordinary dump trucks that may be available locally are usually designed to haul sand, gravel, stone, and other materials much heavier than refuse. For refuse collection work, consequently, the bodies have too small a capacity in relation to the size of the chassis.

It may be possible to induce private companies to purchase equipment specially adapted to the local refuse collection requirements, but such an arrangement is subject to all the objections of contract collection cited in Chapter 10. The owners would insist on contracts for the duration of the life of the equipment, and it would be difficult to get sufficient competition to insure fair rental rates.

Municipalities are sometimes forced to rent equipment for refuse collection because funds cannot be made available to buy the needed vehicles. All that can be done is to rent the best available equipment even though it is not suited to the service, and recognize that operation costs will be higher than they should be.

AMOUNT OF EQUIPMENT NEEDED

Refuse collection must be regularly and systematically conducted since it vitally affects the health and well-being of the citizens and is so intimately related to citizen appraisal of municipal government. Shortage of equipment is not a reasonable excuse for failure to make regular collections.

The total number of collection vehicles should at the very least be sufficient to handle peak requirements. The reserve for breakdowns and for vehicles being repaired should be added to the peak demands to insure adequate performance. The amount of such reserves depends largely on the equipment control methods employed. A minimum number is required under a modern preventive maintenance system, because field breakdowns are almost entirely eliminated, and the time lost for major repairs is negligible. In such cases, the additional number of vehicles is limited to the number given preventive service each day. If peak periods can be predicted with reasonable accuracy, the preventive maintenance work can be scheduled to avoid the times of maximum equipment demands. On the other hand, if the maintenance work is haphazard, a much larger reserve will be necessary. In addition to those vehicles undergoing major repairs, several may break down during periods of peak refuse production. Unless replacements are available, the service is crippled, schedules are destroyed, and citizen complaints become numerous.

INSURANCE

Because cities with a large fleet of automotive equipment often find that risks can be carried by the city at less cost than they can buy insurance, many large cities do not carry liability, theft, or fire insurance on automotive equipment. However, cities cannot safely eliminate insurance with private companies without mair^taining a sufficiently large general insurance reserve fund through appropriations to take care of emergency contingencies. Thus, the vast majority of cities have such insurance with a private company.

A survey of 738 cities in 1956[4] showed that 647 of the cities reporting, or 88 per cent, indicated that they have motor vehicle public liability insurance. The survey also revealed that most motor vehicle public liability business is placed with a group of local agents (58 per cent) and only 25 per cent of the cities used competitive bidding.

The maximum limits of insurance coverage for bodily injury per person, bodily injury per accident, and property damage per accident for city-owned vehicles are normally in the range from $25,000 to $100,000; $50,000 to $300,000; and $5,000 to $50,000, respectively.

ACCIDENT PREVENTION PROGRAMS

A good accident prevention program not only benefits the employee through reduced injury rates but benefits the city in dividends of less personnel time lost and savings realized through reduced workman's compensation premiums.

A uniform accident reporting system is an absolute necessity. A system used effectively is for employees to call the police if they become involved in an accident. A police investigation squad is sent to the scene of the accident immediately and the dispatcher notifies the municipal garage. The garage, in turn, sends a pre-designated individual to the scene to make an estimate of all damages. Such a determination has been found helpful in contesting excessive damage claims against the city at a later date. Reports are prepared by the police (one for the police department, one to the head of the department involved, one to the city attorney's office, and two to the personnel office) and the employee. The employee directs his report to the department head. After an appropriate study, the department head forwards with his recommendations the employee's report to the city attorney's office and the personnel office.

In the public works field, by far the most expensive and frequent type accidents are those involving equipment (both automotive and shop), and control programs should be designed accordingly. There are many tools of accident prevention. These include various forms of employee education such as safety bulletins and regularly scheduled meetings, development and use of on-the-job safe procedures, use of safety clothing and equipment, employee incentive plans which provide for various types of safe driver awards, and physical examinations for drivers being hired and for all drivers who have had accidents.

Some cities have found that punitive, incentive, and educational activities can best be handled by an accident review board. Such boards

---

[4]"Municipal Insurance Data," *The Municipal Year Book 1956* (Chicago: International City Managers' Association), pp. 49-53.

should be composed of officials who are directly concerned with the operation and safety of the city fleet.

EQUIPMENT RECORDS AND REPORTS[5]

Each motor vehicle costs the city from a few hundred to a thousand dollars or more each year for direct operating expenses. With the addition of tangible costs, such as depreciation on the vehicle and on the garage and equipment, interest on the investment, and possibly interest and principal on bonds issued to construct the garage, the total cost amounts to considerably more. Computation of intangible costs, however, is generally so complicated a matter that few cities make any attempt to undertake the task. On the other hand, many cities keep accurate records of operating and maintenance costs.

Each piece of equipment incurs expenses at a different rate, and if a city is to know the facts concerning the relative economies possible in the operation of different types of motor vehicles, carefully kept cost records are an absolute necessity. Thus, a system of itemized records showing the operating and other costs of each car and truck in the municipal motor vehicle fleet is more than desirable; it is an essential part of the city's accounting system for such vehicles. In view of the excessive costs, or even extravagances, which may result if such records are not kept, failure to keep good vehicle records is as much an indication of poor administration as failure to record the annual expenses of any bureau, division, or department.

A certain type or make of motor vehicle may be more economical than others for certain municipal services. The only way to determine this is by a comparison of the operating costs of the different vehicles.

Furthermore, when the operating cost of each car or truck mounts rapidly, due to obsolescence, it is necessary to decide whether it will be more economical to replace the unit than to overhaul it. In the absence of a complete cost record, the best time for replacement is left to guesswork. Proper accounting of equipment costs is also necessary in order to establish an equitable schedule for rental rates. Such rates should approximate the cost of making the equipment available for each hour or mile of use, and should not only include the direct operating costs, such as gasoline, oil, tires, and other supplies, but also maintenance, depreciation, insurance, and overhead costs.

A total of 221 cities, or 73 per cent of those reporting in a recent survey conducted by the International City Managers' Association, indicated that they have an equipment cost system with records to show various elements of cost for oil, supplies, parts, maintenance, and repair of each piece of motor equipment. Only 38 of the 221 cities, however, indicated that their cost records also include overhead and depreciation.

[5]This section from *Municipal Public Works Administration* (Chicago: International City Managers' Association, 1957), pp. 145-146; and *Municipal Public Works Cost Accounting Manual* (Chicago: Public Administration Service, 1955), p. 97.

The detailed cost accounts for automotive equipment are maintained on an individual equipment record in order to provide special cost and performance data. Monthly totals of the several classes of costs and of rentals earned are posted to these records with other data so that operating and dispatching efficiency can be revealed. Quarterly and "to-date" cost and earnings figures are shown on the individual equipment record so that periodically the costs and the operating efficiency of the equipment may be appraised. This form is used for a period of one year. At the end of the year, the annual totals are transferred to an equipment history record which provides a record covering the entire life of the equipment.

SUMMARY

The cost of refuse removal operations and the regularity of collections are influenced markedly by the character of the equipment control practices employed. Good management of equipment services insures minimum equipment cost, whereas the failure to adopt modern controls and sound maintenance procedures increases operating costs in any city and may destroy the effectiveness of the whole removal system.

There is no question as to what constitutes effective equipment management. While many of the practices and procedures in the field of refuse collection must be decided on the basis of local conditions, this is not true of the purchase, maintenance, and servicing of vehicles. Authorities agree on the proper methods of control to obtain the most effective use of equipment and to secure the lowest operating costs. In view of this it is difficult to excuse failure to use the accepted methods.

chapter 15

REPORTING, COST ACCOUNTING, AND BUDGETING

The basic tools of management are complete reports of operations, accurate costs and cost analyses, and well prepared budgets. Sound organization, planning, direction, and expenditure control are wholly impossible without proper data on production and costs. As one authority has said:

> Blind dependence on the judgment of subordinates will ultimately prove disastrous. Casual observations are informative to the trained administrator, but such at best give only an incomplete picture of conditions and performance; they provide no penetrating analysis of the real situation, and they force reliance on memory alone for knowledge of past operations. The public works administrator has need of definite measurements of the amount and character of work done, its costs, the efficiency of its execution, and the quality of results obtained. Such information is indispensable to the effective planning, control, and evaluation of public works activities. The value of such measurements is greatly enhanced if they can be compared with recognized standards.[1]

This situation is widely recognized in the field of refuse collection, and all competent officials endorse the principle that complete information on operations must be regularly and accurately secured and periodically summarized and analyzed. An adequate reporting system need not and should not be complicated or it will defeat its own purpose. Simple field reports and summaries have been shown to be the most satisfactory.

MEASUREMENT OF PERFORMANCE AND EFFICIENCY

A means of measuring the amount of work done by the refuse removal forces is necessary to any meaningful reporting of accomplishments, efficiency or cost. Several possible units of measurement may have significance. The number of families from which refuse is collected may in some cases be a reasonable measure of performance, but such a family or a per capita unit does not consider the quantity of material handled. The distance walked by collectors and that traveled by

---

[1]Donald C. Stone, *The Management of Municipal Public Works* (Chicago: Public Administration Service, 1939), p. 47.

vehicles may be a fairly accurate measure of effort but does not serve to evaluate the accomplishments or performance. The amount of refuse material handled is a good measure of performance for both collection and hauling but may give incomplete information as to effort expended. Perhaps a combination of all these measures would be necessary for precise measurement of the work done, but reporting in such terms would be far too complicated and time-consuming to be practical, at least in the present stage of development of work analysis.

FIG. 15-1. Measurement of the amount of refuse collected is made most accurately on a weight basis. The ton is the unit commonly used. All refuse handled at the incinerators of Philadelphia is weighed in the collection vehicles.

A quantity of measurement is the single unit that most nearly measures performance. A ton of refuse handled is the approved unit of work, for weight is the only quantity measurement that is sufficiently accurate. When facilities for weighing cannot be provided, a volume measure (in cubic yards) may be used, but it introduces several variables that may destroy the accuracy of reports.

The volume of collected refuse normally must be measured in the collection vehicles, but the material may be compacted to varying degerees or not compacted at all, and individual loads may contain unusually heavy or light refuse. Loads in open bodies cannot be measured with reasonable accuracy unless the bodies are level full or unless the material is leveled carefully. The part heaped above the water-level lines can only be estimated. Ashes can be measured fairly accurately by volume because this material does not compress greatly and can be easily leveled. Rubbish, on the other hand, is subject to much compacting and is difficult to level for measuring. The only serious disadvantage to the use of weight of refuse in evaluating performance is that rubbish and ashes may include appreciable quantities of water in rainy or snowy weather. However, weight has so many advantages over volume as a basis of measurement that it should be used wherever possible. For some determinations, refuse density should be known and to obtain this information, weight and volume measurements should be made. These measurements may be made in truck bodies or in certain instances after the refuse is unloaded.

FIG. 15-2. Volume measurement of refuse is used for control purposes in numerous cities. The water-level capacity of the body of each collection vehicle may be accurately determined and then additions or deductions made for each load by measuring or estimating the surcharge or the unfilled portion. A gauge is being used by the employee at this municipal disposal area to measure the amount of refuse above the water level lines of the truck.

Because a quantity measurement does not take all factors of performance into account, it cannot be accepted as an infallible index of cost or efficiency. It will take longer, for example, to collect a ton of refuse in a sparsely settled area than in a solidly built-up district. Similarly, it requires more time and effort to collect a ton of refuse when the containers are a hundred feet from the vehicle than when they are twenty feet away. Also, when refuse production per capita is greater in some areas than in others, the speed of collection is affected. Thus, it should be remembered that ratios based on the quantity of refuse are simply indices of work produced; they do not necessarily portray the whole situation.

Varying unit performance or cost among crews or districts, or unusually low unit performance or high unit cost for certain groups should be viewed as warning signals. The appearance of such signals ordinarily requires investigation to discover if valid reasons exist for the different or unusual unit performance ratios or if a change of efficiency actually has occurred. Sometimes such investigations may involve special analyses, using other measures on a spot check basis to see if differences in the amount of work done or effort expended actually exist. Often these measures will involve the distances walked by collectors or set-out helpers, the number of containers handled, or hauling speed.

FIG. 15-3. Some cities believe it is important to obtain accurate quantity data even when refuse is disposed of in a sanitary landfill. In Los Angeles, trucks hauling combustible rubbish are weighed on a scale at the disposal site.

Measurements of performance are now rather widely used as indices of accomplishment and efficiency, whereas formerly almost sole dependence was placed on unit costs. Performance ratios expressed in terms of man-hours per ton, man-hours per cubic yard, or tons per equipment mile are in many respects superior to unit costs. They are obtained easily and quickly from field data that should be reported daily whether used for performance analysis or not. Knowing the total number of man-hours spent by a collection crew or a collection district and the total amount of refuse collected by that crew or district, the performance ratios can be computed readily by simple division. The figures can be in the hands of the supervisors early the next morning, permitting prompt corrective action if it is needed. Daily measures of performance are invaluable, particularly for comparison with unit costs which ordinarily are available but once a month—and not until several days after the close of a month's work. Performance data is readily provided for each crew, each district, or other unit of organization. If desirable, loading can be reported separately from hauling, and set-out and set-back activities can be computed separately from loading.

These performance measurements make it possible to analyze the use of the labor force. Since labor costs are ordinarily more than half of the total expense and are the cause of the greatest variations, this control is probably the most important. A few cities use labor costs as the only basis for analyzing operations, but ordinarily other controls are needed. If performance ratios are computed for refuse hauling, another useful index of operations is provided, but they produce separate indices that are difficult to combine with labor controls to furnish over-all ratings.

While performance measurements provide valuable daily guides of operation effectiveness, they do not reveal all that needs to be known about collection activities. Unless a complete analysis is made, some elements of expense would never be taken into account—for example, the cost of supplies, materials, and supervision—and over-all control would be lacking. Therefore, performance indices should be supplemented by unit cost analysis whenever possible.

Unit costs are very valuable measures of efficiency and are widely used to compare accomplishments from one period to another and to compare districts, crews, and routes. The most common index is the cost of removing a ton or a cubic yard of refuse. Separate unit costs for actual collection, for set-out and set-back, or for hauling are desirable if the time of employees and equipment can readily be reported separately. Unit costs may also be valuable to divide the hauling cost, when transfer operations are involved, into that for hauling to the station, for transfer, and for hauling from the station to disposal sites. The important analysis, however, is a monthly unit cost for the complete collection activity—for each crew, for each district, and for the entire city—which is then compared with the unit cost of the previous month and the same month of the previous year.

FIELD REPORTING OF REMOVAL OPERATIONS

The foundation of an adequate system of records and costs is accurate, regular, and complete reporting of the field operations of the refuse collection forces. If the information on the use of equipment, the activities of the crews, and the amount of refuse collected is wrong or incomplete, the subsequent summaries, analyses, and standards will be equally erroneous. If the errors are substantial, the resulting records may be misleading instead of helpful.

The truck drivers and the foremen who must be relied upon to report the daily operations and the refuse removal crews are understand-

ably more interested in collecting and hauling the refuse than in keeping records. Unfortunately, sometimes, the value of cost and performance data in administering the removal work is beyond their compre-
hension and interest, with the consequence that omission of some data,
approximation of others, and irregularity in preparing reports are not
regarded as important. Probably the most difficult problem of employee
training is to develop proper habits in field reporting to create an interest in and sense of responsibility for making accurate and complete
records.

Present Status of Field Reporting

All refuse collection agencies require some field reporting. While reports in some cities are limited to daily or weekly labor or pay roll
documents, in other places both labor and equipment use are reported
regularly, and in many municipalities rather complete information is
reported on the amount of work done, location of operations, conditions
of work, and other pertinent aspects, in addition to labor and equipment
use. Of 89 cities reporting on detailed operations, 73 collect refuse with
their own forces, and 62 of these cities require regular field reports showing performance data in addition to pay roll and equipment use data.
All of the 62 cities obtain enough information to permit the separate
analysis of each class of refuse collected, and many of them secure data
from each crew or from each route.

TABLE 15-1
Performance Data Collected By 62 Cities,
By Class of Refuse and Basis of Reporting

		Basis of Reporting		
Class of Refuse	Number of Cities[1]	Tons	Cubic Yards	Tons and Cubic Yards
All refuse together....................	28	15	9	4
Garbage.............................	18	13	3	2
Garbage and combustible rubbish.....	12	7	3	2
Ashes and noncombustible rubbish...	8	3	5	..
Combustible rubbish..................	5	3	..	2
Noncombustible rubbish..............	9	2	5	2
Rubbish and ashes...................	4	1	2	1
Rubbish..............................	5	2	3	..
Ashes................................	4	1	3	..
Yard.................................	5	1	4	..
	98	48	37	13

[1] Because some cities collect two or three classes of refuse, the total exceeds 62.

Table 15-1, compiled from an earlier APWA study, shows, for each
class of refuse, the number of cities that report performance by class
of refuse and by a unit of measurement which determines the amount
of material handled. The fact that approximately 85 per cent of the
cities using their own forces have fairly complete field reporting systems indicates the increasing recognition of the need for accurate performance data in the administration of refuse collection activities. This

Date _2/6/58_   Division_____

Town of Montclair
Department of Public Works
Bureau of Refuse Collection and Disposal

CHAUFFEUR'S DAILY REPORT

No._72_   Name _John Pureno_

Started_6 30_ a.m. ~~p.m.~~   Finished _3 15_ ~~a.m.~~ p.m.   Rate_____   ~~Hourly~~ Daily   Amt _14 84_

8 3/4 Hours

LOAD No.		1	2	3			
TRUCK No.		50	50	50			
ROUTE No.		5	5	6			
Loading Time	Finish	8 30	11 30	2 15			
	Start	6 30	9 30	12 30			
	Total Hours	2	2	1 3/4			
Cubic Yards		23	23	14			
Hauling Time	Finish	9 30	12 30	3 15			
	Start	8 30	11 30	2 15			
	Total Hours	1	1	1			

Explanation of Idle Time_____

_____

Remarks_____

_____

BUREAU OF RECORDS AND ACCOUNTS							
Truck No.	Hours	Miles	Route No.	Loading Time 620	Hauling Time 630	Total Yards
50	8 3/4		5	4	2	46
			6	1 3/4	1	14
TOTALS		XXX	XXX	5 3/4	3	60

Form 9   Approved:_____

FIG. 15-4. The chauffeur's and superintendent's daily field reporting forms used in Montclair, New Jersey, provide for recording the essential information needed for the control of truck operations.

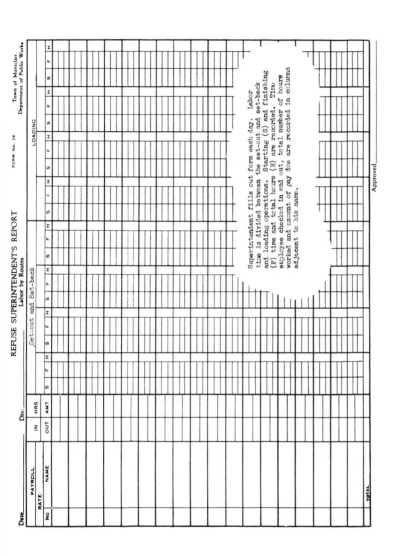

is encouraging; but the salient fact still remains that if the information furnished on field reports is not put to the best use, it is wasted effort. The data must be summarized and analyzed in a form that can be used for management and administrative determinations by operating officials.

Content of Field Reports

The reporting of refuse collection operations is not complicated, even in those cities that require complete daily statements of performance from each unit or crew. The work is of such a routine nature that the necessary information is usually easily and quickly recorded. Moreover, although there are numerous kinds of reports in existence to fit accounting systems, organization arrangements, needs of administrators, and the number of refuse separations, there is little difference of opinion among administrators as to the information that should be included.

The four chief reasons for reporting refuse collection operations may be stated as follows:

1. To provide a means of informing accounting and other headquarters offices of the utilization of equipment and the amount of time worked by each employee, in order that proper distribution of expense can be made and that pay rolls are accurately and promptly prepared.

2. To insure enough information as to the location and extent of work done by various crews to be able to answer complaints and criticisms intelligently.

3. To furnish any data on progress and performance of each unit of the service needed to manage the refuse collection operations effectively.

4. To make it possible to report accomplishments, performance, and cost to city officials and citizens.

Field reports can be designed to provide all the information needed to meet these requirements without duplicating items and without obtaining data that will never be used. Sometimes a single form is used to record all the information for a crew, but frequently the pay roll data are separate. A few cities have three forms, one for pay roll, one for equipment use, and one for performance. As a guide to the kind of information usually secured from the field forces, the following list is suggestive:

1. Date
2. Weather conditions
3. Names and pay roll numbers of employees
4. Names of foremen
5. Class of service (garbage, ashes, rubbish, etc.)
6. District number or name
7. Route number
8. Location of work (when route number may not fully identify location)
9. Number of each piece of equipment used
10. Number of hours each piece of equipment is used

11. Number of hours worked by each employee
12. Kind of work (loading, stowing, driving, set-out and set-back)
13. Number of loads
14. Time for each load (loading, hauling, unproductive travel, idle)
15. Amount of refuse collected, each load (tons, cubic yards)
16. Remarks (cause of delays, breakdowns, or any unusual situation that might affect the work.)

Some cities may not require information on all these items, while others may need further data, particularly if the refuse is transferred. It is desirable, however, to separate the information needed regularly from that required for special studies and investigations. Ordinarily, the data for special analyses should be secured for short periods as the need becomes evident rather than burden the field forces with keeping records that may not be used.

When more than one class of refuse is collected, it is of course essential that the information on the use of labor and equipment and on performance be separated by classes, even though a crew may frequently shift from one collection service to another. The failure to make complete distribution of expense by class will defeat the entire reporting operation.

The daily reports of field operations are of great value to immediate supervisors of the collection system because through them they may be promptly informed of any unusual situation. Such detailed reports, however, are not ordinarily of great value to administrators until the information is properly summarized.

SUMMARY STATEMENTS OF PERFORMANCE AND COST

Much of the information made available by the field reports is required periodically for the proper administration of the operations and for public reporting purposes. To be of greatest value, however, it must be summarized, condensed, and analyzed so as to show the significant information clearly and simply. The contents and form of such statements will depend on the purpose the information is to serve and the individual desires of administrators. Officials most immediately responsible for collection operations are interested primarily in over-all unit costs and over-all performance. Others want to know regularly the comparative performance and efficiency for each crew, route, or district. In some cities separate statements are made for route analyses and for over-all comparisons.

Summaries of Performance

Performance data are normally summarized daily and the information made available to supervisors at various levels as early as practicable the following day. Preferably the summaries will show the performance of each crew in man-hours per ton or per cubic yard and will indicate the class of refuse collected. Sometimes the information is more meaningful if it is summarized by routes or by districts. Equipment utilization should also be summarized daily on the same report.

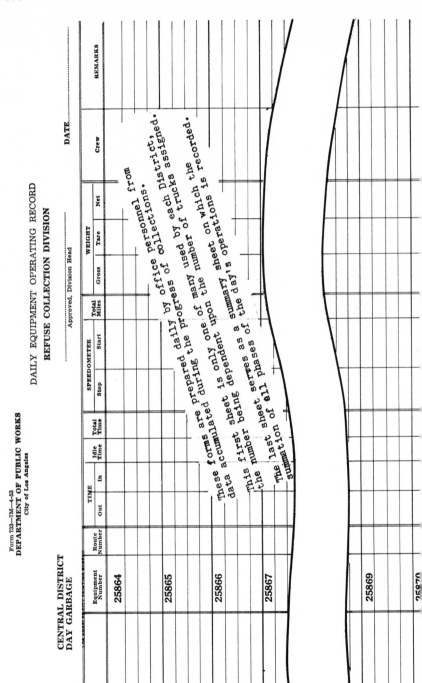

FIG. 15-5. In Los Angeles, a daily equipment operating record is kept for each collection vehicle by the refuse collection division. A summation of all phases of the day's operation is recorded on the last sheet.

Very large cities usually prepare a separate summary report for each district or other major division; other municipalities ordinarily make a single report for the entire operation. In the event more than one daily summary report is made, a summary for the entire city is necessary.

Performance reports should also be prepared for longer periods to permit comparison with past periods. They may be made on a weekly, monthly, or annual basis, depending on the needs of the supervisors and administrators. A customary practice is to develop daily, monthly, and annual summaries. The monthly performance reports permit useful comparisons among the various crews as well as with previous months and with the same month of the previous year. If monthly unit cost reports are prepared, however, the two summaries are usually combined into a single report.

Summaries of Unit Costs

Unit cost summaries are usually prepared monthly and accumulated annually to produce yearly ratios. The unit cost for each activity—such as garbage collection, rubbish collection, and set-out and set-back service—is reported for each crew, each district, and the entire city in terms of cost per ton or cost per cubic yard. Monthly performance data is frequently added to monthly cost summaries to give a more complete analysis.

The complete summary reports should be forwarded each month to each supervisor. Condensed summary reports are valuable to administrators and officials concerned more with general management than with routine operations.

Statements showing the monthly performance of the various crews have proved effective in several cities in stimulating competition among the operating units. Usually, performance and cost ratios are listed, and the reports are posted conspicuously on bulletin boards at employee assembly points.

Annual summaries of the consolidated monthly statements are prepared for public information and for budgeting purposes. Special summary reports may also be made to show information required to plan route adjustments and revise schedules. In some cities, several different bases of measurement are prepared and kept up to date to help determine trends and forecast expenditures, amount of work, and costs.

Performance and cost statements are the basis for critical and scientific evaluation of refuse collection operations. A knowledge of the comparative efficiency of the whole operation as well as of districts and crews is impossible without well prepared summary statements.

COST ACCOUNTING FOR REFUSE COLLECTION

The purpose of cost accounting as applied to refuse collection is to assemble the various expenditures by class of refuse, district, crew, route, or kind of work so that production efficiency and effort can be measured and evaluated. Most of the information on expenditures for

ROUTE SUMMARY OF REFUSE COLLECTION

City of _____
Department of Public Works

Month_____

Day	ROUTE					ROUTE					ROUTE				
	Labor Hours	Equip No.	Equip Hours	Lbs.	Miles	Labor Hours	Equip No.	Equip Hours	Lbs.	Miles	Labor Hours	Equip No.	Equip Hours	Lbs.	Miles
27															
28															
29															
30															
31															
1															
25															
26															
Tot.															

	Cost			Cost			Cost	
	Monthly	Per Ton		Monthly	Per Ton		Monthly	Per Ton
Labor $	_____	_____	Labor $	_____	_____	Labor $	_____	_____
Equip.$	_____	_____	Equip.$	_____	_____	Equip.$	_____	_____
Total $	_____	_____	Total $	_____	_____	Total $	_____	_____

	Tons Per			Tons Per			Tons Per	
Labor Hr.	_____	Mile_____	Labor Hr.	_____	Mile_____	Labor Hr.	_____	Mile_____
Equip Hr.	_____		Equip Hr.	_____		Equip Hr.	_____	

COST ANALYSIS OF REFUSE COLLECTION ROUTES

City of _____
Department of Public Works

Week
For Month Ending_____

Route No. (1)	Kind and Capacity of Equipment (2)	Men in Crew (3)	Labor & Equip. Cost (4)	Tons (5)	Cost per Ton (6)	Labor Cost per Ton (7)	Equip. Cost per Ton (8)	Tons per Mile (9)	No. House-holds per mi. (10)

INSTRUCTIONS: This analysis is prepared from the monthly route summary. Its purpose is to furnish a route comparison of work and costs. Copies go to the superintendent of refuse collection and the director of public works.

FIG. 15-6. A monthly route summary is an accepted means of summarizing collection costs by routes. Entries are made daily from daily route reports. Thus, comparisons can be made among the several crews, and inefficiencies or unequal work loads can be known at once.

FIG. 15-7. This figure provides a convenient summary of collection costs by route. It is posted directly from Fig. 15-6. This is not a complete cost statement because it ignores supplies and overhead expense. However, labor and equipment are the major charges in collection work and are satisfactory for route studies.

REFUSE COLLECTION WORK AND COST STATEMENT

City of _____
Department of Public Works

For Month.......... August, 1956

Operation (1)	Standard Work Units (2)	Work Program Estimate (3)	Work Units Collected				Production Ratios			
			Actual Units Done (4)	Over(+) Under(-) (5)	This Year To Date (6)	Last Year To Date (7)	Men Hours (8)	Units per Man Hour (9)	Equipment Hours (10)	Units per Equipment Hour (11)
Garbage Collection	Tons	1500	1642.17	+142.17	2779.67	2992	5567	.295	2783-1/2	.589
Haul to Hog Farm	Tons	1500	1642.17	+142.17	2779.67	2992	747-3/4	2.196	665-1/4	2.468
Tin Can Collection	Cu.Yds	2465	1837 1/3	-627 2/3	3743 1/3	4736	1446	1.27	1077	1.706
Ash Collection	Cu.Yds									
Dead Animal Collection	No. of	600	649	+49	1276	1147	249	2.606	259	2.506
Landfill Maintenance	Cu.Yds	2465	1837 1/3	-627 2/3	3743 1/3	4736	220	8.35		

Operation (1)	Unit Cost			Total Cost			
	Unit Cost Standard (12)	Actual (13)	Over (+) Under(-) (14)	Work Program Estimate (15)	Actual This Month (16)	This Year to Date (17)	Last Year to Date (18)
Garbage Collection	2.94	2.53	- .41	4420.10	4154.00	7739.74	7703.93
Haul to Hog Farm	.45	.342	- .108	675.00	562.75	936.39	1281.64
Tin Can Collection	.505	.558	+.053	1245.65	1026.05	1873.16	3303.26
Ash Collection							
Dead Animal Collection		.233		133.00	151.28	250.61	284.07
Landfill Maintenance		.059		123.00	109.39	216.05	283.11

NOTE: Copies are submitted to the director of public works and superintendent of refuse collection.

FIG. 15-8. A monthly work and cost statement gives a useful picture of refuse collection operations by comparing the actual results with work program estimates and also with figures from the past year.

the various operations, jobs, and organization units is obtained from the field reports, although the overhead expenses are largely compiled from invoices and pay rolls.

It is apparent that all expenses applicable to the collection of refuse must be charged to the class of refuse, crew, route, or district for which costs are being compiled. If any part of the expense is omitted from the computations, the resulting cost figures will be unreliable and sometimes misleading.

For cost accounting purposes, refuse collection expenses are usually classified in four elements: (1) personal services, (2) equipment, (3) supplies and materials, and (4) overhead. The expense for supplies and materials is negligible, usually limited to expenditures for tools, carrying tubs, protective clothing, and supplies for shelters which cannot easily be charged to particular operations and are therefore ordinarily included with overhead. If the field reports are carefully prepared, little difficulty should be experienced in allocating direct labor charges.

It is practically impossible to make accurate charges for equipment unless rental rates have been established, as described in Chapter 14. Under the rental plan, charges are made to operations simply by applying the rental rate for the particular item of equipment for the number of hours of use as shown by the field reports. Without such a plan, it is necessary to include in the cost accounts all of the component expenses of operating the equipment, including fuel, tires, repairs, storage, insurance, and depreciation. It is obvious that these expenses cannot be accurately allocated unless a particular piece of equipment is used full time in collecting one class of refuse, by one crew, and on one route. Just as soon as any division of cost between two routes or classes is attempted, it is necessary to estimate and guess how to divide repair, fuel, or other items. If cost accounting is to be accurate, a rental system is a practical necessity.

Some refuse collection expense cannot easily or accurately be divided among the organization units, kinds of work, or classes of refuse. Normally such expenses are from 4 to 10 per cent of the total cost of the work, and are grouped as overhead. The main items included in overhead are: personal services of administrators, staff officers, and supervisors; operating expense of shelters, locker rooms, and assembly places; office expense; and small tools. Overhead is not charged day by day to the individual cost accounts, but is usually distributed monthly, in proportion to the labor expense. Sometimes overhead expense is omitted from refuse collection cost accounts because it is less tangible than direct labor and equipment expenses, but its inclusion is essential for completeness and accuracy. Without overhead, the effect of supervision and clerical expense on the whole activity would not be taken into account. Total unit cost is also necessary for some analyses, such as comparing one method with another, or comparing one district with another.

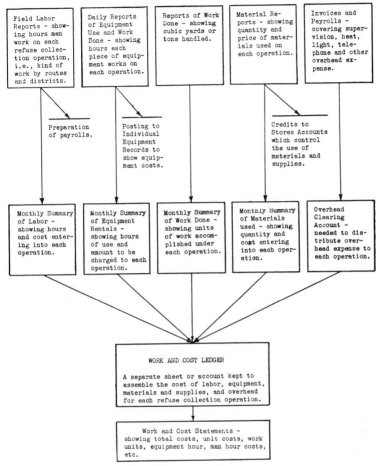

FIG. 15-9. A flow chart of daily summary reports of refuse collection activities. The steps in the cost accounting procedure are shown graphically.

Cost accounting operations should be performed by the central finance department or accounting unit that keeps the budgetary accounts because they can be performed more effectively and with less cost and can be more easily coordinated with the other fiscal records of the city. When proper cooperation cannot be secured, it may be necessary to establish a cost accounting office for the department in which refuse collection is allocated, or at times for the refuse collection agency itself. Wherever the cost accounts are kept, however, the system should be designed to provide for regular reconciliation with the general accounts of the municipality.

PREPARING WORK PROGRAMS

The use of field reports and cost data in planning refuse collection operations is discussed at some length in Chapter 7. There it is shown that the whole process of selecting methods and equipment, laying out routes, and establishing schedules is based on data on actual operations and on carefully prepared analyses and summaries of such data. The same information is invaluable in the development of accurate work programs, in making satisfactory budget estimates, and in conducting sound expenditure control.

Four main steps are involved in the development of work programs for refuse collection operations:

1. Estimating the growth of population and the additional properties to be served in order to know the total probable work load.

2. Forecasting the amount of each kind of work required to collect refuse in accordance with prescribed policies and in accordance with the methods that are shown to be most efficient.

3. Establishing unit costs to be used to translate the forecasted work into estimated expenditures.

4. Consolidating the forecasted work, costs, and expenditures into a comprehensive program which will show for each class of refuse, each kind of work, and each district and route the amount of work necessary and the total cost.

Forecasting the Amount of Work

The plan for conducting refuse collection operations shows in detail the number of collection routes, and for each route, the number and size of crews and the kind and amount of equipment needed to remove the refuse at a predetermined frequency. In other words, in preparing the plan of operation there is always created an accurate forecast of the amount of work that must be done and the amount of labor and equipment required to do it. Obviously such plans must be kept up to date to reflect expansion and increased service if they are to be usable as guides to the total work load.

The form or arrangement of the forecast of work will depend largely on the internal organization, the number of separations of refuse, and the plan for organizing the crews. Usually the main division is made by class of refuse, although in some cities there has to be a separation by districts before a breakdown by class of refuse can be effected. Under each class of refuse it is customary to list the routes laid out for the particular separation and show for each route the number of tons of material that will be collected during each month of the ensuing year and the total amount for the year. The records of past performance prepared from field reports provide a sound basis for determining quantities. If no change in the extent or kind of service is expected, the current quantities and the performance ratios may be used safely. If any changes are expected that will affect the work load or the performance ratio, studies should be made in order to estimate as accurately as practicable the expected changes.

DETAILED FORECAST OF REFUSE REMOVAL WORK

Prepared by _____   For Year Ending _____ 19 __

Route Number	Location of Routes			Frequency of Collection	Number of Stops	Miles in Route	Anticipated Quantities		
	Street or Alley	From	To				Cubic Yards	Tons	Miles Haul

CONSOLIDATED WORK PROGRAM

Department of Public Works   For Year Ending _____ 19 __

Operation	Standard Work Units	Total No. of Work Units for Year	Unit Cost Standard	Total Estimated Cost for Year	January		February	
					Work Units	Cost	Work Units	Cost
1. Garbage Collection	Tons							
2. Haul to Hog Farm	Tons							
Etc.								

FIG. 15-10. Forms used in the preparation of the annual work program for refuse collection. The upper form summarizes by routes the forecasted amount of refuse that will have to be handled during the ensuing year. The bottom form is used to summarize the work and costs for all activities and to show the distribution by months.

Determining Standard Costs

Perhaps the most critical part of preparing work programs is establishing standard unit costs to use in translating forecasted work into estimated expenditures. Unless accurate costs of existing operations are known, it is practically impossible to determine these costs with sufficient accuracy to give the work program any validity. If such costs are known, however, sound predictions can be made, as has been demonstrated by many cities. The unit cost of past and present work must, of course, be adjusted to reflect changing conditions. Changes that are known to have occurred since the unit cost figures were produced can be calculated exactly and the accuracy of the figures will not be destroyed. Allowing for changes in labor or equipment rates for the future period necessarily involves some margin of error, particularly when market conditions are unsettled. However, if some study is given to trends, adjustments can be made with reasonable accuracy.

Consolidating Forecasts and Costs

There are two general forms for preparing work programs, one primarily for controlling operations; the other for controlling expenditures. The first arrangement consists of adding columns for unit cost and total cost to the forecast of performance. Such a program will then show for each route the total estimated cost for refuse removal for the year and for each month of the year. Also, totals of groups of routes will show such totals for each district and for each class of refuse.

The second arrangement lists estimated expenditures, classified by elements of expense for budget and budget control purposes. Such a classification, however, is normally made only by districts and by classes of refuse, and therefore this may be arranged to serve both as a summary and to show the breakdown into personal services, equipment, and overhead. The summary statement, to serve as a budget estimate, should also show the actual expenditure for the previous year for each class of refuse and each district, as well as the estimated expenditures for the current year based on actual expenses to date and the work program forecasts.

Changes in Work Programs

The work program may be changed several times before it becomes a working plan for the year. The original program and summary serve to support the budget request and are usually presented to the budget authorities as a justification of the amount requested. The budget authority, in the process of examining the requests and preparing the whole municipal budget, will probably make some changes, and additional adjustment may be made by the legislature when the appropriation ordinance is passed.

When the amount of the appropriation is determined, the entire work program must be revised if the funds made available do not equal the expenditure called for by the forecast. Ordinarily, adjustments that have been made represent decisions as to the character and the amount of work that is to be undertaken. These changes can be readily made in the program. Sometimes, however, the appropriation is cut or increased arbitrarily and without guidance as to what curtailment in service should be made. This makes the adjustment of the program more difficult and sometimes involves reconstructing much of the plan of operation to conform to the funds made available. During the year additional changes will usually have to be made in the program to take care of emergencies and unusual situations.

BUDGETARY CONTROL

A refuse collection agency must conduct its operations so that the work can be done in accordance with adopted policies and plans and within the amount appropriated by the legislature. The official in charge of the refuse collection activity is usually held accountable for operating the service within the budgeted amount. The work program, as revised to fit the funds made available, is the basis for financial control as well as for spreading the work in accordance with seasonal requirements. Monthly or quarterly allotments are usually set up for each class of refuse or for each district in the amount anticipated in the work program for the particular months. The relation of the allotments to the monthly expenditures is shown on the monthly statements. By comparing the actual expenditures with the estimated costs, as shown in the detailed program, administrators are able to know whether operations are being conducted according to plan, and, if not, where the differences occur. If the variation from the plan is appreciable, it may be necessary to revise the program for the rest of the year to insure that there will be sufficient funds to provide full service throughout the balance of the fiscal period.

DATA PROCESSING—SOLID WASTES COLLECTION APPLICATION

Electronic data processing has in recent years become one of the most significant new tools used by public works departments. While its introduction seems to have been hastened by a rapid and substantial increase in workload in other public works functions, data processing has gradually been expanded to include certain phases of municipal reporting, budgeting and accounting in the area of solid waste disposal.

Principal uses for computers and punched card equipment today seem to be in the areas of program cost reporting, the measurement of individual collection performance, the development of significant projections of service costs and levels and, of course, customer billing for services rendered.

With careful design, for example, a Daily Collection Report for each crew or vehicle can provide the basic data on:

1. Tonnage hauled (or cubic yards or both)
2. Miles traveled to disposal site
3. Identification of the site
4. Waiting time, if any
5. Number of loads hauled

This data can be punched into cards and combined on a daily or weekly basis with similar reports from other trucks or crews. The resultant comparisons can then be anlyzed in terms of both costs and crew performance, and personnel and vehicle charges can be distributed to the appropriate budgetary accounts. The computer can be used to provide bills to be rendered to contractual users of the service, if required.

The same data cards can be manipulated by disposal area to highlight peak dumping periods and also to provide projections based on the rate at which the area is being filled. If required, collection and disposal costs can also be used, in combination with zoning or land use characteristics, as a basis for evaluating the adequacy of both collection schedules and fees.

The above are just a few of the applications of data processing to the reporting, cost accounting, and budgeting for refuse collection. Research, experimentation, and actual usage is currently in process throughout the country. As the body of knowledge in this area increases and additional applications, as well as refinements of current applications, become part of everyday operating procedures, more precise and accurate management decisions will be the result.

SUMMARY

The successful management of refuse collection operations depends in a large measure on the skill exercised in planning and programming the work, and in accurately appraising and evaluating the program, performance, and efficiency. These controls and evaluations, however, rest on accurate and regular field reporting and on carefully prepared analyses and statements of performance and cost. Sound reporting and cost analysis, universally recognized as indispensable in private industry, are just as effective and necessary in municipal work. Equally satisfactory results and savings just as substantial can be realized.

chapter 16

PUBLIC RELATIONS

Because refuse removal forces are in constant contact with the citizens, they are in an excellent position to demonstrate the public relations policy of the local government. Furthermore, as citizens understand the difficulties confronted by the collection forces and recognize a genuine desire to provide satisfactory service, their cooperation will be secured.

The term "public relations" has been mistakenly used as a synonym for publicity. While publicity is a valid and necessary means of bringing about good public relations, it is not the decisive element on which good relations are built. Public approval and good will follow the realization that public services are being rendered efficiently and that public employees are competent, willing, and pleasant.

It is essential, however, that citizens be aware of the sincere desire of public officials to render good service at low cost and, through such an understanding, recognize the need for municipal regulation and the advantages of citizen cooperation. The achievement of these ends depends on the entire governmental organization, from the mayor and council down to the smallest operating unit.

A program of public relations encompasses the policies of the municipal government; it depends on the competence and efficiency of the administration; and it is furthered and developed by the enlightenment and education of the public. Public relations include everything done by government. No act is too small or too large not to be viewed as an integral part of the program.

POLICIES OF THE MUNICIPAL GOVERNMENT

The chief executive of the city and the members of the city council foster the municipal activities they believe the people want. The scope and extent of the refuse collection ordinance determine and are determined by the temper and attitude of the public. If the individual citizen does not believe that he is adequately protected from a public health standpoint, if he does not believe he gets full measure for his tax dollar, his disapproval, however voiced, will operate to the disadvantage of the administration as well as of the refuse collection service.

Council decisions as to the money to be expended for the various government services have a direct bearing on public relations. Somewhere in the process of evolving policies resulting in refuse appropriations, information should be furnished to those responsible, as well as to the public, regarding the implications of limitations on services provided. Failure to make available some means of disposal for wastes normally produced must surely lead to problems involving inconvenience and irritation to the householder and untidy or unsanitary environments because of accumulations on his premises or of clandestine dumping and littering of highways and vacant properties.

When the public and the legislators alike recognize the problems faced by collection agencies and the consequences of inadequate service, sufficient funds are more likely to be appropriated. Failure to win the support of the people, on the other hand, may result in such drastic curtailment that the regularity of the service is interrupted or the scope or collection frequency is reduced. The inevitable result is public antagonism.

INFLUENCES OF PERSONNEL PRACTICES

The caliber of the people employed by the municipality, the quality of their performance, and their attitudes and manner are closely related to the public's reaction to their city government. The role of the refuse collection agency is particularly important. The idea that anyone can be a refuse collector, that only those unsuccessful in other fields will do the job, must be eliminated wherever it exists. When the refuse collection service is hamstrung by political appointments, a nonmerit system, and rapid turnover among the personnel, it is almost impossible for the individual refuse collector or the public to respect the job or the service.

The manner in which refuse collection personnel are chosen is bound to make a very definite impression on the public and on the employee himself. As reported in Chapter 12, the 1964 survey conducted by the American Public Works Association found that only 154 cities, out of a total of 637 reporting, placed all refuse collection employees on a civil service status. Of these 154 cities, 85 were of a population of less than 50,000.

While the form and content of applicant examination need not be discussed here, the atmosphere in which the examinations are given, the attitude of examiners, and the facilities provided all need to be considered from the point of view of public relations. Most cities do not provide a written or oral examination for common laborer, but the mere fact that a physical examination must be passed tends to give some prestige to the service. When the examinations are accompanied by effective publicity, public attitudes are often channeled along favorable lines.

The various aspects of employee relations all have their public relations importance. Vacations, sick leave, hours of work, and physical surroundings all affect the conditions of service. Handling garbage cans every day is not the most pleasant occupation, and for the sake of morale the task must be surrounded with such attractions as can be devised. If grumbling and discontent are allowed to make headway among the workers, the critical attention of the public is soon drawn to the service.

Various devices have been used to raise or maintain employee morale at a fairly high level. Credit unions, safety measures and instruction, recreation programs, and library facilities have been set up for employees. Opportunities are given, either to the workers individually or in group meetings, to criticize present practices and make suggestions for improvement. Open forum meetings, suggestion boxes, and even questionnaires are among the devices used to obtain employee support and suggestions. When the criticism and suggestions issue from the employees themselves, the service benefits more than when they come from the public or are imposed from above by the administration. Moreover, the refuse collection employees are in a good position to get ideas from the public and if helpful suggestions are acted upon by the administrators, much public criticism can be overcome before it acquires general circulation.

EMPLOYEE CONTACTS WITH CITIZENS

In the eyes of the citizen every public employee represents the city, so what any employee does is of vital importance to the maintenance of good public relations. The refuse collection service must be particularly sensitive to its public relations role since few city departments have so many personal contacts with citizens.

Training for Contacts

It is generally conceded that refuse collectors should undergo some training in public relations, but the manner and form of such training have been left to conjecture. Some cities have prepared public relations handbooks for all municipal employees, giving practical advice on telephone procedure, meeting visitors, handling complaints, writing letters, driving habits, and other activities that can make or break municipal public relations.

Group lectures, formal classes, manuals of practice, and personal instruction have all proved to be effective public relations training devices. Of course both the size of the city and the refuse collection force affects the way the instruction is given. Demonstrations before groups of employees of right and wrong tactics and attitudes are of great assistance to collectors as well as to foremen, inspectors, and supervisors. In smaller cities, such methods may not be feasible. Of necessity, most of the training must be given by the officials in charge of the activity. One excellent means consists in stating clearly the municipal public relations policy and then presenting in the form of rules the satisfactory and unsatisfactory ways of dealing with particular situations. Probably the most successful training method is through personal instruction. An official may accompany a supervisor, foreman, or inspector when he goes to answer complaints received by the department. In the same way, foremen and supervisors may counsel with truck drivers or collectors when errors in approach or conduct in public contacts are observed. These methods are not restricted to small communities. They are just as effective in the largest cities. Their successful use, however, depends on the ability of supervisory officials to instruct and their understanding of public relations techniques.

Personal Contacts

The training of an employee for the performance of a task and the actual performance itself are but two sides of a single activity. Training is never complete; the good employee can, and will, learn something new from each succeeding experience. The broad outlines of policy can be carefully worked out, but the action within that framework must be determined in large part by the employee himself.

Individual citizens and the members of the refuse collection service often come into direct contact with one another. Whether these contacts are slight in nature or time consuming, opportunity is present for the collectors to build good will. The kind of impression left by an incapable public servant is all too evident. If the employee is slow to respond, seems to lack interest, is poorly informed, slovenly in appearance, or generally not helpful, the citizen is likely to conclude that he is typical of the municipal service.

It cannot be expected that refuse collectors combine the bearing of military men and the skill of salesmen but some elements of both must be present. When traveling along the collection route or answering a summons from a citizen, the employee who slouches and gives the appearance of extreme weariness is giving the city an unfavorable name. The worker who looks presentable, is courteous, and answers in clear and definite terms whatever queries are put to him—even explaining to the citizen that the nature of his request or demand is outside his authority—will leave that citizen with the idea that his tax dollar is being spent in a businesslike manner.

The ability to answer questions should be cultivated, if not in every member of the service, in at least some members of each collection crew. It is always more effective to settle any controversy amicably and equitably on the spot rather than go through some tedious, time-consuming process. Sometimes a copy of the ordinance or the refuse collection rules and regulations, together with any other information pertaining to the service, can be made available to each crew in a form permitting easy location of answers to citizen questions. Some cities summarize refuse collection rules and practices on cards for placement in a convenient location in the home. The duties and obligations of the refuse collector should be carefully defined and the rights and obligations of the individual citizen should be outlined. Thus, when the occasion demands, the answer to the controversy and the status of all parties concerned are soon determined.

Some cities delegate to inspectors the authority to adjust controversies and to explain possible difficulties. In many communities the supervisors or superintendents of the service combine such public relations work with their other duties. The selection of these individuals should be made very definitely with an eye toward furthering amicable public relations. Here again, considerations of appearance, manner of treating the citizen, and the ability to explain the why of the service and to answer questions about the employee's own department and other city activities are important.

FIG. 16-1. A uniformed district superintendent in the Sanitation Department of New York City. The relations between the citizens and the municipal government will be improved in any community if the refuse removal employees are neat and presentable. The identification provided by the uniform and badge also is of value, particularly for employees who answer complaints or otherwise operate separately from the regular equipment and crews.

Contacts through Correspondence

While most of the contacts between citizens and the refuse collection service are face to face, there are also those who have contact with the service through correspondence. Each request for information should receive a prompt and courteous reply. It should be "personal" in tone rather than like a legal code. Each written inquiry should be routed immediately to the official best equipped to answer it, and everyone responsible for handling inquiries must be properly trained.

Contacts by Telephone

The opinions that citizens form of the city service from telephone inquiries and conversations with individual employees are also important from a public relations standpoint. First of all, physical facilities must be adequate to receive and distribute calls without confusing and irritating delays. The equipment of the city should make it possible for a citizen to reach the proper branch of the municipal service quickly and easily. Tact, courtesy, and helpfulness are the essentials of telephone contacts. Therefore the greatest care should be exercised in selecting and training telephone operators and others who answer inquiries by phone.

If the city has a central information bureau, telephone calls should be routed there so as not to disturb employees whose time can be used for more important matters. Enough information as to routine operation, rules, schedules, and the like can be available so that the more frequent requests can be answered without calling in someone from the collection service.

In smaller cities, or in cities having no central information bureau, the telephone operator should be supplied with enough information of a routine type so as not to interfere unduly with her work and yet take some of the burden from the shoulders of the administrators. When the operator cannot answer a question she should be able to connect the inquirer with the person in the service who has been delegated to reply to such queries.

HANDLING COMPLAINTS

While much of what has been said about handling requests for information applies equally to the treatment of complaints, the latter merit special consideration because of their importance in public relations. Complaints furnish an indication of the success of the city's service program and offer the refuse collection service an opportunity to create good will for the city.

Good complaint procedure involves four principal stages: (1) receiving the complaint; (2) assignment of responsibility for investigation and correction; (3) follow-up; and (4) notification of correction.

The attitude of the public employee receiving the complaint is of particular importance because the citizen filing the complaint is seldom in the best of temper. Tactless employees, or those who like to argue, are not suited to dealing with the public in such situations.

Clear lines of authority or appeal should be established for complaint matters. While most complaints are of a routine nature and can be handled by subordinates, some require a higher decision and should automatically be brought to the attention of the proper officials. When this is done the citizen has the feeling that the city is actually looking after his interests.

Some cities have found that the public likes to deal with a central complaint office which serves all city departments. Any uncertainty as to where complaints should be filed is thus eliminated and it is possible to make one person responsible for following up and reporting on all complaints. In the larger cities, however, it may be advisable for the

Name of Complainant

REFUSE COMPLAINT REPORT
Department of Public Works and Utilities
FLINT, MICHIGAN

Address

Date_____ Time_____ a.m. / p.m.

Garbage_____ Ashes_____ Tin Cans_____
1—Failure To Collect_____ DEAD ANIMALS
2—Spilled Refuse_____ Animal_____
3—Discourtesy_____ Breed_____
4—Cover Not Replaced_____ Sex_____
5—Special Service Request_____ Color_____
6—Misc._____ License_____
Detail of Complaint_____

Regular Route Collector

See back of report for disposition of complaint (state nature and action).
This form is prepared in duplicate.
First copy goes to investigator.   Signed_____
Must be returned.   *Investigator*
FORM P. W. 50

FIG. 16-2. Refuse complaint report, Flint, Michigan. Prepared in duplicate, the first copy goes to the investigator and is returned with a report on disposition of the complaint on the back.

refuse collection service to have its own complaint bureau. Whichever method is employed, the lines of authority should be so clearly marked that the chief executive of the system has direct knowledge that citizen complaints are being investigated and handled promptly.

Various forms are in use to insure that the information received is forwarded to the proper person to investigate a complaint and simplify follow-up procedures. The forms make it possible to analyze the causes and the types of complaints for measuring the effectiveness of the service. Such complaint report forms ordinarily are in triplicate, a copy being dispatched to the investigator, to the superintendent or to the office of the district supervisor, and one copy remaining on file at the complaint bureau. The form is designed for noting subsequent action taken.

As soon as the complaint is received, it should be referred promptly to the appropriate agency or person and an investigation should be made without delay. It is here that the advantages of radio communication can best be exploited for public relations purposes. Regardless of the final disposition, the householder who has just filed a complaint by telephone can hardly fail to be impressed by the efficiency of an organization which has a representative at the house within a few minutes. If a careful investigation reveals the complaint to be unfounded or if the cause cannot be corrected, the complainant should be so advised and a report should be made stating the situation in clear, concise terms. Otherwise the grievance should be quickly corrected so as not to aggravate the citizen's sense of injury. Prompt and smooth procedure which keeps the complainant fully informed is a decided asset in the public relations program.

In addition to noting the action taken, the investigators in some cities secure the signatures of the complainants to indicate that the trouble has been satisfactorily remedied or the service supplied. The copy of the report at the central complaint bureau remains on a pending file for control purposes and is not filed permanently until the investigator's copy is returned. The disposition of the case should also be noted on the copy of the report kept at the field office.

In some cities the notification procedure is less elaborate. The same ends can be served by a letter directed to the complaining citizen; or a postcard or a telephone call stating the action taken may suffice. Whatever measures are taken to notify the citizens are well repaid from a public relations standpoint. This step climaxes the whole complaint procedure for it serves notice to the citizen that his government is looking out for his rights and interests.

To ascertain the trend and cause of complaints, reports should be analyzed periodically. Monthly analyses are desirable to show the total number of complaints for the month and to classify their causes. In addition, a distribution by district, crew, or route serves to keep administrative officers advised and help them take necessary remedial action.

The segregation of justified from unjustified complaints is of significance if it is done impartially, for it separates the complaints which the city cannot prevent from those for which it is to blame. The number of justified complaints is usually a good index of citizen satisfaction with the refuse collection service.

It is effective to see that the monthly analyses come to the attention of the refuse collection personnel as an indication of citizen opinion of the service and as a possible means for forestalling future complaints of a similar nature.

GOOD RELATIONS THROUGH EFFECTIVE OPERATION

Effective and economical operation of the refuse collection system is one of the best ways to gain the good will and approval of the citizens. This may call for the careful training of employees in the proper ways of doing their work, thus eliminating many complaints and promoting better public relations. Over 80 per cent of the 637 cities reporting to the American Public Works Association in the 1964 survey said that they had no organized training programs for collection crews.

MONTHLY ANALYSIS OF WASTE COMPLAINTS
and
MISCELLANEOUS SERVICES

City of Flint
Department of Public Works & Utilities
Division of Waste Collection & Disposal — For the Month of

JUSTIFIED COMPLAINTS		
1. Collector failed to stop		
2.		
3.		
4.		
5.		
TOTAL JUSTIFIED		
UNJUSTIFIED COMPLAINTS		
6. Information wanted		
7. New householder		
8. Request for special service		
9.		
10.		
TOTAL UNJUSTIFIED		
MISCELLANEOUS SERVICES		
Dead Animal removed		
Special services requested		

COMPARISON OF COMPLAINTS

	This Month	Last Month	This Year	Last Year
Justified				
Unjustified				
Total				

FIG. 16-3. Monthly analysis of waste complaints, Flint, Michigan. This analysis is prepared monthly in the waste collection office from the complaint form shown in Fig. 16-2. Copies are sent to the City Manager and Director of Public Works.

Citizens are especially perturbed if the containers they provide are not handled with care. If they are slammed against the collection vehicle, knocked against other containers, or thrown to the ground after they are emptied, they stand a good chance of being damaged. If such treatment is continued, a new container becomes necessary, and a feeling of ill will toward the collection agency is engendered in the householder.

The spilling of offensive refuse cannot always be avoided when containers or vehicles are overloaded, but any spilled matter should be carefully and completely removed. No trespassing of private property for reasons not in the line of duty should be tolerated, and the collectors must be taught that lawns are to be admired and not to be walked upon.

Collection at night or in the early morning hours also raises certain problems that must be overcome by training. Here the elimination of noise is especially important. While it is impossible to collect refuse without some noise, the amount can be greatly reduced through the careful examination of operations and training of the employees. The language and the tone of voice used by the workers should also be given consideration. This is sometimes a serious problem, for the collectors often have little education and the work is not exactly conducive to soft language. The problem becomes even more acute when refuse collection occurs at night. Then noises are not blended with the general hubbub of a city's daytime activity, but stand out by themselves and often travel a long distance.

Citizens usually associate the collection of refuse with the idea of uncleanliness—a negative picture which may be the only one presented. To substitute a different picture, the idea of cleanliness must first be instilled into the habits and thoughts of the refuse collection personnel. A start in this direction can be made by discussing the personal appearance of the collecting force. Nothing is more offensive to the eye and nose than a costume showing evidences of previous collections. The experience of some cities and of many private businesses has been that to furnish uniforms, laundered at frequent intervals, for workers doing even the most disagreeable jobs, goes a long way toward relieving the stigma attached to such tasks. The American Public Works Association, in 1964, found that 213 cities out of 637 reporting required uniforms for collection crews. In 165 cases, uniforms were furnished by the city. Even if uniforms are not worn, some clean, standardized piece of apparel can be used to serve much the same ends.

The cleanliness principle should also apply to the refuse collection equipment. It may be good public relations technique to keep the vehicles freshly painted in colors that suggest cleanliness, even though it costs a little more money. In many cities collection vehicles are unattractive either through lack of paint or the use of colors disturbing to the eye. But paint alone will not prevent an obnoxious appearance, and the collection equipment must be cleaned often in order to remove dirt, particles of refuse, and unpleasant odors. The method and frequency of such cleansing can be brought to the attention of the employee during the training process.

The impression which city equipment makes on the citizens depends on its use as well as on its appearance. A reckless driver or "road hog" is not liked under any circumstances, but if he is driving a municipal vehicle his offense is magnified. Those in charge of the training program should insist that operators of refuse collection vehicles be exemplary in courtesy and safety on the road. The provisions of all related laws should be followed not only to promote safety but also to provide an example for the townspeople. Arguing with others as to the right of way, trying to "beat" the stoplights, and double parking which may lead to hazardous traffic conditions, should not be permitted.

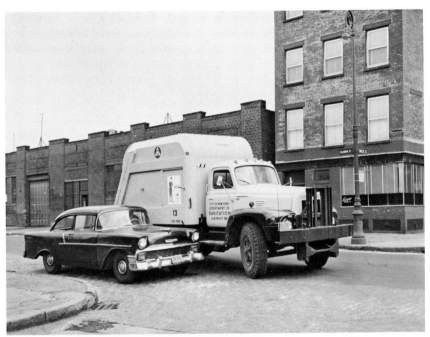

FIG. 16-4. As a part of the training program of the drivers of the refuse collection trucks in New York, demonstrations of right and wrong driving practices are given. This illustration shows a demonstration of an improper right turn. Many public officials believe that the drivers in the municipal service should set an example in safe driving and further believe that public relations can be greatly improved if these drivers are courteous to others using the streets and implicitly obey all traffic regulations.

PUBLIC EDUCATION

The good intentions of conscientious officials to render the best possible refuse collection service, within the limits of budgetary provisions, are frequently thwarted by the carelessness and indifference of citizens and their disregard for even the simplest rules of cleanliness and sanitation. This situation is reflected in littered streets, alleys, parks, vacant lots, and even private premises, tending to produce a slovenly appearance throughout the community and a general lowering of civic pride.

While ordinances, rules, and regulations, with penalties for their violation, have their rightful place in the refuse collection and disposal plan, their enforcement appears to leave much to be desired. This laxness may be due in large measure to the impossibility of financing an enforcement program or possibly to an unwillingness or inability to use compulsion. It has been found that, as part of the public relations program, a much easier and more sensible solution is to secure the helpful cooperation of citizens through intelligent public education.

Obviously the first step in this direction is to advise them what refuse collection services are available, the schedules and rules under which the services are carried on and the obligations of the householder. Especially is this necessary for new arrivals who have no background in local customs. An effective measure to accomplish this is the practice of many cities of furnishing a "kitchen card", containing all of the pertinent information in digest form, such as is shown in Fig. 16-8. It is printed on heavy stock, punched for hanging on a hook as a permanent reminder. When first published it is furnished to all residents and thereafter distributed whenever it would seem helpful. New residents get it automatically by various means, such as when application is made for water service. For simple basic information on changes in practice, illustrated leaflets, such as that shown in Fig. 16-11 are particularly effective.

FIG. 16-5. Good public educational efforts on proper preparation and storage can produce excellent results. Not only is the street made more attractive on collection days, but the cost of refuse collection work is less.

To overcome filthy or insanitary conditions, some cities bestir themselves only once a year in spring "clean-up campaigns" in order to remove from sight the refuse which should have been collected throughout the year in the course of the regular service. Such periodic spurts are commendable in both the quantity of refuse removed and in the amount of public education accomplished. However, unless part of a continuing program, they will fall far short of the desired goal. For this reason, a number of cities look upon public education in the field of refuse collection and disposal as a continuous activity, and have permanently organized it through the cooperative efforts of the public officials and civic groups.

Cleanup campaigns have included sanitation parades and police handing out pink slips to litter offenders reading: "This is not a ticket. Next time you will get one. You are a Litterbug. Keep our city clean."

Mickey Mouse, wearing a street cleaner's uniform, has been used to decorate anti-litter literature, posters, and trash baskets, suggesting that the public keep their city clean. Boy Scouts have gathered cans, bottles, wrappers, and discarded food, placing them in an unappetizing mass in a store window, while a similar exhibit was labeled "Does Any of This Belong to You?" Many such techniques have been employed to maintain continued year-round interest in a cleaner city program.

The "Keep America Beautiful" organization has done an outstanding job of preparing publicity releases and materials for use in all media. These are available to cities and constitute a very useful source of ideas and materials for any effort along this line.

An appropriate opportunity for initiating or especially emphasizing a program of public education is in connection with National Public Works Week when there is a wide-spread and concerted effort to call attention to all public works activities.

Organization for Public Education

City-wide organizations for the purpose of making the public "clean city" conscious usually receive from the outset the official sanction and help of the municipal administration. In fact, several legislative and administrative officials may become active members, to provide liaison with the city departments engaged in street cleaning and refuse collection and disposal.

Membership in such a group most often is recruited from civic clubs, churches, Boy Scout troops, Chambers of Commerce, women's clubs, and similar organizations. Often prominent citizens, including both professional and business leaders, are also solicited to assist in the educational program. After the preliminary recruitment stage has been completed, with all the various groups and interests represented, the organization is put on a permanent basis by the adoption of the customary constitution and by-laws to set forth its purpose and govern its activities. It is then in a position to formulate a definite program of education and publicity.

Newspaper campaigns. Public education through the press is frequently very valuable, especially at the start of a new system of refuse collection or when changes are made in existing services. Otherwise, periodic news releases to the local papers, prepared articles on various phases of the refuse collection and disposal service, photographs of good and bad practices, human interest stories about the personnel, and similar information prepared in attractive and popular style go a long way toward increasing the public's knowledge of what has to be done

FIG. 16-6. Among the many kinds of public education materials distributed by the "Keep America Beautiful" organization are car cards such as the one shown here.

to provide good refuse collection service and arousing interest in having a "clean" city.

Another medium of newspaper publicity is paid display advertisements. When these are effectively composed and prominently set up, they are an excellent method of attracting public attention. If they are accompanied by news releases, they are an especially desirable means of conveying both general and specific information from the administration to the citizens.

Public reports. In many cities the progress, improvements, and problems of each municipal service are presented to the citizens in the form of periodic reports. This medium can very well be used to help educate householders. The efforts being made to provide sanitary and effective removal of refuse and to make the community more attractive can be emphasized. It may be desirable to show pictorially or describe the new methods and equipment, or to state the problems encountered and show the saving that could be realized through citizen cooperation in the preparation and storage of refuse.

Speeches, radio broadcasts and television shows. Addresses to civic groups, improvement associations, and other organizations provide another avenue to make the adult population "clean city" conscious. The same sort of material can be used through the medium of radio and television to assure still wider distribution. For radio broadcast, speakers are generally chosen from the membership of the city-wide organization which has assumed responsibility for the campaign of public education. This provides a stimulating outlet for direct participation of a considerable number of those who have shown a public interest in the problem. A short slogan and "reminders" interjected at intervals during other broadcasts pertaining to health, sanitation, or city beautification have been effectively used to supplement regularly prepared radio talks.

Many city officials are making regular television appearances on public service time programs to tell their municipal story and to seek added citizen cooperation. Competition between programs for audiences is intense, and the city television program must be interesting enough to meet such competition. Interviews and face to face speeches are common types of television programs. The refuse story may not provide a dramatic, moving script, but interest can be added through the use of hand props such as simple charts, diagrams, or maps. It is also sometimes possible to brighten up the television program with short lengths of movie film or slides. As with radio, public service spot announcements can be used on television for such campaigns as clean-up week. The only cost will be to have a good poster-type slide prepared and copy written for use along with it.

Motion pictures and color slides. Two mediums that are becoming increasingly popular in municipal circles are motion pictures and color slides. Some of the more ambitious motion picture programs have called for professional assistance and equipment, but many small cities have found that with a 16 mm. camera and a few dollars worth of film, city officials and employees can produce a report on municipal activities which is inexpensive and effective. The same can be said for color slides. Color slides can be used to excellent advantage and low cost to tell the refuse collection story. Pictures of collection practices, dump, or landfill operations on 35 mm. color film may be assembled in sequence for training new employees. Many of these same color transparencies can be shown to clubs and civic groups to illustrate the story script for talks on clean-up weeks as well as regular operations.

The refuse collection and disposal process lends itself well to such filming for its story makes a complete picture. Unlike most other municipal activities the collection of refuse can be presented in logical order from the preparation of the refuse to its ultimate disposal.

Development of a Campaign

The program to make New York City known as the world's cleanest city is included here because telling it best describes how one city drew together every possible facet of municipal public relations and coordinated them into a comprehensive and effective program. The Department of Sanitation in New York City regards municipal cleanliness as a two-sided affair, with public responsibility on the one hand and governmental responsibility on the other. The public's share of the burden is the greater, for there is no practical way that government can maintain a clean city without public cooperation.

New York City's anti-litter campaign was designed to secure its objective primarily by enlisting the public's assistance, and secondarily by employing its own forces most efficiently and effectively. To do this a plan of action was devised and followed which covered essentially the ten following phases:

1. The opening phase of the campaign was devoted to surveys and investigations—to discover what the problem really was. It was found that streets and sidewalks were being continually littered by a careless and negligent portion of the population; vacant lots and backyards were heaped with refuse that afforded breeding places for vermin and other pests; litter baskets were ignored or misused for garbage or trade waste; garbage cans were filled to overflowing, and were uncovered, insufficient or worn out; gutters were caked with dirt because the parked cars precluded access to them by the sweeper or mechanical brooms; personnel and equipment were insufficient or inadequate to cope with the problems.

2. The second phase consisted of developing plans to meet the litter problem. These plans are of a continuous nature, for when the goal of a clean city is reached, the high degree of cleanliness must be maintained. Plans were prepared with that thought in mind. Every street was classified in accordance with the type and frequency of collection and cleaning service it was to receive. The equipment on hand was checked and it was found necessary to place orders augmenting the equipment already in use. In a two-year period New York City pur-

chased 200 large mechanical sweepers, 80 passenger-car tow trucks, 50 motor flushers, and 400 escalator compactor collection trucks.

3. The third phase of the campaign dealt with the development of interdepartmental participation by other city agencies. It was recognized that activities of any one municipal department of necessity overlap with others. No department can operate successfully as a separate entity. The Mayor established a committee known as the Mayor's Department Committee for a Clean City. It is headed by the Commissioner of Sanitation as chairman and the City Administrator as executive secretary, and numbers among its members the heads of 28 city departments and agencies. These groups worked together in making general inspections, enforcing the law and ferreting out offenses and offenders. The most active departments have been the Fire, Health, Buildings, and Police—all of which have enforcement personnel and inspectional forces.

4. The fourth phase of the campaign called for the appointment of a citizen's committee by the Mayor to take active sustained interest in the clean city program. Unlike many lay committees, the Citizens' Committee for a Clean City was of the ability, power, drive, and desire to accomplish its purpose. The Committee was selected from among the leading businessmen, merchants, and public utility officials. Its organization paralleled that of the Department of Sanitation. To assure continuity, it secured a corporate charter setting it up as a nonprofit charitable and educational organization. The objectives of the Committee are:

    a. To stir and build up the pride of New Yorkers in the appearance of their city.

    b. To use all channels of education and communication to achieve its goal.

    c. To work with all city departments in their effort to take over this voluntary campaign.

    d. Upon reaching its goal, to continue work in maintaining New York as a clean city.

The Citizens' Committee secured cooperation from press, radio, and television and secured professional services for programs at no cost to the City. Messages, appeals and announcements have been made regularly over television and radio; posters have been set up in busses and subways; and groups of public spirited citizens have been organized throughout the city.

5. The fifth phase of the campaign centered around the efforts of the Department of Sanitation to secure cooperation with its own personnel. Without such cooperation, the goal of a clean city was felt to be impossible. From the monetary standpoint, it has been estimated that the value of citizen cooperation saves New York City one hundred million dollars a year—the sum which it would have been necessary to spend if sanitation habits of the public had been uncontrolled. To secure this public assistance, the Department built up an Office of Public Relations

as one of the staff functions on the Commissioner's staff. This office, consisting of 32 people, plans and continues the Department's public relations programs.

Particular emphasis has been placed upon the work of the Sanitary Education Section which is concerned primarily with the city's schools and civic, fraternal, religious, and business groups throughout the city. In 1955, approximately 1,100 school meetings, with a total attendance of 400,000 children, were arranged by members of the Sanitary Education staff. Supplementing this, approximately one million pieces of educational literature were distributed during the year to inform and instruct the people of the city, both young and old, about their obligations as citizens.

6. Appeals to civic pride and community support do not always produce desired cooperation. This led to the sixth phase of the campaign, which is one of enforcement. At the request of the Department, the Mayor and the city authorities increased the Department's inspectional force from a mere handful to an effective striking force of 300 men.

The new personnel were carefully selected from within the Department. A three-week training course was given, the curriculum consisting of orientation courses in interpretation of regulations and other enforcement procedures. Field trips under experienced instructors were included in the training for the purpose of observing and inspecting actual operating conditions.

The Department of Sanitation inspection force are uniformed personnel, and under the law are empowered to issue summonses and in extreme cases make arrests when violations of litter regulations are noted. Approximately 1,000 other sanitation officers have been appointed special patrolmen and also have this power. However, their activity is usually limited to taking action in the flagrant cases which come to their attention. In keeping with the cooperation now being received from other departments, personnel from the Police, Fire, Health Department, and some other departments are now serving summonses for violations for similar offenses.

7. The seventh phase consisted of developing a parking control program to assist street sweeping. Regulations were drawn up forbidding parking of cars on one side of the street or avenue for certain hours for three days a week and on the other side for alternate days of the week. In this manner, each curb is free of parked cars at least three times a week for street cleaning.

8. The eighth phase of the program centered around procurement and distribution of litter baskets and the posting of anti-litter warning signs. The problem caused by litter being thrown on the streets could only be solved by providing a sufficient number of litter baskets to service the need of pedestrians. It was estimated that ultimately 80,000 baskets would be required.

From those baskets already in use, it was estimated late in 1956 that approximately one million pounds of material were deposited annually in baskets each holding an average of 25 pounds. Such baskets are normally emptied by refuse collection crews on their regular routes. In special cases, however, such as on Sundays, trucks are dispatched as basket trucks and are assigned to the sole task of emptying baskets.

9. New York City's ninth step in striving for its cleanliness goal was a littered lot clean-up drive. As a result of surveys, it was disclosed that some 7,000 vacant lots were covered with litter such as garbage, papers, rags, cans, bottles, discarded furniture, and other refuse. Normally, the Department of Sanitation has no jurisdiction over property inside the building lines and so a joint project of the Department with other city agencies was organized to handle the situation.

In keeping with the public relations angle on all phases of this clean-up program, the littered lot clean-up program was the subject of an intensive educational campaign in the vicinity of all vacant lots for two weeks. Circulars were distributed to tenants, janitors, landlords; public notices were posted on the littered lots and cards were displayed in the local stores, schools, and other places. With the cooperation of the Board of Education, lot cleaning was stressed in educational talks on sanitation to school children. Included in this education campaign were city, fraternal, and other organizations who were addressed by public relations personnel of the Department of Sanitation.

10. The last phase of the clean-up program was made against that type of refuse called junk. Junk consists mainly of large bulky objects, such as worn out furniture, mattresses, bed springs, and so on which have outgrown their usefulness and which are often dumped in vacant lots at night. To meet this problem, a regular junk collection service was established.

In its beginning, there had been no intention to set up a regular junk collection service; rather, the idea was to establish a junk collection week. However, so many requests were received by the Department of Sanitation for this service that it was decided to put the activity on a year-round basis. In the first week alone, 5,396 tons of junk were picked up, requiring the employment of 160 trucks manned by 400 men.

It cannot be expected that all cities follow the same procedures used in the "action program for a clean city" in New York. However, its activities do provide a pattern for other areas with a similar problem. The importance of New York City's program does not lie solely in what was done and is being done, but how it was done. City government cannot "go it alone;" it needs the help of the public. Such help can only be achieved through an educational program, and a successful educational program, no matter where the locale, depends upon, and is a part of, good public relations, which is the theme of this chapter but which is constantly being implied in every chapter of this book.

ENFORCEMENT OF ORDINANCES AND REGULATIONS

The most effective cooperation of citizens is that obtained voluntarily through the many informative, educational and persuasive measures

HELP KEEP DETROIT CLEAN!
Courtesy Card
(PLEASE NOTE THE SQUARES CHECKED)

1 ☐ DRUM   Checked receptacle(s) should not be used for waste disposal.

2 ☐ CONCRETE Please furnish a RECEPTACLE metal container (maximum size, 27 gallons) with tight-fitting cover and handles or bails. The DRUM will be picked up if you notify the Division of Sanitation you wish to have it removed. Phone TE 2-2400. You are asked to break up the defective concrete receptacle if you wish to have it removed.

3 ☐ Please WRAP YOUR GARBAGE in several thickness of paper.

4 ☐ OVERFLOWING CONTAINERS show a need for more containers.

5 ☐ Please DO NOT MIX non-burnable with burnable waste (tin cans, bottles, etc. with paper garbage). Furnish SEPARATE CONTAINERS for each.

6 ☐ Do you know that Section 701 of our Sanitation Ordinance prohibits the depositing, or cause to be deposited, sort, scatter or leave any burnable or non-burnable wastes in any public street or alley?

The Division of Sanitation is responsible for collecting municipal waste that is properly prepared and stored. The Police Department is responsible for enforcing the Ordinance which controls the preparation and storage of wastes.

If the squares checked are taken care of, we are quite sure the Sanitary Officer of the Police Department will find no reason to issue a violation ticket.

Representative _____

Telephone: _____

DEPARTMENT OF PUBLIC WORKS
DIVISION OF SANITATION
Form C of D–848

VIOLATION TAGS FOR GARBAGE CANS

REGULATIONS FOR WASTE COLLECTION
CITY OF BISMARCK

The word "garbage" as used herein shall be construed to mean all accumulations of household waste matter including dry kitchen refuse, meat, vegetable and fruit refuse and all tin cans and bottles.

☐ 1. Garbage shall be stored in fly and water tight cans equipped with handles and tight fitting covers.

☐ 2. Cans shall be of a capacity of not less than 15 nor more than 25 gallons.

☐ 3. Cans shall be placed on suitable rack.

☐ 4. Garbage shall be thoroughly drained and wrapped in paper before placing in can.

☐ 5. Cans shall be located not more than 15 feet from serviceable alley and in areas where there is no alley they shall be made as accessible to the street as possible.

☐ 6. Material stored shall conform strictly to the term "garbage" above defined.

— — — — — — — — — — — — — — — — — — — —

Tag attached on ....194......

To..

Address..

Violation..

Signed..

FIG. 16-7. A courtesy card (left) is issued first to ordinance violators in Detroit, Michigan. It is tied to the container by the collector. In Bismarck, North Dakota, violations are noted by attaching a tag (right) to the container to encourage proper handling and storage of refuse materials. The stub is turned over to the refuse collection foreman by the driver for possible follow up action.

described in this chapter. Householders will usually conform if they are convinced that demands of regulations upon them are reasonable and desirable and based on public health or reasonable economic considerations rather than arbitrary whims. However, even the best public relations program may fail to obtain the necessary compliance in a few instances, in which case it becomes necessary to use force as a last resort. Since courts and police officials may be unsympathetic towards enforcement efforts, prosecution is usually best reserved for cases involving habitual and flagrant violations resulting in readily demonstrated health hazards or nuisance conditions.

Where arrests for serious offenses are necessary for the protection of the public health or to prevent a few from interfering with the rights and wishes of the many, there is usually ample legislation available and rather drastic penalties are provided. In some cities, however, police departments are unable to give full cooperation due to limited personnel or other local factors. Health officials will often assist in the correction of insanitary conditions, but for the most part the refuse collec-

PLEASE PRESERVE THIS CARD FOR REFERENCE
VILLAGE OF WINNETKA
What to Do With
Garbage, Tin Cans, Bottles,
Waste Paper and Yard Rubbish

The following information has been prepared to explain the several waste collection services provided for you by the Village. Most of these services are rendered on a scheduled basis free of charge; other services are provided as requested by you at a definite service fee or collection rate.

GARBAGE

Garbage, as a collectable waste, includes all organic kitchen waste. It should be drained and wrapped securely in a newspaper or placed in a paper bag for storage in the garbage receptacle. Storage receptacles for garbage must be provided by each household. Garbage receptacles must be galvanized, or Plastic leakproof cans with handles for lifting, a tight-fitting cover and a capacity of not more than 37 gallons. Such receptacles must be placed outside the building in an accessible location near the rear door at ground level.

Underground, or sunken, storage is also acceptable providing collections can be made easily and the storage vault is kept free of snow and ice and is properly drained to prevent freezing of the receptacles. Garbage collections are made twice each week—either Monday and Thursday or Tuesday and Friday—depending upon your geographic location in the Village. THIS SERVICE IS PROVIDED BY THE VILLAGE WITHOUT CHARGE.

HOUSEHOLD RUBBISH

Household rubbish, as a collectable waste, includes tin cans, bottles, cartons, boxes, wrapping paper and other such debris from normal household operation. An accumulation of newspapers and/or magazines is not considered normal household rubbish and cannot be collected. These accumulations should be disposed of through such service organizations as the Salvation Army. Paper scraps, letters, vacuum cleaner dirt and other fine refuse should be securely wrapped to prevent blowing over the neighborhood when your rubbish can is emptied. Cardboard boxes which are too bulky to place in your rubbish can may be stored open alongside the can for collection. Such boxes should not be used for the storage of smaller refuse as they disintegrate when wet.

Receptacles for household rubbish must be galvanized or Plastic leakproof cans with handles for lifting, a tight-fitting cover and a capacity of not more than 37 gallons. Such receptacles must be placed outside the building in an accessible location at ground level, preferably near your garbage receptacle. Underground, or sunken, storage is also acceptable providing collections can be made easily and the storage vault is kept free of snow and ice and is properly drained to prevent freezing of the receptacles. THE COLLECTION OF YOUR HOUSEHOLD RUBBISH IS MADE WITH YOUR GARBAGE WITHOUT CHARGE.

YARD RUBBISH

Yard rubbish, as a collectable waste, includes grass clippings, leaves, garden and hedge trimmings and ordinary accumulations of tree prunings. It does not include large accumulations of brush from extensive hedge or tree trimmings. The fine accumulations, such as grass clippings, leaves and similar material, must be stored in containers and placed on the parkway. Bulkier accumulations, such as acceptable hedge and tree trimmings, must be cut into pieces not over six (6) feet in length, and piled on the parkway. Such collections, as well as grass clippings and leaves are picked up on Wednesday, except when the demand is heavy causing some collections to be deferred until Thursday. All yard rubbish accumulations must be ready for collection by seven o'clock (7:00 A.M.) on the morning of the scheduled collection day.

THE YARD RUBBISH COLLECTION SERVICE IS PROVIDED UPON REQUEST ON A SEASONAL BASIS FOR A CHARGE OF $5.00. The season normally extends from April 1 to November 15 of each year. No reduction of the seasonal charge can be made for any portion of the season. The Village reserves the right to limit the amount of yard rubbish collected from individual residences to no more than one-half truck load per home per collection.

SPECIAL COLLECTIONS

Objects and materials not acceptable under the foregoing collection service regulations such as large accumulations from extensive yard cleaning, tree trimming, and house cleaning, remodeling or redecorating, may be removed as a special collection upon request. Such special collections are limited to a volume of not over one-half truck load and object weights which can be handled by two men without danger of injury. If you want a special collection, place your order for the service by telephone to, or in person at, the Village Hall prior to Wednesday of the week the pickup is desired. All collections requested after Wednesday must be held until the following week. If immediate collection is required, private haulers should be engaged since all special collections by the Village are made only on Wednesday.

THE SPECIAL COLLECTION CHARGE IS BASED ON THE TIME REQUIRED FOR TWO MEN AND A TRUCK TO MAKE THE COLLECTION, HAUL IT TO THE DISPOSAL POINT AND RETURN TO THE VILLAGE YARD.

ADDITIONAL INFORMATION

Waste collections in the Village will be made only in conformity with these regulations. If you need additional information at any time, you are urged to call the Village offices at HI 6-2500. Your Village office will be happy to handle your call and to receive your suggestions for better service. Do not complain to the collector as he has a heavy schedule of calls to make.

Waste collection of all kinds is a cooperative activity. Your observance of the service regulations will help the Village in providing the efficient collection service you want and expect. 2-62

FIG. 16-8. A card used by the Village of Winnetka, Illinois to gain the coorperation of householders in properly preparing refuse for collection.

tion agency must take the initiative in compelling observance of the laws. Sometimes the refuse supervisors, foremen, and inspectors are deputized as special police officers so that they can make arrests when other methods fail. While this plan has been successful in some cities, it has not always been effective to place so much authority in the hands of people not trained to carry it. In some cities, it has been found more desirable to assign regular police officers to the refuse removal agencies to make the necessary arrests.

Form 871A—2M—1-50

DEPT. OF PUBLIC WORKS **N⁰ 11047**
City of Los Angeles
Bureau of Sanitation
Refuse Collection Division

This container was found in its present damaged condition when the collectors arrived to make the collection today. As a matter of record the address will be reported by the collectors to the Refuse Collection Division Office.

Refuse Collection Division, Bureau of Sanitation

For Information and Complaints call KI-5261

For outlying districts call the following:
Harbor (S. of 120th St.)   TErminal 4-6321
San Fernando Valley   CHase 7-7787
West L. A. and Venice   ARizona 3-1827
or BRadshaw 2-4642

Date..
Lid ☐ was
Container ☐ was
damaged at............................

before truck

No..............................
arrived to make the collection

(Driver)

N⁰ 11047

Form 871B—2M—3-56

DEPT. OF PUBLIC WORKS
City of Los Angeles
Bureau of Sanitation
Refuse Collection Division

This container was damaged accidentally by the collectors today and will be reported by them to the Refuse Collection Division Office. A representative will call upon you within the next few days to make any necessary adjustments.

This Division regrets having caused any inconvenience which may result from this accident.

Refuse Collection Division, Bureau of Sanitation

FOR INFORMATION CALL YOUR DISTRICT OFFICE

Central — LUdlow 8-5261
West L. A., Westchester, and Venice — GRanite 3-1827 or BRadshaw 2-4642
San Fernando Valley — ROgers 7-3130 or STate 5-8311, Sta. 225
Harbor (So. of 120th St.) TErminal 3-9425

Date..
Lid ☐ was
Container ☐ was
damaged by truck

No. ....

at ....

(Address)

(Driver)

FIG. 16-9. When a container is found damaged when the collector arrives to make a collection in Los Angeles, California, a tag is attached to notify the occupant of the premises. Also, when a container is damaged accidentally by the collectors, a tag is attached advising that the city will make any necessary adjustments.

Some of the more minor violations can often be satisfactorily controlled by the refuse collection employees themselves. The failure on the part of the householder to provide proper containers, or to prepare refuse in the required manner can be called to the householder's attention. If suggested corrections are not made within a reasonable time the removal forces may refuse to collect the material or may take still more positive action through the regular city enforcement agencies.

A method commonly employed to call attention to violations is to attach cardboard tags to the refuse containers. These are usually bright-

ly colored to attract attention and may carry a bold-face caption such
as *NOTICE, OFFICIAL NOTICE, CONDEMNED,* or a similar term.
One side of such a tag may consist of a check list of the common violations, including: faulty container, improper separation of refuse, im-

FIG. 16-10. Humorous illustrations are eyecatching and pleasing to the citizen. Above are the
first and last pages of a throw-away leaflet prepared at Des Moines, Iowa, to acquaint the householder with storage container requirements and desirable methods of preparing the garbage for
collection.

proper house treatment of certain classes of refuse, incorrect placement
of receptacles, and the like. The reverse may contain extracts from the
refuse ordinance or list the rules and regulations pertaining to the collection service.

The city of Los Angeles provides collectors with "damaged container
tags" of two types. One notifies the householder that the container was
damaged by the collector and that a supervisor will call relative to correcting or compensating for damages. A second type notifies the householder that the container was found to be damaged when the collectors arrived to make the collection. The tags used in a number of cities
have a perforated stub on which the address of the premises, the nature
of the violation, and the date on which the notice was served are recorded. This stub is detached for future reference and follow-up. Bright-
ly printed gummed stickers are sometimes used instead of cardboard

NOTICE
HOW TO PREPARE GARBAGE *(FOOD WASTES)*
FOR COMBINED COLLECTION
WHEN COLLECTED WITH RUBBISH

EITHER:

KEEP FOOD WASTES SEPARATE FROM OTHER REFUSE
AND STORE IN A COVERED METAL LEAK PROOF PAIL.
PLACE PAIL OUT FOR COLLECTION ON RUBBISH DAY.

OR:

– DRAIN LIQUID FROM FOOD WASTES

WRAP IN SEVERAL THICKNESSES
OF NEWSPAPER

STORE WRAPPED GARBAGE
IN COVERED CONTAINER
WITH OTHER TYPES OF RUBBISH

EITHER METHOD WILL HELP KEEP YOUR LIVING AREA FREE
FROM RATS AND FLIES.   HELP MAKE PHILADELPHIA
A CLEANER, HEALTHIER PLACE TO LIVE.

CITY OF PHILADELPHIA
DEPARTMENT OF STREETS
SANITATION DIVISION

FIG. 16-11. Philadelphia uses one-page flyers like this to remind householders of the proper way to prepare food wastes for collection with rubbish.

JOSEPH F. PERICONI
Commissioner

THE CITY OF NEW YORK
DEPARTMENT OF SANITATION
OPERATIONS OFFICE

HENRY LIEBMAN, P. E.
Director of Operations

Revised 1/66

REFUSE COLLECTION DATA FOR ARCHITECTS AND ENGINEERS

ITEM	MAX. LENGTH	MAX. WIDTH	MAX. HEIGHT	MINIMUM TURNING RADIUS	MAXIMUM AXLE LOAD (lbs)	MAXIMUM TOTAL WEIGHT LOADED (lbs)
 COLLECTION TRUCK	28'-6"	8'-6"	10'-7"	36'	28,000	36,000
 BULK COLLECTION TRUCK	27'-8"	8'-6"	9'-0"	35'	28,750	38,000
 LARGE DETACHABLE CONTAINER & HAULING UNIT	29'-10"	8'-3"	13'-1"	34'	29,477	37,050
 LARGE DETACHABLE CONTAINERS 6 cu. yd. / 8-1/2 cu. yd. / 12 cu. yd.	5'-0" / 6'-8" / 7'-2"	7'-11" / 5'-10" / 8'-0'	5'-9" / 7'-6" / 7'-2"	– / – / –	– / – / –	8,500 / 8,500 / 8,500
 SMALL DETACHABLE CONTAINER 0.8 cu. yd. (used with regular collection truck)	3'-4" (plus 10" for lifting ears)	2'-5"	3'-0"	on casters	–	3,000 (capacity of lifting mechanism)

The Department of Sanitation offers to architects, engineers and property managers, assistance and technical data on its requirements and equipment for refuse collection.
It is suggested that the Department be consulted during the planning of housing developments or other structures eligible for Sanitation service, so that mutually satisfactory facilities and arrangements can be made for refuse collection.
You are invited to telephone the Operations Office, at 566-5546 or 5547 for any other technical information that you may require.
NOTE:- Sunken refuse receptacles in the sidewalk area are illegal encumbrances and should not be installed.

FIG. 16-12. New York City provides an equipment data sheet to architects and engineers concerned with planning housing developments. This enables early consideration of the facilities and arrangements required for satisfactory refuse sanitation service.

tags, apparently because they are less readily removed from the containers.

In a few instances notices of violations are sent through the mail, either as part of a prepared letter, or enclosed with a personal letter. Still other methods include simple printed slips, some prepared for the signature of the inspector or supervisor. These are left at the premises where the violation was discovered.

SUMMARY

The refuse collection service plays an important role in the municipal program of public relations—for either good or ill. By means of its intimate contacts with the majority of citizens, it greatly affects public opinion of municipal operations. To secure and maintain public support is the end toward which all of its activities should be directed.

The character of the service rendered and the efficiency and spirit of the refuse collection employees all have their effect on the amount of cooperation given by the citizens. To secure this cooperation every action of the service should be aimed at building up public relations assets. From the passage of the refuse collection ordinance to the enforcement of its provisions, no opportunity should be lost to convert each action into good will.

APPENDICES

appendix A

PROVISIONS OF

TYPICAL REFUSE COLLECTION ORDINANCES AND REGULATIONS

Typical provisions in municipal ordinances or regulations governing the preparation, storage, and collection of refuse are presented here as a guide to officials in developing suitable local laws or in revising existing ordinances. With one or two exceptions, ordinances are not reproduced in their entirety because it is most improbable that any two cities are confronted with the same set of local conditions. Instead, several different clauses are given under each division to indicate the treatment for widely different circumstances or situations. Examples also include detailed provisions and broad, general statements of intent.

The ordinance and regulation sections quoted have proved satisfactory in certain communities. It must be recognized, however, that they may not be the best ones possible. The requirements or the wording may be conditioned by state laws, court decisions, or other circumstances that do not apply in other places.

The subject matter usually covered by refuse collection ordinances can be grouped under the following headings:

1. Definitions

2. Responsibility for the administration of refuse removal
   a. Ownership of refuse

3. Pre-collection practices
   a. Separation of refuse
   b. Preparation of refuse
   c. Refuse containers
   d. Storing of refuse
   e. Points of collection

4. Collection practices
   a. Limitations on properties served
   b. Availability and extent of service
   c. Responsibility of collectors
   d. Special problems

    e. Control of contract collection
    f. Control of private collectors

5. Financing

6. Penalties for violation

DEFINITIONS

Most accepted and approved ordinances give a clear-cut definition of the numerous terms used to designate the kinds and classes of refuse. Although it is not a set rule, the general plan is to place the identification or terminology clauses near the beginning of the ordinance, preferably in the opening pararaphs. Those terms or definitions should then be used in all published rules and regulations, notices, instructions, and publicity material.

RESPONSIBILITY FOR THE ADMINISTRATION
OF REFUSE REMOVAL

Caldwell, Idaho

The Chief of Police, or such other persons as may be appointed by the Mayor and Council, shall be responsible for the enforcement of the provisions of this chapter and other duties as the Council may prescribe, and there shall be designated as a member of the Police Department, a Sanitary Inspector, who shall enforce the same under the supervision of the Chief of Police.

Calumet City, Ill.

The Street Commissioner (or other designated officer) shall have charge of the collection of garbage, refuse, and ashes in the city.

Lake Forest, Ill.

All ashes, garbage, and rubbish collected, conveyed, and disposed of by the city shall be collected, conveyed, and disposed of under the direction and supervision of the Director of Public Works.

Wilmette, Ill.

The department of public works may collect and dispose of refuse in accordance with such rules and regulations as to service and rates of charge as may be approved by the council from time to time.

Moline, Ill.

[The Sanitation Officer] shall be responsible for the administration of the garbage and refuse fund, prepare payrolls, develop annual budget requirements, determine equipment and supply needs, supervise garbage and refuse collection and disposal and such other duties as the Board of Health, or the Mayor and City Council may impose upon him.

Bluffton, Ind.

The Contractor shall be directly responsible to the Board of Public Works and Safety . . .

In the event of a municipal operation rather than private contract, the Board of Public Works and Safety shall appoint a Superintendent of garbage and rubbish collection and disposal who shall serve for a period of two years from the date of his appointment.

New Castle, Ind.

For the purpose of properly collecting and disposing of trash referred to in this ordinance, the authority for collecting the same is hereby placed in the Street Department of the City, and said Street Commissioner is to direct and supervise the collection of said trash.

Cedar Falls, Iowa

There is hereby established a Department of Sanitation. The Department of Sanitation shall be under the direct supervision of the Mayor and . . . shall have the duty and responsibility of the collection of garbage and refuse . . .

Dubuque, Iowa

The City Manager is hereby authorized and directed to employ city-owned vehicles and equipment, and the necessary operating personnel, to collect all garbage and refuse from dwellings and business places . . .

Ottumwa, Iowa

All refuse accumulated in this city shall be collected, conveyed and disposed of by the contractor under the supervision of the Deputy Health Officer.

Parsons, Kansas

The removal and disposal of garbage and trash shall be at all times under the supervision of the City Health Officer . . .

Salina, Kansas

There is hereby created a Refuse Department within the Department of Service of the City of Salina to provide facilities for the systematic collection and disposal of refuse, as defined herein, from all households, commercial establishments, and other premises within the city at such times and in the manner hereinafter provided.

Wichita, Kansas

The collection and subsequent disposal of all rubbish, trash, and garbage in the city shall be under the supervision of the sanitation director [of the sanitation division of the department of public works].

Lawrence, Kansas

The collection, transportation and disposal of refuse shall be at all times under the general supervision of the City Manager or his duly authorized agent . . .

Newton Center, Mass.

The street department shall have charge of the removal [of refuse] from yards, areas, and premises and the disposal of all ashes, refuse, and garbage.

Ann Arbor, Mich.

All refuse accumulated in the city shall be collected, conveyed, and disposed of under the supervision and direction of the superintendent [of the Public Works Department].

Buchanan, Mich.

The city clerk shall be empowered to license on application any person, firm, or corporation for the purpose of collecting garbage and refuse, ashes and rubbish . . .

Detroit, Mich.

The enforcement of this ordinance shall be the duty of the Commissioner of

Public Works, the Commissioner of Health, the Commissioner of Police, and the Commissioner of Buildings and Safety Engineering, who are hereby jointly authorized to adopt reasonable regulations to carry out the intent of the ordinance.

Ferndale, Mich.

The Director of Public Works shall collect and dispose of all garbage and rubbish, except production or processing refuse, and builders' and contractors' refuse, when properly prepared for collection and placed according to the regulations.

Frankenmuth, Mich.

All refuse accumulated in the City shall be conveyed and disposed of by the City under the supervision of the City Manager.

Grosse Pointe Farms, Mich.

Garbage and rubbish will be collected by the [Highway] Department [of the Village of Grosse Pointe Farms] free of charge on schedules approved by the Village Council.

Livonia, Mich.

The municipal refuse disposal system as herein defined shall be and remain under the management, supervision, and control of the Director of Public Works of the City of Livonia subject to such control reserved by law and the City Charter to the Mayor and City Council.

Muskegon, Mich.

The Board of Health shall have the power to make such rules, regulations, and recommendations as the board may from time to time deem necessary for the collection of garbage and ashes for the best interest of the city. The board shall also divide the city into convenient garbage districts and the city commission shall regulate the gathering, collection, and disposal of said garbage and ashes in such districts, and shall cause the same to be collected and removed therefrom in accordance with the rules and regulations adopted by the board of health, and shall contract for the removal thereof if deemed advisable.

Niles, Mich.

All refuse accumulated within the city shall be collected, conveyed, and disposed of by the city under the supervision of the Systems Director.

OWNERSHIP

Lakeland, Fla.

It shall be unlawful . . . to fail or refuse to dispose of all garbage and similar waste or refuse matter . . . by failing or refusing to place such garbage and similar waste and refuse matter in tightly covered cans or plastic receptacles until the contents . . . are removed by the Department of Public Works.

Fort Myers, Fla.

It is hereby declared unlawful . . . to collect or permit to be collected by any one, the garbage from any garbage can other than by persons regularly employed by the City of Fort Myers for that purpose or by persons working under contract with the City of Fort Myers . . .

Coral Gables, Fla.

In all cases in which garbage and/or trash is removed and disposed of by persons other than the employee of the Public Service Department of the City of Coral Gables, the owner or occupant of the premises from which such removal is made shall previously secure a written permit therefor from the Director of Public Service . . .

Gainesville, Ga.

The City of Gainesville by and through its proper departments shall be responsible for the collection and disposal of all garbage, trash, and refuse within the City, and no person, firm, or corporation shall collect and dispose of, or transport over the streets of the city, any garbage, trash, or refuse without first obtaining a written permit from the city to do so.

Hammond, Ind.

All junk and other materials placed on the disposal area are the property of the City of Hammond, Indiana, and no person is allowed to separate and collect, carry off, or dispose of same except under written direction of the Board of Public Works.

SEPARATION OF REFUSE

Washington, D.C.

Three separations—namely, ashes, garbage and trash—are required by the householder as each class of material is collected and disposed of separately. Mixture of two, or more, classes of refuse in one container is unlawful, and collection will not be made until separated.

Calumet City, Ill.

Refuse which is flammable shall not be mixed or mingled with refuse that is nonflammable. Garbage shall be kept separate from all other types of refuse.

Mount Prospect, Ill.

Building materials, earth, sod, and rocks resulting from "do-it-yourself" home projects will be picked up if placed in bushel baskets or garbage cans, providing such containers can be reasonably lifted by one man without possible physical injury.

Grass clippings, or other small items of debris and rubbish can be placed in garbage cans or bushel baskets.

Wichita, Kansas

The containers used for storage of wrapped garbage may also be used for the storage of trash and rubbish.

Quincy, Mass.

Glass, broken crockery, tin cans or other like substances shall not be mixed with garbage.

Salem, Mass.

Waste (except extraordinary commercial wastes, industrial wastes, and tree wastes) shall be collected by the Health Department if separated as to (1) garbage, (2) burnable rubbish, and (3) non-burnable rubbish . . .

Coldwater, Mich.

You may put anything in your can, except dirt, stones, water, or anything that is forced or wedged that will make it difficult to dump the contents.

Detroit, Mich.

Muncipal waste materials shall be collected by the Department of Public Works, if separated as to (1) garbage, (2) rubbish, provided that such materials be stored in separate receptacles as hereinafter described.

Madison Heights, Mich.

Noncombustibles, ashes, and yard wastes . . . shall be separated from other refuse to allow it to be dumped separately at the disposal site, and shall be picked up on a "special" pickup.

Royal Oak, Mich.

Noncombustible rubbish shall be in separate containers and shall be in no case intermingled with garbage or placed in garbage receptacles.

PREPARATION OF REFUSE

Hartford, Conn.

The following materials shall require special preparation:

(a) Garbage. All garbage shall be drained and securely wrapped in paper.

(b) Food containers. Plastic, metal and glass food containers shall be drained of excess liquids and may be wrapped, either separately or together, with the garbage.

(c) Ashes. All ashes shall be cool and kept dry and stored in a separate, approved container.

Rehoboth, Del.

All kitchen waste, vegetable or animal waste, commonly classified as "garbage" shall be *completely* wrapped in newspaper or other waste paper and *securely* tied before disposal in any waste container.

Wilmington, Del.

It shall be unlawful for any person, firm, or corporation to place or cause or allow to be placed in receptacles, any garbage that is to be collected by this department, unless such garbage has been thoroughly drained of its moisture, wrapped in substantial paper, and placed in metal containers with tightly fitted metal lids. It shall also be unlawful . . . to place . . . any rubbish unless such rubbish is secured in tight packages, so as to prevent scattering . . . tree trimmings, brush, vines, etc., shall be limited to (100 pounds) and shall be tied securely in bundles limited to four feet in length.

Washington, D.C.

Ashes include coal ashes, household incinerator ashes, oyster and clam shells. Ashes must be kept dry.

Do not wrap garbage. No paper, tin cans, or bottles should be mixed with garbage.

Liquids must be removed from all bottles, cans or containers before placing in trash.

Branches must be less than four feet in length and tied securely into compact bundles easily handled by one man, or be placed in proper containers.

Ocala, Fla.

Leaves, newspapers, tree and shrubbery trimmings need not be placed in containers, but shall be placed not more than ten feet from the street right-of-way line in one pile for each property. Newspapers, wrappings, and similar debris shall be securely bundled and tied, or placed in boxes in such a manner that the same will not be scattered by the elements and can be handled easily and quickly by the collection crews.

Hilo, Hawaii

It shall be unlawful for any person, firm, or corporation within the County of Hawaii to abandon refrigerators, ice boxes, wardrobe trunks, or any other containers, equipment, or appliance having self-locking doors without first removing and detaching the doors or covers from the same.

Mount Prospect, Ill.

Empty wooden crates in excess of four feet for any dimension must be knocked down.

Niles, Ill.

It shall be the duty of the occupant of every single dwelling, multiple dwelling, or occupational unit, to cause all refuse produced therein to be deposited in the refuse container, wrapped in paper and in a reasonably dry state.

Riverside, Ill.

Garbage . . . should be well drained and wrapped or put in bags before placing in a garbage can.

Household refuse, such as facial tissues, letters, cartons, paper boxes, and dirt from a vacuum cleaner . . . should be wrapped securely before being placed in a garbage can . . . Although service includes picking up newspapers and magazines when securely tied, it is recommended that they be given to such organizations as the Salvation Army or the Boy Scouts for paper drives . . .

Yard rubbish includes grass clippings, garden and hedge trimmings, leaves, and small branches under one inch in diameter and cut two feet long. A total of four bushels of such rubbish will be collected . . . if it is placed in wooden bushel baskets or metal containers the same size and put on the parkway.

Broken toys, metal scraps, and heavy rubbish should be placed in a metal container on the parkway.

Winnetka, Ill.

[Garbage] should be drained and wrapped securely in a newspaper or placed in a paper bag for storage in the garbage receptacle.

Paper scraps, letters, vacuum cleaner dirt, and other fine refuse should be securely wrapped to prevent blowing over the neighborhood when your rubbish can is emptied. Cardboard boxes which are too bulky to place in your rubbish can may be stored *open* alongside the can for collection. Such boxes should not be used for the storage of smaller refuse as they disintegrate when wet.

. . . acceptable hedge and tree trimmings must be cut into pieces not over six feet in length and piled on the parkway.

Bluffton, Ind.

Garbage shall be carefully drained and wrapped before depositing in receptacles. Trees, limbs, boxes and other articles of unwieldy size or shape will only be acceptable for collection if they are broken or cut down to a size suitable for handling and transportation, and the Board of Public Works and Safety shall have the authority to prescribe the maximum size and weight thereof from time to time.

New Castle, Ind.

. . . those items of trash that are not readily contained in a trash container, such as hedge clippings, tree limbs, and similar trash, shall be tied in bundles, but the length shall not exceed three feet and the diameter of such bundles not to exceed two feet, nor the weight of such bundles to exceed 75 pounds.

Cedar Falls, Iowa

All garbage shall be drained and wrapped for deposit in containers. All refuse shall be placed in metal containers, except that it shall not be necessary to place books, magazines, and newspapers in containers if same are securely tied in bundles of not larger than 20x20x26 inches. Ashes or cinders may be placed in open containers or tubs.

Charles City, Iowa

Drain and wrap in paper all raw garbage to avoid sticking. Do not pack refuse into containers so tight that it will not come out by shaking.

Salisbury, Md.

All wet garbage shall be wrapped in several thicknesses of paper. This will double the life of your garbage can and reduce the cost of incineration.

Berkley, Mich.

All cans, receptacles, and containers of any description *must be broken open* before being placed in the refuse container with combustible refuse. Such refuse may be placed in the same can with garbage.

Small furniture, toys, household materials and utensils must be broken up to have a maximum dimension of not over three feet, with no solid wood over two inches or heavy metal over $\frac{1}{16}$-inch in thickness.

Roseville, Mich.

All cans and bottles which have contained food shall be drained before being deposited for collection.

Saginaw, Mich.

Ashes and small or bulk items of rubbish shall be placed in containers for collection so that it will never be necessary for the men making the collections to use either a shovel or a fork to pick up the rubbish. Newspapers and magazines, when securely tied in bundles, need not be placed in containers. Trimmings from bushes and shrubs with stalks one inch or less in diameter may be cut into small pieces and placed in containers or be securely tied in bundles not over 18 inches in diameter. Large items of rubbish, including branches of trees four inches or less in diameter, shall be placed in neat piles for collection. Small stumps and roots, which may be placed in a bushel basket and not project more than twelve inches above the top of the basket will be picked up. Only between October 1 and December 1 may leaves be raked into the gutter or edge of the roadway for collection. Leaves and grass clippings shall be placed in containers for collection during other times of the year.

REFUSE CONTAINERS

Greeley, Colo.

Every occupant of any house, hotel, restaurant, store building, flat, apartment, or tenement in this city where persons reside, board, lodge, or stay, or where animal or vegetable matter is prepared or served, shall provide and at all times maintain therefor in good condition, one or more sufficient, suitable cans or receptacles for garbage . . . Such garbage receptacles shall be watertight, made of substantial metal with an easy, close-fitting metal cover and have a capacity of not less than ten gallons.

Hartford, Conn.

Approved containers for the storage of garbage, incinerator refuse, and non-combustible refuse shall be galvanized iron or other non-rusting metal of substantial construction with tight-fitting metal covers and adequate handles, watertight, of such size as to be easily handled by one man, and in any case to have a capacity not in excess of twenty-five gallons and not less than ten gallons. Nothing in this section shall be interpreted as preventing the director of public works from approving some other devices which, in his opinion, meet the requirements of this section.

Containers . . . shall be kept covered at all times and maintained in good condition. Any container that does not conform to the provisions of this chapter or that may have ragged or sharp edges, or any other defect liable to hamper or injure the person collecting the contents thereof, must be promptly replaced by an approved container upon receipt of notice to that effect from the director of public works to the responsible person or agent. If not so replaced within ten days after receipt of such notice, such nonconforming or defective container shall be disposed of by the department as waste.

All such containers shall be set out in some accessible part of the premises for removal. The department of public works may designate the location of such receptacles, and specify their number and capacity.

Rehoboth, Del.

All waste material shall be contained in individual containers and each of a capacity not exceeding one bushel.

Containers and contents weighing more than fifty pounds will not be emptied by the collection forces of the city; heavy oil drums are not considered satisfactory containers.

Washington, D.C.

Ashes must be in metal containers (with covers) not larger than 24 gallons.

[Garbage] must be in watertight, covered metal containers not larger than 10 gallons (unless permitted upon application to this division) with handles, and kept tightly covered at all times.

Sunken garbage receptacles must be located at point of collection, or inside can must be covered and set out by the householder to the point of collection on collecting days.

[Trash] must be in lightweight containers (with covers) 30 gallons maximum size, or burlap bags so as to prevent the litter of public space. Oil and chemical drums, paper bags, cardboard boxes, and baskets are not legal containers.

Ocala, Fla.

Garbage shall be placed in galvanized metal containers having a capacity of not more than 32 gallons, but rubbish and refuse may be placed in other containers suitable for the purpose, such as cardboard boxes or galvanized metal containers.

Lakeland, Fla.

. . . for the purpose of this ordinance, the words "garbage can" shall be defined to mean a galvanized metal can or plastic receptacle of the type commonly sold as a garbage can or receptacle, of a capacity not to exceed 30 gallons, and such can shall have two handles upon the sides of the can or receptacles as a bail by which it may be lifted, and shall have a tight fitting metal or plastic top, except storage bins and other containers, which containers shall be approved by the Department of Public Works of the City of Lakeland.

Garbage cans or plastic receptacles shall be kept in a place easily accessible to the inspectors of the Sanitation Department of the City of Lakeland and to the employees of the Department of Public Works of said City, and shall not be kept upon City or public property, or neighboring property not in the ownership or tenancy of the person by whom the garbage is accumulated, whether such neighboring property be vacant or improved . . .

Chattahoochee, Fla.

Garbage Box [defined]. Any wooden or metallic box constructed so that the contents will be kept dry and intact therein and in which dry garbage only shall be deposited. The size, design, and location of all garbage boxes shall be approved by the town council or its authorized agent or assistant.

Hilo, Hawaii

All garbage and swill shall be contained in leak-proof metal receptacles and shall be securely covered at all times so as to exclude insects and animals. All rubbish, except hedge cuttings, stumps, branches, banana leaves, palm and coconut leaves, and other similar materials shall be contained in metal or wood receptacles, or in paper or cardboard cartons of sufficient strength to adequately contain the contents therein.

Caldwell, Idaho

Such containers shall be kept in sanitary condition, with the inside and outside thereof washed at such times as to keep the same free and clean of all accumulating grease and decomposing material and so that no odor nuisance shall exist. All garbage or refuse cans shall be placed in a place accessible to the collector, provided that in the case of isolated dwellings or places of business or where reasonable access cannot be had by a truck, the can may be kept in such places as may be designated by the inspector. Provided further, that where there is no alley entrance, such cans shall be placed on the street curb on collection days.

Elgin, Ill.

A receptacle for ashes, tin cans, and bottles shall be either of metal, wood, or cement, and such receptacles shall have a capacity of not less than ten gallons, nor more than thirty gallons. No hot ashes shall be placed in a wooden receptacle.

Winnetka, Ill.

If [containers are] located underground, the pit shall be drained in such a manner as to prevent freezing during cold weather.

Moline, Ill.

Containers shall be kept in an inconspicuous and inoffensive location between collection days.

Hammond, Ind.

Containers of a permanent nature used for central garbage collection for multiple dwellings must be of such capacity as to provide 20 gallons of space for each family using such containers, and provide that such container is so constructed and designed as to afford a means of emptying the same from a door or gate on a level with the bottom of such container located at ground level . . . Containers shall be located and maintained so as not to create a fire hazard or provide harborage for rodents or the breeding of insects.

New Castle, Ind.

Said trash containers shall be of such material that will not be damaged by weather or repeated handling by the trash collector. This container shall not weigh more than 75 pounds including container and trash. The trash container shall be perforated so that water cannot accumulate. The trash container shall be maintained in good condition so that the trash will not leak or sift out. The container shall never be filled above the highest most part of the container. This does not, however, alter the weight limitation already set forth.

All trash containers shall be placed in the alley immediately adjacent to the premises of the owner thereof abutting upon such alley at such point as shall be farthest removed from any dwelling houses, or least liable to become obnoxious to any of the inhabitants of the neighborhood, providing the containers do not block traffic through the alley. Trash containers may be placed upon the inside of the premises in the rear thereof, provided the same are made easily accessible for the trash collector by convenient door or gate. In case there is no alley abutting upon the premises of any residence of said city, such resident shall place his trash container on his own premises or along the parkway between sidewalks and curb where the same shall be easily accessible to the trash collector and least obnoxious to neighboring residents.

Chariton, Iowa

Any container used shall be kept clean and covered with a tight fitting lid. It shall not be left in alleys or streets except in the business district where the property does not provide sufficient outside area for a garbage rack. It shall also be the duty of each person to provide a storage can of sufficient size that all garbage will be held until picked up. Cans will be held or anchored in such a manner that they cannot be tipped over or the garbage allowed to scatter.

Ottumwa, Iowa

Containers shall be of a type approved by the deputy health officer, and shall be kept in a clean, neat, and sanitary condition at all times.

Hutchinson, Kansas

Such containers shall be kept or placed in a suitable place accessible to the city collectors not to exceed 50 feet from any street or alley, but not on any street, alley, or public place, and such containers shall be kept in such a manner or place that the contents thereof will not freeze.

Salina, Kansas

Trash and nonputrescible substances may be placed in any type of container: provided, that where the Refuse Department makes collections, no container shall exceed 32 gallons and the combined weight of said container and contents shall not exceed 75 pounds.

Ashland, Ky.

Cans or receptacles for garbage from private dwelling houses, from each flat, and from each department shall have a capacity of not less than 20 gallons, nor more than 30 gallons. However, in the conduct of their business and activities, breweries, wholesale produce and grocery dealers, meat packing and meat wholesale dealers, bakeries, fat rendering and hide processing plants, and other business establishments wherein garbage is produced, shall provide such receptacles or method or manner of handling their industrial or commercial garbage or waste as shall meet with the approval of the superintendent of streets and sanitation of the City of Ashland.

Salem, Mass.

Burnable rubbish shall be placed by owner, agent, or occupant in standard size metal barrels or other suitable rigid containers weighing not more than 100 pounds when full for collection by the Health Department. Containers shall be painted around the center with a red stripe at least three inches wide.

Containers [for non-burnable] rubbish shall be painted around the center with a green stripe at least three inches wide.

Coldwater, Mich.

Residential customers will be furnished a 15-gallon garbage can with a tight fitting cover.

Detroit, Mich.

Single or two-family dwellings. A proper and sufficient number of portable receptacles as herein defined for the storage of garbage and of rubbish between collections shall be provided by each family residing in a single-family dwelling or in a two-family dwelling. It shall be the duty of the occupants to maintain such receptacles in good repair and in a clean and satisfactory condition and to store rubbish and garbage properly therein.

Multiple dwellings. In the case of a building housing more than two families, the owner, lessee, or agent of the premises shall provide for each family a proper and sufficient number of receptacles as herein defined for the storage of garbage and of rubbish between collections. The owner, lessee, agent or caretaker of such receptacles shall maintain them in good repair and in a clean and satisfactory condition. Unless a permit for a stationary or large moveable receptacle has been issued as specified in Section 405.6, these receptacles shall be of a portable type as defined in Section 404.

Commercial and other non-residential establishments. The proprietor, manager, or agent or person in charge of a commercial establishment, professional office, church or any other non-residential occupancy where waste accumulates shall provide proper and sufficient receptacles as herein defined for the storage of garbage and of rubbish between collections. All receptacles shall be kept clean and in good repair. Unless a permit for a stationary or large moveable receptacle has been issued as specified in Section 405.6, these receptacles shall be of a portable type as defined in Section 404.

Broken and illegal receptacles. After due notice has been given to the responsible party to dispose of defective or illegal waste receptacles and outdoor trashburners, they may be collected as rubbish by the Department of Public Works if they remain on public property. No defective or illegal receptacle shall be used for storage of garbage or rubbish. Defective concrete receptacles beyond repair shall be broken into small pieces not to exceed 100 pounds and when placed at the regular collection location may be collected by the Department of Public Works.

Portable receptacles. Portable receptacles for garbage shall be adequate in size, number and type to hold two weeks' accumulation, and each portable receptacle shall have a capacity of not less than 20 gallons nor more than 26 gallons except where special permission is granted by the enforcing officer for a receptacle of other size. The receptacle shall be of substantial galvanized metal or other approved construction, fly-tight, and provided with handles or bail and a tight-fitting cover with handle and no single receptacle shall weigh more than 100 pounds when filled.

Portable receptacles for rubbish shall be adequate in size, number and type to hold a three weeks' accumulation of materials and each portable receptacle shall have a capacity of not less than 20 gallons nor more than 26 gallons except where special permission is granted by the enforcing officer for a receptacle of other size. The receptacle shall be of substantial galvanized metal or other approved construction, fly-tight, and provided with handles or bail and a tight-fitting cover with handle, and no single receptacle shall weigh more than 100 pounds when filled. Ashes shall be stored in portable covered containers having a capacity of not over 20 gallons or in a manner approved by the enforcing officer.

Labeling and elevating. All portable waste receptacles shall be labeled with weatherproof letters at least three inches high to designate their use as either a garbage container or a rubbish container. The symbol or letter to be used for such designation shall be designated by the enforcing officer. Occupants of two family dwellings shall in addition designate the apartment served on each receptacle. All portable receptacles shall be placed on a rack or other acceptable device to hold the container not less than 12 inches and not more than 24 inches above the ground, with a clear space under the rack for cleaning out any spilled waste matter. Can covers only shall be separately chained or securely tied with chain or rope fastened to the rack or other stationary object. Container shall not be chained or tied. Hangers from walls or posts or any other acceptable method of elevating the cans as specified above may be used in place of the rack. Underground receptacles may be used if they are fly-tight, rodent-proof, and in a location approved by the enforcing officer.

Stationary and large moveable receptacles. Approval of construction details. Plans, specifications and details of construction for any waste receptacle other than portable as described in Section 404, shall be approved by the Department of Public Works and the Department of Health, along with the application for permit to install such receptacle in the City of Detroit. The manufacturer of pre-fabricated receptacles shall be responsible for obtaining the approval of each size and model before it is made available for sale and installation with the City of Detroit. Each such stationary receptacle hereafter installed shall have a capacity of not less than 250 gallons and not more than 500 gallons unless special permission is granted by the enforcing officer for a receptacle of other size.

Identification and labeling. Stationary receptacles shall be legibly and permanently labeled with the following information: (1) Name of manufacturer; (2) Capacity of the receptacles in gallons; (3) "No Burning" or equivalent; (4) Appropriate symbols on both front and rear to designate use for either garbage or rubbish as suggested by the enforcing officer, in letters at least three inches high.

Accessibility. The owner or installer of every stationary receptacle shall install the receptacle so that both doors are accessible for use. Any space existing between any side of such receptacle and any adjacent receptacle, building or other object shall be at least 12 inches in least dimension, unless the space is small enough to be effectively sealed.

Steps. Any receptacle with the top reception door located over 42 inches above the adjacent ground after installation shall have approved steps or platforms. Steps shall be maintained in good repair and in a safe condition at all times.

Limited use. All receptacles for the storage of garbage, rubbish, and ashes shall be of a portable type as defined in Section 404 except where portable receptacles because of space limitations are found impractical by the enforcing officer. Where a caretaker is designated as required in Section 707, the enforcing officer may approve an application and permit for the use of one or more stationary or large moveable receptacles at the following building occupancies:

(1) For storage of garbage in dwellings containing nine families or more.

(2) For storage of rubbish in dwellings containing five families or more.

(3) For storage of garbage from an individual commercial establishment whose monthly bill for garbage collection from the City of Detroit establishes the need for nine or more portable legal garbage cans of 26 gallons capacity between collection.

(4) For storage of rubbish from an individual commercial establishment whose monthly bills for waste collection from the City of Detroit establishes the need for a total of nine or more legal portable cans of 26 gallons capacity between collections.

Permits required. Where stationary or large moveable receptacles are authorized they shall not be installed until a permit has been obtained from the Department of Public Works. A permit shall be issued only after payment of a fee not to exceed five dollars. Sufficient receptacles shall be provided to hold a two weeks' accumulation of garbage and a three weeks' accumulation of rubbish. Permits will not be issued and concrete receptacles shall not be provided for joint use of two or more commercials or for joint use of residences and commercial establishments. The concrete receptacles must be properly installed to comply with all conditions stated on permit. Any permit shall be revoked for cause by the Commissioner of Public Works.

Permits for existing receptacles. An existing installation of one or more stationary receptacles may be continued in use if each has between 100 gallons and 500 gallons capacity, is maintained in good repair, and is on a rat wall or slab as required by the enforcing officer. This shall apply only to premises that meet all "Limited Use" requirements specified in Section 405.5. An application for a permit for an existing receptacle may be approved by the enforcing officer after he has determined that the location is conveniently accessible for use and collection service. Any receptacle relocated to another multiple dwelling or commercial establishment shall be subject to all requirements for a new receptacle.

Location of Receptacles. Receptacles shall be conveniently accessible for collection service and for all users. All receptacles for garbage or rubbish shall be located on private property except on collection days. All trash burners shall be kept on private property except while being used and attended. In alley collection areas the receptacles shall be located as near as possible to the alley line but not in any alley, street, or other public property; except that where it has been deemed impractical by the enforcing officer to provide access to the receptacles on private property, revocable permission may be granted for the storage of receptacles on public property. The Commissioner of Public

Works shall have the authority to designate the location from which receptacles shall be serviced. A notice of any change in location where receptacles are to be placed for service shall be given to all persons concerned before the change is put into effect.

Space for receptacles. To insure sufficient space for the storage of garbage and rubbish receptacles, there shall be provided and maintained on private property an open or unoccupied space not less than 50 square feet in area, directly adjoining the street or alley where service is rendered which is accessible through a passageway not less than three feet wide from the exit of any building to said street or alley. In the case of a commercial building where compliance with this requirement is impracticable, an approved rubbish room may be provided in lieu of outside space. No person shall obstruct access to receptacles.

Garbage and rubbish chutes. After the effective date of this ordinance garbage and rubbish chutes shall not be installed unless a permit is obtained from the Department of Buildings and Safety Engineering. Existing garbage and rubbish chutes shall not be used unless in combination with an incinerator acceptable to the Department of Buildings and Safety Engineering. Any other garbage and rubbish chute shall be effectively sealed to prevent its use or shall be removed from the premises.

Rubbish rooms. The location, capacity and use of any new or existing room for storage of municipal waste for collection by the Department of Public Works shall be subject to approval, and such room shall be used only for storage of portable receptables and not for bulk storage of waste. Rubbish rooms or refuse bins shall be constructed only in accordance with requirements of the Building Code.

Ferndale, Mich.

All rubbish containers are to be kept in a sanitary condition by the users thereof. Failure to place a container in a sanitary condition after notice by the collector will be sufficient reason for refusing to pickup the refuse on the collection following the one on which the notice was given.

Location of refuse container: (a) The owner of the property, or his agent, shall provide a suitable place for the storage of the containers between collection periods off from public property. The containers are to be placed on a platform not less than one foot above the general ground level and protected so as not to be easily disturbed by animals. The location of the storage space shall be accessible for collection and subject to approval by the Director of Public Works.

Frankenmuth, Mich.

Containers shall be made of metal or plastic, equipped with suitable handles and tight-fitting covers, and shall be watertight. Disposable waterproof paper bags may also be used.

Monroe, Mich.

Buildings housing less than six families—each occupant must supply his own containers. Residents in multiple family dwellings must identify their containers by name of owner. Buildings housing six or more families— owner of the building shall provide the necessary number of containers.

Roseville, Mich.

Clean refuse containers shall be maintained in place at or near the rear of the building in a location where they shall not interfere with the healthful enjoyment of adjoining property . . .

STORING OF REFUSE

Greeley, Colo.

It shall be the duty of all householders, hotel keepers, restaurant keepers, store keepers, and all other persons having garbage, to deposit the same in the garbage can provided for such premises; provided an incinerator approved by the chief of police may be utilized for the immediate burning of garbage. Garbage cans shall be placed on such premises where same can be conveniently removed by the garbage collector, abutting on an alley if possible. In case of controversy over the location of such garbage can, same to be determined by the chief of police.

Washington, D.C.

Public wastepaper boxes are not to be used for disposal of refuse from households or business establishments.

Material for collection must be kept in lawful containers on private property at all times.

Lakeland, Fla.

All residents or occupants of residences, apartments, or places of business . . . are required to provide a garbage can, or cans, or plastic receptacle, or receptacles, of sufficient capacity to hold four days' accumulation of garbage in the residential districts and areas of the city.

Fort Myers, Fla.

All garbage shall be daily deposited in the garbage cans or containers herein above required. Garbage cans and containers shall be kept tightly covered at all times, except when it is necessary to lift the cover to deposit garbage in the garbage can or container.

Coral Gables, Fla.

All residents or occupants of residences, apartments, or places of business within the City of Coral Gables are hereby required to provide a garbage can, or cans, and a trash container, or containers, as hereintofore defined, of sufficient capacity to hold four days' accumulation of garbage and trash in the residential and apartment districts and areas, and three days' accumulation of garbage and trash in the business and industrial districts and areas. Whenever a large proportion of garbage and trash accumulation are subject to decay or putrefaction, such accumulation may be kept in a covered bin, or other container not subject to deterioration.

Gainesville, Ga.

No person, firm, or corporation who shall own or occupy a premise or premises within the city shall permit garbage, trash or refuse to collect or remain on such premise or premises except during periods between City Sanitary Department pickups, and no person, firm or corporation . . . shall permit garbage, trash, or refuse to be scattered from such premise or premises into the public streets or alleys of the city.

Caldwell, Idaho

It shall be unlawful for any person to permit or to suffer to accumulate in or about any yard, lot, place, or premises, owned or occupied by such person, any garbage or refuse so as to cause such yard, lot, premise, or the street, alley or sidewalk adjacent thereto to be, or remain in such condition as to cause or create a nuisance or offensive odor or atmosphere or rodent harborage, or thereby to be or to become, or cause or create, a public nuisance.

Barrington, Ill.

It shall be unlawful for any person, firm, or corporation to burn garbage within the village, to permit garbage to accumulate in any manner so as to create a nuisance and to attract flies, vermin or rats, or to permit garbage to accumulate for more than seven days; provided, however that gas incinerators or similar equipment properly installed so that such installation does not constitute a health hazard or fire hazard, may be used for the burning of garbage, and properly installed kitchen garbage disposal units may be used for the disposal of garbage into sewer lines within the Village.

Parsons, Kansas

. . . any trash which, because of its bulk or nature, cannot be placed in such container. shall be so located as not to constitute a fire hazard and shall be located in such places as to be accessible to the city trash collector.

POINTS OF COLLECTION

Hartford, Conn.

All such containers shall be set out in some accessible part of the premises for removal.

Rehoboth, Del.

The owner or occupier of any given lot shall place all waste material in containers or disposable containers along the curb in front of such lot in order that it may be conveniently collected by the city collection forces. All waste material containers shall be removed from city property within eight hours after the same shall have been collected.

Containers for collection on private property shall be placed along the curb in front of the property prior to 7:00 a.m. of the day of collection, but in no case shall such full containers be placed on city property prior to 12 hours preceding the day of collection. The normal hours of collection are between the hours of 7:00 a.m. and 5:00 p.m. daily, except Sundays.

Containers for collection from commercial houses on Rehoboth Avenue and any other commercial district shall be placed for collection normally after closing hours of the commercial establishments involved.

Whenever waste collections are made on Saturdays and Mondays, no waste containers shall be placed on property of the city, either in the area of the sidewalk or streets, between the hours of 12 noon on Saturdays until 11:00 p.m. on Sundays.

Wilmington, Del.

All garbage and rubbish from buildings and premises where there is no suitable means of ingress or egress to rear of same, and all refuse, shall be placed for collection on the sidewalk abutting the premises respectively from which the same are brought, or they may be placed on any roadway abutting the premises from which the same are brought, provided such a roadway has a suitable roadbed, is at least eleven feet wide, has at least twelve feet vertical clearance under obstructions, sufficient room at corners, and is open at both ends; the placing of said containers, receptacles and packages on the sidewalk or roadway shall be before six o'clock a.m. of the day of collection, but not before six o'clock p.m. of the day preceding the day set for collection, and said containers and receptacles shall be removed from the sidewalk or roadway by householders the same day they are emptied by the collector.

Washington, D.C.

On collection days, containers must be placed adjacent to public property, not in alley or street, but just inside of alley gate, at front building line, or inside of front or side gate depending on the point of collection (point of collection determined by Division of Sanitation). Emptied containers will be returned to the point of collection.

Material must be at the proper point of collection and gates or doors unlocked before the arrival of collectors. Collections start at 7:00 a.m.

Coral Gables, Fla.

. . . said can and containers are hereby required to be kept at a point upon the premises of the owner or occupant within 20 feet of the rear lot line of the premises and, in the case of corner lots, not closer to any side street than one-half the breadth of the premises at the rear property line. Whenever premises abut an alley, the garbage cans and trash containers shall be placed within easy and convenient access from such alley and not closer to any side street than one-half of the breadth of the premises at the rear property line.

Caldwell, Idaho

All garbage or refuse cans shall be placed in a place accessible to the collector provided that in the case of isolated dwellings or places of business or where reasonable access cannot be had by a truck, the cans may be kept in such places as may be agreed upon by the owner and collector, or at such place as may be designated by the inspector. Provided further, that where there is no alley entrance, such cans shall be placed on the street curb on collection days.

Glencoe, Ill.

Garbage, tin cans, and bottles are collected twice a week at your back door beginning at 7:00 a.m. Collectors cannot go onto porches or inside buildings. Rubbish is collected once a week beginning at 7:00 a.m. from the parkway next to your home.

Lake Forest, Ill.

Containers . . . to be collected shall be placed for collection at or near ground level on the property and at or near the rear or service door of the principal building or buildings on the premises. Collectors shall not be permitted to enter houses, enclosed porches, garages, or similar enclosures to make collections. Containers of refuse, or refuse not in containers for collection, shall not be placed within the right-of-way of any street or alley.

Where circumstances warrant, exceptions may be made to the above, but only upon express authorization by the Director of Public Works.

Underground or sunken container storage vaults will be acceptable provided that collections can be made easily; that the storage vault is kept free of snow and ice; and is properly drained. The city will assume no responsibility for the protection or maintenance of any underground storage vault, or parts thereof.

Ottumwa, Iowa

Residential refuse containers shall be placed for collection at ground level on property and not within right-of-way of street or alley, and at a point accessible to the street or alley from which collection is made. Containers may be placed for collection at other than ground level, at points not easily accessible, upon payment of an additional and reasonable fee for the extra service as agreed upon by both parties. Refuse containers at commercial and industrial locations should be placed in suitable containers outside of the building, but may be stored inside if space is unavailable outside the building, and provided that access is provided to refuse hauling contractors.

Salem, Mass.

Garbage containers shall be placed at the rear of the house or building of the producer or owner, and shall not be placed upon the street, sidewalk, or other public place, and shall be securely covered at all times.

Burnable and non-burnable rubbish containers or bundles of ordinary commercial waste and garden and lawn waste. These shall be placed at the outer edge of the sidewalk appurtenant to the premises of the owner . . .

Buchanan, Mich.

Rubbish containers and bundles to be picked up on collection days shall be placed at the curb where the premises are served from the street and at the rear of the lot of those premises served from alleys or otherwise served from the rear.

Garbage containers may be placed at the curb, at the back door of the buildings, or at the rear of the lot, if such lot is served from the rear.

Fremont, Mich.

All refuse to be collected by the City Manager shall be placed at the curb unless the City Manager determines that alley collection is preferable.

LIMITATIONS ON PROPERTIES SERVED

Hartford, Conn.

The department of public works shall collect and remove, or cause to be removed under its direction, such garbage, refuse and other waste material from all private dwellings as provided for in this chapter and such limited quantities from all manufacturing and commercial establishments as provided for in the rules and regulations of said department.

Wilmington, Del.

It shall be the duty of the Chief Engineer, acting for the Board of Directors of the Department to collect and remove, or cause to be collected and removed, all rubbish and refuse, excepting industrial and commercial rubbish and refuse, but including schools, hospitals, and commercial establishments where they are located in a residential building and the total volume of garbage, rubbish and refuse does not exceed the contents of two twenty-gallon containers twice weekly for each occupancy . . .

Fort Myers, Fla.

Any place or abode or any place of business occupied and/or in operation shall be prima facie evidence that garbage and/or trash is being produced and accumulated in such premises, and it shall be the duty of the Sanitary Director of the City, or his representatives to inspect and supervise said premises and to remove therefrom any and all garbage found thereon, provided that the owner or occupant of such premise is not in default in the payment of the required fees and charges imposed pursuant to the terms of this ordinance.

Coral Gables, Fla.

Industrial wastes and non-combustible refuse as defined herein must be removed by the owner, occupant, operator, or contractor performing such work, or other person creating or causing the accumulation of such materials, as the case may be. Spent oils or greases accumulated at garages, filling stations or similar establishments will not be removed except for the convenience and use of the City of Coral Gables.

Gainesville, Ga.

The City of Gainesville by and through its proper departments shall be responsible for the collection and disposal of all garbage, trash, and refuse within the city, and no person, firm, or corporation shall collect and dispose of, or transport over the streets of the city any garbage, trash, or refuse without first obtaining a written permit from the city to do so.

Caldwell, Idaho

Every owner and occupant of premises within the prescribed limits of the city must use the refuse collection and disposal system herein provided and shall deposit or cause to be deposited in accordance with this regulation all rubbish and garbage that is of such nature that it is perishable, or may decompose, or may be scattered by wind or otherwise.

Mount Prospect, Ill.

All commercial businesses or industrial establishments shall be required to make private arrangements for the collection and disposal of all garbage, refuse, or waste in a prompt and sanitary manner.

Sioux City, Iowa

The term "residential property" shall be deemed to mean all single family residences, duplexes, residences which have been converted to apartments, churches, schools, orphanages, and all structures owned or occupied by the City of Sioux City.

Wichita, Kansas

The sanitation division, with the approval of the board of city commissioners, is hereby authorized to engage, with the equipment and facilities of the city, in the collection and disposal of any refuse in any part of the city.

Ashland, Ky.

. . . the proper maintenance of health and sanitation in the City of Ashland, Kentucky requires, and it is the intention by this ordinance to make the collection, removal, and disposal of garbage, offal, and other refuse matter within the City of Ashland, Kentucky, compulsory and universal . . .

Brunswick, Maine

Whenever the town appropriates for the removal of garbage or rubbish at public expense, collection shall be made regularly within the territory comprised within a radius of one and one-fourth miles from the town hall, unless the town otherwise specifies.

Coldwater, Mich.

Whenever the Common Council of the City of Coldwater shall deem it necessary or advisable they shall, either by advertising for bids or in any other manner at their discretion, enter into a contract and grant a license to such person, persons, firm or corporation as the said Common Council may deem best able to collect garbage in the said City of Coldwater, or any part of district thereof for the purpose of the best disposal of such garbage and to conserve the public health of said City.

Marquette, Mich.

The Manager is hereby empowered, subject to approval of the Commission to determine the areas of the City to be serviced by the garbage collection service, and/or rubbish collection service . . .

Niles, Mich.

All refuse accumulated in the City shall be collected, conveyed and disposed of by the City.

AVAILABILITY AND EXTENT OF SERVICE

Greeley, Colo.

It shall be the duty of city garbage collectors, without charge therefor, to collect and remove at least daily, except Sunday, from public places and private property in the business district and at least twice each week from the first day of May to the thirty-first day of October, and once each week from the first day of November to the thirtieth day of April in the residence district of the city, all garbage in accordance with his contract and the ordinances of the city.

Wilmington, Del.

The time for collection and removal of garbage, rubbish, and refuse as hereinbefore described, shall be between the hours of six o'clock a.m. and six o'clock p.m. and the city shall be divided and served as follows:

Monday and Thursday—all of the city north of Brandywine Creek and all of the city east of Washington Street south of Brandywine Creek, excepting the area from the west side of Shipley Street to the east side of King Street from Front Street to 10th Street. Tuesday and Friday—all of the city south of Brandywine Creek west of Washington Street.

Daily, excepting Saturday and Sunday, the area from the west side of Shipley Street to the east side of King Street from Front Street to 10th Street. When weather conditions make it impracticable to collect and remove garbage, rubbish, and refuse on the day or days appointed, the work shall be done as soon thereafter as practicable, excepting Sundays and legal holidays.

Fort Myers, Fla.

All garbage cans and containers shall be emptied and disposition made of the contents thereof as many times weekly as shall be designated by the Director of Sanitation.

Coral Gables, Fla.

All garbage cans and trash containers shall be required to be emptied, and the contents thereof disposed of, at least twice each week in all residential districts, and as designated by the City Manager in business and industrial districts. It shall be unlawful, and a violation of this ordinance, to permit an accumulation of garbage and/or trash upon any premises in the City of Coral Gables in any event for a period longer than four days without having arranged for disposal of such accumulation by some person qualified and licensed under the ordinance to perform such service or by the Public Service Department of the City of Coral Gables.

Gainesville, Ga.

Collections from residential premises shall be made twice weekly.

Collections from business or commercial premises hereinafter designated as commercial Class A shall be made twice weekly.

Collections from business and commercial premises other than those hereinafter designated as Class A shall be made daily except Sundays and holidays.

Calumet City, Ill.

Whenever the collection of garbage from any establishment or place shall exceed the normal amount from such a place so that the fee prescribed for such collection is not fair and reasonable as applied to that particular place, the Street Commissioner (or other designated officer) shall recommend to the city council the establishment of a special rate for such food place.

Glencoe, Ill.

Abnormal sizes or quantities of rubbish are collected separately following the regular rubbish pickup. Also, yard clippings are collected separately, but on Monday or, if the demand is heavy, on Tuesday and Wednesday.

Lake Forest, Ill.

Ashes, garbage and rubbish accumulated on premises shall be collected by the City's collection services on such schedule and in such manner, with or without charge, as may be prescribed by the regulations for such collection services made by the Director of Public Works and approved by the' City Council, all in accordance with the provisions of this Article.

Ashes, garbage and rubbish accumulated on residential premises shall be collected by the City's collection services on a schedule as prescribed in the regulations for collection services, except where equipment breakdowns, holidays, weather conditions, road conditions or other circumstances beyond the control of the City shall interfere with the prescribed collection schedule, and except where it is agreed between the Director and the occupant of a residence that less frequent collections will suffice for that particular residence.

Stores, offices, restaurants, hotels, clubs, and such other establishments and institutions as deem it necessary may enter into an agreement with the City for a greater frequency of collection than is provided for by the regulations for collection services, or may contract with private scavengers or collectors, licensed by the City, for collection services. Where necessary, in the interests of sanitation and the public health, the Director shall have the authority to require that more frequent collections be made.

The quantity of ashes, garbage or rubbish to be collected at any single collection with special charge shall not exceed the equivalent of the contents of four 21 gallon containers.

The quantity of ashes, garbage or rubbish to be collected from stores, offices, restaurants, hotels, clubs, and other similar establishments without special charge shall not exceed the equivalent of the contents of eight 21 gallon containers in any calendar week.

All collections from schools, hospitals and other institutions shall be subject to the regulations made by the Director of Public Works as approved by the City Council.

The special charges to be made for collections of quantities in excess of those stated in paragraphs above or for any special collections, shall be as established in the regulations made by the Director, as approved by the City Council. The Director shall have the authority to refuse to collect unreasonable amounts of ashes, garbage, rubbish or other refuse or to make any additional charge for such collections.

Mount Prospect, Ill.

Building materials, earth, sod, and rocks resulting from "do-it-yourself" home projects will be picked up . . . The inclusion of these items with the regular pickup has improved the service to the level of unlimited normal refuse collection.

Large items, such as hot water tanks, washing machines, pianos, toys, bicycles, household furniture and appliances of all kinds will be picked up on the regular garbage collection days, thereby eliminating the necessity of telephone notification or special arrangements.

The acceptable size of garbage cans has been increased from 26 gallons to 30 gallons in capacity.

Please remember that all material may be put out on your regular pickup day, with the exception of large trees, and there is no limit as to the number of cans or baskets.

Chariton, Iowa

All garbage must be taken from dwellings at least once a week and from business establishments as frequently as the council may require, but not less than twice a week from food handling and service establishments.

Dubuque, Iowa

Collections shall be made not more than twice weekly, at such times and in such areas of the City as shall be set out in schedules prepared by the City Manager.

Parsons, Kansas

Garbage shall be collected and removed daily from the business districts, hotels, restaurants, public boarding houses boarding five or more individuals, and hospitals; and twice each week from the residence districts.

Lawrence, Kansas

The employees or agents of the City shall make collection of refuse at such regular intervals as shall be prescribed by the Governing Body from time to time. Collection of refuse by others shall not be less frequent than the intervals thus prescribed . . .

Takoma Park, Md.

Collection will be made twice each week for the collection of all "Class 1. Food Waste" . . . and all "Class 1. Dry Waste" . . .

Collections will be made once each week during the heating season (at the request of those persons desiring the service) for all "Class 1. Ashes" . . .

"Class 1. Yard Refuse" . . . and . . . "Class 1. Miscellaneous Refuse" . . . will be collected by the Department of Public Works without charge, as its schedule permits, upon request of those persons desiring the service.

Ferndale, Mich.

The Director of Public Works shall be authorized to arrange dates and schedules for public collection of refuse in the various sections of the City, provided, however, that such schedules shall provide one collection each week from the residential areas and such collections not to exceed five each week (except by special arrangements by the Director of Public Works) from those business establishments and multiple family residences requiring more frequent service.

Niles, Mich.

Refuse accumulated by residences shall be collected at least once each week, except during the months of June, July and August when such refuse shall be collected at least twice each week. Hotels, hospitals, restaurants and other such businesses and institutions as deem it necessary may enter into an agreement for a greater frequency of collection at an increased charge. Where necessary to protect the public health, the System Director shall have the authority to require that more frequent collections be made.

Wyandotte, Mich.

. . . special six to ten yard containers shall be emptied during regular working hours as often as they are filled.

RESPONSIBILITY OF COLLECTORS

Washington, D.C.

Tips or gratuities should not be offered to District employees to perform special or unlawful service. Solicitation of tips or gratuities by collectors are prohibited and should be reported to the Division of Sanitation.

Newton Center, Mass.

Employees of the street department shall not enter upon private property to remove ashes, garbage, or refuse, except when and where directed by the street commissioner.

Quincy, Mass.

Persons using iron receptacles above ground in freezing weather do so at their own risk, as it is practically impossible to remove frozen garbage from an iron receptacle without damage to the receptacle.

Niles, Mich.

The System Director, after identifying himself, shall have authority to enter, at all reasonable times, upon private and public property for the purpose of inspecting and investigating conditions relating to the enforcement of the provisions of this ordinance.

SPECIAL PROBLEMS

Hartford, Conn.

No hazardous refuse will be collected by the department of public works, but shall be transported by the owner, responsible person, or agent to the municipal disposal area and disposed of as prescribed by the director of public works.

Radioactive materials, drugs, poisons, and like substances shall be disposed of under the supervision of the director of health.

Hilo, Hawaii

It shall be unlawful for any person, firm, or corporation within the County of Hawaii to dump, place, or remove to any county dumping grounds any explosives, blasting materials, fuses, live ammunition or any other substance or material that may explode upon contact with heat or fire.

Caldwell, Idaho

Dirt or earth debris from construction or lawn renovation, rocks, stones, automobile bodies and parts, dead animals, building materials such as masonry, plaster, scrap lumber, and wood shavings, are not acceptable for collection and such items shall be collected and disposed of by the building contractor, owner, or occupant of the premises.

Moline, Ill.

No person shall place or caused to be placed in containers provided for garbage or refuse, any bedding, clothing, or other articles contaminated by infectious or contagious diseases. All such refuse shall be burned on the premises and the ashes shall be placed in suitable containers for collection. If the burning of such refuse is impossible, the refuse shall be placed in containers for disposal under the supervision of the Sanitation officer in accordance with the rules and regulations of the Board of Health and the ordinances of the city.

No person shall place or caused to be placed in containers provided for the collection of garbage or refuse, such materials as motion picture film or similar material, celluloid, rags or paper products saturated with inflammable substances or other inflammable or explosive materials . . .

Iowa City, Iowa

Dogs, cats, or any other dead animals shall not be placed in garbage containers. The dead animal pickup service of the Department of Sanitation of the City of Iowa City will, upon notice to it, remove such dead animals.

Wichita, Kansas

The collection of remodeling or construction wastes, dead animals, and animal excrement shall not be deemed to constitute a part of the regular residential collection service provided by the city; provided, however, such refuse may be collected by the city as a special pickup service. The charge for such services shall be determined by the sanitation director and shall be based on the volume of refuse to be collected.

New Orleans, La.

Waste materials, such as soiled dressings, bandages, wearing apparel and bedding that are discarded by households, hospitals, boarding homes for the aged, or other places where infectious or contagious diseases have prevailed, shall be prepared for removal in accordance with instructions from the Director, Department of Health of the City of New Orleans. All such materials shall be wrapped in moisture-proof paper, placed in boxes, and marked "Hospital Waste." Upon notice to the Department of Sanitation, special trips will be made for the removal of such refuse.

The producers of such waste materials as celluloid trimmings, motion picture films, rags or other materials soaked with gasoline, kerosene or other inflammable materials shall place such materials in metal containers with tight covers and remove the same for disposal as instructed by the Director, Department of Sanitation.

Takoma Park, Md.

"Non-Collectable Waste" shall include poisons, acids, caustics, explosives, materials that may cause damage to collection equipment or personal injury to collectors; residue resulting from landscaping, repairs, or alteration of buildings or other structures; human or animal excreta, or any article or substance soiled by human or animal excreta.

Newton Center, Mass.

Discarded or broken furniture, stoves, pipes, machinery, ruins of buildings, remnants of wood and metal from building construction or repairs, wooden boxes and large junk, trimmings from trees and vines and other large bulky or unwieldy refuse may be removed and disposed of by the street department upon application by the owner or occupant of the building or premises who shall pay to the city therefor the actual cost of removal and disposal as determined by the street commissioner; provided, however, that the mayor may suspend for one week in the year, to be determined by him, the provision of this section requiring payment for removal. All the materials offered for removal by application shall be of such form and so prepared and placed as the street commissioner may specify or accept, otherwise they shall not be removed by the city.

Quincy, Mass.

The contractor will not be responsible for the collection of excessive amounts of lobster or clam or crab shells, and in the case of undue amounts, the property owner will have to dispose of them, himself.

Monroe, Mich.

Christmas trees, when set out at the point of collection, will be picked up with the regular collection.

CONTROL OF CONTRACT COLLECTION

Hartford, Conn.

The director of public works, in conjunction with the director of health, may, subject to the authority of the division of purchases and insurance, and with the consent of the council, arrange for contracts, or otherwise provide for the removal and disposition of garbage, ashes, rubbish, waste material, dead animals, night soil, or other offensive substances, and require and receive bonds in such form and for such amounts as they may jointly approve for the performance of the provisions of such contracts. All such contracts shall be signed by the city manager. Such contracts when made shall be carried out under the supervision and control of the department of public works, but cognizance shall always be taken of any complaint or request of the department of health, and such contracts may be canceled or revoked by the director of public works and the director of health whenever the contractor refuses or neglects to perform any of the terms thereof.

Caldwell, Idaho

The Mayor and Council shall be the sole authority to license, contract, or perform all services pertaining to sanitary collection and disposal, and to establish reasonable fees for licenses and is hereby authorized to enter into contracts with one or more contractors, and establish reasonable rules and regulations governing the conduct and operation of such licensees or contractors.

The Council may require of any such collector or contractor a bond in a reasonable amount, the condition of which shall be the satisfactory performance of the contract.

Peoria, Ill.

Extracts from the garbage collection contract:

1. *Definitions.* Said Collector will collect all refuse (deposited in any container, vessel or receptacle) as defined in Sections 18 and 18(a) of Chapter 120 of the Muncipal Code of Peoria (1940) as amended, and said Sections, together with all other applicable provisions of the Municipal Code of Peoria (1940) as amended, are herewith incorporated in this contract in their entirety as an integral part and covenant hereof, as fully as though set forth herein verbatim.

4. *Time of collections.* The Collector agrees to make said collections not less than once each week from each residence, apartment, dwelling, lot or tract within the city limits of said City, and shall submit to the City for approval, a regular weekly schedule subdividing said City by areas and fixing the day of the week upon which collections shall be made from said areas. At the election of the City, it may be required that the City be divided into as many areas as there are refuse collectors in use and that one collecting vehicle be assigned permanently to each area. In any event the schedule of collection shall be subject to the approval of the City and shall become effective upon its approval thereof. Such schedule shall not be changed without the consent of the City, nor without giving at least (15) days' notice to all parties affected. In the event that any alley shall be impassable, the City shall have authority to direct that the refuse be collected on the curb line in the vicinity of said alley, or that routes may be temporarily changed until alley collection is possible.

5. *To furnish equipment.* The Collector agrees to furnish the necessary equipment to remove Christmas trees from the City of Peoria, on the following basis: The City Manager shall designate a Friday and Saturday during the month of January in each year during the term of this contract, at which time the public shall be notified to deliver their trees to certain locations in the City of Peoria designated by the City Manager, and the Collector shall remove such trees from said locations and dispose of the same at the disposal site hereinafter provided for.

7. *Gratuities—Special Service.* Neither the Collector nor his employees shall request or accept any gratuities from any persons, firms or corporations for services required to be performed under this contract; provided that where residents desire a special service over and above that provided by the Ordinance and this contract, they may make such arrangements therefor as they so desire and make any payment therefor to the Collector's office. Where the special service consists of anything other than the removal of the containers, vessels or receptacles of the regular weekly schedule from some place on resident's property other than alley or curb, the work shall be done by special truck and shall not be handled by the collectors on regular routes.

The equipment for the special service in this paragraph described shall be in addition to the equipment required for regular collections, and the equipment for regular collections shall not be utilized for this service except in the case of emergencies.

11. *Transporting refuse.* The Collector shall transport said refuse in such a manner as to be inoffensive to the public, shall exert all reasonable precautions to prevent the spilling or scattering of same while in transit or loading, and in the event that any of such refuse does spill or scatter, he shall immediately clean up and remove such spillage.

12. *Additional territory*. Should the present city limits be extended through annexation, said Collector shall immediately provide collection service to such new residents and shall, in addition to the sum hereinabove agreed to be paid, be compensated at a rate per annum per inhabitant of said additional territory equivalent to the annual sum payable by the City under this contract, divided by 115,000.

16. *Complaints*. All complaints by residents made either to the Collector or the City shall be preserved in writing, in duplicate, which complaint shall set forth the name of party complaining, his address, the date of the complaint and a brief description as to the nature of the complaint. One copy shall be retained by the party receiving such complaint, and one copy shall be delivered to the opposite party; where the opposite party is the Collector, he shall receive the copy, and where the opposite party is the City, one copy shall be delivered to the City.

17. *Disputes with collectors*. Where any dispute arises between a resident and a Collector as to the manner of placing refuse or the nature of the contents or the like, the Collector agrees that in the specific instance, the refuse will be immediately removed even though, in his opinion, it is improperly placed or contained; and that he will immediately report the same to the City so that the two may adjust the same, if possible, before additional collection becomes necessary, it being intended in this article to avoid disputes or disagreements between residents and Collector's employees, and permitting the same to be handled by mutual discussion between the Collector and the City.

20. *Additional services*. The Collector agrees that he will remove all dead dogs and cats from the streets, avenues and alleys of the City and dispose of such animals, without additional compensation.

The Collector further agrees that notwithstanding the provisions of paragraph 4 of this contract, he will make collections twice each week from all housing projects operated within the City of Peoria by the Peoria Housing Authority.

Bluffton, Ind.

The person or firm contracting to provide the service of collecting and disposing of garbage and rubbish shall give a good and sufficient bond to the City of Bluffton, Indiana, in the sum of $25,000.00 dollars for satisfactory performance of duty. The Contractor shall procure and keep in force such liability insurance as the Board of Public Works and Safety may require. The Contractor shall be directly responsible to the Board of Public Works and Safety, whose duty it shall be to see that the collection and disposal of garbage and rubbish is carried out according to the agreement between the Contractor and the City.

Parsons, Kansas

Sample Contract

This agreement, Made and entered into in duplicate this 7th day of December, 1959, by and between the City of Parsons, Labette County, Kansas, a municipal corporation of the first class, Party of the First Part, and Harry Price, an individual doing business as Parsons Sanitation Service, Party of the Second Part:

Witnesseth: That Party of the First Part, in consideration of the covenants and agreements to be kept and performed by the Party of the Second Part, hereinafter set forth, does hereby agree to issue to Party of the Second

Part an exclusive license to engage in the business of hauling garbage and trash within the City of Parsons, Kansas, for a period of ten (10) years, from and after the 1st day of January, 1960.

First Party further agrees that during the period of this Contract, it will keep in effect and as vigorously as reasonably possible enforce Ordinances which will not allow any other person, firm or corporation to engage in the business of hauling garbage and trash within the City of Parsons.

In consideration of the issuance of said exclusive license and the protection thereof as herein set out, Party of the Second Part does hereby covenant and agree with the Party of the First Part as follows:

FIRST: That he will collect and remove daily from the Business District, hotels, restaurants, public boarding houses, hospitals and any and all other places of business, all garbage and trash. That he will collect all garbage and trash from the residential district of said City not less than twice each week. That he will collect all trash and garbage from the Municipal Building, the Police and Fire Department of the City of Parsons, Kansas, free of charge.

SECOND: To conduct such business and to dispose of all garbage and trash during the term of this Contract in strict compliance with the terms and provisions of Ordinance No. 3748 or any amendments thereto, except as the same may be changed by this Contract, and in compliance with the general health and sanitary Ordinances and rules of the City of Parsons, Kansas, where applicable, and the applicable Ordinances of said City are hereby made a part of this Contract by reference.

THIRD: It is agreed that the Party of the Second Part will submit to the Governing Body of the City of Parsons, Kansas, his proposed charges for services to be rendered to the citizens of the City of Parsons, Kansas in collecting and removing garbage and trash. Upon the approval of said proposed charges by the Governing Body of the City of Parsons, Kansas, said charges shall be the legal charges that may be charged and collected by Second Party herein and no charge in excess thereof will be made by Second Party without the consent of the Governing Body of the City of Parsons, Kansas. Said charges may be changed from time to time if agreed upon by both parties.

FOURTH: Party of the Second Part further agrees to keep an office in the City and maintain a listed telephone for the purpose of receiving calls and complaints concerning services; and further agrees that he will give prompt attention to any complaints made and see that any just cause for the complaint is removed. Party of the Second Part agrees to maintain a truck for the purpose of taking care of any calls which are the basis of a complaint and for all emergency uses.

FIFTH: Party of the Second Part further agrees that he will at his own expense maintain in a good manner and according to the best accepted practices a sanitary land fill, and place a man in charge thereof and relieve the City of the necessity of caring for said land fill and city dump. The City shall construct at its expense a permanent fence around the city dump and place appropriate signs and instructions for the use of the land fill by the general public. It is agreed that Second Party shall have the control of anything deposited in the city dump and the right to the use of the salvage therefrom.

SIXTH: Second Party further agrees to pay to First Party during the term of this contract the sum of Three Hundred Dollars ($300.00) per year, payable at the rate of Twenty-five dollars ($25.00) per month, the first monthly payment to be due and payable upon the execution of this contract and a like monthly payment being due and payable each month thereafter.

SEVENTH: Party of the Second Part further agrees to execute and deliver to Party of the First Part a good and sufficient surety bond executed by a reliable corporate surety company authorized to do business in the State of Kansas, subject to the approval of Party of the First Part, in the penal sum of Two Thousand Dollars ($2,000.00) and conditioned upon the faithful performance of this Contract and to save the City from any loss or damage on account of Second Party's conduct of said business.

EIGHTH: Party of the Second Part further agrees that Party of the First Part has the right to cancel and revoke this Contract at any time for cause upon a showing being made that Party of the Second Part has failed or refused to comply with any of the terms thereof.

NINTH: This Contract shall not be assignable by Party of the Second Part without the written consent of Party of the First Part. This contract shall be binding upon the parties hereto, and their successors, heirs, administrators and assigns.

TENTH: Party of the Second Part further agrees that in addition to the removal and disposal of trash as trash is defined in Ordinance No. 3748 or any amendments thereto, he will remove and dispose of all cold ashes, yard trash and tree leaves placed in a receptacle, and tree limbs and trimmings which are properly located in a place readily accessible to Second Party's collectors for removal.

ELEVENTH: It is further agreed that Second Party shall, during the term provided for herein, provide and keep in a clean and neat condition and good repair all necessary automotive and other equipment in order that he can properly and in a good and businesslike manner comply with the terms of this Contract in order that good service may be rendered to the citizens of the City of Parsons, Kansas. To assure the clean and neat condition and good repair of said equipment, First Party shall have the right through its officers or agents, to make periodic inspection of said equipment and Second Party agrees to comply with any reasonable requests made by First Party in regard to maintaining said equipment in a clean and neat condition and in good repair.

TWELFTH: Upon the expiration of the term of this Contract, or in the event of the death or disability of Second Party by reason of health or otherwise, to continue to comply with this Contract, First Party shall have the option to purchase from Second Party, his heirs, executors or administrators, any or all of said equipment used by Second Party in the Parsons Sanitation Service at its fair market value, said value to be determined by three appraisers, one to be chosen by First Party, one to be chosen by Second Party, or his heirs, executors or administrators, and said two appraisers to choose the third, and the appraisal made by said appaisers shall be binding on the parties.

THIRTEENTH: It is further understood and agreed that upon the expiration of the term provided for by this Contract and in the event First Party does not renew said Contract or extend to Second Party an exclusive license to engage in the business of hauling garbage and trash within the City of Parsons, Kansas, Second Party, if requested by First Party, hereby agrees to continue the same service provided for by this Contract for an additional period of sixty days after the expiration of the original term of this Contract in order that First Party shall have sufficient time to make arrangements to provide permanent sanitation service to the citizens of Parsons, Kansas.

FOURTEENTH: No contractor will be permitted to dispose of waste building material in the city dump, nor will any industry be permitted to dispose of industrial waste or refuse in the city dump without first obtaining permission to do so from Second Party and entering into a contract with Second Party for the disposal of such material, waste and refuse in the manner and for the consideration as is fixed by Second Party in said contract.

IN WITNESS WHEREOF, The party of the First Part has caused these presents to be signed by its Mayor, and attested by its Clerk and the seal of the City affixed thereto, and Party of the Second Part has hereunto set his hand the day and year above written.

Florence, Ky.

An ordinance authorizing the city clerk to advertise for bids for the exclusive right and privilege of entering in and upon the streets and public ways of the city of Florence, Kentucky for the collection of garbage, trash and refuse, and providing for the regulations of the manner in which said garbage, trash and refuse shall be collected and disposed of.

Whereas, the City does not now have a contract or franchise agreement concerning the collection of garbage, trash and refuse within the City, and

Whereas, there are now more than one persons or firms attempting to collect same with results in duplication of services, irregular schedules, different charges and other undesirable effects, and

Whereas, the Public Works Committee of this Council has recommended that an exclusive franchise be granted for this purpose.

Now, therefore, the Common Council of the City of Florence, Kentucky does ordain as follows:

Section I. That the City Clerk be, and he is hereby directed to advertise that sealed bids will be received by the Common Council of the City of Florence, Kentucky, (hereinafter referred to as "The City") at a regular meeting to be held on the 12th day of February, 1963, for the exclusive right and privilege of entering in and upon the streets and other public ways of the City of Florence for the purpose of collecting and hauling away from businesses, homes and dwellings and other places where necessary, garbage, trash, and refuse, and providing for the regulation of the manner in which same shall be done.

Section II. The right and privilege to be granted hereunder shall be, and continue for a period of two years from and after the date of acceptance of the bid or proposal hereunder, as herein provided. All bids shall be sealed and marked on the outside with the words, "Bid for Garbage Collection."

Said bids shall be opened at said meeting of this council in open session, and said right and privilege shall be awarded to the bidder who offers to provide the lowest and best rates for the service to be rendered hereunder. The Council reserves the right to reject any and all bids.

Section III. The successful bidder will be required, and by his bid must agree to the following terms and conditions:

(1) To make said collection of garbage, trash and refuse from all homes, dwellings and business places desiring same in the entire city, at least twice a week and on the same day each week, unless a legal holiday occurs during said week, in which event, the successful bidder must give reasonable notice of any variation by newspaper publication.

(2) To furnish a place to, and dispose of said garbage, trash and refuse

outside of the City Limits of Florence, Boone County, Kentucky, and in a manner approved by the Kentucky State Health Department, and all other applicable laws and regulations.

(3) Do his own billing and collecting for said service, it being understood and agreed that there is no responsibility on The City for same.

(4) Use only covered packer type trucks and a sufficient number thereof for the collection of said garbage, trash and refuse.

(5) State the rates to be charged for both residential and business collection and guarantee that said rates will not be increased during the term of this franchise agreement.

(6) State and furnish proof of Workmens Compensation and Unemployment Insurance on his employees and state and furnish proof of Liability Insurance covering both bodily injury and property damage and agree and guarantee to save The City harmless from any and all liability, claims and damage of every kind and nature arising or growing out of said collection of garbage, trash and refuse.

Section IV. Said bid or proposal shall contain the rate per month to be charged to residences and dwellings, and to business places in The City for the collection of garbage, trash and refuse as described herein.

Section V. This ordinance together with the bid or proposal and the resolution of the Council accepting the successful bid, shall constitute a contract for the purposes as hereinabove set out.

Section VI. All ordinances, resolutions or parts thereof in conflict herewith are, to the extent of such conflict, hereby repealed.

Section VII. If any section, paragraph or clause of this ordinance be held by a proper court to be invalid, such invalidity shall not affect the remaining sections, paragraphs or clauses, it being hereby expressly declared that the remainder of said ordinance would have been passed despite such invalidity.

Livonia, Mich.

Whenever any contingency shall in the judgment of the City make such action necessary or advisable the Council may determine to have the City enter into a contract or contracts and to grant a license or licenses to such person, persons, firm or corporation as the Council may deem best able to collect municipal refuse in the City of Livonia in accordance with the best interests of the City and its citizens. The contract shall be for such term as the Council may determine. Any such contract authorized by the Council may be, but need not be, exclusive and the Council may authorize the making on the part of the City of one or more contracts and if the Council shall deem it necessary it may limit such contract to a certain part or parts of the City or to certain types of premises such as residential, commerical and industrial and the like.

Contract or contracts shall be awarded on a competitive basis and the Council shall be responsible for the control of letting and making such contract or contracts. The procedures established by the City Charter and all ordinances in connection with the awarding of contracts shall be observed.

Each person, persons, firm, partnership or corporation entering into a contract with the city for the collection and disposal of garbage and refuse shall furnish the city with a performance bond in an amount established by the Council and in such form as may be approved by the Department of Law, which bond shall be signed by an approved corporate surety authorized to do business in the State of Michigan and which bond shall be conditioned on the satisfactory performance of all obligations assumed under the particular contract and further conditioned on the due observance during the term of the contract of all laws of the State of Michigan, or ordinances of the City of Livonia and all legal rights of all persons who are served by or insured by the Contractor.

Each City Contractor shall carry for each truck public liability insurance sufficient to pay $100,000.00 for one person injured in an accident, $300,000.-00 for all persons injured in one accident and $20,000.00 for property damage and shall deposit with the City Clerk certificates of insurance indicating this coverage prior to the execution of the contract.

The City may require of the City Contractors other bonds and insurance including Workman's Compensation Insurance to insure the City that the obligations of the Contractor will be sufficiently performed and/or discharged and protecting the City in the event that they are not.

The City Clerk shall issue to the Contractor immediately after the execution of the contract a license, without charge, to collect municipal refuse as required by the terms and conditions of the contract for the period of the contract.

No license or contract issued, granted, or entered into, to any City Contractor under the provisions of this ordinance shall be transferable, assignable or sublet without the express permission of the Council in the form of a resolution, unless otherwise expressly provided in the contract.

CONTROL OF PRIVATE COLLECTORS
Coral Gables, Fla.

In all cases in which garbage and/or trash is removed and disposed of by persons other than the employees of the Public Service Department of the City of Coral Gables, the owner or occupant of the premises from which such removal is made shall previously secure a written permit therefor from the Director of the Public Service Department of the City of Coral Gables. The application for such permit shall show the names and addresses of the person or persons by which such removal is to be made, the nature of the vehicle in which it is to be transported, the location at which and the manner in which the ultimate disposition of the garbage is to be accomplished. No person shall contract for or permit himself to be employed for such private disposition of garbage or trash unless he shall have first procured a license therefor, from the City of Coral Gables as provided hereafter.

No person shall remove garbage or trash from any premises in the City of Coral Gables, or transport garbage or trash through the streets or alleys or public ways of the City of Coral Gables, or dump, incinerate, or in any other manner dispose of garbage or trash originating in the limits of the City of Coral Gables, or contract for or permit himself to be employed or engaged for any such removal, transportation or disposal without first having secured a license for such services from the Tax Collector of the City of Coral Gables, evidencing the payment to the City of Coral Gables of the necessary license fee as provided and required by the Occupational License ordinances of the city. Before issuing any such license, the Tax Collector shall require the execution of an application form, to be furnished by him, showing the name or names of the person or persons to be licensed, or, in the case of a corporation, the names of the principal officers and the name of the person or persons who are to actually perform such services for the corporation, together with the business and home addresses of each such person; the description of the equipment to be used in such removal, transportation and disposal;

and the exact location of and the method of disposal. Said application shall be submitted to and approved by the Director of the Public Service Department of the City of Coral Gables as a prerequisite to the issuance of the license. When such application specifies a point of disposal beyond the limits of the City of Coral Gables, the City Manager shall determine that the disposal of garbage at the point named, and by the method described in the application are satisfactory to the proper authorities of Dade County or of the municipality, if such point be within a municipality. No licensee under this section shall change any of the personnel named in such application, nor any of the equipment used for removal or transportation, nor the location or method of disposal, as described in such application, without first having reported such changes to the City Manager and secured his approval and permission therefor, and in the case of changes in the location and method of disposal, if beyond the limits of the City of Coral Gables, such changes shall also be approved by the proper authorities of Dade County or of the municipality within which such disposal point is located. The City of Coral Gables hereby reserves the right to reject any such application without the necessity for showing cause of such action, provided such contractor undertakes to perform work not in the best interests of the City of Coral Gables.

Hilo, Hawaii

It shall be unlawful for any person, firm, or corporation to engage in any business involving the collection and removal of any refuse from any premises within the limits of the City of Hilo, County of Hawaii, without having first received a license from the Treasurer of the County of Hawaii to do so.

All vehicles used for the collection and removal of refuse shall be kept in a clean, inoffensive, and sanitary condition. All refuse shall be handled in such a manner as to prevent the scattering, spilling, or leaking of the same.

Ames, Iowa

License Required. It shall be unlawful for any person, firm or corporation to collect garbage and/or refuse within the City of Ames, except from his own residence or business property without first obtaining a license from the City of Ames.

Application for License. Application for a license to collect garbage and/or refuse shall be made at the office of the city clerk on forms provided by said office. The applicant shall file with his application a certificate or affidavit of insurance as hereinafter set forth and shall pay the required license fee. Upon receipt of such application properly executed the city clerk shall refer the same to the city manager for his approval before issuing the license.

Insurance. The certificate or affidavit to be filed with the application shall be executed by representatives of a duly qualified insurance company evidencing that said insurance company has issued liability and property damage insurance policies covering the following: First, all operations of the applicant, or any other person, firm or corporation employed by him in garbage and refuse collection within the corporate limits of the City of Ames; Second, the disposal of such garbage and refuse to and within any area designated as a sanitary land fill by the City of Ames; Third, protecting the public and any person from injuries or damages sustained by reason of carrying on the work of garbage and refuse collection and disposal. The certificate or affidavit shall specifically evidence the following amounts of insurance coverage which shall remain in effect for the term of the license, and shall provide that written notice shall be given the city clerk thirty (30) days prior to any change in the conditions of the certificate or affidavit, or any expiration or cancellation thereof.

(a) Public liability insurance: $25,000 per person, $50,000 per accident.

(b) Motor vehicle bodily injury liability: $25,000 per person, $50,000 per accident.

(c) Property damage: $10,000 per accident.

Inspection by City Manager. Upon notice from the city clerk that an application has been received, the city manager shall cause to be made an inspection of the applicant's equipment proposed to be used, the pick-up service to be maintained and his methods of operation; and if they meet the requirements herein specified, he shall file his approval with the city clerk.

Issuance of License. Upon receipt of approval from the city manager, the filing of the proper certificates or affidavits of insurance and the payment of the license fee, the city clerk shall issue the applicant a license. All licenses shall expire on December 31st of the year of issue.

Renewal of License. The annual license of all persons licensed under this chapter shall be automatically renewed from year to year upon the payment of the fee herein provided, and the filing of certificate of proper insurance coverage. Licenses may be revoked only upon compliance with the procedures set out at sections 59-20 and 59-21 of this chapter.

The license fee shall be five dollars ($5.00) per year per truck. If issued after July 1st of any year the license fee for the remainder of that year shall be three dollars ($3.00) per truck.

Condition of Vehicles. All vehicles used in the transportation of garbage and refuse within the city shall be kept in a sanitary condition and shall be so constructed as to prevent leakage in transit. The body of the truck shall be wholly enclosed or shall at all times while in transit be kept covered with an adequate cover, or canvas cover, provided with eyelets and rope for tying down. Loading of vehicles shall be done in such manner as to prevent spilling or loss of contents. On or after July 1, 1957, all persons licensed under the terms of this chapter shall use packer type trucks for normal collection purposes.

Frequency of Collections. Collections of garbage from private residences shall be made not less than three times per week from May 1st to November 1st, and not less than two times per week from November 1st to April 30th.

Collections of garbage from hotels, restaurants, clubs, boarding houses or other places of like character where considerable garbage is produced daily shall be made on each week day.

Pick-up Service. Each garbage collector shall maintain an adequate and prompt pick-up service to service all complaints from patrons on missed service and improper handling. Such service shall be promptly available for servicing complaints from the office of the city manager for any material improperly deposited within the limits of streets or highways during transit.

Hauling to Disposal Site. All garbage and refuse collected shall be hauled to a designated sanitary land fill disposal site. All operations including that of unloading shall be as directed by the custodian of the area.

Disposal Sites Under Control of City Manager. The schedule of operation, and all matters pertaining to the control and disposition of garbage and refuse material at sanitary land fill disposal sites shall be under the supervision, inspection, and direction of the city manager.

Periodic Inspection of Equipment. Frequent inspections shall be made by the custodian of disposal sites of equipment used in the transportation of garbage and refuse; and repeated violations of the requirements herein specified shall be called to the attention of the city manager.

Revocation of license. The city council may for repeated violations of the provisions of this chapter upon recommendation of the city manager revoke any license issued after notice and hearing to the person or persons affected.

Port Huron, Mich.

All vehicles used for this collection or disposal of garbage and trash must be certified by the Health Officer as meeting the following minimum standards of sanitation.

1. All trucks should be enclosed trucks and so constructed that the bed of the truck is watertight to prevent spillage of liquid from the body and compartments or sections.

2. The trucks shall be so constructed and enclosed to prevent access by flies and other insects and to prevent the spillage of garbage and the blowing of paper and other debris.

3. The construction of the vehicles shall be such that they are easily cleanable.

4. Where trucks are used for the purpose of hauling trash *only* where no garbage or liquids are hauled, then only that section pertaining to the prevention of the blowing and spilling of paper and debris shall be required as minimum standard.

All trucks must also be certified by the Port Huron Police Department as to compliance with the safety standards of the State of Michigan motor vehicle laws.

All trucks must have the name of the owner or the name of the business clearly displayed on both sides of the truck in letters not less than 3 inches high.

FINANCING

In cases where municipal collection service is financed from general revenue funds, that fact is seldom specifically stated in ordinances. The case of Bluffton, Indiana, shown below is an exception. On the other hand, ordinances are frequently quite specific as to the use of service charges and fees as the other examples given show.

Fort Myers, Fla.

Whereas, City of Fort Myers now owns, operates and maintains a system for the collection and disposal of garbage, trash and other refuse within said City, the operation and maintenance of which system has been and is being financed from the general revenues derived by the City for the purpose of operating the government of said City; and,

Whereas, it is not only necessary but vital to the health, safety and general welfare of the City of Fort Myers and its inhabitants that such system for the sanitary collection and disposal of garbage, trash and other refuse be efficiently and adequately operated and maintained by said City; and,

Whereas, the City Council of the City of Fort Myers deems and considers it equitable and fair and to the best interest of the City and persons using and desiring to use the services and facilities of the garbage collection and disposal system that the operation of said system be made self-supporting as nearly as practicable; Now, Therefore, Be it enacted by the City Council of the City of Fort Myers, Florida . . .

That there is hereby established the following minimum uniform schedule of rates and charges for the services and facilities of the municipal sanitary garbage and trash collection and disposal system of the City of Fort Myers by the owner, tenant, or occupant of the premises using the services and facilities of said system: . . .

Caldwell, Idaho

Collection Fees: Fees and rates for the collection of garbage and refuse shall be set by rules and regulations of the Council. The fee for the collection at residences shall be one dollar and twenty-five cents ($1.25) per month for single family residences. The fee for business houses or multiple family residence shall be set by negotiation and contract between the City and the business houses.

Provided further, that where the enforcement of the provisions of this Chapter will work a financial hardship, or where the amount of refuse and garbage is of such small amount as not to warrant the collection of the full charges as herein provided, the Mayor and Council may issue a special permit altering the provisions of this Chapter.

Method of Collection: Fees shall be carried on the water and sewer bill, and the same shall be paid with the water and sewer bills, and the Water and Sewer Department is authorized to discontinue service to any premises if the entire water, sewer and garbage bill shall not be paid, said charges to become delinquent as provided for water charges, and shall be subject to the same penalties provided for in the case of water and sewer collections.

Sanitary Fund: The proceeds from the collection of fees and charges herein provided shall be placed in a special fund to be known as the Sanitary Service Revenue Fund, and all expenses of the City in the operation of the sanitary collection and disposal system shall be paid out of such fund and any surpluses remaining therein at the end of each fiscal year may be transferred by the Council to the General Fund of the City.

Bluffton, Ind.

All costs and expenses accruing or arising by virtue of General Ordinance No. 264 in the collection and disposal of garbage and rubbish, and all other incidental costs therewith, shall be financed and paid for exclusively from the General Fund of the City of Bluffton, raised by General Tax levy and budgeted or appropriated in accordance with the existing statutes of Indiana.

Newton Center, Mass.

There shall be charged by the city for the collection of ashes, shrubbery, clippings, tree branches and any other refuse, but not for the collection of garbage, the sum of ten cents for each barrel, parcel, box, or other container in excess of two containers.

Clawson, Mich.

The Finance Director shall from time to time make studies of the costs of collecting garbage and other refuse, making suitable allowance for all direct and indirect costs, including wages, supervision, supplies, equipment and depreciation thereon, pension costs, overhead, and all other matters which would be a proper element of cost under accepted principles of accounting for concerns operating for a profit. The City Manager shall from time to time fix the charges required under this ordinance in the light of such studies.

Detroit, Mich.

Domestic Wastes. Domestic waste shall be collected without charge except that waste material scattered on the ground or placed in other than proper receptacles as specified in Article IV may be classed as commercial waste and may be charged for at special rates to be determined by the Commissioner of Public Works and approved by the Common Council.

Commercial Wastes. The Department of Public Works shall collect garbage and/or rubbish from a commercial establishment, subject to payment therefor as provided in this Article. Nothing herein shall be construed to prohibit the party or parties responsible for creating commercial waste from entering into a contract with an authorized private collector or otherwise disposing of such waste, provided it is stored and disposed of in such a manner as to create no nuisance.

Charges for Collection of Commercial Wastes. The Commissioner of Public Works with the approval of the Common Council shall from time to time determine rates for the service of collection of commercial wastes. These rates shall provide for an exemption of not to exceed 20 bushels of commercial rubbish or 200 gallons of commercial garbage in any calendar month from any one establishment, provided this establishment has entered into an agreement to pay for amounts collected in excess of such exemption.

Charges for Disposal of Garbage and Rubbish. The Commissioner of Public Works with the approval of the Common Council shall from time to time establish rates which shall be charged for the disposal of all commercial garbage, commercial rubbish or other wastes delivered to a city-operated incinerator or other disposal location approved by the Commissioner.

Contracts for Service. The Commissioner of Public Works may enter into a contract with a party or parties responsible for creating commercial waste or construction waste. This contract shall provide for payment in accordance with the approved rates for all wastes collected or received by the Department of Public Works. Payment shall be made on the basis of periodic billing, and shall be due in full within 30 days from first date of each bill; provided, that payment may be made by surrender of collection tickets purchased from the Department of Public Works.

PENALTIES FOR VIOLATION

Rehoboth, Del.

Any person violating any provision of this Ordinance upon conviction thereof, shall be subject to a fine of not more than Ten ($10.00) Dollars, or in default of payment thereof, be imprisoned for a period of not exceeding five (5) days for each offense.

Wilmington, Del.

Any person or persons, firm or corporation violating any of the provisions or regulations of this Resolution, shall upon conviction thereof before the Municipal Court be subject to a fine of not less than Five ($5.00) Dollars—nor more than Twenty ($20.00) Dollars for each offense, besides costs of suit.

Longboat Key, Fla.

Any person found guilty of violating the terms of this Ordinance shall be fined a sum not in excess of Two Hundred Dollars ($200.00), or may be imprisoned for a term not in excess of thirty (30) days, or both.

Gainesville, Ga.

Any person, firm or corporation charged with a violation of any Section or provision of this Ordinance shall upon conviction in the Recorder's Court of the City of Gainesville be fined not more than $100.00 or imprisoned not exceeding ninety (90) days or both.

Barrington, Ill.

Any person, firm or corporation violating any provision of this ordinance shall be fined not less than one dollar nor more than Two Hundred Dollars ($200) for each offense, and a separate offense shall be deemed committed on each day during which a violation occurs or continues.

Calumet City, Ill.

Any person, firm, or corporation violating any provision of this ordinance shall be fined not less than five dollars ($5.00) nor more than two hundred dollars ($200.00) for each offense; and a separate offense shall be deemed committed on each day during or on which a violation occurs or continues.

When an occupant of any premises fails to pay the fee for removal of garbage, refuse or ashes the Street Commissioner (or other designated officer) shall notify the occupant of this fact and shall refuse further collection until the required fee is paid.

The fact that garbage, refuse or ashes remains on any occupant's premises in the city in violation of this ordinance shall be prima facie evidence that the occupant of such premises is responsible for the violation of the ordinance occurring.

Ann Arbor, Mich.

Any person who shall violate any provision or provisions of this Chapter shall be guilty of a misdemeanor, punishable as provided in Section 1:13 of the Code.

appendix B

REFUSE COLLECTION IN 1964: SELECTED DATA FROM 956 CITIES

The questionnaire from which most of the statistical data used in this edition of Refuse Collection Practice was derived was distributed in 1964 to all cities in the United States and Canada of more than 5,000 population.

A total of 1,116 replies were received, of which 995 proved to be usable. The data was transferred to IBM cards and processed by the United States Public Health Service under the direction of Mr. John Wheeler and Mr. Larry Crane.

These cards were then re-processed by APWA—when 39 proved to be unusable—to yield the print-out reproduced on the following pages. The data, therefore, relate to 956 cities.

Seven key characteristics of refuse collection practices from among the numerous questions asked in the survey and reported in the various chapters of this volume are represented in the print-out.

Included is the frequency of collection of combined refuse, garbage, ashes, rubbish, and other during Summer and Winter months, from both residential (Res.) and commercial (Com.) sites.

The following code is used to present that data:

1. *Population:* given in thousands.
2. *Systems Used:* M = Municipal; C = Contract; P = Private.
3. *Areas Served:* R = Residential; C = Commercial; M = Manufacturing and Industrial; I = Institutional and Public.
4. *Collection Points:* A = Alley; C = Curb; F = Front of house; R = Rear of house; V = All four collection points used; VO = All four collection points used, plus others.
5. *Set-out/Set-back:* O = Set-out; B = Set-back; OB = Set-out and Set-back.
6. *Frequency of Collection:* Numerals = pickups per week, e.g., 1 = once a week. + = more than four times a week in residential column only; M = Monthly; B = Bi-weekly, every 2 weeks; R = As Required; S = Special, such as Clean-up Week.
   NOTE: Replies to survey on frequency of collection required interpretation and should be used with that in mind.
7. *Method of Financing:* GT = General Tax; SC = Service Charge; TC = General Tax and Service Charge; O = Other.

City	Population Thousands	Systems Used	Areas Served	Collection Points	Set-out Set-back	Method of Financing
ALABAMA						
AUBURN	16	M	ALL	VO	OB	SC
BAYMINETTE	10	M	ALL	C		GT
CHICKSAW	7	M	RCI	AF		SC
FORT PAYNE	5.0	M	ALL	AF		TC
GADSDEN	58.0	M	ALL	ACF		GT
LEEDS	10	M	RCI	CR		GT
MOUNTAIN BROOK		C	MOUNTAIN BROOK	CR		TC
ALASKA						
ANCHORAGE	6	MP	ALL	AC		SC
KETCHIKAN		MP	RCI	O		TC
ARIZONA						
FLAGSTAFF	18	MP	ALL	AC		GT
PHOENIX	439	MP	RCI	ACF		GGT
SCOTTSDALE	27.5	MP	ALL	ACF		TC
TEMPE	21.3	MC	RCI	C		SGTC
TUCSON	213	MP	ALL	AC		GTC
VANCOUVER			ALL	AC		TC
ARKANSAS						
CAMDEN	16	M	ALL	CR		SC
NEWPORT	8	M	ALL	AR		SC
RUSSELLVILLE	9	C	AGC	RR	B	SC
SPRINGDALE	12	C	RC		O	
CALIFORNIA						
ALAMEDA	64	C	ALL	VO		SGT
ANAHEIM	118	C	ALL	ACR		O
ARCADIA	41	P	RCI	CF	O	SC
ARCATA	5	R	ALL	O		
ATWATER	7	C	RC	AC		
AZUSA	21	M	C	AR		SGT
BAKERSFIELD	54	C	ALL	VC	O	O
BALDWIN PARK	34	C	ALL	AC		SC
BANNING	13	P	RC			
BARSTOW	12	C	RC	AC		TC
BELMONT	16	C	C	R		GT
BERKELEY	111	H	RCI	V		GCTC
BEVERLY HILLS	34	M	ALL	ACO		SC
BUENA PARK	46	C	ALL	ACO		SC
BURBANK	92	H	ALL	ACF		GTC
CHULA VISTA	48	M	ALL	ACR		SC
CLAREMONT	19	M	CM	R		SC
COLTON	19	C	RCI	AC		GT
COMPTON	72	C	RCI	AC		SC
CORONADO	18	C	RC	R		GT
CORTE MADERA	6	U	LL	V		TC
COSTA MESA	59	P	ALL	AC		SC
CULVER CITY	32	H	RCM	AC		SC
DELANO	15	M	ALL	AC		SC
DUARTE	14	C	ALL	AC		GT

City	Population Thousands	Systems Used	Areas Served	Collection Points	Set-out / Set-back	Comb. Refuse Summer	Comb. Refuse Winter	Garbage Summer	Garbage Winter	Ashes Summer	Ashes Winter	Rubbish Summer	Rubbish Winter	Other Summer	Other Winter	Method of Financing
EL CAJON	40	P	ALL	AF		1	1	1	1							GT
EL SEGUNDO	15	C	ALL	AC		1	1	1	1					R	R	SC
ESCONDIDO	16	C	ALL	AC	O	R	2									SC
FREMONT	44	C	ALL	R		1	1									SC
FRESNO	156	H	JC	ARC		R	R									
FULLERTON	36	C	RC	C		1	1									SC
GARDENA		Q	ALL	O		1	1	7	7							SC
GILROY	7	D	JC	AC		1	1									TC
GLENDALE	120	P	ALL	V		6	2									
HANFORD	10	M	JC	R		R	1									
HAYWARD	93	X	RC	R		1	1	1	1	6	6	6	6	R	R	TC
HOLLISTER	87	R	RC													
HUNTINGTON BEACH	11	C	ALL	AC		6	2									TC
INGLEWOOD	63	M	CM	AC		R	7									SC
INGLEWOOD		C	I	AOF		R	1									SC
LA MESA	30	C	ALL	ACC		2	2									TC
LA MIRADA	28	P	ALL	ACU		1	1									T
LA PUENTE	70	P	RC	C		1	1									S
LAKEWOOD	80	A	ALL	AV		R	1									
LARKSPUR	16	U	RC	R		R	1									
LIVERMORE	22	U	I	R		6	1	1	1							SC
LODI		O	RCM	C												
LOMPOC	247	M	ALL	AC		1	1									SC
LOS ANGELES	9	C	RCI	ACC		2	2	2	2					R	M	TC
LOS BANOS	75	U	ALL	AFR		6	2									SC
LYNWOOD	32	M	RCM	ACC		R	1									SC
MADERA	14	C	ALL	AV		1	1									
MANTECA	8	C	ALL	F		1	1				R	R		R	R	
MARIN COUNTY	0	C	ALL	R		1	1	1	1							
MARTINEZ	10	P	I	C		R	1	1	1							
MERCED	21	M	AR	R		R	R									
MIDWAY DIST		X	ALL	AC		5	2									SC
MILPITAS	7	C	ACM	CRR		5	5									TC
MODESTO	37	P	RCM	ACC		R	R							6	6	
MONCTON		P	ALL	AC		R	1							1	1	
MOUNTAIN VIEW	31	C	ALL	CR		R	1	1	1					6	1	GT
NAPA	27	P	ALL	VC		5	5							1	1	SC
NORTH SACRAMENTO	14	MC	R	AC		R	1							1	1	GT
NORTH SACRAMENTO		MC	AR	R												GT
NORWALK	89	P	AC	AC		1	1							1	1	
OAKLAND	361	C	RCM	R		R	1	6	6	6	6	6	6	6	6	SC
OCEANSIDE	25	M	ALL	CR		R	1							1	1	GT
ONTARIO	48	M	ALL	ACF		1	1	2	2							SC
ORANGE	26	C	AC	AFR		R	R	1	1			R	R			SC
OROVILLE	52	L	RCI	ACC		R	2	7	7							SC
OXNARD	12	M	RC	AV		1	1	R	R	R	R	R	R			TC

City	Population Thousands	Systems Used	Areas Served	Collection Points	Set-out/Set-back	Comb. Refuse Summer (R,C,O,m,s)	Comb. Refuse Winter (R,C,O,m,s)	Garbage Summer	Garbage Winter	Ashes Summer	Ashes Winter	Rubbish Summer	Rubbish Winter	Other Summer	Other Winter	Method of Financing
PALM SPRINGS	16	M	ALL	R		R 1	R 1									TC
PALO ALTO	56	C	ALL	R		R 1	R 1									SC
PARAMOUNT	28	CP	ALL	V		R 1	R 1									SC
PASADENA	116	MP	RI	V	O											TC
PASADENA	19	C	ALL	CRO		R 1	R 1	R	R	R	R	R	R			SC
PITTSBURG	5	P	R	ACO		R 1	R 1									
PLACENTIA	67	MP	CMI	AC		R 5	R 5									TC
POMONA	16	M	ALL	AR		C 2	C 2									SC
REDDING	30	M	RC	AR		R 1	R 1	6	6	6	6	6	6			SC
REDLANDS	49	M	ALL	ACF		R 6	R 6									TC
RIVERSIDE	100	M	ALL	AR		6 1	6 1									SC
ROSEVILLE	15	C	RC	ACR		R 1	R 1									SC
SALINAS	50	CP	ALL	ACR		R 2	R 2	2	2			R	R			GT
SAN BUENAVENTURA	33	P	RCI	ACC		R 1	R 1									GT
SAN BUENAVENTURA	525	P	ALL	ACC		5 2	5 2									
SAN DIEGO COUNTY	225	CP	ALL	F		R 1	R 1									
SAN DIMAS	7	P	CMI	AC		R 2	R 2	2	2							SC
SAN FERNANDO	16	MP	ALL	AC												
SAN JOSE	203	CP	ALL	CR		6 1	6 1									SC
SAN RAFAEL	204	P	ALL	AC		R 1	R 1									TC
SANTA ANA	100	C	RCI	AC		R 1	R 1	R	R					R	R	SC
SANTA CLARA	159	MC	R	VOR		R 2	R 2	2	2	1	1	5	5	R	R	SC
SANTA CLARA	28	M	ALL	AC		R 1	R 1									
SANTA CRUZ	160	P	ALL	AC		R 1	R 1			1	1	1	1			GT
SANTA FE SPRINGS	20	MP	ALL	AC		R 1	R 1			1	1	1	1			SC
SANTA MARIA	84	MP	ALL	AC												TC
SANTA MONICA	13	M	CMI	AC												SC
SANTA PAULA	6	C	ALL	R		5 1	5 1									SC
SAUSALITO	54	C	CM	AC		R 1	R 1							R	R	
SOUTH GATE	86	CP	R	AR		R 1	R 1							R	R	SC
SOUTH GATE	26	P	ALL	ARF		1	1							R	R	SC
SOUTH PASADENA	31	A	ALL	ACF		2 1	2 1	2	2	1	1	5	5			
STOCKTON	61	C	ALL	ACF		R 1	R 1									SC
TEMPLE CITY	16	MP	ALL	ACR		R 1	R 1									SC
UPLAND	16	C	ALL	CR		R 1	R 1							R	R	CC
VALLEJO	14	M	RC	AC		R 1	R 1							R	R	SC
VISALIA	57	MC	ALL	AC		R 1	R 1									SC
WALNUT CREEK	16	MC	ALL	CC		R 1	R 1									GC
WATSONVILLE		MC					1					1	1		1	SC
WEST COVINA																
WHITTIER																
WOODLAND																
COLORADO																
ARVADA	19	CP	ALL	AR								R	R			

City	Population Thousands	Systems Used	Areas Served	Collection Points	Set-out / Set-back	Method of Financing
ARVADA	48	CP	RC	R		GT
AURORA	38	P	RCM	ACR		
BOULDER	7	CP	RCM	ACF		GT
BRIGHTON		CP	ALL	V		
COLORADO SPRINGS	70	P	CM	AR		GT
DENVER		MP	ALL	AC		GT
ENGLEWOOD	33	CP	ALL	AC	O	
FORT COLLINS	25	C	ALL	C		GT
GREELEY	27	MP	ALL	CR		GT
GREELEY		MPC	RI	ARC		O
LONGMONT	15	MPC	CM	V		TC
LONGMONT		MPC	ALL	C		SC
MONTROSE	5	M	ALL	AC		SC
PUEBLO	91	CP	ALL	V		GT
PUEBLO		CP	ALL	AC		
STERLING	11	MP	ALL	AC		SC
WALSENBURG	5	P	RC	AR		
CONNECTICUT FARMINGTON	12	CP	RCI	CR	O	SC
GREENWICH	54	C	ALL	R		SC
HARTFORD	162	MP	CMI	CR		GT
MANCHESTER	42	MP	RCI	CR	O	SC
MIDDLETOWN	31	CP	ALL	AC		GT
NEW LONDON	34	M	ALL	CCR		GT
PLAINVILLE	14	CP	RCI	CR	B	GT
ROCKVILLE	10	MC	ALL	V		GT
ROCKVILLE	93	MP	ALL	CR		GT
STAMFORD		MP	RCM	AR		GT
TORRINGTON	30	CP	RCM	AR		GT
WEST HARTFORD	62	CP	ALL	AR		GT
WETHERSFIELD	21	M	CM	I		SC
WETHERSFIELD		CP	RI	V		
WINCHESTER	11	P	ALL			
WINDSOR	20	CP	ALL	V		SC
WINDSOR		CP	RC	C	O	
DELAWARE WILMINGTON	96	M	RI	ACR		GT
DISTRICT OF COLUMBIA WASHINGTON	764	MP	CMI	AFR		GT
WATERLOO		MP	ALL	AC		GT
WELLAND		MC	RC	C		GT

Table — Refuse Collection Practice (Florida, Georgia, Idaho)

City	Population Thousands	System Used	Areas Served	Collection Points	Set-out / Set-back	Comb. Refuse (Summer / Winter)	Garbage (Summer / Winter)	Ashes (Summer / Winter)	Rubbish (Summer / Winter)	Other (Summer / Winter)	Method of Financing
FLORIDA											
BARTOW	13	M	ALL	ACR	OB		2/2				SC
CLEARWATER	34	M	RC	VO		6/2	5/2		1/1	B/B	SG
CORAL GABLES	35	C	ALL	ACR		2/2	2/2		1/1	1/1	GC
DAYTONA BEACH	17	M	ALL	AFR			2/2		1/1		SC
DUNEDIN	3	P	ALL	V	5/5	2/2		3/3			SG
EAU GALLIE		M	ALL	ACR			2/2		2/2		S
FORT MYERS	30	P	ALL	ACR		5/5	6/6		3/3		SG
GAINESVILLE	46	MC	C				1/1	R/R	R/R		I
HOLLYWOOD											
KISSIMMEE	4	MP	RC	AC		R/2	5/2		5/1		SG
KISSIMMEE	5	MC	ALL	CR	R/2	R/2		R/1			GC
LAKELAND	29	MP	RC	ACR		R/2	R/2	R/1	1/1		CG
LARGO	7	MP	RCI	ACR		3/3	1/1	1/1	1/1		GT
MELBOURNE	4	M	ALL	CAFRO			2/2		1/1		SC
MIAMI	11	MC	RC	ACR		7/7	7/7		2/2		GC
MIRAMAR			RC	ACR		1/1	1/1				
NAPLES		MC	ALL	ACF			3/3		6/6		S
OCALA	19	M	ALL	R		6/6	6/6		2/2		SC
PALM BEACH	40	MC	ALL	CFR	8/8	1/1	1/1	2/2	1/1		SC
PINELLAS PARK	50	MC	RCM	ACC		2/2	2/2		8/8		CS
PINELLAS PARK	276	MP	RCI	ACR		R/R	R/R		1/1		SC
SANFORD	19	MP	ALL	CR		6/6	6/6	6/6			GT
SARASOTA	18	M	ALL	ACR		R/R	R/R		R/R		C
GEORGIA											
ATLANTA	487	MP	RCI	O		R/2	5/5		2/2		GT
ATLANTA	70	MP	RCM	ACR		3/3	3/3	6/6	2/2		GG
AUGUSTA	7	MC	RCM	ACR		*/*	*/*		R/R		GG
AUGUSTA	7	M	RCI	VOU		3/3	3/3	2/2	1/1		GG
CAIRO	117	MPC	RCI	ACC		2/2	2/2		1/1		TC
CHAMBLEE	36	MPC	ALL	ACR		2/2	2/2	2/2	6/6		GC
CHAMBLEE	17	M	ALL	ACR		2/2	2/2				TC
COLUMBUS	27	M	AR	AR		5/2	5/2		1/1		GT
EAST POINT	25	M	AC	AC		5/2	5/2	R/R	2/1		GG
GAINESVILLE	120	M	ALL	R		R/2	R/2		1/1		TC
GRIFFIN	140	M	ALL	V				1/1	1/1		GG
JESUP	18	M	ALL	V		5/2	5/2		R/R		TC
MARIETTA	31	M	ALL	V							TC
IDAHO											
BLACKFOOT	8	M	ALL	AC		5/5	5/5		R/R		TC

City	Population Thousands	Systems Used	Areas Served	Collection Points	Set-out Set-back	Comb. Refuse Summer R C e S m	Comb. Refuse Winter R C e S m	Garbage Summer	Garbage Winter	Ashes Summer	Ashes Winter	Rubbish Summer	Rubbish Winter	Other Summer	Other Winter	Method of Financing
BOISE	74	CC	ALL	V		2 6 6	2 6 6									SC
CALDWELL	13	CC	ALL	V		2 6 2	2 6 2									SC
IDAHO FALLS	33	M	RCI	AC		1 6 R	1 6 R									TC
ILLINOIS																
ADDISON	9	C	ALL	ACR	8	1 5 R 6	1 1 2 R 1									SC
ALTON	44	E	RL	AFR		1 5 R 6	1 1 2 R 1									GT
ARLINGTON HEIGHTS	29	C	ALL	AC		1 5 R 6	1 1 2 R 1									SC
BARRINGTON	5	C	RCC	A												SC
BLOOMINGTON	36	C	CMI	AFU												GT
CALUMET CITY	25	M	ALL	AOU												SC
CARMI	6	P	CMI	AC		1 6 1	1 2 1									
CHAMPAIGN		MP	RCI	AC												G
CHICAGO	3550	MP														TC
CHICAGO																
DE KALB	19	M	RCM	AC		2 6 1	2 2 1	1 1	1 1		5	5		S	S	GT
DEERFIELD	12	A	RCR	ARC				1	1							
DIXON	9	P	RCM	A												I
ELGIN		MPC	RCC	AV							1	1				
ELGIN		MPC	RCI	CR										M	M	GT
ELK GROVE	10	P	RCI	CR												C
ELMHURST	40	A	RCI	FRC		5	1	1 1	1 1		1	1				SC
ELMHURST		P	RCR	AC				1	1							
EVERGREEN PARK	25	C	AR	AV												
FRANKLIN PARK	18	MPC	RL	AC		1 6 1	1 3 1							S	S	GT
FRANKLIN PARK		MPC	AR	A		1 6 1	1 3 R									G
FREEPORT	27	MPC	RI	CR		1 6 1	1 R 3 R									TC
FREEPORT		MPC	ALL	CR		2 1 2	2 1 1	2	2							SC
GLENVIEW		MPP	RCC	AC		R 2 1	1 2 1	1	1		1	1				SC
LAKE FOREST	11	MP	RCI	V		R 2 1	1 1 1	1	1		1	1				
LAKE FOREST	11	MP	RL	AC												
LAWRENCEVILLE		CC	ALL	AC		R 6 R	1 1 2 R									
METROPOLIS	27	CC	RCI	AV		1 R 6	1 1 R 6									
MOLINE	43	MP	RL	AC		R 2	1 2 1							S	S	GT
MORTON GROVE	23	CC	A	AC		R 2	1 2 1	1	1	1						SC
MOUNT PROSPECT	20	CC	RI	OAC				1	1							GT
NILES	16	C	RI	CAC		R 6	R 1 1 1									GT
OAK PARK	50	P	ALL	V		R 6	R 1 1 1									TC
PALATINE	10	AP	RCI	VV												IC
PARK FOREST	33	MP	RCI	AC		R 6	R 1 1 1									SC
PARK RIDGE	28	MP	ALL	AC												SC
PEKIN			RI	AC												
PEORIA	103	CMP	RI	AC		R	1 1 2									GT
QUINCY	45	MP	RCI	AR		R	N 1 1									TC
RIVERSIDE	10	AP	ALL	OQ												SC
ROCK ISLAND	54	PP	RCI	AC		R	1 1 2									GT
ROCK ISLAND	6	CP	RL	AC		R	1 1 2									SC
SCHILLER PARK	59	MP	R	AC												GT

City	Population Thousands	Systems Used	Areas Served	Collection Points	Set-out Set-back	Comb. Refuse Summer R/C	Comb. Refuse Summer e/S	Comb. Refuse Winter R/C	Comb. Refuse Winter e/S	Garbage Summer R/C	Garbage Summer e/S	Garbage Winter R/C	Garbage Winter e/S	Ashes Summer R/C	Ashes Summer e/S	Ashes Winter R/C	Ashes Winter e/S	Rubbish Summer R/C	Rubbish Summer e/S	Rubbish Winter R/C	Rubbish Winter e/S	Other Summer R/C	Other Summer e/S	Other Winter R/C	Other Winter e/S	Method of Financing
TAYLORVILLE	9	MPC	RC	AC	—	1	2	—	2	1	—	M	—	R	—	R	—	R	—	R	—	R	—	R	—	GT
VANDALIA	6	P	RC	AC	—	5	2	5	2	—	—	—	—	—	—	—	—	—	—	—	—	—	—	—	—	—
WEST CHICAGO	7	P	ALL	—	—	5	1	5	1	—	—	—	—	—	—	—	—	—	—	—	—	—	—	—	—	—
WESTERN SPRINGS	12	C	RCI	ACR	—	R	2	R	2	—	—	—	—	—	—	—	—	—	—	—	—	—	—	—	—	SC
WILMETTE	30	MC	RTI	ACR	—	—	—	—	—	2	2	2	—	—	—	—	—	—	—	1	—	—	—	—	—	TC
WINNETKA	13	MC	ALL	AR	—	R	2	R	2	1	—	1	—	1	—	1	—	1	—	1	—	—	—	—	—	TC
INDIANA																										
AUBURN	7	CP	CMI	O	—	R	1	R	1	—	—	—	—	—	—	—	—	—	—	—	—	—	—	—	—	T
AUBURN	7	CP	RC	AR	—	R	2	R	2	2	—	2	—	1	—	1	—	—	—	—	—	—	—	—	—	GT
BLUFFTON	6	M	ALL	ACFR	—	R	1	R	1	—	—	—	—	—	—	—	—	—	—	—	—	—	—	—	—	T
CHARLESTOWN	15	M	R	ACR	—	4	2	4	2	—	—	—	—	—	—	—	—	—	—	—	—	—	—	—	—	GT
CRAWFORDSVILLE	12	M	ALL	AC	—	6	1	6	1	—	—	—	—	—	—	—	—	—	—	—	—	—	—	—	—	GT
ELWOOD	11	M	RC	AC	—	5	1	5	1	—	—	—	1	—	1	—	1	—	1	—	1	—	—	—	—	GT
GREENSBURG	7	M	ALL	C	—	1	1	1	1	—	—	—	1	—	1	—	1	—	1	—	1	—	—	—	—	GT
GRIFFITH	9	MPC	RC	AC	—	1	2	1	2	—	—	—	—	—	—	—	—	—	—	—	—	—	—	—	—	GT
HAMMOND	117	MPC	RC	—	—	2	2	2	2	—	—	—	—	—	—	—	—	—	—	—	—	—	—	—	—	—
KOKOMO	48	MC	RC	AC	—	R	2	R	2	—	—	—	—	—	—	—	—	—	—	—	—	—	—	—	—	GT
LAFAYETTE	42	MC	RI	AR	—	2	2	2	2	—	—	—	—	—	—	—	—	—	—	—	—	—	—	—	—	GT
LAFAYETTE	20	M	ALL	AC	—	1	1	1	1	—	—	—	—	—	—	—	—	—	—	—	—	—	—	—	—	GT
NEW CASTLE	13	M	ALL	O	—	1	1	1	1	—	—	—	—	—	—	—	—	—	—	—	—	—	—	—	—	—
WABASH		P	ALL	—	—	1	1	1	1	—	—	—	—	—	—	—	—	—	—	—	—	—	—	—	—	—
IOWA																										
AMES	27	P	RC	V	—	3	3	3	3	—	—	—	—	—	—	—	—	—	—	—	—	—	—	—	—	TC
ASPALOOSA	12	MP	RI	O	—	6	1	1	1	—	—	—	—	—	—	—	—	—	—	—	—	—	—	—	—	SC
BETTENDORF		M	AC	AC	—	2	1	1	1	—	—	—	—	—	—	—	—	—	—	—	—	—	—	—	—	G
BETTENDORF	21	M	RI	AC	—	1	1	1	1	—	—	—	—	—	—	—	—	—	—	—	—	—	—	—	—	T
CEDAR RAPIDS	92	MP	CMI	—	—	1	2	1	2	—	—	—	—	—	—	—	—	—	—	—	—	—	—	—	—	T
CEDAR RAPIDS		MP	RC	ACR	—	R	2	R	2	—	—	—	—	—	—	—	—	—	—	—	—	—	—	—	—	G
CENTERVILLE	7	P	ALL	AC	—	5	1	5	1	—	—	—	—	—	—	—	—	—	—	—	—	—	—	—	—	SC
CHARITON	5	P	ALL	O	—	6	2	6	2	—	—	—	—	—	—	—	—	—	—	—	—	—	—	—	—	G
CLARINDA	6	P	ALL	V	—	R	1	R	1	—	—	—	—	—	—	—	—	—	—	—	—	—	—	—	—	—
CLEAR LAKE	5	M	RC	ACR	—	R	2	R	2	—	—	—	—	—	—	—	—	—	—	—	—	—	—	—	—	SC
COUNCIL BLUFFS	58	M	RI	AR	—	1	1	1	1	—	—	—	—	—	—	—	—	—	—	—	—	—	—	—	—	SC
DES MOINES	209	M	ALC	O	—	2	2	2	2	—	—	—	—	—	—	—	—	—	—	—	—	—	—	—	—	G
DUBUQUE	57	M	RC	AC	—	2	1	2	1	—	—	—	—	—	—	—	—	—	—	—	—	—	—	—	—	G
DUBUQUE		CP	R	AC	—	1	2	1	2	—	—	—	—	—	—	—	—	—	—	—	—	—	—	—	—	G
FAIRFIELD	8	P	ALL	LO	—	2	2	2	2	—	—	—	—	—	—	—	—	—	—	—	—	—	—	—	—	G
FORT MADISON	15	M	ALL	AR	—	2	2	2	2	—	—	—	—	—	—	—	—	—	—	—	—	—	S	S	S	SC
INDEPENDENCE	5	M	RCM	AR	—	R	2	R	2	—	—	—	—	—	—	—	—	—	—	—	—	—	S	S	S	SC
IOWA CITY	33	P	R	O	—	R	2	R	2	—	—	—	—	—	—	—	—	—	—	—	—	—	—	—	—	G
IOWA FALLS	6	P	ALL	V	—	R	1	R	1	—	—	—	—	—	—	—	—	—	—	—	—	—	—	—	—	G
KEOKUK	17	M	RCM	AF	—	1	2	1	2	—	—	—	—	—	—	—	—	—	—	—	—	—	—	—	—	—
KNOXVILLE	8	C	RCM	AR	—	R	1	R	1	—	—	—	—	—	—	—	—	—	—	—	—	—	—	—	—	—
LE MARS	7	P	RC	ACR	—	R	2	R	2	—	—	—	—	—	—	—	—	—	—	—	—	—	—	—	—	—
MAQUOKETA		P	R	R	—	1	1	1	1	—	—	—	—	—	—	—	—	—	—	—	—	—	—	—	—	—
MASON CITY	31	MP	ALL	AR	—	R	2	R	2	—	—	—	—	—	—	—	—	—	—	—	—	—	—	—	—	G
MASON CITY		HP	ALL	AR	—	R	2	R	2	—	—	—	—	—	—	—	—	—	—	—	—	—	—	—	—	—
OTTUMWA	34	C	ALL	—	—	R	2	R	2	—	—	—	—	—	—	—	—	—	—	—	—	—	—	—	—	SC

City	Population (Thousands)	Systems Used	Areas Served	Collection Points	Set-out / Set-back	Method of Financing
PERRY CITY	6	M	ALL	V	—	SC
SIOUX CITY	9	CP	CM	AO	—	GT
SIOUX CITY	89	CP	RI	AC	—	
STORM LAKE	8	CP	RC	ACR	—	SC
URBANDALE	6	M	RC	C	—	GT
WATERLOO	73	M	RA	AR	—	GT
WAVERLY	6	MP	ALL	A	—	SC
WEST DES MOINES	12	MP	R	I	—	
WEST DES MOINES		MP	R	—	—	GT
KANSAS AUGUSTA	7	MP	CM	ACR	—	SC
AUGUSTA	17	MP	ALL	ACR	—	SC
COFFEYVILLE	130	P	ALL	AR	—	SC
HAYS	40	MCC	RMI	ACR	—	SC
HUTCHINSON	19	MP	ALL	A	—	SC
HUTCHINSON	5	M	RCI	F	—	SC
JUNCTION CITY	30	C	ALL	ACR	—	SC
LAWRENCE		C	ALL	AC	—	TC
MCPHERSON		CCP	ALL	F	OB	
OTTAWA	114	C	ALL	AR	—	SC
PARSONS	28	CCP	RCI	V	—	SO
PRAIRIE VILLAGE	39	MPP	RCI	I	—	
SALINA		MP	R	O	—	SC
WICHITA	270	MP	ALL	AFRO	—	SC
KENTUCKY ASHLAND	33	M	RC	AR	—	SC
FLORENCE	5	M	RCI	C	—	GT
FORT THOMAS	10	M	RCI	U	—	GT
GLASGOW	69	M	RCI	CF	—	TC
HAZARD	30	M	RCI	AR	—	GT
MURRAY		MP	RCI	ACF	—	GT
NEWPORT	153	M	RCI	AC	—	
LOUISIANA BATON ROUGE	40	M	RCI	ACF	—	GT
BOSSIER CITY	67	MP	ALL	ACR	—	SC
CROWLEY	657	M	RCI	AC	—	SC
LAKE CHARLES		M	CM	I	—	SC
NEW ORLEANS	9	M	RC	AFR	—	GT
PINEVILLE		MPC	RCI	U	—	GT
MAINE AUBURN	24	MP	ALL	C	—	GT
BANGOR	40	MPC	RCM	AFR	—	SC
BANGOR		MP	RCI	L	—	
BRUNSWICK	16	MPC	RCI	UFR	—	GT
BRUNSWICK		MP	U	C	—	SC
MADAWASKA	6	MPC	R	C	—	GT
PORTLAND	73	MPC	CR	CR	—	GT

City	Population Thousands	Systems Used	Areas Served	Collection Points	Method of Financing
RUMFORD	10	MP	CMI	U	GT
RUMFORD	6	MP	CM	U	GT
SCARBOROUGH	23	MP	RC	L	GT
SCARBOROUGH		PC	RC	L	GT
SOUTH PORTLAND		MC	RC	F	
SOUTH PORTLAND					
MARYLAND					
ABERDEEN	10	MP	RCI	AC	TC
ANNAPOLIS	25	MP	CI	AR	
ANNAPOLIS			RCI	ACF	TC
BALTIMORE COUNTY	500	CM	RC	AF	GT
CAMBRIDGE	20	MP	ALL	RC	GT
CARROLLTON	100	MP	AR	AC	GT
COLLEGE PARK	207	MP	CMI	AC	GT
HAGERSTOWN	17	MC	CR	AC	GT
SALISBURY					
SALISBURY					GT
SEAT PLEASANT	17	CI	RCI	RC	TC
TAKOMA PARK	14	M	CM	ACR	TC
MASSACHUSETTS	697				
AMHERST	60	CP	RCI	RC	TC
BOSTON	34	CP	CM	RC	TC
BOSTON	65	M	ALL	AC	TC
BROOKLINE	26	MM	ALL	RC	GT
CHELSEA	93	MU	RCILM	RLF	TC
CHICOPEE FALLS		CM	RCLM	CR	GT
LEOMINSTER		MC	ALL	AC	TC
NEEDHAM					
NEWTON CENTRE	20	CP	ALL		GT
NEWTON CENTRE	87	CP	CM	RC	TC
NORTH ADAMS	209	CP	RI	UCR	TC
QUINCY	34	CP	RCILM	FR	GT
QUINCY	190	M	RCILM	FR	GT
RANDOLPH	190	UM	RCI	AR	GT
READING	20		R		
SALEM		MP	CM	OC	GT
WALPOLE		MP	ALL	RC	GT
WINCHESTER		P	RCILM	RC	GT
WORCESTER		MP	RCILM	CR	GT
MICHIGAN			RCUM	CF	GT
ADRIAN		MPC	CM	AC	GT
ADRIAN		MPC	R		
ALBION	20				
ALPENA					
ANN ARBOR					
BAY CITY					
BENTON HARBOR					
BERKLEY					
BIRMINGHAM					
BIRMINGHAM	15	M	RCI	ACR	GT
BUCHANAN	15	M	RCI	AC	GT
CLAWSON					

City	Population Thousands	Systems Used	Areas Served	Collection Points	Method of Financing
COLDWATER	9	MP	RCI	R	SC
DETROIT	1670	MP	CM	ACO	TC
DEARBORN	46	M	ALL	F	GT
EAST DETROIT	30	M	RCI	AC	GG
EAST LANSING	15	M	RCI	AC	GG
ESCANABA	13	M	ALL	C	
FERNDALE	31	MP	CMI		
FLINT	197	M	RCI	AR	GT
GRAND HAVEN	11	MC	RCI	ARC	GSC
GRAND RAPIDS	202	P	ALL	AC	GG
GRANDVILLE	8	CM	ALL	AC	GG
GREENVILLE	7	C	RCI	C	GG
GROSSE POINTE FARMS	14	M	RCI	ACF	GT
GROSSE POINTE WOODS	19	M	ALL	ACF	CG
HANCOCK	5	M		ACR	GG
HAZEL PARK	27	M			
HILLSDALE	8	M	ALL	V	GT
IRON MOUNTAIN	9	M	ALL	RR	GS
IRONWOOD	11	MP	RCI	RC	GG
LANSING	113	M	ALL	CFR	GG
LAPEER	5	P	ALL	AC	GT
LINCOLN PARK	54	C	RCI	AC	CG
LUDINGTON	9	M	RCI	AR	GT
MADISON HEIGHTS	33	C	ALL		GG
MANISTEE	8	P	ALL	RI	
MARQUETTE	20	MP	RCM		
MARSHALL	7	MP	RCM	AC	GT
MENOMINEE	11	M	ALL	AC	GT
MIDLAND	30	M	RCI	ALL	GS
MONROE	22	M	ALL	C	GG
MT CLEMENS	15	PC	RCI	AR	GG
MT PLEASANT	6	CM	ALL	AR	GG
MUSKEGON	47	CP	ALL	AR	SG
NILES	13	P	CMI	RI	
OAK PARK	37				
PETOSKEY	6				
PONTIAC	85	MP	RCI	ACC	GT
PORT HURON	36	MB	RCI	CRC	GI
RIVER ROUGE	19	MP	ALL	AC	GG
ROSEVILLE	51	M	RCI	ACF	TG
ROYAL OAK	82	M	ALL	RRC	GG
SAGINAW	98	M	ALL	AC	SG
SAULT STE MARIE	19	CP			
ST JOHNS	6		ALL		
ST JOSEPH	12	MC	RCI	AC	TC
ST JOSEPH		MC	ALL	AR	

City	Population Thousands	Systems Used	Areas Served	Collection Points	Method of Financing
THREE RIVERS	7	MP	ALL	F	SC
TRAVERSE CITY	18	MP	ALL	AFR	GT
TRENTON	9	MM	RCI	AC	GT
WATTEN	09	MM	RCI	C	GT
WYANDOTTE	01	CC	ALI	CC	TC
WYANDOTTE	44	MC	RCI	ACC	GT
WYOMING	50	P	ALL	CR	
MINNESOTA					
BLOOMINGTON	51	P	ALL	OO	
BROOKLYN CENTER	24	P	ALL	A	
COLUMBIA HEIGHTS	18	PU	RCM	AC	
COON RAPIDS	14	MM	ALL	CR	
FERGUS FALLS	14	MP	ALL	AO	SC
MAPLEWOOD	485	PU	ALL	C	
MINNEAPOLIS	25	C	R	AC	GT
MINNETONKA	6				
NORTH MANKATO					
NORTH ST PAUL	9	P	ALL	R	
OWATONNA	13	PP	ALL	ACR	GT
RICHFIELD	43	PP	ALL	V	GT
ROBBINSDALE	16	CC	CMI	ACO	SC
ROSEVILLE	24	PP	RLL	C	
ST CLOUD	34	MP	CMI	AC	
ST LOUIS PARK	43	C	ALL	AR	
WEST ST PAUL	13	PP	RCL	IO	GT
WINONA	25	CP	ALL	AR	
MISSISSIPPI					
CLEVELAND	10	MM	RCM	ACR	GT
GREENVILLE	42	MM	ALL	ACO	TC
MERIDIAN	50	MM	RCI	AF	GT
NATCHEZ	24	MM	RCM	ACR	GT
STARKVILLE					
MISSOURI					
BELLEFONTAINE NEIGHBORS	14	PU	ALL	C	
BRENTWOOD	11	CC	ALL	AC	SC
CARTHAGE	14	AP	RCM	AR	SC
CLAYTON	16	PU	ALL	AR	SC
CLAYSTOWN	37	CC	RCM	CFR	
COLUMBIA		MM	CMI	AO	
DE SOTA	25	MC	RC	C	
FERGUSON	15	P			
GLADSTONE					
JOPLIN	39	MP	R	AC	GTO
KANSAS CITY	552	MP	ALL	R	GT

City	Population Thousands	Systems Used	Areas Served	Collection Points	Set-out / Set-back	Comb. Refuse Summer R C e o s m	Comb. Refuse Winter R C e o s m	Garbage Summer R C e o s m	Garbage Winter R C e o s m	Ashes Summer R C e o s m	Ashes Winter R C e o s m	Rubbish Summer R C e o s m	Rubbish Winter R C e o s m	Other Summer R C e o s m	Other Winter R C e o s m	Method of Financing
MOBERLY	13	MP	RCM	O		6 2	6 2									TC
MOBERLY	45	MC	ALL	A		1 3	1 3									TC
NO KANSAS CITY	16	QP	R	CF												
POPLAR BLUFF		P	ALL	V												GT
ST LOUIS	750	MP	RI	C												
MONTANA																
BOZEMAN	13	MP	CI	A		6 1	6 1									TC
BOZEMAN		MM	RCI	V		1 1	1 1									GT
HAVRE	11			AC		R	R									
NEBRASKA																
BELLEVUE	9	C	RCI	R		6 2	1 2									SC
FREMONT	20	QP	ALL	V		6 2	2 2						R	R		SC
GRAND ISLAND	26	MP	ALL	OO		6 5	2 1									SC
HASTINGS	21	QP	ALL	AR		5 R	1 1						R	R		TC
KEARNEY	14	P	M													
LINCOLN	129	QP	ALL	ACR		R 2	1 2	1	1			1	1	R	R	GT
OMAHA	301	QM	RCI	ACF		6 6	1 2	1	1			1	1	6	6	SC
PLATTSMOUTH	6	P	ALL	AC		R	R									
SCOTTSBLUFF	13	QQ	ALL	AC		R R	2 1			R	R					SC
YORK	64	QP	ALL	ACUR		R 5	2 1									SC
NEVADA	51		RCL	AR		R R	1 1									
HENDERSON	18	MM	ALL	C		3 R	1 1									GT
LAS VEGAS	309	MM	RC	U		1 1										GT
RENO	197	MM	ALL	C		3 1										GT
SPARKS	30	QC	RCM	CO		1 1	2 1									GT
NEW HAMPSHIRE	30	UU	RCLI	O												GT
BERLIN	39	QP	CMI			1	1	1	1			1	1			GT
CONCORD	16	QP	RCI	OOO				1	1			1	1			GI
DOVER		M	R			2	1									GT
EXETER	9		RCI	AC		6	6	1	1	1	1	1	1			GI
HAMPTON	52	QP	ALL	CR												GI
MERIDITH	8	MC	RIH	CR				2	2	2	2	2	2	R	R	
MERIDITH	10	QQ	RCI	OO		2	2	2	2	2	2	2	2	R	R	
NASHUA	82	QP	CMI	OO		6 1	6 1	5	5	1	1	1	1	6	6	GT
NASHUA	7	QC	RCM	CP												GT
ROCHESTER	9	MM	RCI	AC												GT
NEW JERSEY	36		R													
SOMERSWORTH		M	CI	CF		2 2	2 2			1 1	1 1	1 1	1 1	5	5	GT
BELMAR	52	QC	ALL	CR		6 2	6 2	2 2	2 2	2	2	2	2	R	R	GT
BLOOMFIELD	8	P	ALL	CRC		1	1	3 2	3 2			2 1	2 1	R	R	GT
BOGOTA	10	QP	RCL	RU		1	1									GG
BUTLER	82	QC	CM	R		2 2	2 2	1	1	1	1			6	6	GT
CHATHAM	7	QC	ALL	C		2 2	2 2	1	1					5	5	
CLIFTON	9	MP	ALLM	OO		2 2	2 2									GT
CLIFTON	36	P	ALL	CU		6 2	6 2									GI
CRESSKILL	5	QC	RCM	R												GT
DUMONT	9	UC	RCI	R		2 2	2 2	2 2	2 2	1	1	1	1	5	5	GT
FAIR LAWN	7	QP	RCI	C		1 1	1 1									GT
GARWOOD	5	MM	RCI	OO		1 1	1 1			1	1					GT
HILLSIDE	9	MP	RCI	LO		R R	R R									TC
KEYPORT	7	P		C		2 2	2 2			1	1					

City	Population Thousands	Systems Used	Areas Served	Collection Points	Set-out / Set-back	Comb. Refuse Summer R C e o s m	Comb. Refuse Winter R C e o s m	Garbage Summer R C e o s m	Garbage Winter R C e o s m	Ashes Summer	Ashes Winter	Rubbish Summer	Rubbish Winter	Other Summer	Other Winter	Method of Financing
LEONIA	8	M P	ALL	R	O	3 3 3 3	3 3 3 3									GT
LIVINGSTON	24	M	ALL	R		2 2 2 2	2 2 2 2									GT SC
METUCHEN	14	C	RCM	F	B	1 2 1 2	1 2 1 2									SC
MIDLAND PARK	8	M P	RCI	R	O B	6 2 6 2	R 2 R 2									GT
MONTCLAIR	43		ALL	R												
MORRISTOWN	18	M P	RI	CR												GT
MORRISTOWN																
NEW BRUNSWICK	40	C	ALL	C		6 2 6 2	2 2 2 2									GT GT
NEW SHREWSBURY	7	M P D	ALL	R		2 2 2 2	2 2 2 2									
NEWTON	7	D	RC	R		5 5 5 3	2 3 2 3									GT GT
NORTH PLAINFIELD	17	C	I	R		3 3 3 3	2 2 2 2	3 3 3 3	3 3 3 3							GT GT
OAKHURST	14	M	ALL	AC												GT GT
ORADELL	9	M P	RCI	C		6 6 6 6	2 2 2 2	1 1 1 1	2 2 2 2	1 1 1 1	1 1 1 1	1 1 1 1	1 1 1 1			
PHILLIPSBURG	19	C P	RI		AFRO	R R R R	R R R R	R R R R	R R R R	1 1 1 1	1 1 1 1	1 1 1 1	1 1 1 1			
PITMAN	9	C P	ALL	CR												
PLAINFIELD	45		RCI	AC												
PRINCETON	10	C P	ALL													
PRINCETON																
RAMSEY	21	C P	RCI	CR	O	1 2 1 2	2 2 2 2	3 3 3 3				7 7 7 7	7 7			SC GT
RUTHERFORD	6	M P	ALL	CR		5 5 5 5	2 2 2 2	3 3 3 3	3 3 3 3			1 1	1 1			GT GT
SPARTA	24	C	RC	CF		R R R R	3 3 3 3									GT SC
SUMMIT	42	M	RC			2 2 2 2	2 2 2 2	2 2 2 2	2 2 2 2	1 1 1 1	1 1 1 1	1 1 1 1	1 1 1 1	1 1 1 1	1 M 1	GT SC
TEANECK	30	M P C	RCI	CR	O	6 2 6 2	2 2 2 2									GT
TEANECK	40	M P C	ALL	CR		2 2 2 2	2 2 2 2									SC SC
WAYNE	22	M	RCM	AC		1 1 1 1	1 1 1 1	1 2 1 2	1 1 1 1							SC GT SC
WEST ORANGE	9	M	RCI	AC		1 1 1 1	1 1 1 1	2 3 2 3	2 3 2 3							
NEW MEXICO																
ALAMOGORDO	28	M	ALL													
CLOVIS	38	M	RCI	C	O	1 1 1 1	1 1 1 1	1 2 3 R	R 2 3 R			R R	R R			GT GT
LAS VEGAS	18	C	ALL													GT GT SC
NEW YORK																
AMSTERDAM	6	M	RCI	CR		1 1 1 1	1 1 1 1	2 2 3 2	3 2 3 2	1 1 1 1	1 1 1 1	1 1 1 1	1 1 1 1			GT GT SC
AUBURN	19	C P	RCI	AC				2 2 2 2	2 2 2 2	2 2	2 2	1 1	1 1			
BATAVIA		M P P	ALL	O						1 1	1 1	1 1	1 1			GT GT
BINGHAMTON	18	M C	RCU	CR	O	2 2 2 2	2 2 2 2	2 2	2 2	1 1	1 1	1 1	1 1	6	6	GT GT
CORTLAND	7	M P	ALL	AC		1 1 1 1	1 1 1 1	2 3 2 3	2 3 2 3			1 1	1 1			GT GT SC
CORTLAND	8		RCI	O												
DUNKIRK	5		ALL	CR												
EAST HILLS	47	M M M	RC	AR		2 2 2 2	2 2 2 2					1 1 1 1	1 1 1 1			GT GT
EAST ROCHESTER	34		RCI	CR								1 1	1 1			GT GT
ELLENVILLE	17	C P	ALL	AR												GT GT SC
ELMIRA	22	M M M	CM	ARO												
FREEPORT	767	M P P	RI	O		2 2 2 2	2 2 2 2									
GARDEN CITY	11	M P P	CMI	AC		2 2 2 2	2 2 2 2									GT GT
GLOVERSVILLE		M P P	ALL													GT GT
HEMPSTEAD																
HUDSON																
ITHICA	29	M	ALL	AC		2 2 2 2	2 2 2 2									GT

City	Population Thousands	Systems Used	Areas Served	Collection Points	Set-out Set-back	Comb. Refuse Summer R C e e o s m	Comb. Refuse Winter R C e e o s m	Garbage Summer R C e e o s m	Garbage Winter R C e e o s m	Ashes Summer R C e e o s m	Ashes Winter R C e e o s m	Rubbish Summer R C e e o s m	Rubbish Winter R C e e o s m	Other Summer R C e e o s m	Other Winter R C e e o s m	Method of Financing
JAMESTOWN	42	C	ALL	O		1 1 1	1 1 1									GT
JOHNSTOWN	30	C	R	C		1 1 1	1 1 1	2 1	2 1	2	3 2 1	2	2 1			GT
LACKAWANNA	75	H	R	CR	OB			1	1		1		1			GT
LONG BEACH	28	H	C	A												TC
LYNBROOK	21	H	RCM	R		1 1	1 1									GT
MAMARONECK	16	P	R	C		1 1 R	1 1 R	6 1	6 1	2 1	2 1	2 1	2 1			GT
MASSAPEQUA PARK		MP	C	U												
MASSENA	24	M	RCI	C		6	6									GT
MASSENA	77	MP	CMI	R		1 1	1 1	1 2 1	1 2 1	1 1	1 1	1 1	1 1			GT
MIDDLETOWN	100	MP	ALL	I	O	2 1	2 1	2 1	2 1	1	1					GT
MT KISCO		P	CM	C		1	1	2 1	2 1			1	1			GT
MT KISCO	8100	MP	RI	R		1	1									
NEW ROCHELLE	13	P	RCM	F		R 2	R 2									
NEW ROCHELLE	35	MP	ALL	L		1 2	1 2									TC
NEW YORK CITY	6	C	ALL	A	O	1 2	1 2									TC
NEW YORK CITY		MP	CM	C		2	2									GT
NO TONAWANDA	23	MP	ALL	O		1 2	1 2									GT
NORTHPORT	29	P	ALL	AR		2	2	5	5			1	1			GT
OLEAN	6	MP	RCM	I		R 2 5	R 2 5							5 6	5 M	TC
OLEAN	380	P	L	AC	O	3 1	3 1							5 6	5 M	GT
OSWEGO	327	MP	ALL	RC		1 1	1 1			1	1			5 6	5 M	GT
PATCHOGUE		MP	ALL	RR		1 1	1 1			1	1			5 6	5 M	
PATCHOGUE		MP	CM	F		1 2 1	1 2 1									
PENN YAN	14	MP	ALL	CF		1	1									GT
PLEASANTVILLE	18	C	ALL	R	O	1	1	1	1	1	1	1	1			GT
POUGHKEEPSIE	82	MP	C	R		1 1	1 1									GT
ROCHESTER		MP	RCI	O		2 1	2 1									GT
ROCKVILLE CENTRE	8	M	C	U		2 1	2 1									GT
ROCKVILLE CENTRE	55	MP	C	C		2 1	2 1									GT
RYE	67	MP	RCI	R		1	1									GT
SCARSDALE		MP	ALL	V	OB											GT
SCARSDALE	5	M	RCI	AFR		6 R R 6	6 R R 6	6 5	6 5	6	6	6 1 7	6 1 7			GT
SCHENECTADY	12	M	ALL	AC	OB	R R 6	R R 6	5 7	5 7	1	1	1 2	1 2		S	TC
SCHENECTADY	13	M	RCI	CF	OB	6	6									GT
SCOTIA	278	M	ALL	R	OB	1	1	3 2	3 2	2	2	2 1	2 1			GT
SUFFERN	14	M	ALL	ACR		1	1	3 2	3 2	1	1	1 1	1 1	1	1	GT
SYRACUSE	120	M	RCI	AC				2	2	2	2					GT
TROY	9	M	RC	AC		5	5	2	2							GT
NORTH CAROLINA	11	M	ALL	V				2	2			6 1 6	6 1 6			TC
ALBEMARLE																
CANTON																
CHAPEL HILL																
CHARLOTTE																
DURHAM																
ELIZABETH CITY																
GRAHAM																
GREENSBORO																
HICKORY																
MONROE																

City	Population Thousands	Systems Used	Areas Served	Collection Points	Set-out / Set-back	Comb. Refuse Summer	Comb. Refuse Winter	Garbage Summer	Garbage Winter	Ashes Summer	Ashes Winter	Rubbish Summer	Rubbish Winter	Other Summer	Other Winter	Method of Financing
MOORESVILLE	7	M	ALL	ACR		2 R	2 R									TC
MORGANTON	9	M	RCI	ACR	OB	1 6	1 6									GT
MOUNT AIRY	19	P	ALL	ACR		2 R	2 R							7 R	7 R	GT
NEW BERN	9	M	M			2 5	2 5							8	8	
RALEIGH	14	M	RCI	AR		1 5	1 5							7	7	GT
REIDSVILLE	13	M	ALL	V		R 6	R 6									GT
ROANOKE RAPIDS	35	M	RCI	AC		6	6	6	6					R	R	GT
ROCKY MOUNT	18	M	ALL	RC	OB	R	R			R	R	R	R	R	R	GT
ROXBORO						R	R			R	R	R	R	R	R	GT
SHELBY	10	M	RC	FR		3 2	3 2									GT
SOUTHERN PINES	7	M	ALL	CR	OB	2	2	2	2							GT
STATESVILLE	45	M	RCI	AR		6 2	6 2									GT
THOMASVILLE	29	M	RCM	ACO		6 2	6 2	2	2							GT
WASHINGTON	11	M	RCM			1 3	1 3									GT
WILMINGTON		M	ALL	AC		6 2	6 2	2	2							GT
WILSON		M	ALL	AR		R 5	R 5									TC
WINSTON-SALEM		M	RCI	AR		5 2	5 2									GT
NORTH DAKOTA																
BISMARCK	30	M	RC	AR		1 2	1 2	R	1	R	R	R	R	R	R	SC
JAMESTOWN	15	MC	RCI	A	O	6 1	6 1	1	1	1	1	S	S	S	S	SC
JAMESTOWN		MC	ALL	AC		2 1	2 1	1	1	1	1	1	1	1	1	SC
MANDEN	12		C			1	1									GT
OHIO																
ASHLAND	17	MP				2 1	2 1	R	1	R	1	R	1	1	1	SC
BARBERTON	34	MP	RCI	FC		1 1	1 1	1	1	1	1	1	1	S	S	GT
BAY VILLAGE	15	MP	ALL	CR		1 1	1 1	1	1	1	1	1	1	1	1	SC
BEDFORD	17	P	RCL	VR		2 1	2 1							S	S	
BELLEVUE	8	MP	ALL			1 1	1 1									GT
BEREA	17	P	ALL	C		1 1	1 1							R	R	
BEXLEY	14	MP	RI	ARF		R 1	R 1	R	1	R	1	R	1	R	R	
BOWLING GREEN	13	M	ALL	AC		2 1	2 1	R	1	R	1	R	1	1	1	
BRYAN	17	M	RCI	AF		7	7									GT
BUCYRUS	12	M	RCI	AC	OB	R 1	R 1	R	1	R	1	R	1	S	S	SC
CAMBRIDGE	14	M	RCI	V	O	5 1	5 1	1	1	1	1	1	1	R	R	SC
CHILLICOTHE	25	MP	RCL	AC		2 1	2 1	R	1	R	1	R	1	1	1	SC
COLUMBUS	471	MP	RCU	ACR		R 1	R 1							R	R	SC
CUYAHOGA FALLS	262	P	RCM	R		2 1	2 1							R	R	GT
DAYTON	13	MP	CM	I R		R 2	R 2									SC
DELAWARE	38	MP	CM	I		1 3	1 3									GT
EAST CLEVELAND	20	M	RCI	C		R 1	R 1							R	R	SC
EAST CLEVELAND		MP	RCI	AR		R 1	R 1							R	R	SC
FAIRBORN	15	MP	ALL	V		1 2	1 2							R	R	SC
FAIRBORN PARK	8	MP	RCI	O		R 1	R 1							R	R	GT
FAIRVIEW PARK	9	P	AC			1	1									SC
FRANKLIN	9	P	RCI	AC		2 1	2 1							R	R	TC
GRANDVIEW HEIGHT	72	M	ALL	C		1 2	1 2							R	R	SC
GROVE CITY	5	C	ALL			1 3	1 3							R	R	GT
HAMILTON																
HURON																

City	Population Thousands	Systems Used	Areas Served	Collection Points	Set-out Set-back	Comb. Refuse Summer/Winter	Method of Financing
IRONTON	16	M	RC	AC	—	1 5 / 1 5 / 1 2	GT
KETTERING	55	M	RCI	R	—	5 5 / 2	—
LEBANON	6	P	RC	R	—	2 2 / —	—
LEBANON	7	M	AL	AC	B	R 5 / 1 1 / R R	SC
LOVELAND	34	P	LL	C	O	5 5 / 2 2 / 5 5	—
LOVELAND	17	P	RCI	C	O	5 5 / 1 1 / 5 5	SC
MAPLE HEIGHTS	17	C	LL	C	—	1 1 / 1 1 / 1 1	GC
MARIETTA	30	C	LL	R	—	R R / 1 1 / R R	SC
MARION	30	M	AC	AC	—	6 6 / 1 1 / 6 6	SC
MASSILLON	42	P	RCM	—	—	1 1 / 1 1 / 1 1	SC
MIDDLETOWN	—	P	RCI	ACR	O	R R / 1 1 / R R	TC
NEW PHILADELPHIA	14	M	RCI	C	—	R R / 1 1 / R R	GT
NORWALK	13	C	AL	R	—	R R / 1 1 / R R	SC
OAKWOOD CITY	8	M	RCC	VO	O	5 5 / 1 1 / 5 5	GT
OBERLIN	6	M	RCC	AR	—	1 1 / B 1 / 1 B	—
ORRVILLE	16	C	RCC	CR	—	R R / 1 1 / R R	SC
PAINESVILLE	8	P	RC	C	—	1 1 / 1 1 / 1 1	GT
PERRYSBURG	6	M	AL	U	O	R R / 1 1 / R R	
REYNOLDSBURG	8	C	RCI	C	—	1 1 / 1 1 / 1 1	GT
ROCKY RIVER	18	P	RCI	—	—	R R / 1 1 / R R	
SHAKER HEIGHTS	36	M	RCI	RO	O	1 1 / 1 1 / 1 1	GT
SIDNEY	15	M	AL	C	O	R R / 1 1 / R R	SC
SILVERTON	7	P	ALL	ACR	—	2 2 / 2 2 / 2 2	SC
ST EUCLID	28	M	ALL	AC	—	R R / 1 1 / R R	GT
SPRINGFIELD	83	M	RCL	V	O	3 3 / 1 1 / 3 3	TC
SPRINGFIELD	8	P	AL	—	B	R R / 1 1 / R R	
ST MARYS	14	M	RC	AC		2 2 / 2 2 / 2 2	
TOLEDO	28	M	RCI	—	O	1 1 / 1 1 / 1 1	GT
TROY	11	M	RCI	ACR	O	6 6 / 2 2 / 6 6	SC
UPPER ARLINGTON	60	M	RCM	AC	B	6 6 / 2 2 / 6 6	SC
WADSWORTH	7	M	RC	CR	B	5 5 / 2 2 / 5 5	SC
WARREN	8	M	ALL	AC		6 6 / 2 2 / 6 6	SC
WESTERVILLE	41	M	RCI	V		6 6 / 2 2 / 6 6	GT
WYOMING	14	M	RCM	AC		6 6 / 2 2 / 6 6	TC
ZANESVILLE	17	M	ALL	VO		6 6 / 2 2 / 6 5	SC
OKLAHOMA							
ADA	20	M	ALL	F		6 6 / 1 1 / 6 6	SC
ANADARKO	12	M	ALL	AR		5 5 / 1 1 / 5 5	SC
ARDMORE	7	M	ALL	AR	O	R R / 2 2 / R R	SC
BARTLESVILLE	29	M	ALL	ACR	B		SC
BETHANY	9						
CLAREMORE	6						
EDMOND	38						
NORMAN	40	M	ALL	AFR	—	2 2 / 2 2 / 2 R	SC

City	Population Thousands	Systems Used	Areas Served	Collection Points	Set-out / Set-back	Comb. Refuse Summer	Comb. Refuse Winter	Garbage Summer	Garbage Winter	Ashes Summer	Ashes Winter	Rubbish Summer	Rubbish Winter	Other Summer	Other Winter	Method of Financing
OKLAHOMA CITY	324	MP	RCM	V		R2R	R2R							1R	1R	SC
OKLAHOMA CITY	24	MP	ALL	VO		R2R	R2R							R1	R1	SC
STILLWATER		MP	RCM	ACF		626	626									
TULSA	262	MP	RCM	AR		1R	1R									SC
TULSA	15		RCM	AR		R2R	R2R									SC
OREGON	10															
ALBANY	7	C	ALL	AF		R5R	R5R									
ASTORIA	21	C	ALL	AR		1R1	1R1									
BAKER	11	C	ALL	AC		6R6	6R6									
COOS BAY	6	P	RCI	V		1R1	1R1									
CORVALLIS	24	P	ALL	AFR		R2R	R2R									
FOREST GROVE	5	P	ALL	AR		1R1	1R1									
GRANTS PASS		P	ALL	AC												
LEBANON		C	ALL			R6R	R6R									
MEDFORD		P	ALL													
ONTARIO		P	RC			1R1	1R1									
PENDLETON	3	P		R		R	R	2	2							
PORTLAND	322			R		2	1	1	1			1	1			
SPRINGFIELD	11			V	0											
THE DALLES					B	1R1	2						1	1	S	S	SC
PENNSYLVANIA																
ABINGTON	56	MP	ALL	C		R	2									
ALTOONA	69		ALL	AC		R2R										
BELLEFONTE	6	HP	ALL	ACO		1R2	2									
DOYLESTOWN	11	HP	RCI	ACF		R								X	X	GT
DU BOIS	35	P	RCI	ACF		R2R	2							X	X	SC
EASTON	10		ALL	CR		5R5	5R5			X	X					SC
EDGEWOOD	8	C	RCI	CR		6R6	2			X	X					SC
FRANKLIN		C	RC			1R2	2									GT
GROVE CITY					0	1R3	2									
HANOVER	16	MP	ALL	AC		R	2									SC
HAZLETON	32	CP	ALL	O		R	2									GT
HAZLETON		HP			B	R	2	2	2							SC
JOHNSTOWN	54	MP	AL	R		RR	R	1	1			1	1			SC
LATROBE	59	HP	RCI	ACO		5R2	5	2	2			1	1			GT
LOWER MERION	8	P	CML	C		6R1	6					2	2			SC
LOWER MERION	6	HP	ALL	ACR		1R2	2									GT
MECHANICSBURG		CP				2	2									
MEDIA	8	P	RCM	AR		5R2	R2R	2	2	1	1	1	1			GT
MEDIA	305	MPC	RCC	CR		R2R	R2R							X	X	GT
MILTON		MPC	RCC	R	0	1	1									SC
MORRISVILLE	10	C	C	V		R	2	2	2	1	1	1	1			GT
MT LEBANON	9	U	CML	ACO		2	2									GT
NARBERTH	7		RC	ACR		1R2	R2R					1	1			
NARBERTH	6		ALL	ACO		R2R	R2R									SC
NEW CUMBERLAND		MPC	RCI	ACO		1	2	2	2	1	1	1	1			GT
PHILADELPHIA	2002															

City	Population Thousands	Systems Used	Areas Served	Collection Points	Set-out / Set-back	Comb. Refuse Summer	Comb. Refuse Winter	Garbage Summer	Garbage Winter	Ashes Summer	Ashes Winter	Rubbish Summer	Rubbish Winter	Other Summer	Other Winter	Method of Financing
PHILADELPHIA	9	MPC	CM	ACO	B											
PHILADELPHIA	27	MPC	RC													GT
PLEASANT HILLS BORO	6	C	ALL	CFC	O											GTC
POTTSTOWN	6	C	RC	AC												GTC
RIDGWAY	6	C	ALL	ACR	OB											GTC
SCHUYLKILL	6	M	RC	ACR												SC
SEWICKLEY	6	C	ALL	AC												
SHARPSVILLE	6	C	RC	AC												
SHILLINGTON		C	ALL	AC												
SHIPPENSBURG		C	RCI	AC												
STATE COLLEGE	22	M	ALL	AC						1	1	1	1			SC
TYRONE	8	P	RCM	R				2								
UNIONTOWN	17	C	RC	C	OB											SC
WAYNESBURG	5	C	ALL													GTC
WEST YORK BORO	30	C	RC	CR												GT
WILKINSBURG	5	M	RCI	AC												
WYOMISSING		C	RCI	AC												
YORK	55	M														
RHODE ISLAND																
BARRINGTON	17	MPC	RI	CO					R	R	R				R	SC
BARRINGTON	67	MPC	CI												R	
CRANSTON	42	CP	RR	CR	O			1	1							GTC
EAST PROVIDENCE			R					1	1							GT
SOUTH CAROLINA																
ABBEVILLE	5	M	RCM	RCM	O								2	2	R	R
AIKEN	11	M	ACU	VO												GT
BEAUFORT	65	M	ALL	FR				1				2	2	R	R	GT
BELTON	66	M	RCI	V												
GREENVILLE		M	RCI					5	3			2	2			
SOUTH DAKOTA																
ABERDEEN	23	M	ALL	VAC												GT
HURON	150	MP	ALL	AC												GT
PIERRE	42	MP	RCI	AC												GT
RAPID CITY	6	MP	CMI	AR	O											TC
VERMILLION		P	ALL													GT
TENNESSEE																
ALCOA	6	M	ALL	R												SC
CHATTANOOGA	130	M	RCM	ACF				2								GT
COOKEVILLE	100	M	RCI	AC	B											GTC
EAST RIDGE	31	M	ALL	FAC	O					2	2					GT
JOHNSON CITY	26	M	RCI	AC					1							GT
KINGSPORT	27	CC	ALL	AR												SC
OAK RIDGE	10	MC	RCM	OFR	B			2	2							GT
PULASKI		M														
RED BANK WHITE OAK	11	M	RCI	CC								1	1	1		GT
SHELBYVILLE	10	MP	ALL	C				2	2			M	M	M	M	GT
TEXAS																
ABILENE	90	MP	ALL	AC												SC
ALICE	20	M	ALL	AC										R	R	SC

City	Population Thousands	Systems Used	Areas Served	Collection Points	Set-out / Set-back	Comb. Refuse Summer (R e o m / R e s)	Comb. Refuse Winter (R e o m / R e s)	Garbage	Ashes	Rubbish	Other Summer	Other Winter	Method of Financing
ALVIN	6	M	ALL	AC	—	6 / 2	6 / 2	—	—	—	— / —	— / —	SC
AMARILLO	138	MP	C	AR	—	R / 2	R / 2	—	—	—	R / B	R / B	SC
AMARILLO	138	MP	RCI	AR	—	R / 2	R / 2	—	—	—	1 / 1	1 / 1	SC
ANDREWS	11	C	ALL	V	—	5 / 2	5 / 2	—	—	—	— / —	— / —	SC
ARLINGTON	44	MP	ALL	AR	—	R / 2	R / 2	—	—	—	— / —	— / —	TC
AUSTIN	187	M	ALL	AC	—	R / 2	R / 2	—	—	—	R / B	R / B	SC
BEAUMONT	119	MP	ALL	L	—	R / 3	R / 3	—	—	—	B / B	B / B	TC
BELLAIRE	20	M	RCI	AC	—	5 / 2	5 / 2	—	—	—	— / 1	— / 1	—
BIG SPRING	31	MP	CMI	AC	—	R / 2	R / 2	—	—	—	— / —	— / —	SC
BIG SPRING	31	MP	ALL	AC	—	R / 2	R / 2	—	—	—	R / R	R / R	TC
BORGER	21	MP	ALL	ACR	—	R / 2	R / 2	—	—	—	— / 2	— / 2	SC
BRYAN	28	C	RCI	A	—	6 / 2	6 / 2	—	—	—	2 / 2	2 / 2	TC
BURKBURNETT	6	MP	RC	CR	—	R / 2	R / 2	6 / 1	—	1 / 1	2 / 5	2 / 5	TC
CANYON	168	M	ALL	AC	—	6 / 3	6 / 3	—	—	—	1 / 1	1 / 1	—
CHILDRESS	20	M	ALL	AC	—	6 / 2	6 / 2	—	—	—	— / —	— / —	—
CORPUS CHRISTI	673	M	RCI	AC	—	5 / 2	5 / 2	—	—	—	1 / 1	1 / 1	TC
CORSICANA	23	MP	ALL	ACRO	—	R / 2	R / 2	6 / —	—	—	R / M	R / M	SC
CRYSTAL CITY	28	M	RCM	AC	—	R / 2	R / 2	—	—	—	— / —	— / —	TC
CUERO	9	MP	ALL	R	—	R / 2	R / 2	—	—	—	— / —	— / —	GC
DALLAS	7	MP	ALL	AC	—	5 / 2	5 / 2	—	—	—	— / —	— / —	SC
DENISON	356	MP	RCM	AF	—	R / 1	R / 1	—	—	—	— / —	— / —	TC
DENTON	6	M	ALL	ACRO	—	R / 2	R / 2	—	—	—	— / R	— / R	SC
ENNIS	—	—	ALL	AR	—	6 / 2	6 / 2	—	—	—	6 / M	6 / M	—
FALFURRIAS	41	M	ALL	AF	—	R / 2	R / 2	—	—	—	1 / 1	1 / 1	SC
FORT WORTH	18	M	RCI	AC	—	— / 2	— / 2	6 / 6	—	6 / 6	— / R	— / R	TC
FORT WORTH	115	M	RCM	AC	—	R / 2	R / 2	2 / 2	—	1 / 1	— / 1	— / 1	TC
GLADEWATER	106	C	ALL	RO	—	6 / 2	6 / 2	—	—	—	6 / 6	6 / 6	SC
HARLINGEN	46	M	ALL	AR	—	1 / 2	1 / 2	—	—	—	1 / R	1 / R	TC
HEREFORD	25	M	ALL	AF	—	R / 2	R / 2	—	—	R / R	— / —	— / —	—
HIGHLAND PARK	14	M	RCI	AC	—	R / 2	R / 2	2 / 2	—	—	2 / 2	2 / 2	SC
HITCHCOCK	10	M	R	RC	—	2 / 2	2 / 2	—	—	—	1 / 1	1 / 1	TC
HURST	—	C	RCM	CF	—	R / 2	R / 2	—	—	—	— / —	— / —	SC
IRVING	12	M	RCI	AC	—	R / 2	R / 2	—	—	—	— / —	— / —	GC
KILGORE	107	M	ALL	AC	—	6 / 2	6 / 2	—	—	—	— / —	— / —	TC
KINGSVILLE	9	M	RCM	AC	—	7 / 2	7 / 2	—	—	—	5 / 5	5 / 5	SC
LA MARQUE	129	M	ALL	AR	—	R / 2	R / 2	—	—	—	5 / 5	5 / 5	SC
LAKE JACKSON	24	M	RC	C	—	6 / 2	6 / 2	—	—	—	5 / 5	5 / 5	SC
LAMESA	28	M	ALL	AC	—	6 / 2	6 / 2	—	—	—	— / —	— / —	TC
LAMPASAS	63	M	ALL	AC	—	6 / 2	6 / 2	—	—	R / R	5 / R	5 / R	TC
LEVELLAND	12	M	RCI	AC	—	6 / 2	6 / 2	—	R / R	—	5 / 5	5 / 5	GC
LITTLEFIELD	26	M	ALL	CR	—	R / 2	R / 2	—	—	—	5 / 5	5 / 5	TC
LUBBOCK	—	M	ALL	AC	—	6 / 2	6 / 2	—	—	—	R / R	R / R	SC
MARSHALL	—	M	RC	AC	—	6 / 2	6 / 2	—	—	—	1 / 1	1 / 1	SC
MESQUITE	—	M	ALL	VO	—	— / —	— / —	—	—	—	— / —	— / —	SC
ORANGE	26	M	RC	VO	—	2 / 2	2 / 2	—	—	—	1 / 1	1 / 1	SC

City	Population Thousands	Systems Used	Areas Served	Collection Points	Set-out Set-back	Comb. Refuse Summer R e s.	Comb. Refuse Winter R e s.	Garbage Summer R e m.	Garbage Winter R e m.	Ashes Summer R e s.	Ashes Winter R e s.	Rubbish Summer R e s.	Rubbish Winter R e s.	Other Summer R e s. m.	Other Winter R e s. m.	Method of Financing
PALESTINE	14	MH	ALL	C		2 6	2 6									TC
PAMPA	25	MH	RCM	A		2 R	2 R									SC
RICHARDSON	16	MP	ALL	A		2 R	2 R									SS
RICHARDSON	8	MH	ALL	C		2 6	2 6									SS
RIVER OAKS	10	MH	RLL	R		2 6	2 6	R	R	R	R			1	1	SS
ROBSTOWN	4	MH	ALL	C		2 6	2 6							1	1	SS
SEGUIN	25	MH	ALL	A		2 6	2 6							6		SS
SHERMAN		MH	RCM	V		2 2	2 2									SS
SLATON	6	MH	RCM	A		2	2									
SNYDER	14	MH	RCM	AC		2	2							S	S	SC
SWEETWATER	14	MP	RCM	V		1	1							1	1	
SWEETWATER	3	MP	RIL	VO		3	3									SC
TEXARKANA	11	MP	ALL	OCR		3	3							S	S	TC
TYLER	5	MH	ALL	ARC		6	6	R	R	R	R			1	1	TC
UNIVERSITY PARK	20	MH	RCI	RC		6	6	R	R	R	R			R	R	SS
UVALDE	10	MP	RIL	AC		2	2									SS
VICTORIA	32	MH	ALL	C		2	2									SC
WACO	102	MH	RIC	AC		2	2			R	R			S	S	SC
WAXAHACHIE	14	MH	RC	A		2	2							1	1	
WESLACO	16	MH	ALL	AC		2 6	2 6									SC
WICHITA FALLS	101	MH	ALL	V		2	2	1		R	R					SC
UTAH																
BOUNTIFUL	17	M	RI	C	OB	1 6	1 6			1	1			S	S	SC
BRIGHAM CITY	12	MP	RCI	AC	OB	1 R	1 R			1	1			1	1	TC
LOGAN CITY	17	MP	RCI	AC		1	1									GT
OGDEN	71	MP	RRI	ACC		1	1							S	S	GT
TOOELE	9	MC	RRI	C	OB	1	1							1	1	GC
WASHINGTON TERRACE	6	U	R	F		1	1	2								GC
VERMONT																
BURLINGTON	36	C	ALL	LV		1	1									GT
ESSEX JUNCTION	7	U	ALL	V		1	1									
VIRGINIA																
ALEXANDRIA	61	MP	RCM	AC	OB	R	R			1	1			S	S	SC
ALEXANDRIA	91	MP	RC	I		1	1			1	1			1	1	GT
ARLINGTON COUNTY		MP	RCM	R		R	R			1	1					SI
ARLINGTON COUNTY		MP	RCI	ACC	OB	R	R							S	S	GT
BEDFORD	6	MP	RCI	ACR		3	3							1	1	SI
BUENA VISTA	6	MH	RCI	ACC		5 R	5 R							S	S	GT
CHARLOTTESVILLE	34	MM	RCI	AC		R 6	R 6							R	R	TC
CHARLOTTESVILLE		MH	ALL	R		3	3									GT
CLIFTON FORGE		MH	RC	F		R 6	R 6							1	1	SI
COVINGTON	9	MH	ALL	R		R 6	R 6							S	S	GT
DANVILLE	47	MH	ALL	AC		R 2	R 2							1	1	
EMPORIA	6	MH	RC	CR		1	1							1	1	GT
FAIRFAX	14	MH	RI	V		2	2							S	S	GT
FALLS CHURCH	10	MM	R	R		N 2	N 2							1	1	SI
FREDERICKSBURG	13	MH	RCI	R		2 6	2 6							S	S	GT
FREDERICKSBURG		MH	ALL	AF		2	2									TC
HAMPTON	90	MH	RC	CR		2	2									GI
HARRISONBURG	13	MH	ALL	V		2	2							1	1	GI
HOPEWELL	18	MH	RCI	RC		1	1							1	1	GT

City	Population Thousands	Systems Used	Areas Served	Collection Points	Set-out Set-back	Comb. Refuse Summer r.s.	Comb. Refuse Summer c.o.m.	Comb. Refuse Winter r.s.	Comb. Refuse Winter c.o.m.	Garbage Summer r.s.	Garbage Summer c.o.m.	Garbage Winter r.s.	Garbage Winter c.o.m.	Ashes Summer r.s.	Ashes Summer c.o.m.	Ashes Winter r.s.	Ashes Winter c.o.m.	Rubbish Summer r.s.	Rubbish Summer c.o.m.	Rubbish Winter r.s.	Rubbish Winter c.o.m.	Other Summer r.s.	Other Summer c.o.m.	Other Winter r.s.	Other Winter c.o.m.	Method of Financing
MARTINSVILLE	19	MP	RC	AR	OB	2	5	2	5	2	1	2	1	1	1	1	1	1	1	1	1	R	R	R	R	GT
NEWPORT NEWS		MP	ALL	V		1	1	1	1																	GT
NORFOLK		MP	ALL	C		1	1	1	1																	GT
PORTSMOUTH		MP	ALL	AC		2	R	2	R	R	1	R	1	R	1	R	1	R	1	R	1	R	R	R	R	TC
PULASKI		MP	CM	V		1	R	1	R																	SC
RADFORD			ALL	R																						
RICHMOND			ALL	V																						GT
RICHMOND	220	MP	RC	AC																						GT
SALEM																										GT
STAUNTON																										GT
VIENNA	16	MP	RCI	V																		R	R			GT
WILLIAMSBURG	22	MP	RC	C		2	3	2	3																	TC
WINCHESTER						2	1	2	1																	SC
WASHINGTON																										
AUBURN	14	CC	ALL	AC		R	1	R	1	2		2		2		2		2		2		R	R	R	R	SC
BELLINGHAM	17	MC	CMI	O		5	1	5	1													S	S			GT
CENTRALIA	15		RC	ACR		R	1	R	1													S	S	R	R	SC
CHEHALIS	12	CC	ALL	AC		5	1	5	1	2		2		2		2		2		2						SC
CLARKSTON	35	MC	RCU	O		3	1	3	1																	GT
ELLENSBURG	9	P	ALL	ACU		6	1	6	1																	SC
KELSO	5	MP	RCI	ACF		R	1	R	1																	SC
LONGVIEW	9	CC	ALL	V		R	1	R	1													R	R	R	R	SC
MOSES LAKE	24	MP	RCI	VOR		R	1	R	1																	SC
PORT ANGELES	13	MC	RCI	ACR		R	1	R	1													S	S	S	S	SC
PUYALLUP	12	MC	ALL	V		R	1	R	1																	SC
RICHLAND	557	MC	ALL	ACU		6	1	6	1																	
SEATTLE	181	CC	ALL	ACU		1	1	1	1																	SC
SPOKANE	46	MC	ALL	V		R	1	R	1																	
SUNNYSIDE	148					6	1	6	1																	SC
TACOMA	25	MC	RI			3	1	3	1																	
WALLA WALLA	18	MP	ALL	AC		6	1	6	1																	
WALLA WALLA																										
WENATCHEE																										
WEST VIRGINIA																										
BLUEFIELD	19	MP	RCM	ACR	OB	R	1	R	1	1	2	1	2	1	1	1	1	1	1	1	1	R	R	R	R	SC
CLARKSBURG	268	MC	ALL			R	1	R	1	2	1	2	1	1		1		1		1		R	R	R	R	SC
NEW MARTINSVILLE	45	CC		V						6		6		1		1		1		1		R	R	R	R	SC
PARKERSBURG	19	MC	ALL	AR				2		1		1		1		1		1		1		R	R	R	R	TC
SOUTH CHARLESTON	48	MP	RCI	ACR		1	1	1	1	1	2	1	2	1	R	1	R	8	R	8	R	R	R	R	R	TC
WISCONSIN	37	MP	ALU	AAR		N	2	N	2	N	1	N	1	1	1	1	1	1	1	1	1	R	R	R	R	GT
APPLETON	18	CM	RCU	AF																						GT
BEAVER DAM	3	OP	RCI			R	1	R	1	R	2	R	2	R	1	R	1	R	1	R	1					GT
BELOIT	3	MP	ALL	CR		3	2	3	2	1	1	1	1	1	1	1	1	8	1	8	1					GT
BROWN DEER	7	MC	AJU																							GT
CUDAHY	63	MM	RCI	ACR	OB					2	1	2	1	R	1	R	1	R	1	R	1	R	R	R	R	GT
EAU CLAIRE																										
FOND DU LAC																										
FORT ATKINSON																										
FOX POINT																										
GREEN BAY																										

City	Population Thousands	Systems Used	Areas Served	Collection Points	Set-out Set-back	Comb. Refuse Summer r c e / s m	Comb. Refuse Winter r c e / s m	Garbage Summer	Garbage Winter	Ashes Summer	Ashes Winter	Rubbish Summer	Rubbish Winter	Other Summer	Other Winter	Method of Financing
GREENDALE	7	M	RCI	C	—	1 / 1	1 / 1	—	—	—	—	—	—	—	—	GT
HARTFORD	6	MP	R	ACR	—	1 / 1	1 / 1	1 / 1	1 / 1	1 / 1	1 / 1	1 / 1	1 / 1	—	—	I
KENOSHA	68	C	RCI	AR	—	—	—	2 / 1	2 / 1	2 / 1	2 / 1	2 / 1	2 / 1	S / S	S / S	GT
LA CROSSE	48	MP	RI	AC	—	—	—	—	—	—	—	—	—	—	—	I
MADISON	127	MP	CM	AC	—	—	—	1 / 1	1 / 1	1 / 1	1 / 1	—	—	S / S	S / S	GT
MADISON	741	MP	CMI	—	—	—	—	R / 1	R / 1	B / 1	B / 1	B / 1	B / 1	—	—	I
MILWAUKEE	8	M	ALL	AFRO	—	—	—	1 / 1	1 / 1	M / M	M / M	M / M	M / M	2 / 2	2 / 2	TC
MILWAUKEE	18	M	ALL	CR	—	—	—	2 / 2	2 / 2	R / R	R / R	R / R	R / R	S / S	S / S	GT
NEW BERLIN	16	P	ALL	F	—	—	—	—	—	—	—	—	—	—	—	—
OSHKOSH	45	MP	CMI	ACR	—	R / 1	R / 1	—	—	—	—	—	—	—	—	GT
OSHKOSH	89	MP	RCI	ACR	—	1 / 1	1 / 1	1 / 1	1 / 1	1 / 1	1 / 1	1 / 1	1 / 1	1 / 1	1 / 1	GT
RACINE	9	M	ALL	ACR	—	1 / 1	1 / 1	1 / 1	1 / 1	1 / 1	1 / 1	1 / 1	1 / 1	1 / 1	1 / 1	GT
RHINELANDER	16	MC	RCI	AR	—	—	—	1 / 1	1 / 1	1 / 1	1 / 1	1 / 1	1 / 1	—	—	GT
SHOREWOOD	200	C	ALL	AO	O	1 / 1	1 / 1	1 / 1	1 / 1	B / B	B / B	B / B	B / B	1 / 1	1 / 1	GT
SOUTH MILWAUKEE	20	M	ALL	AR	—	2 / 2	2 / 2	2 / 2	2 / 2	B / B	B / B	B / B	B / B	5 / 5	5 / 5	GT
ST FRANCIS	34	UC	ALL	AR	—	1 / 1	1 / 1	1 / 1	1 / 1	1 / 1	1 / 1	1 / 1	1 / 1	—	—	GT
TWO RIVERS	12	C	RCI	AC	—	1 / 1	1 / 1	—	—	—	—	—	—	—	—	GT
WAUKESHA	30	MC	RCM	CU	—	—	—	2 / 2	R / R	—	—	—	—	—	—	GT
WAUKESHA	8	M	RCM	AR	—	R / 1	R / 1	R / 1	R / 1	—	—	M / M	M / M	M / M	M / M	GT
WAUPON	32	P	RCI	AC	—	1 / 1	1 / 1	1 / 1	1 / 1	—	—	—	—	—	—	TC
WAUSAU	57	M	RCI	IR	—	1 / 1	1 / 1	1 / 1	1 / 1	1 / 1	1 / 1	—	—	—	—	TC
WAUWATOSA	18	M	RC	R	—	1 / 1	1 / 1	1 / 1	1 / 1	B / B	B / B	B / B	B / B	—	—	TC
WHITEFISH BAY	—	—	—	—	—	—	—	—	—	—	—	—	—	—	—	—
CASPER	39	M	ALL	AC	—	6 / 6	6 / 6	1 / 1	1 / 1	1 / 1	1 / 1	—	—	M / M	M / M	SC
CHEYENNE	44	MP	RCI	AFR	—	R / 1	R / 1	R / R	R / R	1 / 1	1 / 1	—	—	S / S	S / S	SC
LARAMIE	18	MP	ALL	AC	—	R / 1	R / 1	1 / 1	1 / 1	1 / 1	1 / 1	—	—	S / S	S / S	TC
RIVERTON	7	C	ALL	AC	—	R / 2	R / 2	2 / 1	2 / 1	2 / 1	2 / 1	—	—	—	—	SC
CANADA																
ALBERTA																
CAMROSE	7	MP	ALL	A	—	6 / 1	6 / 1	1 / 1	1 / 1	—	—	—	—	S / S	S / S	GT
EDMONTON	269	MP	RCI	AFR	—	R / 1	R / 1	1 / 1	1 / 1	—	—	—	—	—	—	TC
JASPER PLACE	36	MC	RCM	AC	—	R / 1	R / 1	—	—	—	—	—	—	S / S	S / S	TC
LETHBRIDGE	34	MC	CMI	AO	—	1 / 1	1 / 1	—	—	—	—	—	—	—	—	GT
RED DEER	20	C	ALL	ACR	—	1 / 1	1 / 1	—	—	—	—	—	—	—	—	SC
BRITISH COLUMBIA																
CRANBROOK	7	MP	CMI	A	—	R / R	R / R	—	—	2 / 1	2 / 1	—	—	—	—	GT
KIMBERLY	14	MP	RCI	AO	—	R / 1	R / 1	R / R	R / R	R / 1	R / 1	—	—	S / S	S / S	TC
NANAIMO	6	C	RCM	ACR	—	1 / 1	1 / 1	R / R	R / R	—	—	2 / 2	2 / 2	1 / 1	1 / 1	GT
NORTH KAMLOOPS	10	MP	CMI	ACR	—	1 / 1	1 / 1	—	—	—	—	—	—	—	—	TC
PORT COQUITLAM	380	MP	ALL	ACR	OB	R / R	R / R	2 / 2	2 / 2	—	—	—	—	S / S	S / S	GT
VANCOUVER	10	MP	CMI	VCO	—	6 / 6	6 / 6	R / R	R / R	—	—	—	—	S / S	S / S	TC
VERNON	55	MP	ALL	AR	—	R / R	R / R	R / R	R / R	—	—	—	—	R / R	R / R	TC
MANITOBA																
BRANDON	29	MP	ALL	AC	—	1 / 1	1 / 1	—	—	—	—	—	—	—	—	TC
EAST KILDONAN	26	CP	RCI	AF	—	6 / 6	6 / 6	—	—	B / B	B / B	—	—	R / R	R / R	GT
WEST KILDONAN	26	CP	ALL	AR	—	2 / 2	2 / 2	—	—	7 / 7	7 / 7	—	—	R / R	R / R	TC
WINNIPEG	265	MP	—	—	—	1 / 1	1 / 1	—	—	R / R	R / R	—	—	R / R	R / R	TC

City	Population Thousands	Systems Used	Served Areas	Collection Points	Set-out / Set-back	Comb. Refuse Summer	Comb. Refuse Winter	Garbage Summer	Garbage Winter	Ashes Summer	Ashes Winter	Rubbish Summer	Rubbish Winter	Other Summer	Other Winter	Method of Financing
NEW BRUNSWICK																
MONCTON	43	P	CMI	R		1	1			1 2	1 3			R	R	TC
SAINT JOHN	56	CP	RCM	R		5	1			2	3					
NEWFOUNDLAND																
GANDER	5	M	R	C		1	1							S	S	GT
NOVA SCOTIA																
AMHERST	11	P	RCI	R		R	1							S	S	
DARTMOUTH	47	MC	RCI	C		1	1							S	S	GT
GLACE BAY	24	P	RCI	F		1	1									
ONTARIO																
BARRIE	21	C	RCI	C		2	2							S		GT
BROCKVILLE	18	C	RCI	AC		2	2									GT
CORNWALL	44	C	RCI	CR		3	2							M		GT
FOREST HILL	20	C	RCI	AC		1	1									GT
FORT FRANCES	9	C	RCI	CR		1	1									GT
HAMILTON	264	H	RCI	ACR		6	1	4	4	2	2	1	1			GT
KITCHENER	81	C	ALL	R		2	1									GT
LONDON	176	MP	ALL	C		2	1	1	1	1	1	1	1			GT
OAKVILLE	44	MP	ALL	AC		1	1	2	2	1	1	1	1			GT
OTTAWA	259	C	ALL	CR		2	1	2	2	2	2	2	2			
PORT ARTHUR	44	M	ALL	AC		1	1	2	2	2	2	2	2			GT
PORT COLBORNE	17	C	ALL	ACR		R	R	R	R	1	1	2	2			GT
PORT CREDIT	11	C	RCI	CR		1	1	1	1	1	1	1	1			
PRESTON	9	C	ALL	V		2	2									GT
RIVERSIDE	19	H	RI	C		1	1	1	1							GT
ST. THOMAS	20	C	RCI	C		1	1									GT
SARNIA	50	M	RCI	C		2	2							S	S	GT
SAULT STE MARIE	42	M	ALL	A		1	2									GT
SCARBOROUGH	199	P	RCI	AF		R	R	R	R	2	2	2	2			GT
SUDBURY		M	ALL	AR		1	1	2	2	1	1	1	1			GT
TORONTO	645	MP	RCI	R		2	2	2	2	2	2	2	2	S	S	GT
WATERLOO	21	MC	ALL	AC		2	2	1	1	1	1	1	1			GSC
WELLAND	36		ALL	AF		1	1									GT
QUEBEC																
BEACONSFIELD	10	C	RC	R		2	2							S	S	GT
POINTE-CLAIRE	21	C	ALL	AC		2	2									GT
SEPT-ILES		MC	ALL	AF		R	2			2	2					GSC
WESTMOUNT	32		ALL	R		5	2									GT
SASKATCHEWAN																
SWIFT CURRENT	12	M	ALL	AC		5	1									GT
WEYBURN	9	M	ALL	AF		R	R									GT

appendix C

ANALYSIS AND PLANNING
OF REFUSE COLLECTION SYSTEMS

PART I

The University of California Sanitary Engineering Research Project carried on investigations in the field of community refuse collection and disposal in 1950 and 1951. A report of the results of their work was published in December, 1952. It is titled "An Analysis of Refuse Collection and Sanitary Landfill Disposal," Technical Bulletin No. 8, Series 37. This work is the first comprehensive scientific effort to develop basic refuse collection system design criteria on a broad basis that has been made in almost three decades. Consequently, it is believed desirable to reproduce a synopsis of the data and analytical techniques developed from the study.[1] It should be kept in mind, however, that the data is based on California conditions and should be interpreted accordingly.

REFUSE PRODUCTION

Table 1 reports the unit production of combined refuse observed in the thirteen California cities investigated, grouped according to frequency and type (combined or separate) of collection. Inspection of Table 1 reveals that the average unit production of refuse in eight California cities employing primarily once-per-week collection (Group I) was 32.3 pounds per service per week. The three cities employing essentially twice per week collection reported an average unit production of 47 pounds per service per week. Two cities employing separate collection of garbage (including commercial swill) and rubbish, with twice per week collection of garbage and once per week collection for the remainder, had an average total refuse production of 84.5 pounds per service per week. It would appear from these data that twice per week collection and separate collection of garbage and rubbish encourage greater unit production. It should be pointed out, however, that a portion of the difference in refuse production may attributed to differences in the extent of collection service rendered. The production figures for Group III, Burbank and Long Beach, include the commercial

---

[1]Reproduced with permission, Sanitary Engineering Research Project, University of California.

swill contribution, whereas the data for all other cities excludes commercial swill.

The collection operation including the round trip haul to the disposal site constitutes the major cost of the refuse activity. The cost of collection averages approximately 84 per cent of the total cost of the refuse activity in the thirteen California cities included in this investigation, all of which employ some form of land disposal.

Labor Requirements

The refuse collection operation may be subdivided into four unit operations: (1) pickup, (2) haul, (3) off-route, and (4) at disposal site. "Pickup" includes the time consumed during the actual collection of ref-

TABLE I

Unit Production of Combined Refuse in Thirteen California Cities
(1950-1951)

| | | Unit Production Volume | | Unit Production Pounds per | |
City	Collection Frequency	Cu. Yds. per Service per Week	Cu. Ft. per Capita per Day	Service per Week	Capita per Day
Group I					
Berkeley......		0.11	0.14	27.4	1.25
Fresno........		0.11	0.12	34.1	1.52
Lodi..........	Primarily	0.09	0.12	39.8	1.95
Oroville.......	Once	0.09[1]	0.11[1]	34.0	1.62
Palo Alto......	per	0.15	0.19	36.0	1.70
Sacramento..	Week	0.06[1]	0.07[1]	23.0	1.03
Santa Rosa...		0.08[1]	0.11[1]	32.0	1.63
Stockton......		0.10	0.11	32.5	1.36
Avg. Group I..		0.10	0.12	32.3	1.51
Group II					
Bakersfield...	Primarily	0.16[1]	0.19[1]	67.4	3.01
Riverside.....	Twice	0.11[1]	0.14[1]	41.3	1.90
Watsonville...	per	0.09[1]	0.11[1]	32.3	1.55
Avg. Group II.	Week	0.12	0.15	47.0	2.15
Group III					
Burbank......		0.15	0.18	88.9	4.05
Long Beach..	[2]	0.23	0.32	80.1	4.15
Avg. Group III...		0.10	0.25	84.5	4.10

[1]Mechanical packer yards and cubic feet.
[2]Separate Collection: Garbage—twice per week, includes commercial swill.
Rubbish—one per week.

use from the premises and consists of the net working time from the pickup of the first container until the last container of refuse is loaded on the collection vehicle. "Haul" designates the time required for the round trip to the disposal site and is measured from the time of pickup of the last container on the collection route until the collection vehicle returns to the first container of the succeeding route, excluding the time spent unloading or waiting at the disposal site. "Off-route" time includes such activities as organized rest periods; time out for smoking, eating, refreshments, personal reasons, contacting residents and supervisors; and other miscellaneous activities not devoted to the other three operations.

Table II reports the labor requirements for pickup of commercial refuse for seven California cities.

Table III reports the labor requirements for the pickup operation in combined refuse collection in eleven cities as well as in Burbank and Long Beach, where separate collection is practiced. The average pickup time for ten cities, excluding Burbank, Long Beach, and Oroville, was 148 man-minutes per ton or approximately 2½ man-hours per ton of refuse collected.

It is notable that the man-minutes per ton required for the collection of commercial refuse is about seven per cent less than that of residential.

TABLE II

Average Labor Requirements for Pickup of
Commercial Refuse, for Seven California Cities

City	Year	Number of Men per Collection Vehicle	Commercial Pickups, Per Cent of Total[1]	Curb or Alley Pickups, Per Cent of Total[1,2]	Tons per Trip	Pickup Time, Man-Minutes per Ton
Bakersfield......	1951	3	87	86	2.52	160
Burbank[3]........	1950	3	100	100	2.13	127
Fresno...........	1950	4	100	90	3.32	125
Long Beach[3].....	1950	2	98	100	1.27	112
Riverside........	1950	2	100	100	1.79	184
Sacramento.....	1950	3 & 2	92	64	2.57	137
Watsonville......	1950	2	93	100	1.70	115
Average........		2.6	96	90	2.19	136

[1]Percentage of trips sampled—not necessarily representative of average for entire city.
[2]Remainder are pickups from the street—with container at rear of premises.
[3]Rubbish.

Effect of Collection Frequency on Labor Requirements

The quantity of refuse collected per week from a given area where twice weekly collection is provided may be expected to be about 1.4 times that which would be collected if once per week collection service is provided. At the same time, other potential variables being constant, it would require some 1.2 times the manpower (or man-minutes per ton) to pick up a ton of refuse on a twice weekly frequency. This results from the lesser quantity of material collected per man per pickup or service where the collection frequency is twice weekly. Thus, if three men were required to provide one weekly pickup service to a given area, theoretically 3 x 1.2 plus 3(1.4−1.0) = 3.6 + 1.2 or 4.8 men would be required to supply the same area with twice weekly service.

TABLE III
Tabular Summary of Refuse Pickup Time Studies in Thirteen California Cities
1950 - 1951

City	Year	Type of Truck	Men per Truck	Per Cent Rear of House Pickups	Per Cent Residential Pickups	Services per Mile	Pickup Only—Per Cent of Time Spent							Pickup Time Man-Minutes per Ton
							On Truck	On Street	On Property	At Container	Loading	Waiting	Resting	
Bakersfield	1951	Packer	3	26	87	69	24	20	9	14	18	9	6	158
Berkeley	1950	Open	3	90	85	118	16	18	24	18	16	1	7	123
Berkeley	1951	Open	2.9	100	99	114	17	22	28	20	7	2	4	138
Burbank¹	1950	Packer	3	0	87	61	47	5	0	0	39	7	2	104
Fresno	1950	Open	2.2	32	82	47	27	19	24	9	18	0	3	125
Fresno	1951	Open	2	41	90	50	33	20	15	9	12	4	7	117
Lodi	1950	2/3 Open	2.6	46	73	44	28	14	13	14	27	1	3	124
Lodi	1951	2/3 Open	3	62	84	51	28	14	18	16	18	3	3	142
Long Beach¹	1950	Open	2.2	0	66	83	26	6	0	0	63	1	4	98
Oroville	1951	Packer	3	53	76	31	42	10	12	12	12	4	8	291
Palo Alto	1950	Open	2.6	91	82	20	22	11	19	23	19	3	3	158
Riverside	1950	1/2 Open	2.3	83	83	49	22	11	14	15	27	5	3	160
Riverside	1951	Packer	2.5	71	96	78	21	14	23	19	13	6	4	167
Sacramento	1950	Packer	2.8	71	69	58	29	17	17	11	14	5	7	157
Santa Rosa	1951	Packer	2	85	82	42	19	18	22	19	13	6	3	155
Stockton	1950	Open	3.3	83	72	56	13	25	31	19	10	1	1	194
Stockton	1951	Open		94	90	54	22	20	24	20	10	1	3	170
Watsonville	1950	1/2 Open	2.4	—	45	77	22	12	10	9	38	3	6	111
Watsonville	1951	Packer	3	87	99	125	16	15	31	20	7	8	3	165
Average			2.69	61.9	81.4	64.9	24.9	15.5	17.6	14.1	20.1	3.7	4.2	148²

¹Collection of rubbish and ashes—separate garbage collection not included.
²Excluding Burbank, Long Beach, and Oroville.

Effect of Container Location

Chart 1 illustrates the effect of the container location on the pickup time. The curve represents the trend line of the field data. The pickup time varies from approximately 103 man-minutes per ton for zero per cent rear-of-house pickups (100 per cent alley or curb) to 165 man-minutes per ton for 100 per cent rear-of-house collection (zero per cent alley or curb). The effect of container location (pickup point) upon the cost of collection may be readily computed using the pickup time-unit, man-minutes per ton, and average wage rate. For example: Assuming an average wage rate of $1.50 per hour (2.5 cents per man-minute) and employing the trend line in Chart 1, the cost of labor is approximately $2.56 per ton and $4.15 per ton for 100 per cent rear-of-house pickup. The difference in cost between rear-of-house and alley and/or curb refuse collection is approximately $1.59 per ton. Actually, it will be somewhat greater than $1.59 per ton because the fixed, operation, and maintenance costs will also be greater for rear-of-house collection.

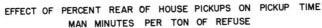

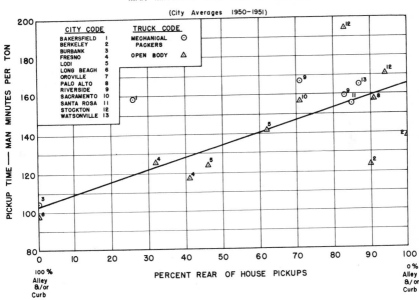

Chart 1

Pickup Density

Although the field investigation did not specifically study the labor requirements of rural refuse collection, it is possible to analyze the effect of population or pickup density on the pickup requirements. Chart 2 reports the relationship between pickup time in man-minutes per ton (percentage of city average) and the average pickup density in services per route mile. In preparing this chart, collection trips within a range of pickup density of 10 services per mile were grouped together. The chart indicates that pickup densities between 30 and 180 services per mile have relatively little effect on the labor requirements of the pickup operation. However, at pickup densities less than 30 services per mile, the labor requirement increases markedly.

Equipment Requirements

The relationship between the total volume of collection vehicle capacity in daily use and the number of services in eleven California cities investigated is shown in Chart 3. There appears to be no significant difference in the equipment requirements for the collection of combined refuse with open-body trucks or mechanical compaction-type vehicles. This may partially be explained by the general failure to utilize compaction-type collection vehicles to capacity in the cities investigated.

A comparative analysis of the efficiency of mechanical packers and open-body trucks in the pickup of combined refuse is reported in Tables IV and V.

It would appear that the open-body truck is somewhat more efficient from the standpoint of labor requirements of the pickup operation. It should be noted, however, that the average number of containers per service was slightly greater for the mechanical packer truck group than for the open-body trucks. Thus, a portion of the increased pickup time for the mechanical packers should be attributed to the handling of a greater number of containers per service.[2] Based upon the average refuse density in open-body vehicles, an average compaction ratio of approximately 1.36 was found to obtain in the field for refuse collection with mechanical compaction type vehicles.

The best single index of the labor efficiency of the haul operation is the unit, man-minutes per ton mile. This may be defined as the man-minutes per ton for the round trip haul distance divided by the number of miles traveled in the haul operation.

For maximum labor efficiency in the haul operation, the combination of number of men per truck, weight of refuse collected per trip, and the number of trips per day should be adjusted to require the minimum man-minutes per ton mile possible. A summary analysis of the labor requirement in man-minutes per ton mile as observed in each of the thirteen cities showed that the man-minutes per ton mile ranged from a low of 1.75 at Lodi, for a 21.9 mile haul with an average of 4.34 tons per trip, to a high of 7.63 at Oroville, for a 7.8 mile haul with an average of 1.83 tons per trip. For a given haul distance, the magnitude of the man-minutes per ton reflects the efficiency of the haul operation—the lower the value, the more efficient the operation.

---

[2] It should be noted that a number of significant efficiency improvements have been made on compactor vehicles since this data was collected.

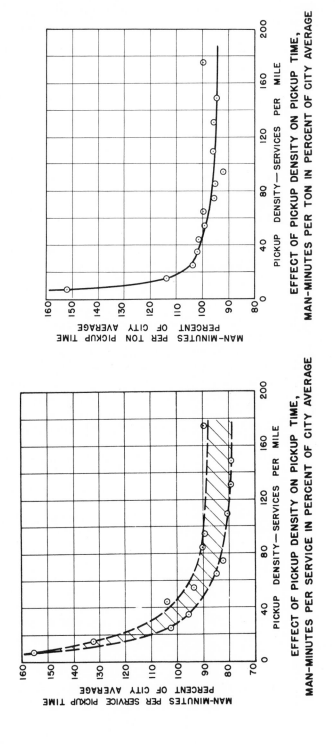

EFFECT OF PICKUP DENSITY ON PICKUP TIME,
MAN-MINUTES PER SERVICE IN PERCENT OF CITY AVERAGE

EFFECT OF PICKUP DENSITY ON PICKUP TIME,
MAN-MINUTES PER TON IN PERCENT OF CITY AVERAGE

Chart 2

Pickup labor, per ton of refuse collected, increases rapidly on sparsely settled routes, that is, on routes with less than 30 services per mile.

TABLE IV

Comparative Analysis of Efficiency of Mechanical Packers
and Open-Body Trucks in Refuse Pickup Operation

Average of Field Data from Nine California Cities, 1950-1951

Type of Truck	Total Number of Trips	Number of Men per Truck	Per Cent Rear-of-House Pickups	Per Cent Residential Pickups	Pickup Density		Pickup Only—Man-Minutes				Unit Weight of Refuse, Lb. per Cu. Yd.
					Services per Mile	Containers per Mile	Per Ton	Per Yard	Per Service	Per Container	
Mechanical packers	971[1]	2.7	65.8	88.6	76	103	159	34.2	2.24	1.59	440
Open-body trucks	87[2]	2.5	65.4	87.2	69	70	135	21.4	1.84	1.73	323

[1] Data from Bakersfield, Lodi, Riverside, Sacramento, Santa Rosa, and Watsonville.
[2] Data from Berkeley, Fresno, Lodi, Riverside, and Stockton.

TABLE V

Where Pickup Time is Spent with Mechanical Packers
and Open-Body Refuse Collection Trucks

Average of Field Data from Nine California Cities, 1950-1951

Type of Truck	Characteristics of Group	Pickup Time, Man-Minutes per Ton	Per Cent of Pickup Time Spent							Pickup Time, Per Cent of Total Trip
			On Truck	On Street	On Property	At Container	Loading	Waiting	Resting	
Mechanical Packers	Same as Table IV	159	21.2	18.1	19.9	16.5	12.8	7.0	4.4	71.7
Open-body trucks	Same as Table IV	135	25.9	18.8	21.0	14.7	13.2	1.9	4.5	68.6

REFUSE COLLECTION TRUCK CAPACITY
WITH RESPECT TO NUMBER OF SERVICES

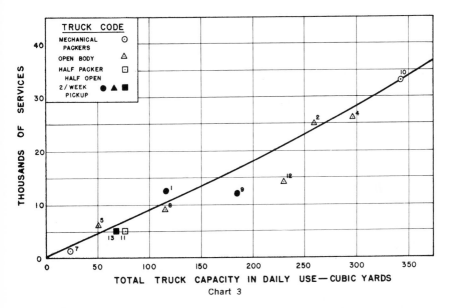

Chart 3

Chart 4 illustrates the relationship existing between the man-minutes per ton mile and the average haul distance. It should be noted that the longer the haul the smaller the man-minutes per ton mile. This may be explained by the fact that the average truck speed increases with the distance traveled; hence, the haul time (man-minutes) increases at a slower rate than the ton miles. Therefore, the quotient or man-minutes per ton mile decreases as the haul distance increases. Assuming a reasonable value for the man-minutes per ton mile for a given haul distance, it is possible to estimate the labor cost of the haul operation in dollars per ton.

Haul speed. The average rate of travel during the haul operation determines the time required for any given haul distance. The average rate of travel or haul speed is defined as the average truck speed for the round trip haul, excluding stops en route or at the disposal site. In other words, it is the net haul speed while the collection vehicle is en route to and from the disposal site.

Numerous factors affect the haul speed, such as the total distance traveled, the size and street layout of the city, and the type of vehicle Studies were made in the field to determine the actual haul speed obtained for the haul operation in each of the thirteen cities studied. Chart 5 shows the relationship existing between the average haul

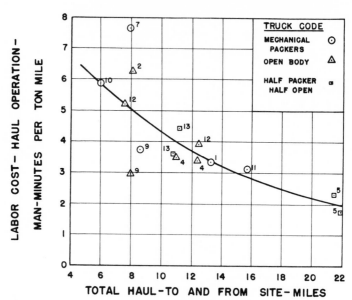

MAN-MINUTES PER TON MILE WITH RESPECT TO HAUL DISTANCE

Chart 4

speed in miles per hour and in minutes per mile, and the average total haul distance in miles. Insufficient data were obtained to establish definitely the relation between the haul speed and the haul distance. The data, however, clearly indicate the general trend, familiar to transportation specialists, that within the limit of haul distances normally encountered in refuse collection, the average haul speed increases as the total haul distance increases.

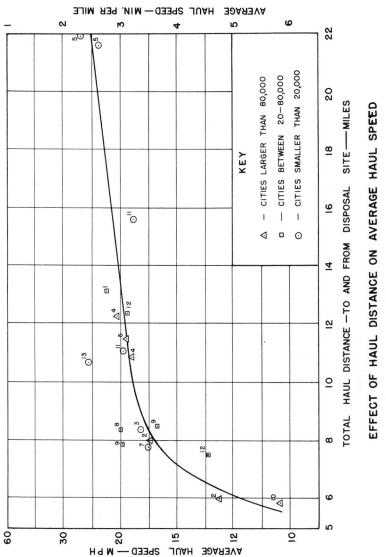

EFFECT OF HAUL DISTANCE ON AVERAGE HAUL SPEED

Chart 5

PART II

GENERAL CONSIDERATIONS

The principal reason for resolving refuse collection into the four unit operations previously discussed—pickup, haul, off-route, and at disposal site—is to permit a rational analysis and design of the collection system. The field studies evaluated the general magnitude of these unit operations and the effect of each on the over-all problem. In addition, it is known that the cost of collection is made up essentially of two items: (1) the cost of labor necessary to load the refuse on the collection vehicles, and (2) the expense of operating the vehicles. From these considerations a method for design and analysis of a system can be developed.

Efficiency of Existing Systems

Municipal officials have frequently expressed an interest in a simple method of evaluating the efficiency of their refuse collection and disposal systems. If refuse collection is a municipal function, the city officials can compute the cost of their individual operation. Evaluation is meaningless, however, unless data from other cities are available for comparison. Unfortunately most of the data reported in this field are not comparable because they represent total over-all costs and include significant variables, such as the haul distance, which hinder a direct cost comparison of one system with another. A rational method of evaluating a system is needed both for determining the efficiency of municipal collection and for establishing an equitable charge for service when contracts for the collection of refuse are arranged with private organizations.

An economic analysis of refuse collection systems entails the evaluation of the two principal components of cost: the labor cost and the operating expense.

Labor cost. A part of the total labor cost is chargeable to each of the unit operations of pickup, haul, off-route, and at disposal site. Pickup time accounts for from 67 to 75 per cent of the total labor requirement. The principal part of the remainder is chargeable to the haul operation. The variables involved in each of these operations are discussed in previous chapters.

The off-route, and at disposal site time requirements of the haul operation are essentially constants, although the latter may be somewhat variable, depending on the type of unloading mechanism employed on the collection vehicles.

It is possible to develop the following expression for the total labor requirements in man-minutes per ton.

$$\underset{\text{Minutes per Trip}}{\text{Total Man-}} = \underset{\text{Time}}{\text{Pickup}} + \underset{\text{Time}}{\text{Haul}} + \underset{\text{Time}}{\text{Off Route}} + \underset{\text{Time}}{\text{At Site}}$$

$$f = bc + ade + 15a + 5a$$

in which: a = number of men per truck
(assume 15 minutes off-route and 5 minutes at disposal site per trip.)

b = pickup time in man-minutes

c = average tons of refuse per trip

d = mileage to and from disposal site

e = average haul speed in minutes per mile

f = total man-minutes per trip

x = total man-minutes per ton

If both sides of the equation are divided by c, the average tons of refuse per trip, then $f/c = x$. Dividing out and simplifying, the following basic expression is obtained.

$$x = b + \frac{ade}{c} + \frac{20a}{c}$$

Knowing the average haul distance, haul speed, and men per truck, and estimating the pickup time in man-minutes per ton, the labor cost in dollars per ton may be readily computed for any wage rate.

Charts 6 and 7, entitled "Chart for Analysis of Refuse Collection Systems" are nomographic expressions of the preceding equation and have been prepared to facilitate its ready solution. They are of particular value in reviewing the efficiency of refuse collection systems.

Since the general range for each characteristic of refuse collection systems has been evaluated for thirteen California cities, the values presented in this report should be adequate for the analysis of collection systems where similar conditions obtain. Other cities may require a short field study in order to develop local design data. In most cities information or estimates are readily available regarding the average haul distance to and from the disposal site, the number of men per truck, and the average tons of refuse collected per trip. Data not so easily obtainable may be the pickup time in man-minutes per ton and the average haul speed to and from the disposal site. These data may be estimated from typical data presented in this report, or they can be observed for a few typical collection trips in any city concerned. Local data will, of course, provide the best basis for analysis of a collection system.

The total labor requirements for the collection operation may be readily computed by means of the nomograph employing the basic data outlined above. A hypothetical example may best illustrate its application.

HYPOTHETICAL CITY

Basic data:

Average distance to disposal site (From center of city) (Round-trip— 16 miles)	8 miles
Average haul speed to and from site	20 mph
Number of collectors per truck	3
Number of collection trips per day (per truck)	3
Average tons of refuse collected per trip	3
Average refuse pickup time	150 man-minutes per ton
Average wage rate of refuse collectors	$1.50 per hour

Required:

Labor cost of collection operation.

Employing Chart 6 the labor cost equation may be solved as follows:

1. By means of a straightedge, connect 16 on "average total haul to and from site—miles," with 20 on "speed, miles per hour" scale and mark intersection point on "index."

2. Similarly, connect intersection point on "index 1" with 3, on "tons per trip, 3 men per truck," and mark intersection on "index 2."

3. Connect point on "index 2" with 150 on "pickup time—man-minutes per ton" scale and read answer, approximately 218 man-minutes per ton total trip time.

Assuming an average wage scale of $1.50 per hour (2.5¢ per man-minute), the labor cost of the collection operation is found to be $5.45 per ton.

Operating cost. The operating cost of refuse collection includes the fixed costs of the collection vehicles and is best expressed in terms of dollars per ton of refuse collected. Several methods may be used to evaluate these costs. Probably the most common method for a city is to evaluate the total annual cost of the operation and divide this by the estimated annual tonnage of refuse collected. Such a method entails a city-wide evaluation of the type, number, and cost of all collection equipment, allowance for depreciation, vehicle operation and maintenance costs, and an estimate of the total annual tonnage of refuse collected. Because the rational design of a refuse collection system frequently necessitates an economic comparison of several types of collection vehicles, a method of evaluating the operating cost on a single collection vehicle basis is presented.

A significant advantage of the analysis of fixed, operation, and maintenance costs on a single truck basis is that it permits a simple and direct comparison of different sizes and types of collection vehicles on a cost per ton basis. It does not, however, give directly the over-all city average cost per ton of refuse collected because each type of collection vehicle

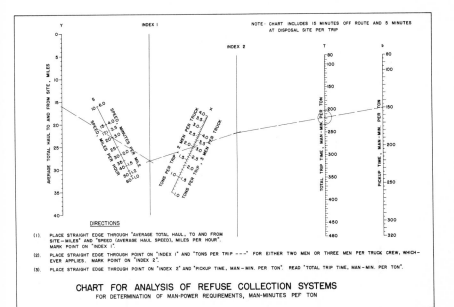

CHART FOR ANALYSIS OF REFUSE COLLECTION SYSTEMS
FOR DETERMINATION OF MAN-POWER REQUIREMENTS, MAN-MINUTES PEF TON

Chart 6

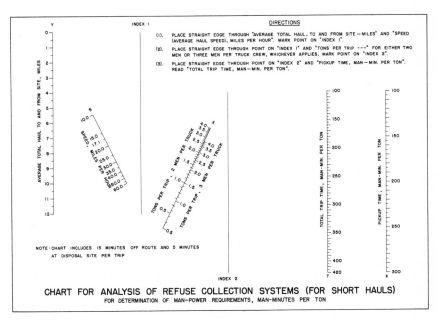

CHART FOR ANALYSIS OF REFUSE COLLECTION SYSTEMS (FOR SHORT HAULS)
FOR DETERMINATION OF MAN-POWER REQUIREMENTS, MAN-MINUTES PER TON

Chart 7

employed will incur a different operating cost. Since most cities operate a fleet of uniform or similar refuse collection vehicles, the difference in the over-all cost per ton due to nonuniform collection equipment such as the use of a special type of truck for downtown business collection, may not be significant. The single truck economic analysis permits a ready evaluation of the cost of collection for each type of vehicle; thus, the weighted average cost per ton of refuse collected may be computed on the basis of the number of each type of equipment in use.

The seven principal factors affecting the operating cost of refuse collection systems are:

1. Initial cost of the refuse collection vehicle
2. Effective or useful life of the vehicle
3. Current interest rate on capital
4. Operation and maintenance cost of the vehicle
5. Average quantity of refuse collected per trip
6. Number of collection trips per year
7. Average total mileage traveled per collection trip or per year

The operating cost on a single truck basis may be expressed by means of the following mathematical expression.

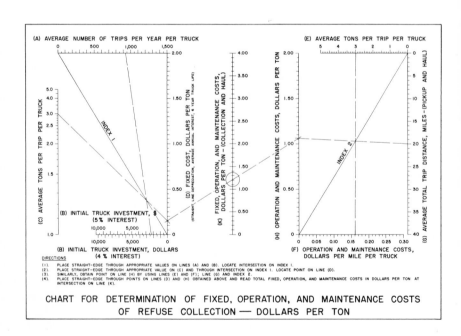

CHART FOR DETERMINATION OF FIXED, OPERATION, AND MAINTENANCE COSTS OF REFUSE COLLECTION — DOLLARS PER TON

Chart 8

Total Operating Cost per Year per truck	=	Annual Depreciation (St. Line)	+	Average Annual Interest	+	Operation and Maintenance per year

$$q = \frac{h}{s} + \frac{hi + \dfrac{hi}{s}}{2} + kmo$$

in which: c = average tons of refuse per trip
h = initial cost of truck, dollars
i = interest rate on capital
k = total number of trips per year
s = useful life of truck in years
m = total mileage per trip, pickup plus haul
o = Operation and maintenance of truck, dollars per mile
q = total operating cost per year per truck
y = total operating cost (fixed charges, operation, and maintenance) in dollars per ton of refuse collected

Since the above expression gives the total operating cost per year per truck, the operating cost per ton may be obtained by dividing both sides of the expression by ck, the number of tons of refuse collected per year per truck.
then:

$$y = \frac{h}{cks} \frac{[1 + i(s + 1)]}{2} + \frac{mo}{c}$$

Total Operating Cost (Dollars per ton)	=	Fixed Charges (Dollars per ton)	+	Operation and Maintenance (Dollars per ton)

In order to simplify the above equation and facilitate its solution by means of a nomograph, interest rates on capital of 4 and 5 per cent and a useful truck life of 6 years were assumed. Six years is a conservative estimate of the useful life of a collection vehicle. But since it corresponds to a truck life of approximately 100,000 miles for an average collection operation employing a sanitary landfill for disposal, a truck life of approximately 6 years appears to be justified for economic analyses of refuse collection systems.

Chart 8 is a nomographic chart to facilitate the solution of the preceding equation for the fixed, operation, and maintenance costs of refuse collection.

The utility of Chart 8 is illustrated by the solution of an example dealing with the hypothetical city previously cited. The problem entails the determination of the operating expense per ton of refuse collected. Additional characteristics of the refuse collection system are given below.

HYPOTHETICAL CITY

Basic data: (supplemental to data given on pp. 488-89)

Average total trip distance (Pickup plus haul)	20 miles
Average tons of refuse collected per trip	3
Number of collection trips per day	3
6-day week, trips per year	936
Type of truck	Open-body
Initial cost of truck	$2300.00
Average truck life—assumed	6 years
Operation and maintenance of truck	$0.16 per mile
Interest rate on capital	4%

Required:

Fixed charges, operation and maintenance in dollars per ton.

Solution by means of Chart 8 is accomplished in the following manner.

1. By means of straightedge, connect 936 "trips per year" on scale "A" with 2300, "initial truck investment, dollars, 4% interest" on scale "B." Mark intersection on "index 1."

2. Connect 3 "tons per trip," scale "C" with previously located point on "index 1" and mark appropriate point on scale "D," fixed cost, dollars per ton." The fixed charge portion of the operating cost appears to be approximately $0.15 per ton.

3. Connect 3 "tons per trip," scale "E," on right-hand side of figure with 0.16 "operation and maintenance cost—dollars per mile" on scale "F" and mark intersection on "index 2."

4. Similarly, connect 20, "average total trip distance, miles" with point on "index 2" and mark off appropriate point on scale "H," "operation and maintenance costs—dollars per ton." In this case, the operation and maintenance cost is approximately $1.06 per ton.

5. To obtain the total operating cost, connect the appropriate points on scales "D" and "H" and read off the total fixed, operation, and maintenance cost of $1.21 per ton on scale "K." Or, the values obtained for fixed and operation and maintenance cost may be added together to obtain the total operating cost.

For the hypothetical example given, the labor cost was found to be $5.45 per ton, and $1.82 per ton for fixed charges, operation, and maintenance, making a total cost, exclusive of administration of $7.27 per ton. The nomographs provide a ready means of estimating the cost of refuse collection and provide a basis for comparison with the actual cost computed from the annual budget and estimates of the annual tonnage of refuse collected. Gross differences in the unit cost of refuse collection by the two methods indicate the relative efficiency of the collection operation. For example, the collection routes may be laid out so that the prescribed number of trips per day fail to utilize the entire working period, resulting in considerable loading or waiting on the part of the collection crews. Similarly, numerous trips to the dis-

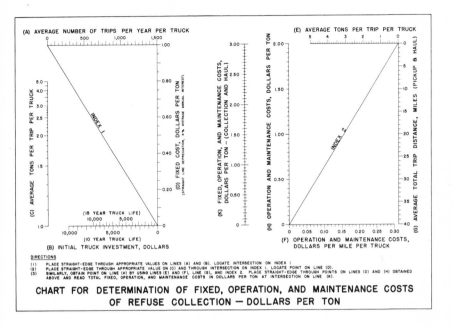

CHART FOR DETERMINATION OF FIXED, OPERATION, AND MAINTENANCE COSTS
OF REFUSE COLLECTION — DOLLARS PER TON

Chart 9

posal site with below capacity loads may result in inefficiency in the collection operation.

Chart 9 is a nomographic chart for the determination of fixed, operation and maintenance costs of refuse collection employing a longer useful truck life than used in Chart 8. The chart is based on a 4 per cent interest rate and a useful truck life of either 10 or 15 years. Its inclusion is to facilitate the determination of fixed charges for collection systems where local conditions indicate a useful truck life appreciably longer than 6 years.

Design of Collection Systems

The rational design of a refuse collection system is an engineering problem. The efficiency of a collection system depends on the judicious combination of the size of the collection vehicle, number of men per vehicle, the type of refuse pickup, and the number of trips per day for a given haul distance to the disposal site.

Because of the many variables affecting the collection operation, it is difficult to select the appropriate combination of size of truck, number of men per truck, and number of trips per day that will result in the minimum total cost of collection without an economic analysis of each collection system. Several desirable characteristics of collection systems are readily apparent. Each collection route should be laid out so that for a given number of collectors per truck, the full working day is utilized in making the prescribed number of collection trips per day. That is, it should not require more than the working day to complete the daily quota of collection trips, nor, for the sake of efficiency, should it require appreciably less. The relatively common practice of having each vehicle collect two full loads, and a third or last which is only a half-load, does not efficiently utilize the collection equipment. It is apparent that for a city with a given haul distance employing a given number of men per truck and collection trips per day, the amount of refuse collected per trip is definitely fixed, since these factors determine the amount of time in man-minutes devoted to the pickup operation each trip. Therefore, the average tons of refuse collected per trip depends on the magnitude of the average pickup time for the city.

For a fixed length of haul, the collection system requiring the minimum number of man-minutes per ton for the haul operation will be most desirable from the standpoint of labor efficiency. A hypothetical example may best illustrate this point. Assume that a certain city employs two men per collection vehicle, that each vehicle makes three collection trips per day, and that it collects on the average, two tons of refuse per trip. If the city changed to three trips per day, each truck would have to collect three tons of refuse per trip to maintain the same labor efficiency. If less than three tons of refuse were carried per trip, the labor cost per ton would increase. The operating cost per ton, however (fixed charges, operation, and maintenance costs) would decrease slightly.

In order to perform the rational design of a refuse collection system, it is necessary to know the effect of using two or three men per collection vehicle on the total cost of collection. Similarly, the effect of making two or three collection trips per day on the size of vehicle required is of interest. The quantitative evaluation of the economy of different collection schemes necessitates relating the variables in a single mathematical expression. Assuming an eight-hour work day for refuse collectors, the following relationship was developed for the refuse operation.

$$\frac{\text{Man-minutes}}{\text{per trip}} = \frac{\text{Pickup}}{\text{Time}} + \frac{\text{Haul}}{\text{Time}} + \frac{\text{Off Route}}{\text{Time}} + \frac{\text{At}}{\text{Site}}$$

$$f = \frac{480a}{g} = bc + ade + 15a + 5a$$

In which: a = number of men per truck
           b = pickup time in man-minutes per ton
           c = average tons of refuse per trip
           d = mileage to and from disposal site
           e = average haul speed in minutes per mile
           f = total man-minutes per trip
           g = total number of trips per day
           x = total man-minutes per trip

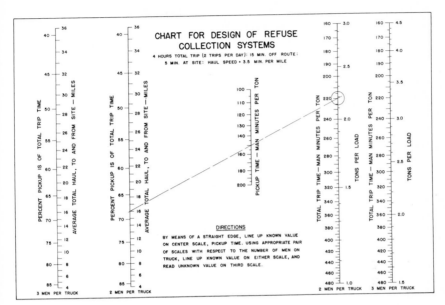

Chart 10

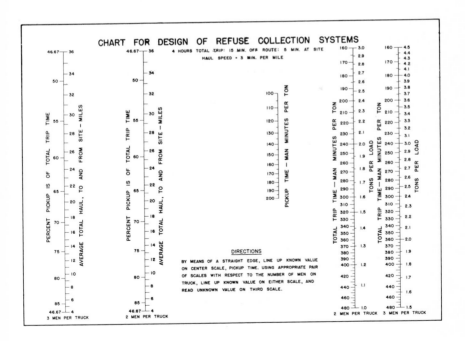

Chart 11

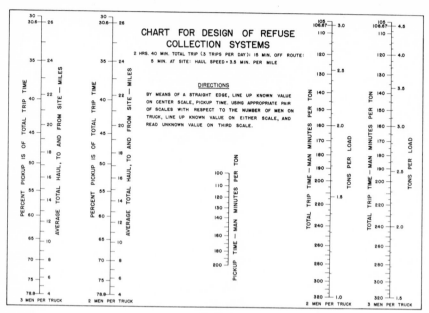

Chart 12

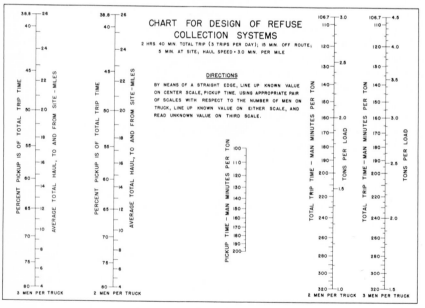

Chart 13

Dividing both sides of the equation by a, the number of men per truck, and simplifying, the following expression may be obtained.

$$\frac{480}{g} = \frac{bc}{a} + de + 20$$

It should be noted that the above expression is similar to the equation developed for the analysis nomograph (Chart 6). Both relationships include a 15-minute allowance for time off route and a 5-minute allowance for the time at disposal site, making a total of 20 minutes per trip in nonpickup activity exclusive of the haul time.

Charts 10, 11, 12 and 13 are design nomographs developed from the above expression for particular values of e and g; namely, the average haul speed in minutes per mile, and different numbers of collection trips per day. Charts 10 and 11 are charts for the nomographic solution of the above equation when g is 2 trips per day and the haul speed, e, is 3.5 and 3.0 minutes per mile (17.1 and 20 mph) respectively. Similarly, Charts 12 and 13 are design nomographs for use when 3 collection trips are made each day and the average haul speed is 3.5 and 3.0 minutes per mile, respectively.

To use these charts, simply select the appropriate chart for the number of trips per day and the estimated haul speed, and by means of a straightedge connect any known characteristic of the system, such as the average total haul to and from site, with the appropriate value for the pickup time, and read off the unknown characteristics.

For example, a city has a suitable location for a refuse disposal site 8 miles from the center of the city. If 2 collection trips per day and 2 man trucks are employed and an average haul speed of 17.1 mph (3.5 minutes per mile) is attained: what size of truck will be required and what will be the total labor cost of the collection operation in man-minutes per ton? Also, what per cent of the total trip time will be devoted to the pickup operation? The pickup time for the city is estimated to be approximately 150 man-minutes per ton. Connecting 150 man-minutes per ton and 16 miles average total haul on the appropriate 2 men per truck scales as noted on Chart 10, the average tons per load is observed to be approximately 2.18, the labor is 220 man-minutes per ton, and the pickup time approximately 68 per cent of the total trip time. All design charts are used in a similar manner.

PART III

Illustrative example of the design of a refuse collection and disposal system for a typical western community of 12,000 services (about 45,000 population). *This example is presented as a guide. Certain of the design factors vary according to local conditions and these should be determined in each case.*

ASSUMED CONDITIONS TO BE USED AS BASIS FOR DESIGN

1. Residential services 12,000
2. Commercial services 800
3. Average residential density of services .... 90 per mile
4. Average commercial service density .... 50 per mile
5. Twice per week collection of combined refuse in residential districts and three collections per week in commercial districts.
6. Fifty per cent of the community, "rear of house" collection service, the remainder receiving either curb or alley service.
7. Landfill disposal sites available at distances of 5 to 10 miles from the geographical center of the city (therefore, average haul = 10 to 20 miles).
8. A suitable incinerator site on municipally owned land—available at a distance of 2 miles from the geographical center of the city (therefore, average total haul = 4 miles).

DESIGN CRITERIA TO BE ESTIMATED OR DETERMINED FROM FIELD SURVEY

1. Residential production of combined refuse—48 pounds per service week.
2. Commercial production of combined refuse, excluding commercial swill (assume commercial swill collected by private contractor at no cost to the producer)—250 pounds per service per week.
3. Average density of mixed refuse in open-body collection vehicles—350 pounds per cubic yard; in packer-body vehicles—490 pounds per cubic yard (1.4 x the density in open-body vehicles).
4. Labor requirements for pickup only of residential combined refuse with 60 services per mile; 82 per cent residential services, and 71 per cent "rear of house" collection average 148 man-minutes per ton (Chart 1).
5. Labor requirements for pickup only of commercial combined ref-

use (exclusive of commercial swill) averages 136 man-minutes per ton. (Table II)

6. Land requirements for sanitary landfill—3.5 acre-feet per year per 1,000 services at 2.5 compaction ratio and 10 foot depth.

FACTORS INVOLVED IN FINANCING SYSTEM

1. Cost of incineration of one ton of refuse and rubbish including fixed, operation, and maintenance charges (straight line depreciation, 4 per cent average annual interest, 20-year period) averages $2.15. (Excludes administration, employee benefits, and cost of land.)

2. The cost of disposal of one ton of refuse by the sanitary landfill method with all inclusions and exclusions as per above but including debt retirement on land at $200.00 per acre, and on equipment averages $0.66 per ton. This figure based upon a land-use requirement of approximately 3.5 acre-feet per year per 1,000 services and an assumed 30 per cent increase in population over a 20-year period, the design life of the site. Cost also included amortization of a $20,000 dragline

3. Average cost of collection labor—$1.50 per hour.

4. Other cost factors:
   a. for collection vehicles, straight-line depreciation, 4 per cent average annual interest, 6-year (100,000 miles) truck life;
   b. $0.16 per mile for operation and maintenance of a packer-type collection vehicle and $0.12 per mile for an open-body type vehicle;
   c. initial cost of packer-body type vehicle—$7,500, and cost of open-body type vehicle—$2,500 (both costs include truck and body)

TOTAL ANNUAL PRODUCTION

Residential production of combined refuse—(48 lbs/serv/week)

$$[12,000 + (0.20)(800)^1](52)\frac{(1)}{(2000)} = 15,175 \text{ tons per year}$$

Commercial production—250 lbs/serv/week

$$(0.80)^1(800)(52)\frac{(1)}{(2000)} = 4160 \text{ tons per year}$$

The total community production of combined refuse (excluding commercial swill) will be 19,335 tons annually.

PICKUP TIME

From Chart 1, the pickup time for 50 per cent "rear of house" collection routes is 134 man-minutes per ton. A survey showed that the pick-

---

[1] 20 per cent of total commercial services assumed to be "residential business" contributing to the unit production of 48 lbs/service/week.

up time with a packer type truck is approximately 10 per cent greater than that for open-body trucks. Therefore, the pickup time will be assumed at 134 man-minutes per ton for open-body collection vehicles and 147 man-minutes per ton for packer-body collection vehicles.[2]

The cost relationship between "rear of house" collection and curb or alley collection may be estimated from data in Chart 1. For 0 per cent "rear of house" collection (100 per cent "curb" or "alley" collection) the pickup time averages 104 man-minutes per ton. For 100 per cent "rear of house" collection, the pickup time averages 162 man-minutes per ton. Thus, 100 per cent "rear of house" collection requires $\dfrac{(162 - 104 \text{ x } 100)}{104} = 56$ per cent more pickup time, or pickup time for 100 per cent "curb" or "alley" pickup is $\dfrac{(104 \text{ x } 100)}{162} = 64$ per cent of that required for 100 per cent "rear of house" pickup. If the cost of man-power in the collection and haul operation involves 90 per cent of the total cost of collection, then the cost of "curb" or "alley" collection is $(0.90 \text{ x } 36) = 32$ per cent less than the cost for 100 per cent "rear of house" collection. Further, if collection and haul approximate 85 per cent of the total cost of the refuse system (collection and haul, disposal, and administration) then 100 per cent "curb" or "alley" collection will result in a cost for the whole system of $(0.85 \text{ x } 32) = 29$ per cent less than that for a system built around 100 per cent "rear of house" collection. (Or, the cost of a 100 per cent "curb" or "alley" system, considering total cost, is $\left(\dfrac{1}{1.28} \text{ x } 100 \right) = 78$ per cent of the cost of a 100 per cent "rear of house" system.)

THE PROBLEM

In general, the city is faced with three problems associated with its refuse disposal system.

1. How far can combined refuse be hauled in the collection vehicle at a cost which is equal to or less than the total cost of collection and disposal by incineration?

2. What is the most economical combination of type and size of truck, number of trips per day, and number of collectors per truck, for the given set of conditions?

3. How much more does it cost to collect refuse and haul it to a disposal site 5 to 10 miles from the city compared to an alternate, but more expensive disposal site 2 miles from the city?

THE DESIGN

Using the design criteria previously cited, and employing Charts 8 through 13 (Charts 10 through 13 for determination of pickup and haul

---

[2]It should be noted that a number of significant improvements have been made on compactor vehicles since this data was collected.

labor costs, and Chart 8 for determination of fixed, operation, and maintenance costs), the total costs for various collection schemes plus disposal by incineration may be determined. These costs are reported in Table VI.

An analysis of the data in Table VI indicates the following conclusions:

1. The use of open trucks reduces the cost of the operation by an appreciable amount. If it is believed by the community that the aesthetic value of the use of the mechanical packer-trucks is equal to the additional cost, the selection of the type of truck may be made on that basis.

2. The table shows that in each case, the use of 3-man crews on the collection truck reduces the cost of collection. It should be pointed out, however, that in each comparison in Table VI *the additional man must add ½ again as much refuse by weight to the load.*

TABLE VI

Costs of Collection and Disposal of Combined Refuse for Various Collection Systems Employing Disposal by Incineration

| System | Tons Hauled Per Trip | Cost Per Ton—Dollars | | Disposal | Total |
| | | Collection | | | |
		Pickup and Haul	Fixed, Operation and Maintenance		
Packer-body Vehicles					
3 Trips Per Day					
3 Men per Truck	2.57	4.67	1.02	2.15	7.84
2 Men per Truck	1.72	4.67	1.54	2.15	8.36
2 Trips Per Day					
3 Men per Truck	4.21	4.27	0.80	2.15	7.22
2 Men per Truck	2.82	4.27	1.20	2.15	7.62
Open-body Vehicles					
3 Trips Per Day					
3 Men per Truck	2.83	4.25	0.47	2.15	6.87
2 Men per Truck	1.87	4.25	0.71	2.15	7.11
2 Trips Per Day					
3 Men per Truck	4.61	3.90	0.35	2.15	6.40
2 Men per Truck	3.10	3.90	0.51	2.15	6.56

3. The cost analysis indicates that a two-trip per day schedule is more economical than three trips per day both from the standoint of pickup and haul labor cost (less total time off route and at disposal site per day), as well as the fixed, operation, and maintenance costs (more tons per trip hence lower fixed, operation, and maintenance costs per ton). A determining factor is the size of truck required to carry the amount of refuse collected on a two trips per day basis.

Employing the data reported in Table VI, it is possible to compute, by means of nomographic charts, the distance the refuse may be hauled to a sanitary landfill and yet not exceed the total cost of collection and disposal by incineration.

The most economical packer-type collection system is observed to be a two-trip per day, three-men per truck combination; however, noting that with such a system is would be necessary to haul 4.21 tons of refuse per trip which is slightly beyond the capacity of a conventional size truck. The second best collection scheme from an economic point of view is the two-trips per day, two-men per truck combination which will be used for the illustrative example. This collection combination should pick up, on the average, 2.82 tons of refuse per trip, which is a load of conventional size. Since disposal by sanitary landfill will cost $0.66 per ton, the refuse may be hauled a distance such that the total cost of collection (including labor, fixed, operation, and maintenance costs) will be $7.62 less $0.66, or $6.96 per ton. The solution of this problem involves a trial and error method using various haul distances, 147 man-minutes per ton pickup time, and two and three-man crews (Chart 11). It is found that a two-trip per day, three-men per truck system allows a haul of over 18 miles carrying a load of 3.38 tons per trip; and a two-trip per day, two-men per truck system allows a 14-mile haul of a load of 2.42 tons per trip. Chart 11 is used because of the higher haul speed (20 miles per hour) found in hauls from 10 to 20 miles.

Thus, a haul of 18 miles to a sanitary landfill located 9 miles from the geographical center of the city can be made at a total cost (collection and disposal) which is equal to that of a system employing incineration. Let it be assumed that this system will be adopted, and the remainder of the design will be based upon it.

From the information derived from the economic analysis of the collection systems, it is possible to select the appropriate size and number of trucks and to lay out the collection routes. In accordance with the packer design, it is necessary to collect 3.38 tons of refuse per trip. Assuming a density of 490 pounds per cubic yard of packer refuse, a $\dfrac{(3.38)\ (2000)}{(490)}$ = 14 cubic yard body will be required. For adequate capacity and to employ standard size units, 15 cubic yard packer bodies will be used. In order to collect 3.38 tons per trip with an average domestic refuse production of 48 pounds per service per week or 24 pounds per pickup for twice per week collection, it will require on the average approximately $\dfrac{(3.38)\ (2000)}{(24)} = 282$ services or pickups per trip

At the assumed pickup density of 90 services per mile, the designated route would require slightly more than three miles for the pickup operation employed in the design. Assuming 20 per cent of the business or commercial services are "residential" or "outlying" business, then approximately $\dfrac{(12160)\ (2)}{(2)\ (282)} = 44$ routes, each representing a day's work per truck, will be required. This is actually 22 separate routes with twice per week collection. If trucks are worked 6 days per week, then $\dfrac{(44)}{(6)} = 7 +$ trucks will be required, Thus 8 trucks distributed over the 22 routes will handle the job.

The truck requirements for commercial refuse collection may be estimated in a similar manner. Assuming an accumulation of commercial refuse of 250 pounds per service per week, two trips per day, and an average of 3.38 tons per trip, each truck will be able to handle $\dfrac{(2)\ (3.38)\ (2000)\ (6)}{(250)} = 324$ services per day. If each service is picked up

TABLE VII

Comparison of Costs of Collection and
Disposal of Refuse for Round Trip
Hauls of 10 and 20 Miles

System (2 Trips per day)	Tons Hauled Per Trip	Cost per Ton—Dollars		Disposal (Operation and Maintenance)	Total (Less Cost of Land)
		Collection			
		Pickup and Haul	Fixed, Operation andMaintenance		
10 Mile Haul (3.4 min./mile average speed)					
3 men/truck	3.78	4.77	1.14	0.57	6.48
2 men/truck	2.54	4.77	1.70	0.57	7.04
20 mile Haul (3.0 min./mile average speed)					
3 men/truck	3.26	5.53	1.80	0.57	7.90
2 men/truck	2.17	5.53	2.70	0.57	8.80

each day, then $\dfrac{(640)}{(324)} = 2$ trucks will be required for the commercial district.

Thus, a total of 10 collection vehicles are required to handle 22 residential and 2 commercial routes in the city. Each residential route will receive twice per week service, and each commercial route will receive daily service. Additional vehicles may be required for miscellaneous rubbish pickup and for standby equipment.

The cost of refuse collection and disposal has been estimated to be $7.62 per ton. To obtain the total cost of the refuse operation it is necessary only to add a percentage allowance of approximately 10 per cent for general administration and employee benefits. Assuming 10 per cent for administration, etc., the unit cost of the refuse operation is approximately $8.38 per ton or in terms of 19,320 tons of refuse collected per year, the refuse budget is (8.38) $(19,320) = \$161,902.00$ per year.

MAXIMUM HAUL

The foregoing example shows that disposal by a sanitary landfill located 9 miles from the city or an incinerator 2 miles from the city is possible at a cost per ton of $7.62 (plus administration, etc.).

For that cost ($6.96 + 0.66 for disposal), however, a much longer haul can be used if, for example, 100 per cent curb or alley pickup is imposed. In that case, using 110 man-minutes per ton pickup with packers, a total haul of approximately 25 miles can be used. Thus, if the conditions imposed upon the system are changed to include 100 per cent curb or alley collection, a much longer haul can be used for the same cost per ton. The system employing incineration with 100 per cent "curb" or "alley" collection would, of course, also be reduced in cost from that employing 50 per cent "curb" or "alley" collection.

DIFFERENCE IN COST BETWEEN TWO LAND-DISPOSAL SITES

If the problem is one of choosing between two sanitary landfill disposal sites, then the solution involves simply the determination of the cost of each using the charts without the "trial and error" method previously employed.

From the previous problem it was found that the most satisfactory combination of factors (assuming the use of packer body vehicles and 147 man-minutes per ton pickup) involves a two-trip per day system. Of the $0.66 per ton for disposal costs by the sanitary landfill, $0.18 per ton is for amortization of land and equipment, of which, in the example previously cited, one half is for amortization of land. Thus, in the problem, it will be assumed that operation and maintenance of a sanitary landfill site and the amortization of the necessary equipment costs $0.57 per ton of refuse disposed. It will be assumed that there are two possible sites, one at a distance of 5 miles and one at a distance of

10 miles from the geographical center of the city. The former site will be assumed to cost significantly more than the latter.

Using all of the design and cost factors employed in the previous problem, and assuming 50 per cent "curb" or "alley" collection, the costs of collection, haul, and disposal of the refuse (exclusive of land cost) at the two sites may be determined using Charts 10, 11, and 8. These costs are shown in Table VII. The heavy load per trip which would be necessary for the three men per truck system would preclude its use with the 10-mile haul. The cost for the 10-mile haul would therefore be $7.04 per ton (excluding cost of land), and that for the 20-mile haul would be $7.90 per ton. The difference in cost is seen to be $0.86 per ton. The effect of haul upon the refuse collection system is vividly illustrated in this example, and it is obvious that a much more expensive site at a distance of 5 miles from the city, when amortized over a 20-year period, could be used while still keeping the cost well below that involving the longer haul.

appendix D

SELECTED BIBLIOGRAPHY

CHAPTER 1. THE REFUSE COLLECTION PROBLEM

American Public Works Association and U. S. Department of Health, Education, and Welfare, Public Health Service. *Refuse Collection and Disposal for the Small Community*. November, 1953. (Reprinted Washington, D.C.: DHEW, December, 1955.)

American Society of Civil Engineers. "Refuse Collection," and "State Activities and Fiscal Aspects." Reports of subcommittees of the Committee on Refuse Collection and Disposal of the Sanitary Engineering Division. *Proceedings*, Vol. 80, No. 473 and No. 557, 1954.

American Society of Civil Engineers. "Status of Refuse Collection and Disposal." Report of the Solid Wastes Engineering Section of the Sanitary Engineering Research Committee. *Proceedings*, Vol. 83, No. SA1, February, 1957, pp. 1176-1 to 1176-7.

Foster, W. A. "Municipal Officials Handbook, Part I," *American City*, October, 1952, pp. 26-30.

Hollis, M.D., and Hope, M.C. "Public Works and Community Health," *Public Works Engineers' Yearbook, 1955*. Chicago: American Public Works Association, pp. 118-123.

Hope, M. C., Johnson, C. C., and Weaver, L. "Refuse Handling Practices in the United States," *Public Health Reports*, February, 1956, p. 204.

Institute for Training in Municipal Administration. *Municipal Public Works Administration*. 5th ed. Chicago: International City Managers' Association, 1957, 449 pp.

Smith, C. N., and Keller, J. C. "Fly Control for Cities," *Public Works*, June, 1956, p. 122.

Weaver, L. *Refuse Collection and Disposal, An Annotated Bibliography, 1954-1955*. Washington, D.C.: Department of Health, Education, and Welfare, Public Health Service, 1956.

CHAPTER 2. REFUSE MATERIALS

Martin, D. "Sanitary Fills Are the Answer," *American City*, November, 1953, p. 112.

Planned Refuse Disposal. A report to the Directors of the County Sanitation Districts of Los Angeles County, California, September, 1955, Part II, Chapter 6, "Nature and Quantity of Refuse," pp. 26-32.

Schneider, C. "Present Trends in Refuse Collection and Disposal," *Public Works Engineers' Newsletter*, April, 1952, pp. 1, 3, 6, 7.

State Water Pollution Control Board, Sacramento, California. "Report on the Investigation of Leaching of a Sanitary Landfill," *Publication No. 10,* 1954.

University of California. "Muncipal Incineration," *Technical Bulletin No. 6,* November, 1951, Chapters I-V, pp. 1-47.

University of California. "An Analysis of Refuse Collection and Sanitary Landfill Disposal" *Technical Bulletin No. 8,* 1952, Chapter I, "The Collection Operation," pp. 9-50.

Weaver, L., and Keagy, D. *The Sanitary Landfill in Northern States.* Washington, D. C.: U. S. Department of Health, Education, and Welfare, Public Health Service Publication 226, 1952, 31 pp.

CHAPTER 3. PREPARATION OF REFUSE FOR COLLECTION

American Public Works Association and U. S. Department of Health, Education, and Welfare, Public Health Service. *Refuse Collection and Disposal for the Small Community.* November, 1953. (Reprinted Washington, D. C.: DHEW, December, 1955.)

Barnes, W. R. "Big Containers Better Collection," *American City,* May, 1956, p. 11.

"City-Owned, City-Cleaned Garbage Cans," *American City,* February, 1955, p. 101.

Coffee, J. H., and Dunn, W. L. "How To Make Refuse Collection Sanitary," *American City,* January, 1952, p. 90.

Hope, M. C., Johnson, C. C., and Weaver, L., "Refuse Handling Practices in the United States," *Public Health Reports,* February, 1956, p. 204.

Lipp, M. N. "Miami Beach Makes Community Cleanliness a Habit," *American City,* June, 1955, p. 149.

"Paper Bags for Household Refuse Handling." Allan H. Rogers and Robert K. Lockwood. American Public Works Association Research Foundation Project No. 115. Chicago: American Public Works Association, August 1963.

Safe and Sanitary Home Refuse Storage. Washington, D. C.: U. S. Department of Health, Education, and Welfare, Public Health Service Publication No. 183, 1952.

Schneider, C. "Present Trends in Refuse Collection and Disposal," *Public Works Engineers' Newsletter*, April, 1952, pp. 1, 3, 6, 7.

University of California. "An Analysis of Refuse Collection and Sanitary Landfill Disposal," *Technical Bulletin No. 8,* 1952, Chapter I, "The Collection Operation."

CHAPTER 4. FACTORS AFFECTING REFUSE COLLECTION COST

American Public Works Association and U. S. Department of Health, Education, and Welfare, Public Health Service. *Refuse Collection and Disposal for the Small Community.* November, 1953. (Reprinted Washington, D. C.: DHEW, December, 1955.)

Planned Refuse Disposal. A report to the Directors of the County Sanitation Districts, Los Angeles County, California, September, 1955, Part II, Chapter 3, "Factors Affecting Collection," pp. 9-14.

Riker, I. R. "Ten Years of Municipal Costs," *Public Works,* July, 1950, p. 33.

"Refuse Collection Cost Cut—Service Improved," *Public Works,* June, 1957, p. 103.

Screvane, P. R. "Equipment Replacement," *Public Works,* March, 1957, p. 123.

University of California. "An Analysis of Refuse Collection and Sanitary Land-fill Disposal," *Technical Bulletin No.* 8, 1952, Chapter I, "The Collection Operation," and Chapter II, "The Haul."

CHAPTER 5. REFUSE COLLECTION METHODS

American Public Works Association and U. S. Department of Health, Education, and Welfare, Public Health Service. *Refuse Collection and Disposal for the Small Community.* November, 1953. (Reprinted Washington, D. C.: DHEW, December, 1955.)

Foster, W. S. "Municipal Officials Handbook, Part II," *American City,* October, 1952, pp. 31-39.

Geisheker, B. J. "Progress Is the Key," *American City,* December, 1956. p. 82.

Goerlick, H. L. "Zone-Type Refuse Contracts," *American City,* October, 1956, p. 167.

Hope, M. C., Johnson, C. C., and Weaver, L. "Refuse Handling Practices in the United States," *Public Health Reports,* February, 1956, p. 204.

Mann, David. "The Change Came Gradually," *American City,* June, 1956, p. 120.

Planned Refuse Disposal. A report to the Directors of the County Sanitation Districts of Los Angeles County, California, September, 1955, Chapter 4, "Methods and Costs for Refuse Collection," pp. 14-17.

Taylor, R. C. "Modern Refuse Demands Modern Collection Methods," *American City,* September, 1955, p. 142.

University of California. "An Analysis of Refuse Collection and Sanitary Land-fill Disposal," *Technical Bulletin No.* 8, 1952, Chapter I, "The Collection Operation."

CHAPTER 6. REFUSE COLLECTION EQUIPMENT

American Society of Civil Engineers. "Refuse Collection." Report of a subcommittee of the Committee of Refuse Collection and Disposal of the Sanitary Engineering Division. *Proceedings,* Vol. 80, No. 473, 1954.

American Public Works Association and U.S. Department of Health, Education, and Welfare, Public Health Service. *Refuse Collection and Disposal for the Small Community.* November, 1953. (Reprinted Washington, D. C.: DHEW, December, 1955.)

Foster, W. S. "Municipal Officials Handbook, Part II," *American City,* October, 1952, pp. 31-39.

Graydon, S. W. "We Are Trying a King-sized Truck," *American City,* February, 1956, p. 125.

"Refuse Collection Cost Cut—Service Improved," *Public Works,* June, 1957, p. 103.

University of California. "An Analysis of Refuse Collection and Sanitary Landfill Disposal," *Technical Bulletin No. 8,* 1952, Chapter I, "The Collection Operation."

CHAPTER 7. PLANNING REFUSE COLLECTION SYSTEMS

American Public Works Association and U. S. Department of Health, Education, and Welfare, Public Health Service. *Refuse Collection and Disposal for the Small Community.* November, 1953. (Reprinted Washington, D. C.: DHEW, December, 1955.)

Arthur, G. B. "Engineering Solves the Refuse Problem," *Public Works,* April, 1956, p. 116.

Giles, J. H. L. "Developing a Refuse Collection Program—Case Study," *Public Works Engineers' Yearbook, 1955.* Chicago: American Public Works Association, pp. 135-153.

Howell, E. S. "The Challenge of Automation for Cities," *Public Management,* July, 1957, pp. 147-150.

"Integration and Coordination of Public Works, A Forum," *Public Works Engineers' Yearbook, 1956.* Chicago: American Public Works Association, pp. 119-140.

"Madison Heights Sanitary Garbage Collection Service," *Virginia Health Bulletin,* November, 1956, pp. 1-2.

Martin, J. C., Hammerstrom, R. J., and Waldrop, R. H. "The Laredo Story of Sanitation Progress," *American City,* February, 1957, p. 116.

Mocine, C. R. "Trends in City Planning," *Public Management,* October, 1956, pp. 221-225.

"Technical and Planning Aspects of Solid Wastes," Proceedings of A Short Course sponsored by the Ohio Department of Health and the United States Public Health Service in cooperation with the American Society of Mechanical Engineers, American Society of Civil Engineers, American Institute of Planners, American Public Works Association, and Ohio Municipal League, Columbus, Ohio, September 20-24, 1965.

University of California. "An Analysis of Refuse Collection and Sanitary Landfill Disposal," *Technical Bulletin No. 8,* 1952, Chapter II, "The Haul," and Chapter III, "Analysis and Design of Refuse Collection Systems."

CHAPTER 8. SUPPLEMENTAL TRANSPORTATION OF REFUSE

Planned Refuse Disposal. A report to the Directors of the County Sanitation Districts of Los Angeles County, California, September, 1955, Part III, Chapter 3, "Transfer and Haul," pp. 58-67.

University of California. "An Analysis of Refuse Collection and Sanitary Landfill Disposal," *Technical Bulletin No. 8*, 1952, Chapter II, "The Haul," and Chapter III, "An Analysis and Design of Refuse Collection Systems."

Xanten, W. A. "Large-Scale Odor and Dust Control," *Heating and Ventilating*, August, 1951, pp. 65-67.

—. Transfer Station Expedites Refuse Handling," *American City*, September, 1950, p. 108.

CHAPTER 9. SPECIAL REFUSE COLLECTION PROBLEMS

Bailey, J. A. "Philadelphia Alley Cats," *American City*, July, 1954, p. 92.

Foster, W. S. "Municipal Officials Handbook, Part IV," *American City*, October, 1952, pp. 59-68.

Peterson, O. C. "Public Liability in Public Works," *Public Works Engineers' Yearbook, 1955*. Chicago: American Public Works Association, pp. 36-43.

"Sawmill Makes Tree Disposal Profitable," *American City*, October, 1956, p. 105.

"Volume of Roadside Rubbish and Debris," *Public Works*, May, 1957, p. 190.

Wentz, J. B. "Cleaner Alleys," *American City*, March, 1956, p. 152.

Wright, C. E. "Refuse Collection Problems in a Resort City," *Public Works*, February, 1955, p. 271.

CHAPTER 10. MUNICIPAL, CONTRACT, OR PRIVATE COLLECTION OF REFUSE

Eagle, G. H., and Overman, S. M. "Good Refuse Sanitation Is Not Impossible," *Public Works*, December, 1956, p. 83.

Hope, M. C., Johnson, C. C., and Weaver L. "Refuse Handling Practices in the United States," *Public Health Reports*, February, 1956, p. 204.

CHAPTER 11. FINANCING REFUSE COLLECTION OPERATIONS

American Public Works Association and U. S. Department of Health, Education, and Welfare, Public Health Service. *Refuse Collection and Disposal for the Small Community.* November, 1953. (Reprinted Washington, D. C.: DHEW, December, 1955.)

American Society of Civil Engineers. "State Activities and Fiscal Aspects." Report of a subcommittee of the Committee on Refuse Collection and Disposal of the Sanitary Engineering Division. *Proceedings*, Vol. 80, No. 557, 1954.

Clark, J. F. "Trends in Municipal Finance," *Public Management*, October, 1956, pp. 218-220.

"Public Works Financing, a Forum," *Proceedings, 58th Annual Public Works Congress*, August, 1952, pp. 53-75.

Schneider, C. "Refuse Service Charges," *American City*, May, 1953, p. 92.

Sherman, W. H. "Financing Essential Municipal Services," *Public Management*, April, 1952, pp. 77-81.

CHAPTER 12. ORGANIZATION

Arnold, D. S. "Sources of Management Information," *Public Management*, August, 1956, pp. 173-177.

Craig, J. C. "The Administrative Manual—A Tool of Management," *Public Works Engineers' Yearbook, 1955*. Chicago: American Public Works Association, pp. 104-110.

"Communication in Administration," *Public Management*, October, 1955, pp. 218-222.

King, K. K. "Public Works Organization" *Proceedings, 56th Annual Public Works Congress*, October, 1950, pp. 76-82.

Liebman, H. "The World's Largest Municipal Refuse Collection System," *Public Works*, November, 1951, pp. 43-45, 52.

"Solid Wastes Management," Proceedings of a National Conference held April 4-5, 1966, University of California, Davis, and sponsored by the U.S. Public Health Service.

Warren, Carl D. "Organization: Key to Good Sanitation," *American City*, March, 1954, pp. 90-92.

CHAPTER 13. PERSONNEL

"Development of Management Personnel," *Public Management*, February, 1955, pp. 29-36.

"Employee Development in Public Works, a Forum," *Public Works Engineers' Yearbook, 1956*. Chicago: American Public Works Association, pp. 64-80.

Martin, R., Colter, E. R., Baughman, J. D., and Welsh, J. T. "Relations with Employee Organizations," *Public Management*, January, 1956, pp. 2-7.

McClure, R. E., "Spiritual Understanding As a Part of Management," *Public Management*, November, 1956, pp. 247-251.

Pearson, S. "Developing Salary and Wage Plans," *Public Management*, July, 1957, pp. 153-155.

Posey, R. B. "Analysis of City Employee Strikes," *Public Management*, June, 1952, pp. 122-127.

——. "Handling City Employee Grievances," *Public Management*, March, 1954, pp. 54-58.

Richetta, E. F. "Trends in Municipal Personnel," *Public Management*, October, 1956, pp. 226-229.

Schneider, C. "Present Trends in Refuse Collection and Disposal," *Public Works Engineers' Newsletter*, April, 1952, pp. 1, 3, 6, 7.

Spriegel, W. R., and Bailey, J. K. "The Use of Committees in Management," *Public Management*, March, 1954, pp. 56-59.

Warner, K. O. "Looking Ahead at City Personnel Problems," *Public Management*, March, 1956, pp. 50-52.

Zander, A. S. "Labor and the Council Manager Plan, Views of a Labor Official," *Public Management*, June, 1957, pp. 126-129.

CHAPTER 14. EQUIPMENT MANAGEMENT

"Equipment Management, a Forum," *Public Works Engineers' Yearbook, 1955.* Chicago: American Public Works Association, pp. 49-62.

Guider, C. H. "Automatic Lubrication for City Vehicles," *Public Works,* June, 1956, p. 95.

——. "Equipment Replacement Policies," *Public Works Engineers' Yearbook 1954.* Chicago: American Public Works Association, pp. 42-47.

Liebman, H. "New York Makes Careful Equipment Maintenance Pay," *Public Works,* June, 1952.

——. "The World's Largest Muncipal Refuse Collection System," *Public Works,* November, 1951, pp. 43-45, 52.

"Motor Equipment, a Round Table Discussion," *Proceedings, 59th Annual Public Works Congress,* October, 1950, pp. 102-108.

Screvane, P. R. "Equipment Replacement," *Public Works,* March, 1957, p. 123.

CHAPTER 15. REPORTING, COST ACCOUNTING, AND BUDGETING

Ervien, H. G. "Performance Budgeting—Its Value and Shortcomings," *American City,* March, 1957, p. 129.

Howell, E. S. "Reporting the City's Annual Budget," *Public Management,* June, 1956, pp. 126-128.

Jacoby, H. "Applications of Electronics in Public Works," *Public Works Engineers' Yearbook, 1956.* Chicago: American Public Works Association, pp. 81-88.

"Performance Budgeting in Public Works, a Symposium," *Proceedings, 59th Annual Public Works Congress,* October, 1953, pp. 46-74.

Pinel, S. I. "Testing Performance in Public Works Operations," *Public Works Engineers' Yearbook, 1954.* Chicago: American Public Works Association, pp. 34-41.

Rogus, C. A. "Weigh Refuse Electronically," *American City,* April, 1957, p. 128.

Screvane, P. R. "Equipment Replacement," *Public Works,* March, 1957, p. 123.

CHAPTER 16. PUBLIC RELATIONS

Martin J. C., Hammerstrom, R. J., and Waldrop, R. H. "The Laredo Story of Sanitation Progress," *American City,* February, 1957, p. 116.

Mulrain, A. W. "An Action Program for a Cleaner City," *Public Works Engineers' Yearbook, 1956.* Chicago: American Public Works Association, pp. 107-109.

"Public Relations Techniques, a Forum," *Proceedings, 56th Annual Public Works Congress,* October, 1950, pp. 56-67.

"Relations of the Manager with the Public," *Public Management,* April 1955, pp. 77-83.

Walker, C. H. "Solving a Public Works Problem Through Community Relations," *Public Works,* May, 1952, pp. 62-63.

Papers on various aspects of refuse collection practices and problems will also be found in the various issues of the *Yearbook*, American Public Works Association, Chicago, Illinois 60637, and the reports of the annual conferences of the Institute of Public Cleansing, London W1, England.

Related volumes prepared by the American Public Works Association and published by Public Administration Service, Chicago, include:

Municipal Refuse Disposal, Revised Edition, 1966

Public Works Equipment Management, 1964

Street and Urban Road Maintenance, 1963

Street Cleaning Practice, 1959.

INDEX

INDEX